PROBLEMS
IN
GENERAL PHYSICS

PROBLEMS IN

GENERAL PHYSICS

By

I.E. IRODOV

G.K. PUBLISHERS

G.K. Publishers (P) Ltd.
H-205, Sector-63
NOIDA - 201307 (U.P.)
☎ (0120) - 3250473, 4267181, 182, 184 Telefax : 4267183
email : gkp@gkpublications.com
website : www.gkpublications.com

Edition : 2008

ISBN 978-81-8355-215-8

Price : Rs. 90.00

Printed at : **Shubham Offset**, Delhi-110032

PREFACE

This book of problems is intended as a textbook for students at higher educational institutions studying advanced course in physics. Besides, because of the great number of simple problems it may be used by students studying a general course in physics.

The book contains about 1900 problems with hints for solving the most complicated ones.

For students' convenience each chapter opens with a time-saving summary of the principal formulas for the relevant area of physics. As a rule the formulas are given without detailed explanations since a student, starting solving a problem, is assumed to know the meaning of the quantities appearing in the formulas. Explanatory notes are only given in those cases when misunderstanding may arise.

All the formulas in the text and answers are in SI system, except in Part Six, where the Gaussian system is used. Quantitative data and answer are presented in accordance with the rule of approximation and numerical accuracy.

The main physical constants and tables are summarised at the end of the book.

The Periodic System of Elements is printed at the front end sheet and the Table of elementary Particles at the back sheet of the book.

In the present edition, some misprints are corrected, and a number of problems are substituted by new ones, or the quantitative data in them are changed or refined (1.273, 1.361, 2.189, 3.249, 3.97, 4.194 and 5.78).

In conclusion, the author wants to express his deep gratitude to colleagues from MIPhI and to readers who sent their remarks on some problems, helping thereby to improve the book.

I.E. Irodov

CONTENTS

Preface 5
A Few Hints for Solving the Problems 9
Notation 10

PART 1. PHYSICAL FUNDAMENTALS OF MECHANICS 11
1.1. Kinematics 11
1.2. The Fundamental Equation of Dynamics 20
1.3. Laws of Conservation of Energy, Momentum, and Angular Momentum 30
1.4. Universal Gravitation 43
1.5. Dynamics of Solid Body 47
1.6. Elastic Deformations of Solid Body 58
1.7. Hydrodynamics 62
1.8. Relativistic Mechanics 67

PART 2. THERMODYNAMICS AND MOLECULAR PHYSICS 75
2.1. Equation of the Gas State, Processes 75
2.2. The First Law of Thermodynamics, Heat Capacity 78
2.3. Kinetic Theory of Gases. Boltzmann's Law and Maxwell's Distribution 82
2.4. The Second Law of Thermodynamics, Entropy 88
2.5. Liquids. Capillary Effects 93
2.6. Phase Transformations 96
2.7. Transport Phenomena 100

PART 3. ELECTRODYNAMICS 105
3.1. Constant Electric Field in Vacuum 105
3.2. Conductors and Dielectrics in an Electric Field 111
3.3. Electric Capacitance. Energy of an Electric Field 118
3.4. Electric Current 125
3.5. Constant Magnetic Field. Magnetics 136
3.6. Electromagnetic Induction, Maxwell's Equations 147
3.7. Motion of Charged Particles in Electric and Magnetic Fields. 160

PART 4. OSCILLATIONS AND WAVES 166
4.1. Mechanical Oscillations 166
4.2. Electric Oscillations 180
4.3. Elastic Waves. Acoustics 188
4.4. Electromagnetic Waves. Radiation 193

PART 5. OPTICS 199
5.1. Photometry and Geometrical Optics 199
5.2. Interference of Light 210
5.3. Diffraction of Light 216
5.4. Polarization of Light 226
5.5. Dispersion and Absorption of Light 234
5.6. Optics of Moving Sources 237
5.7. Thermal Radiation. Quantum Nature of Light 240

PART 6. ATOMIC AND NUCLEAR PHYSICS 246

6.1. Scattering of Particles, Rutherford-Bohr Atom 246
6.2. Wave Properties of Particles. Schrö dinger Equation 251
6.3. Properties of Atoms. Spectra 257
6.4. Molecules and Crystals 264
6.5. Radioactivity 270
6.6. Nuclear Reactions 274
6.7. Elementary Particles 278

ANSWERS AND SOLUTIONS 281

APPENDICES 365

1. Basic Trigonometrical Formulas 365
2. Sine Function Values 366
3. Tangent Function Values 367
4. Common Logarithms 368
5. Exponential Functions 370
6. Greek Alphabet 372
7. Numerical Constants and Approximations 372
8. Some Date on Vectors 372
9. Derivatives and Integrals 373
10. Astronomical Data 374
11. Density of Substances 374
12. Thermal Expansion Coefficients 375
13. Elastic Constants. Tensile Strength 375
14. Saturated Vapour Pressure 375
15. Gas Constants 376
16. Some Parameters of Liquids and Solids 376
17. Perimitivities 377
18. Resistivities of Conductors 377
19. Magnetic Susceptibilities of Para- and Diamagnetics 377
20. Refractive Indices 378
21. Rotation of the Plane of Polarization 378
22. Work Function of Various Metals 379
23. K Band Absorption Edge 379
24. Mass Absorption Coefficients 379
25. Ionization Potentials of Atoms 380
26. Mass of Light Atoms 380
27. Half-life Values of Radionuclides 380
28. Units of Physical Quantities 381
29. The Basic Formulas Electrodynamics in the SI and Gaussian Systems ... 383
30. Fundamental Constants 386

A FEW HINTS FOR SOLVING THE PROBLEMS

1. First of all, look through the tables in the Appendix, for many problems cannot be solved without them. Besides, the reference data quoted in the tables will make your work easier and save your time.

2. Begin the problem by recognizing its meaning and its formulation. Make sure that the data given are sufficient for solving the problem. Missing data can be found in the tables in the Appendix. Wherever possible, draw a diagram elucidating the essence of the problem; in many cases this simplifies both the search for a solution and the solution itself.

3. Solve each problem, as a rule, in the general form, that is in a letter notation, so that the quantity sought will be expressed in the same terms as the given data. A solution in the general form is particularly valuable since it makes clear the relationship between the sought quantity and the given data. What is more, an answer obtained in the general form allows one to make a fairly accurate judgement on the correctness of the solution itself (see the next item).

4. Having obtained the solution in the general form, check to see if it has the right dimensions. The wrong dimensions are an obvious indication of a wrong solution. If possible, investigate the behaviour of the solution in some extreme special cases. For example, whatever the form of the expression for the gravitational force between two extended bodies, it must turn into the well-known law of gravitational interaction of mass points as the distance between the bodies increases. Otherwise, it can be immediately inferred that the solution is wrong.

5. When starting calculations, remember that the numerical values of physical quantities are always known only approximately. Therefore, in calculations you should employ the rules for operating with approximate numbers. In particular, in presenting the quantitative data and answers strict attention should be paid to the rules of approximation and numerical accuracy.

6. Having obtained the numerical answer, evaluate its plausibility. In some cases such an evaluation may disclose an error in the result obtained. For example, a stone cannot be thrown by a man over the distance of the order of 1 km, the velocity of a body cannot surpass that of light in a vacuum, etc.

NOTATION

Vectors are written in **boldface** upright type, e.g., **r**, **F**; the same letters printed in lightface **italic type** (r, F) denote the modulus of a vector.

Unit vectors

i, **j**, **k** are the unit vectors of the Cartesian coordinates x, y, z (sometimes the unit vectors are denoted as e_x, e_y, e_z),
e_ρ, e_φ, e_z are the unit vectors of the cylindrical coordinates ρ, φ, **z**, n τ are the unit vectors of a normal and tangent.

Mean values are taken in angle brackets ⟨ ⟩, e.g., ⟨v⟩, ⟨P⟩.

Symbols Δ, d and δ in front of quantities denote:
Δ, the finite increment of a quantity, e.g. $\Delta \mathbf{r} = \mathbf{r}_2 - \mathbf{r}_1$; $\Delta U = U_2 - U_1$,
d, the differential (infinitesimal increment), e.g. dr, dU,
δ, the elementary value of a quantity, e.g. δA, the elementary work.

Time derivative of an **arbitrary** function f is denoted by *dfront*

or by a dot over a letter, $\dot{f}$.

Vector operator ∇ (**"nabla"**). It is used to denote the following operations:
∇_ϕ, the gradient of φ (grad φ)
$\nabla \cdot$ E, the divergence of **E** (div **E**),
∇ × **E**, the curl of **E** (curl **E**).

Integrals of any multiplicity are denoted by a single sign $\int$ and differ only by the integration element: dV, a volume elements, $d\mathbf{S}$, a surface element, and d , a line element. The Sign $\oint$ denotes an integral over a close surface, or around a closed loop.

1

PHYSICAL FUNDAMENTALS OF MECHANICS

1.1. KINEMATICS

• Average vectors of velocity and acceleration of a point:

$$\langle \mathbf{v} \rangle = \frac{\Delta \mathbf{r}}{\Delta t}, \quad \langle \mathbf{w} \rangle = \frac{\Delta \mathbf{v}}{\Delta t}, \tag{1.1a}$$

where $\Delta \mathbf{r}$ is the displacement vector (an increment of a radius vector)

• Velocity and acceleration of a point:

$$\mathbf{v} = \frac{d\mathbf{r}}{dt}, \quad \mathbf{w} = \frac{d\mathbf{v}}{dt} \tag{1.1b}$$

• Acceleration of a point expressed in projections on the tangent and the normal to a trajectory:

$$w_\tau = \frac{dv_\tau}{dt}, \quad w_n = \frac{v^2}{R}, \tag{1.1c}$$

where R is the radius of curvature of the trajectory at the given point.

• Distance covered by a point:

$$s = \int v\, dt, \tag{1.1d}$$

where v is the modulus of the velocity vector of a point.

• Angular velocity and angular acceleration of a solid body:

$$\omega = \frac{d\varphi}{dt}, \quad \beta = \frac{d\omega}{dt} \tag{1.1e}$$

• Relation between linear and angular quantities for a rotating solid body:

$$\mathbf{v} = [\boldsymbol{\omega}\mathbf{r}], \quad w_n = \omega^2 R, \quad |w_\tau| = \beta R, \tag{1.1.f}$$

where $\mathbf{r}$ is the radius vector of the considered point relative to an arbitrary point on the rotation axis, and R is the distance from the rotation axis.

1.1. A motorboat going downstream overcame a raft at a point A; $\tau = 60$ min later it turned back and after some time pased the raft at a distance $l = 6.0$ km from the point A. Find the flow velocity assuming the duty of the engine to be constant.

1.2. A point traversed half the distance with a velocity v_0. The remaining part of the distance was covered with velocity v_1 for half the time, and with velocity v_2 for the other half of the time. Find the mean velocity of the point averaged over the whole time of motion.

1.3. A car starts moving rectilinearly, first with acceleration $w = 5.0\ m/s^2$ (the initial velocity is equal to zero), then uniformly, and finally, decelerating at the same rate w, comes to a stop. The total time of motion equals $\tau = 25$ s. The average velocity during that time is equal to $\langle v \rangle = 72$ km per hour. How long does the car move uniformly?

1.4. A point moves rectilinearly in one direction. Fig. 1.1 shows

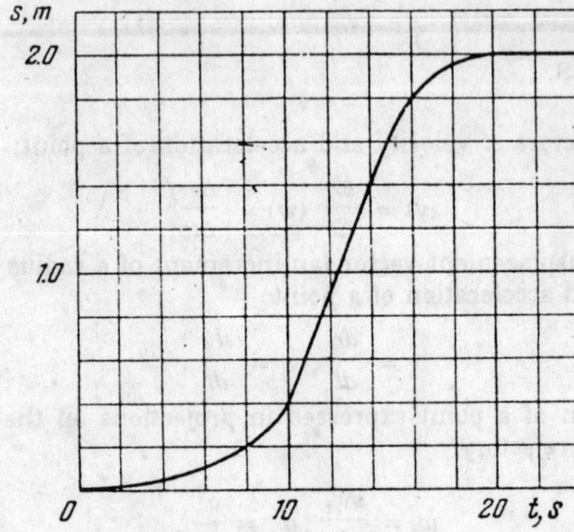

Fig. 1.1.

the distance s traversed by the point as a function of the time t. Using the plot find:

(a) the average velocity of the point during the time of motion;

(b) the maximum velocity;

(c) the time moment t_0 at which the instantaneous velocity is equal to the mean velocity averaged over the first t_0 seconds.

1.5. Two particles, *1* and *2*, move with constant velocities $\mathbf{v}_1$ and $\mathbf{v}_2$. At the initial moment their radius vectors are equal to $\mathbf{r}_1$ and $\mathbf{r}_2$. How must these four vectors be interrelated for the particles to collide?

1.6. A ship moves along the equator to the east with velocity $v_0 = 30$ km/hour. The southeastern wind blows at an angle $\varphi = 60°$ to the equator with velocity $v = 15$ km/hour. Find the wind velocity v' relative to the ship and the angle φ' between the equator and the wind direction in the reference frame fixed to the ship.

1.7. Two swimmers leave point A on one bank of the river to reach point B lying right across on the other bank. One of them crosses the river along the straight line AB while the other swims at right angles to the stream and then walks the distance that he has been carried away by the stream to get to point B. What was the velocity u

of his walking if both swimmers reached the destination simultaneously? The stream velocity $v_0 = 2.0$ km/hour and the velocity v' of each swimmer with respect to water equals 2.5 km per hour.

1.8. Two boats, A and B, move away from a buoy anchored at the middle of a river along the mutually perpendicular straight lines: the boat A along the river, and the boat B across the river. Having moved off an equal distance from the buoy the boats returned. Find the ratio of times of motion of boats τ_A/τ_B if the velocity of each boat with respect to water is $\eta = 1.2$ times greater than the stream velocity.

1.9. A boat moves relative to water with a velocity which is $n = 2.0$ times less than the river flow velocity. At what angle to the stream direction must the boat move to minimize drifting?

1.10. Two bodies were thrown simultaneously from the same point: one, straight up, and the other, at an angle of $\theta = 60°$ to the horizontal. The initial velocity of each body is equal to $v_0 = 25$ m/s. Neglecting the air drag, find the distance between the bodies $t = 1.70$ s later.

1.11. Two particles move in a uniform gravitational field with an acceleration g. At the initial moment the particles were located at one point and moved with velocities $v_1 = 3.0$ m/s and $v_2 = 4.0$ m/s horizontally in opposite directions. Find the distance between the particles at the moment when their velocity vectors become mutually perpendicular.

1.12. Three points are located at the vertices of an equilateral triangle whose side equals a. They all start moving simultaneously with velocity v constant in modulus, with the first point heading continually for the second, the second for the third, and the third for the first. How soon will the points converge?

1.13. Point A moves uniformly with velocity v so that the vector $\mathbf{v}$ is continually "aimed" at point B which in its turn moves rectilinearly and uniformly with velocity $u < v$. At the initial moment of time $\mathbf{v} \perp \mathbf{u}$ and the points are separated by a distance l. How soon will the points converge?

1.14. A train of length $l = 350$ m starts moving rectilinearly with constant acceleration $w = 3.0 \cdot 10^{-2}$ m/s²; $t = 30$ s after the start the locomotive headlight is switched on (event *1*), and $\tau = 60$ s after that event the tail signal light is switched on (event *2*). Find the distance between these events in the reference frames fixed to the train and to the Earth. How and at what constant velocity V relative to the Earth must a certain reference frame K move for the two events to occur in it at the same point?

1.15. An elevator car whose floor-to-ceiling distance is equal to 2.7 m starts ascending with constant acceleration 1.2 m/s²; 2.0 s after the start a bolt begins falling from the ceiling of the car. Find:

(a) the bolt's free fall time;

(b) the displacement and the distance covered by the bolt during the free fall in the reference frame fixed to the elevator shaft.

1.16. Two particles, *1* and *2*, move with constant velocities v_1 and v_2 along two mutually perpendicular straight lines toward the intersection point O. At the moment $t = 0$ the particles were located at the distances l_1 and l_2 from the point O. How soon will the distance between the particles become the smallest? What is it equal to?

1.17. From point A located on a highway (Fig. 1.2) one has to get by car as soon as possible to point B located in the field at a distance l from the highway. It is known that the car moves in the field η times slower than on the highway. At what distance from point D one must turn off the highway?

1.18. A point travels along the x axis with a velocity whose projection v_x is presented as a function of time by the plot in Fig. 1.3.

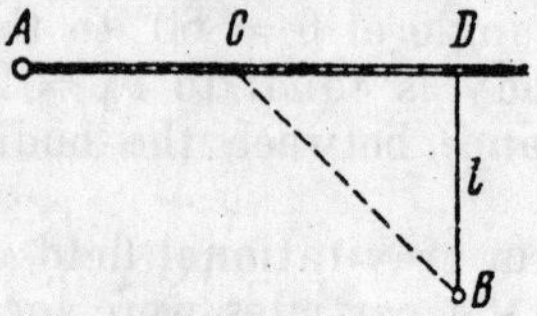

Fig. 1.2.

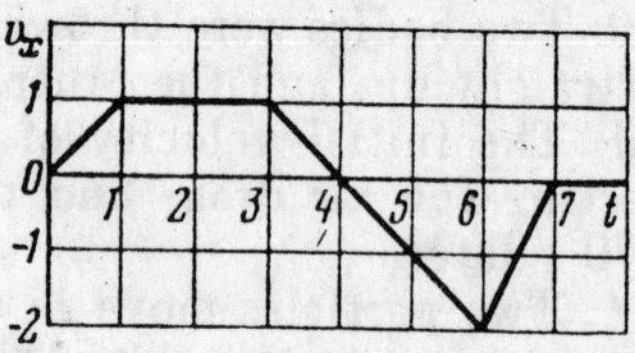

Fig. 1.3.

Assuming the coordinate of the point $x = 0$ at the moment $t = 0$, draw the approximate time dependence plots for the acceleration w_x, the x coordinate, and the distance covered s.

1.19. A point traversed half a circle of radius $R = 160$ cm during time interval $\tau = 10.0$ s. Calculate the following quantities averaged over that time:

(a) the mean velocity $\langle v \rangle$;

(b) the modulus of the mean velocity vector $|\langle \mathbf{v} \rangle|$;

(c) the modulus of the mean vector of the total acceleration $|\langle \mathbf{w} \rangle|$ if the point moved with constant tangent acceleration.

1.20. A radius vector of a particle varies with time t as $\mathbf{r} = \mathbf{a}t\,(1 - \alpha t)$, where $\mathbf{a}$ is a constant vector and α is a positive factor. Find:

(a) the velocity $\mathbf{v}$ and the acceleration $\mathbf{w}$ of the particle as functions of time;

(b) the time interval Δt taken by the particle to return to the initial points, and the distance s covered during that time.

1.21. At the moment $t = 0$ a particle leaves the origin and moves in the positive direction of the x axis. Its velocity varies with time as $\mathbf{v} = \mathbf{v}_0\,(1 - t/\tau)$, where $\mathbf{v}_0$ is the initial velocity vector whose modulus equals $v_0 = 10.0$ cm/s; $\tau = 5.0$ s. Find:

(a) the x coordinate of the particle at the moments of time 6.0, 10, and 20 s;

(b) the moments of time when the particle is at the distance 10.0 cm from the origin;

(c) the distance s covered by the particle during the first 4.0 and 8.0 s; draw the approximate plot $s(t)$.

1.22. The velocity of a particle moving in the positive direction of the x axis varies as $v = \alpha\sqrt{x}$, where α is a positive constant. Assuming that at the moment $t = 0$ the particle was located at the point $x = 0$, find:

(a) the time dependence of the velocity and the acceleration of the particle;

(b) the mean velocity of the particle averaged over the time that the particle takes to cover the first s metres of the path.

1.23. A point moves rectilinearly with deceleration whose modulus depends on the velocity v of the particle as $w = a\sqrt{v}$, where a is a positive constant. At the initial moment the velocity of the point is equal to v_0. What distance will it traverse before it stops? What time will it take to cover that distance?

1.24. A radius vector of a point A relative to the origin varies with time t as $\mathbf{r} = at\mathbf{i} - bt^2\mathbf{j}$, where a and b are positive constants, and $\mathbf{i}$ and $\mathbf{j}$ are the unit vectors of the x and y axes. Find:

(a) the equation of the point's trajectory $y(x)$; plot this function;

(b) the time dependence of the velocity $\mathbf{v}$ and acceleration $\mathbf{w}$ vectors, as well as of the moduli of these quantities;

(c) the time dependence of the angle α between the vectors $\mathbf{w}$ and $\mathbf{v}$;

(d) the mean velocity vector averaged over the first t seconds of motion, and the modulus of this vector.

1.25. A point moves in the plane xy according to the law $x = at$, $y = at(1 - \alpha t)$, where a and α are positive constants, and t is time. Find:

(a) the equation of the point's trajectory $y(x)$; plot this function;

(b) the velocity v and the acceleration w of the point as functions of time;

(c) the moment t_0 at which the velocity vector forms an angle $\pi/4$ with the acceleration vector.

1.26. A point moves in the plane xy according to the law $x = a \sin \omega t$, $y = a(1 - \cos \omega t)$, where a and ω are positive constants. Find:

(a) the distance s traversed by the point during the time τ;

(b) the angle between the point's velocity and acceleration vectors.

1.27. A particle moves in the plane xy with constant acceleration $\mathbf{w}$ directed along the negative y axis. The equation of motion of the particle has the form $y = ax - bx^2$, where a and b are positive constants. Find the velocity of the particle at the origin of coordinates.

1.28. A small body is thrown at an angle to the horizontal with the initial velocity $\mathbf{v}_0$. Neglecting the air drag, find:

(a) the displacement of the body as a function of time $\mathbf{r}(t)$;

(b) the mean velocity vector $\langle\mathbf{v}\rangle$ averaged over the first t seconds and over the total time of motion.

1.29. A body is thrown from the surface of the Earth at an angle α

to the horizontal with the initial velocity v_0. Assuming the air drag to be negligible, find:

(a) the time of motion;

(b) the maximum height of ascent and the horizontal range; at what value of the angle α they will be equal to each other;

(c) the equation of trajectory $y(x)$, where y and x are displacements of the body along the vertical and the horizontal respectively;

(d) the curvature radii of trajectory at its initial point and at its peak.

1.30. Using the conditions of the foregoing problem, draw the approximate time dependence of moduli of the normal w_n and tangent w_τ acceleration vectors, as well as of the projection of the total acceleration vector w_v on the velocity vector direction.

1.31. A ball starts falling with zero initial velocity on a smooth inclined plane forming an angle α with the horizontal. Having fallen the distance h, the ball rebounds elastically off the inclined plane. At what distance from the impact point will the ball rebound for the second time?

1.32. A cannon and a target are 5.10 km apart and located at the same level. How soon will the shell launched with the initial velocity 240 m/s reach the target in the absence of air drag?

1.33. A cannon fires successively two shells with velocity $v_0 = 250$ m/s; the first at the angle $\theta_1 = 60°$ and the second at the angle $\theta_2 = 45°$ to the horizontal, the azimuth being the same. Neglecting the air drag, find the time interval between firings leading to the collision of the shells.

1.34. A balloon starts rising from the surface of the Earth. The ascension rate is constant and equal to v_0. Due to the wind the balloon gathers the horizontal velocity component $v_x = ay$, where a is a constant and y is the height of ascent. Find how the following quantities depend on the height of ascent:

(a) the horizontal drift of the balloon $x(y)$;

(b) the total, tangential, and normal accelerations of the balloon.

1.35. A particle moves in the plane xy with velocity $\mathbf{v} = a\mathbf{i} + bx\mathbf{j}$, where $\mathbf{i}$ and $\mathbf{j}$ are the unit vectors of the x and y axes, and a and b are constants. At the initial moment of time the particle was located at the point $x = y = 0$. Find:

(a) the equation of the particle's trajectory $y(x)$;

(b) the curvature radius of trajectory as a function of x.

1.36. A particle A moves in one direction along a given trajectory with a tangential acceleration $w_\tau = \mathbf{a}\boldsymbol{\tau}$, where $\mathbf{a}$ is a constant vector coinciding in direction with the x axis (Fig. 1.4), and $\boldsymbol{\tau}$ is a unit vector coinciding in direction with the velocity vector at a given point. Find how the velocity of the particle depends on x provided that its velocity is negligible at the point $x = 0$.

1.37. A point moves along a circle with a velocity $v = at$, where $a = 0.50$ m/s². Find the total acceleration of the point at the moment when it covered the n-th ($n = 0.10$) fraction of the circle after the beginning of motion.

1.38. A point moves with deceleration along the circle of radius R so that at any moment of time its tangential and normal accelerations

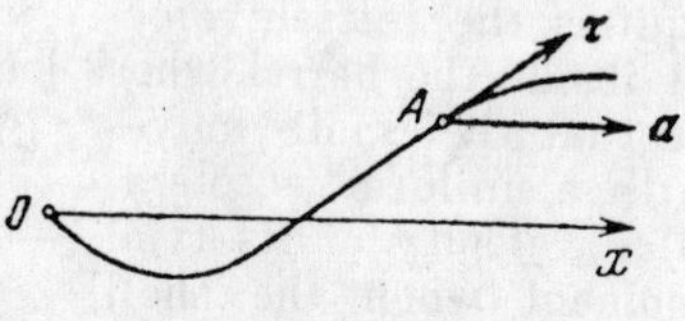

Fig. 1.4.

are equal in moduli. At the initial moment $t = 0$ the velocity of the point equals v_0. Find:

(a) the velocity of the point as a function of time and as a function of the distance covered s;

(b) the total acceleration of the point as a function of velocity and the distance covered.

1.39. A point moves along an arc of a circle of radius R. Its velocity depends on the distance covered s as $v = a\sqrt{s}$, where a is a constant. Find the angle α between the vector of the total acceleration and the vector of velocity as a function of s.

1.40. A particle moves along an arc of a circle of radius R according to the law $l = a \sin \omega t$, where l is the displacement from the initial position measured along the arc, and a and ω are constants. Assuming $R = 1.00$ m, $a = 0.80$ m, and $\omega = 2.00$ rad/s, find:

(a) the magnitude of the total acceleration of the particle at the points $l = 0$ and $l = \pm a$;

(b) the minimum value of the total acceleration w_{min} and the corresponding displacement l_m.

1.41. A point moves in the plane so that its tangential acceleration $w_\tau = a$, and its normal acceleration $w_n = bt^4$, where a and b are positive constants, and t is time. At the moment $t = 0$ the point was at rest. Find how the curvature radius R of the point's trajectory and the total acceleration w depend on the distance covered s.

1.42. A particle moves along the plane trajectory $y(x)$ with velocity v whose modulus is constant. Find the acceleration of the particle at the point $x = 0$ and the curvature radius of the trajectory at that point if the trajectory has the form

(a) of a parabola $y = ax^2$;

(b) of an ellipse $(x/a)^2 + (y/b)^2 = 1$; a and b are constants here.

1.43. A particle A moves along a circle of radius $R = 50$ cm so that its radius vector $\mathbf{r}$ relative to the point O (Fig. 1.5) rotates with the constant angular velocity $\omega = 0.40$ rad/s. Find the modulus of the velocity of the particle, and the modulus and direction of its total acceleration.

1.44. A wheel rotates around a stationary axis so that the rotation angle φ varies with time as $\varphi = at^2$, where $a = 0.20$ rad/s^2. Find the total acceleration w of the point A at the rim at the moment $t = 2.5$ s if the linear velocity of the point A at this moment $v = 0.65$ m/s.

1.45. A shell acquires the initial velocity $v = 320$ m/s, having made $n = 2.0$ turns inside the barrel whose length is equal to $l = 2.0$ m. Assuming that the shell moves inside the barrel with a uniform acceleration, find the angular velocity of its axial rotation at the moment when the shell escapes the barrel.

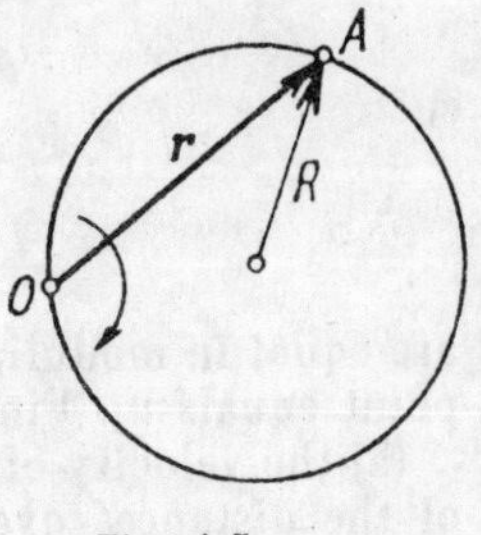

Fig. 1.5.

1.46. A solid body rotates about a stationary axis according to the law $\varphi = at - bt^3$, where $a = 6.0$ rad/s and $b = 2.0$ rad/s^3. Find:

(a) the mean values of the angular velocity and angular acceleration averaged over the time interval between $t = 0$ and the complete stop;

(b) the angular acceleration at the moment when the body stops.

1.47. A solid body starts rotating about a stationary axis with an angular acceleration $\beta = at$, where $a = 2.0 \cdot 10^{-2}$ rad/s^3. How soon after the beginning of rotation will the total acceleration vector of an arbitrary point of the body form an angle $\alpha = 60°$ with its velocity vector?

1.48. A solid body rotates with deceleration about a stationary axis with an angular deceleration $\beta \propto \sqrt{\omega}$, where ω is its angular velocity. Find the mean angular velocity of the body averaged over the whole time of rotation if at the initial moment of time its angular velocity was equal to ω_0.

1.49. A solid body rotates about a stationary axis so that its angular velocity depends on the rotation angle φ as $\omega = \omega_0 - a\varphi$, where ω_0 and a are positive constants. At the moment $t = 0$ the angle $\varphi = 0$. Find the time dependence of

(a) the rotation angle;

(b) the angular velocity.

1.50. A solid body starts rotating about a stationary axis with an angular acceleration $\boldsymbol{\beta} = \boldsymbol{\beta}_0 \cos \varphi$, where $\boldsymbol{\beta}_0$ is a constant vector and φ is an angle of rotation from the initial position. Find the angular velocity of the body as a function of the angle φ. Draw the plot of this dependence.

1.51. A rotating disc (Fig. 1.6) moves in the positive direction of the x axis. Find the equation $y(x)$ describing the position of the instantaneous axis of rotation, if at the initial moment the axis C of the disc was located at the point O after which it moved

(a) with a constant velocity v, while the disc started rotating counterclockwise with a constant angular acceleration β (the initial angular velocity is equal to zero);

(b) with a constant acceleration w (and the zero initial velocity), while the disc rotates counterclockwise with a constant angular velocity ω.

1.52. A point A is located on the rim of a wheel of radius $R = 0.50$ m which rolls without slipping along a horizontal surface with velocity $v = 1.00$ m/s. Find:

(a) the modulus and the direction of the acceleration vector of the point A;

(b) the total distance s traversed by the point A between the two successive moments at which it touches the surface.

1.53. A ball of radius $R = 10.0$ cm rolls without slipping down an inclined plane so that its centre moves with constant acceleration

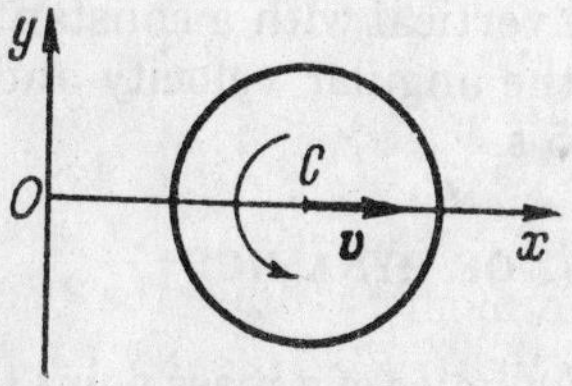

Fig. 1.6.

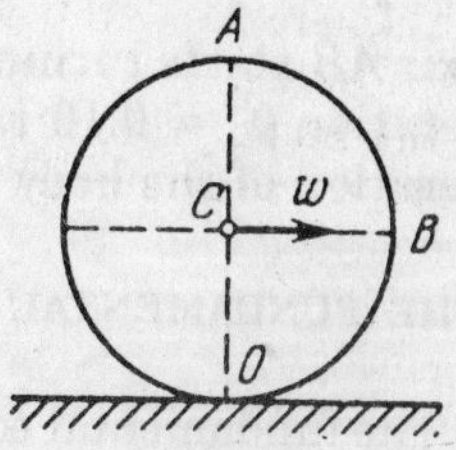

Fig. 1.7.

$w = 2.50$ cm/s^2; $t = 2.00$ s after the beginning of motion its position corresponds to that shown in Fig. 1.7. Find:

(a) the velocities of the points A, B, and O;

(b) the accelerations of these points.

1.54. A cylinder rolls without slipping over a horizontal plane. The radius of the cylinder is equal to r. Find the curvature radii of trajectories traced out by the points A and B (see Fig. 1.7).

1.55. Two solid bodies rotate about stationary mutually perpendicular intersecting axes with constant angular velocities $\omega_1 = 3.0$ rad/s and $\omega_2 = 4.0$ rad/s. Find the angular velocity and angular acceleration of one body relative to the other.

1.56. A solid body rotates with angular velocity $\boldsymbol{\omega} = at\mathbf{i} + bt^2\mathbf{j}$, where $a = 0.50$ rad/s^2, $b = 0.060$ rad/s^3, and $\mathbf{i}$ and $\mathbf{j}$ are the unit vectors of the x and y axes. Find:

(a) the moduli of the angular velocity and the angular acceleration at the moment $t = 10.0$ s;

(b) the angle between the vectors of the angular velocity and the angular acceleration at that moment.

1.57. A round cone with half-angle $\alpha = 30°$ and the radius of the base $R = 5.0$ cm rolls uniformly and without slipping over a horizontal plane as shown in Fig. 1.8. The cone apex is hinged at the point O which is on the same level with the point C, the cone base centre. The velocity of point C is $v = 10.0$ cm/s. Find the moduli of

(a) the vector of the angular velocity of the cone and the angle it forms with the vertical;

(b) the vector of the angular acceleration of the cone.

1.58. A solid body rotates with a constant angular velocity $\omega_0 =$ 0.50 rad/s about a horizontal axis AB. At the moment $t = 0$.

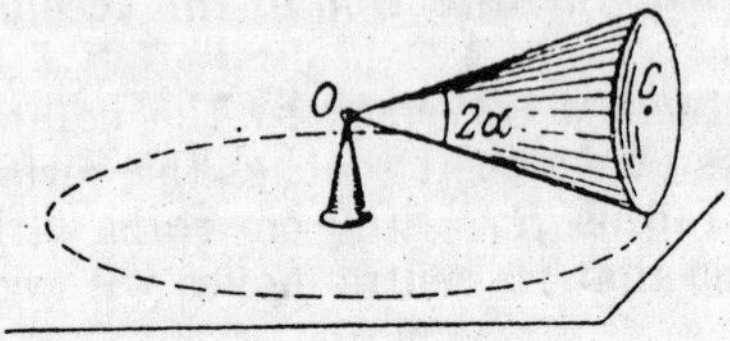

Fig. 1.8

the axis AB starts turning about the vertical with a constant angular acceleration $\beta_0 = 0.10$ rad/s^2. Find the angular velocity and angular acceleration of the body after $t = 3.5$ s.

1.2. THE FUNDAMENTAL EQUATIONS OF DYNAMICS

• The fundamental equation of dynamics of a mass point (Newton's sec. and law):

$$m \frac{dv}{dt} = \mathbf{F}. \tag{1.2a}$$

• The same equation expressed in projectio s on the tangent and the normal of the point's trajectory:

$$m \frac{dv_\tau}{dt} = F_\tau, \; m \frac{v^2}{R} = F_n. \tag{1.2b}$$

• The equation of dynamics of a point in the non-intertial reference frame K' which rotates with a constant angular velocity ω about an axis translating with an acceleration w_0:

$$m\mathrm{w}' = \mathbf{F} - m\mathrm{w}_0 + m\omega^2\mathbf{R} + 2m\,[\mathrm{v}'\omega], \tag{1.2C}$$

where $\mathbf{R}$ is the radius vector of the point relative to the axis of rotation of the K' frame.

1.59. An aerostat of mass m starts coming down with a constant acceleration w. Determine the ballast mass to be dumped for the aerostat to reach the upward acceleration of the same magnitude. The air drag is to be neglected.

1.60. In the arrangement of Fig. 1.9 the masses m_0, m_1, and m_2 of bodies are equal, the masses of the pulley and the threads are negligible, and there is no friction in the pulley. Find the acceleration w with which the body m_0 comes down, and the tension of the thread binding together the bodies m_1 and m_2, if the coefficient of friction between these bodies and the horizontal surface is equal to k. Consider possible cases.

1.61. Two touching bars *1* and *2* are placed on an inclined plane forming an angle α with the horizontal (Fig. 1.10). The masses of the bars are equal to m_1 and m_2, and the coefficients of friction between

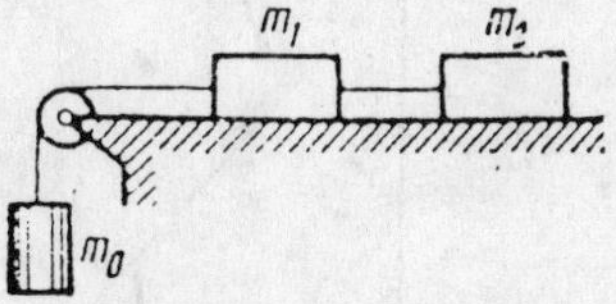

Fig. 1.9

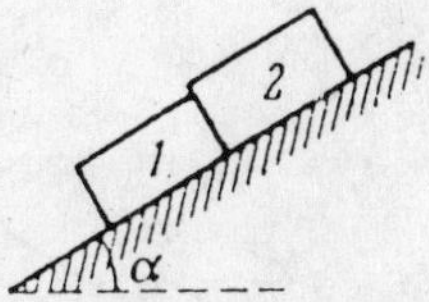

Fig. 1.10

the inclined plane and these bars are equal to k_1 and k_2 respectively, with $k_1 > k_2$. Find:

(a) the force of interaction of the bars in the process of motion;

(b) the minimum value of the angle α at which the bars start sliding down.

1.62. A small body was launched up an inclined plane set at an angle $\alpha = 15°$ against the horizontal. Find the coefficient of friction, if the time of the ascent of the body is $\eta = 2.0$ times less than the time of its descent.

1.63. The following parameters of the arrangement of Fig. 1.11 are available: the angle α which the inclined plane forms with the horizontal, and the coefficient of friction k between the body m_1 and the inclined plane. The masses of the pulley and the threads, as well as the friction in the pulley, are negligible. Assuming both bodies to be motionless at the initial moment, find the mass ratio m_2/m_1 at which the body m_2

(a) starts coming down;

(b) starts going up;

(c) is at rest.

1.64. The inclined plane of Fig. 1.11 forms an angle $\alpha = 30°$ with the horizontal. The mass ratio $m_2/m_1 = \eta = 2/3$. The coefficient of friction between the body m_1 and the inclined plane is equal to $k = 0.10$. The masses of the pulley and the threads are negligible. Find the magnitude and the direction of acceleration of the body m_2 when the formerly stationary system of masses starts moving.

1.65. A plank of mass m_1 with a bar of mass m_2 placed on it lies on a smooth horizontal plane. A horizontal force growing with time t as $F = at$ (a is constant) is applied to the bar. Find how the accelerations of the plank w_1 and of the bar w_2 depend on t, if the coefficient of friction between the plank and the bar is equal to k. Draw the approximate plots of these dependences.

1.66. A small body A starts sliding down from the top of a wedge (Fig. 1.12) whose base is equal to $l = 2.10$ m. The coefficient of friction between the body and the wedge surface is $k = 0.140$. At what value of the angle α will the time of sliding be the least? What will it be equal to?

1.67. A bar of mass m is pulled by means of thread up an inclined plane forming an angle α with the horizontal (Fig. 1.13). The coefficient of friction is equal to k. Find the angle β which the thread must form with the inclined plane for the tension of the thread to be minimum. What is it equal to?

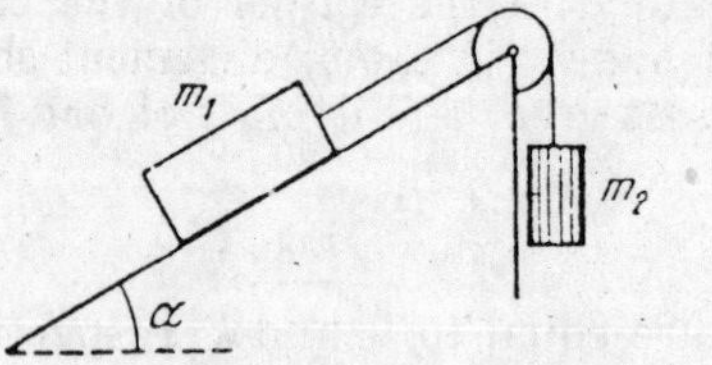

Fig. 1.11

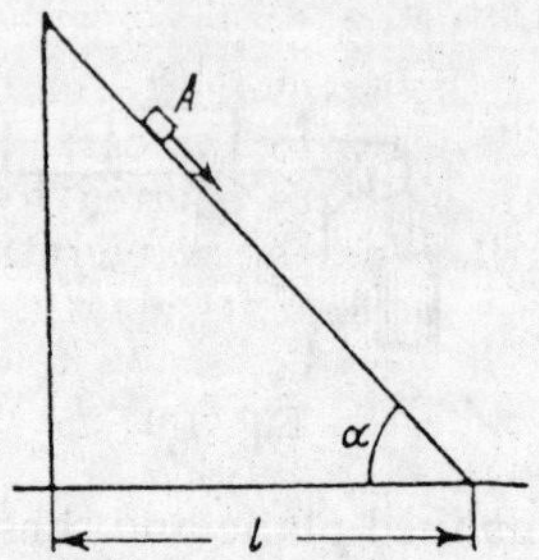

Fig. 1.12

1.68. At the moment $t = 0$ the force $F = at$ is applied to a small body of mass m resting on a smooth horizontal plane (a is a constant).

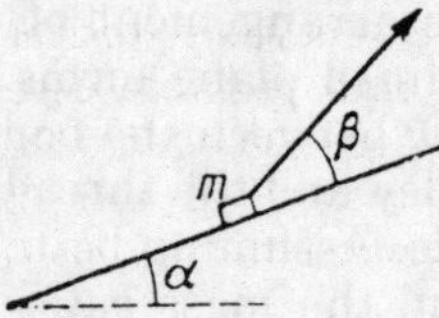

Fig. 1.13

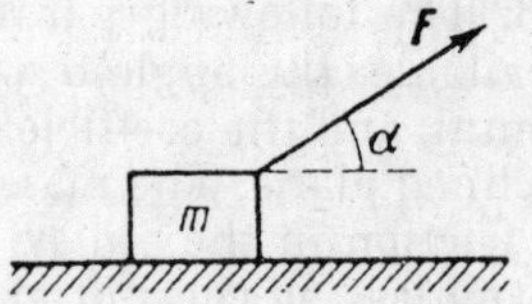

Fig. 1.14

The permanent direction of this force forms an angle a with the horizontal (Fig. 1.14). Find:

(a) the velocity of the body at the moment of its breaking off the plane;

(b) the distance traversed by the body up to this moment.

1.69. A bar of mass m resting on a smooth horizontal plane starts moving due to the force $F = mg/3$ of constant magnitude. In the process of its rectilinear motion the angle α between the direction of this force and the horizontal varies as α = as, where α is a constant, and s is the distance traversed by the bar from its initial position. Find the velocity of the bar as a function of the angle α.

1.70. A horizontal plane with the coefficient of friction k supports two bodies; a bar and an electric motor with a battery on a block. A thread attached to the bar is wound on the shaft of the electric motor. The distance between the bar and the electric motor is equal to l. When the motor is switched on, the bar, whose mass is twice as great as that of the other body, starts moving with a constant acceleration w. How soon will the bodies collide?

1.71. A pulley fixed to the ceiling of an elevator car carries a thread whose ends are attached to the loads of masses m_1 and m_2. The car starts going up with an acceleration $\mathbf{w}_0$. Assuming the masses of the pulley and the thread, as well as the friction, to be negligible find:

(a) the acceleration of the load m_1 relative to the elevator shaft and relative to the car;

(b) the force exerted by the pulley on the ceiling of the car.

1.72. Find the acceleration $\mathbf{w}$ of body *2* in the arrangement shown in Fig. 1.15, if its mass is η times as great as the mass of bar *1* and

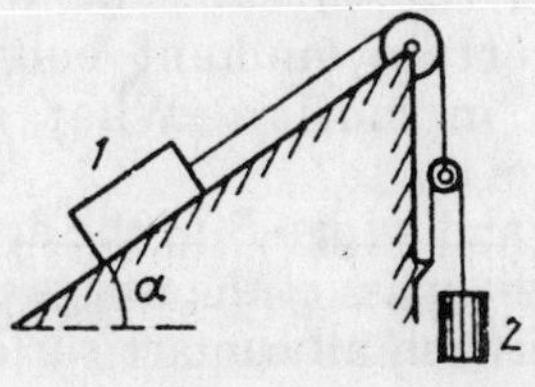

Fig. 1.15.

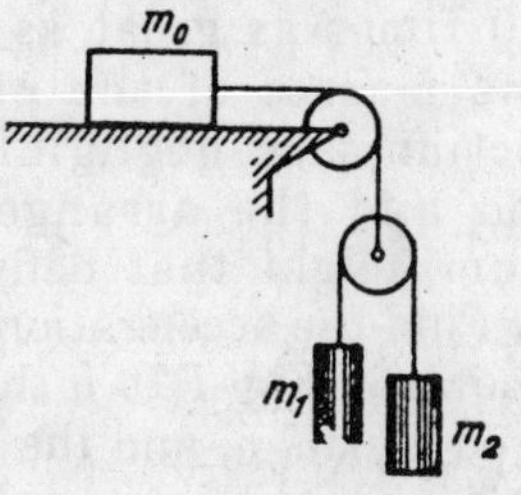

Fig. 1.16.

the angle that the inclined plane forms with the horizontal is equal to α. The masses of the pulleys and the threads, as well as the friction, are assumed to be negligible. Look into possible cases.

1.73. In the arrangement shown in Fig. 1.16 the bodies have masses m_0, m_1, m_2, the friction is absent, the masses of the pulleys and the threads are negligible. Find the acceleration of the body m_1. Look into possible cases.

1.74. In the arrangement shown in Fig. 1.17 the mass of the rod M exceeds the mass m of the ball. The ball has an opening permitting

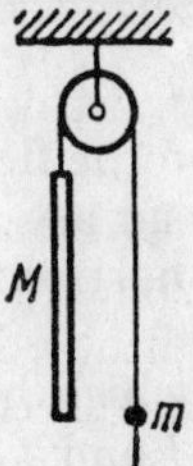

Fig. 1.17.

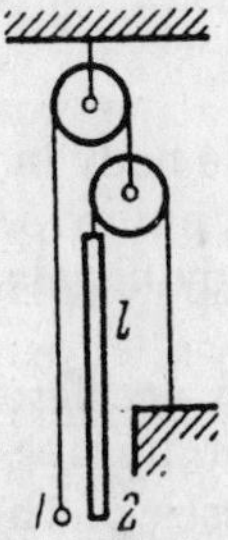

Fig. 1.18.

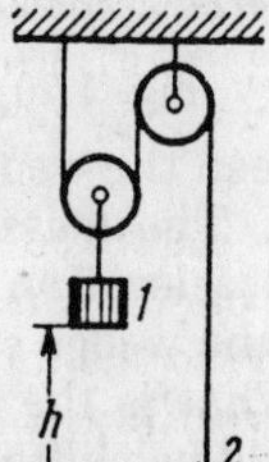

Fig. 1.19.

it to slide along the thread with some friction. The mass of the pulley and the friction in its axle are negligible. At the initial moment the ball was located opposite the lower end of the rod. When set free, both bodies began moving with constant accelerations. Find the friction force between the ball and the thread if t seconds after the beginning of motion the ball got opposite the upper end of the rod. The rod length equals l.

1.75. In the arrangement shown in Fig. 1.18 the mass of ball 1 is $\eta = 1.8$ times as great as that of rod 2. The length of the latter is $l = 100$ cm. The masses of the pulleys and the threads, as well as the friction, are negligible. The ball is set on the same level as the lower end of the rod and then released. How soon will the ball be opposite the upper end of the rod?

1.76. In the arrangement shown in Fig. 1.19 the mass of body *1* is $\eta = 4.0$ times as great as that of body *2*. The height h = 20 cm. The masses of the pulleys and the threads, as well as the friction, are negligible. At a certain moment body *2* is released and the arrangement set in motion. What is the maximum height that body *2* will go up to?

1.77. Find the accelerations of rod A and wedge B in the arrangement shown in Fig. 1.20 if the ratio of the mass of the wedge to that of the rod equals η, and the friction between all contact surfaces is negligible.

1.78. In the arrangement shown in Fig. 1.21 the masses of the wedge M and the body m are known. The appreciable friction exists

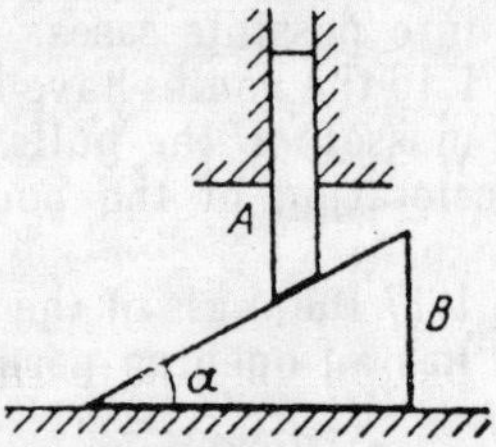

Fig. 1.20

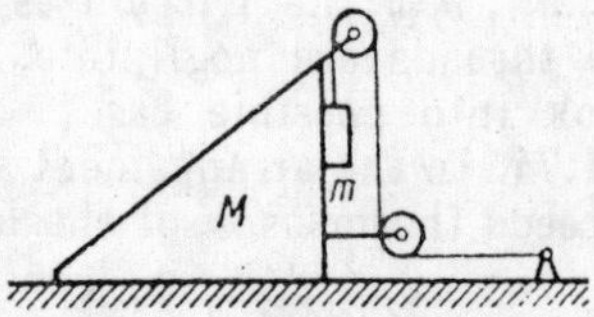

Fig. 1.21

only between the wedge and the body m, the friction coefficient being equal to k. The masses of the pulley and the thread are negligible. Find the acceleration of the body m relative to the horizontal surface on which the wedge slides.

1.79. What is the minimum acceleration with which bar A (Fig. 1.22) should be shifted horizontally to keep bodies *1* and *2* stationary relative to the bar? The masses of the bodies are equal, and the coefficient of friction between the bar and the bodies is qual to k. The masses of the pulley and the threads are negligible, the friction in the pulley is absent.

1.80. Prism *1* with bar *2* of mass m placed on it gets a horizontal acceleration w directed to the left (Fig. 1.23). At the what maximum value of this acceleration will the bar be still stationary relative to the prism, if the coefficient of friction between them $k < \cot \alpha$?

1.81. Prism *1* of mass m_1 and with angle α (see Fig. 1.23) rests on a horizontal surface. Bar *2* of mass m_2 is placed on the prism. Assuming the friction to be negligible, find the acceleration of the prism.

1.82. In the arrangement shown in Fig. 1.24 the masses m of the bar and M of the wedge, as well as the wedge angle α, are known.

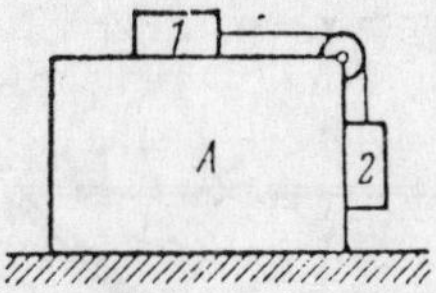

Fig. 1.22

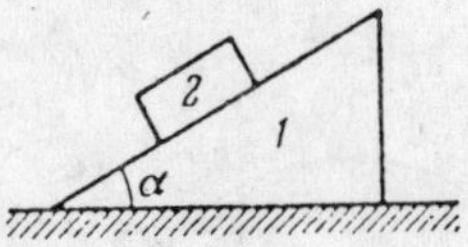

Fig. 1.23

The masses of the pulley and the thread are negligible. The friction is absent. Find the acceleration of the wedge M.

1.83. A particle of mass m moves along a circle of radius R. Find the modulus of the average vector of the force acting on the particle over the distance equal to a quarter of the circles, if the particle moves.

(a) uniformly with velocity v;

(b) with constant tangential acceleration w_τ, the initial velocity being equal to zero.

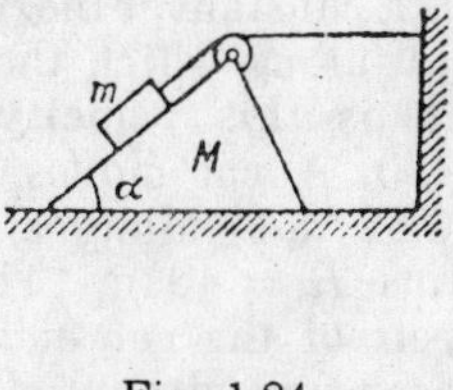

Fig. 1.24

1.84. An aircraft loops the loop of radius R = 500 m with a constant velocity v = 360 km per hour. Find the weight of the flyer of mass m = 70 kg in the lower, upper, and middle points of the loop.

1.85. A small sphere of mass m suspended by a thread is first taken aside so that the thread forms the right angle with the vertical and then released. Find:

(a) the total acceleration of the sphere and the thread tension as a function of θ, the angle of deflection of the thread from the vertical;

(b) the thread tension at the moment when the vertical component of the sphere's velocity is maximum;

(c) the angle θ between the thread and the vertical at the moment when the total acceleration vector of the sphere is directed horizontally.

1.86. A ball suspended by a thread swings in a vertical plane so that its acceleration values in the extreme and the lowest position are equal. Find the thread deflection angle in the extreme position.

1.87. A small body A starts sliding off the top of a smooth sphere of radius R. Find the angle θ (Fig. 1.25). Corresponding to the point at which the body breaks off the sphere, as well as the break-off velocity of the body.

1.88. A device (Fig. 1.26) consists of a smooth L-shaped rod located in a horizontal plane and a sleeve A of mass m attached by a weightless spring to a point B. The spring stiffness is equal to $\varkappa$. The whole system rotates with a constant angular velocity ω about a vertical axis passing through the point O. Find the elongation of the spring. How is the result affected by the rotation direction?

1.89. A cyclist rides along the circumference of a circular horizontal plane of radius R, the friction coefficient being dependent only on

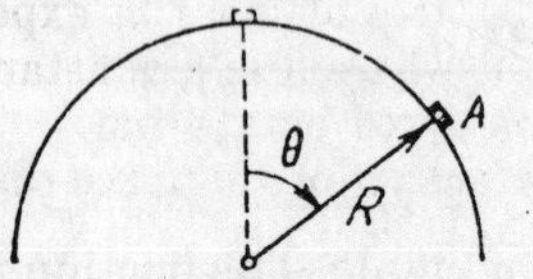

Fig. 1.25.

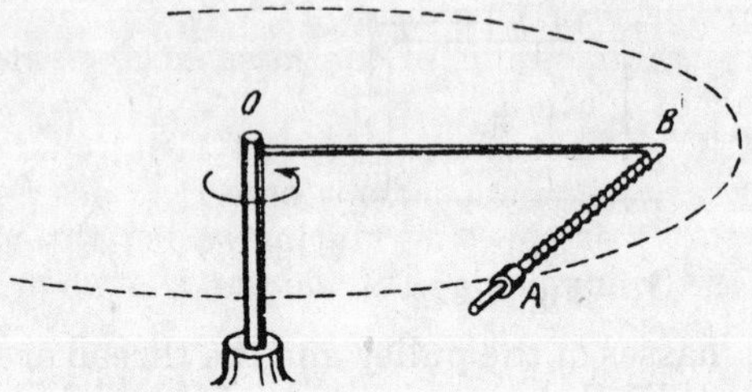

Fig. 1.26.

distance r from the centre O of the plane as $k = k_0(1 - r/R)$, where k_0 is a constant. Find the radius of the circle with the centre at the point along which the cyclist can ride with the maximum velocity. What is this velocity?

1.90. A car moves with a constant tangential acceleration $w_\tau = 0.62\ \text{m/s}^2$ along a horizontal surface circumscribing a circle of radius $R = 40$ m. The coefficient of sliding friction between the wheels of the car and the surface is $k = 0.20$. What distance will the car ride without sliding if at the initial moment of time its velocity is equal to zero?

1.91. A car moves uniformly along a horizontal sine curve $y = a \sin(x/\alpha)$, where a and α are certain constants. The coefficient of friction between the wheels and the road is equal to k. At what velocity will the car ride without sliding?

1.92. A chain of mass m forming a circle of radius R is slipped on a smooth round cone with half-angle θ. Find the tension of the chain if it rotates with a constant angular velocity ω about a vertical axis coinciding with the symmetry axis of the cone.

1.93. A fixed pulley carries a weightless thread with masses m_1 and m_2 at its ends. There is friction between the thread and the pulley. It is such that the thread starts slipping when the ratio $m_2/m_1 = \eta_0$. Find:

(a) the friction coefficient;

(b) the acceleration of the masses when $m_2/m_1 = \eta > \eta_0$.

1.94. A particle of mass m moves along the internal smooth surface of a vertical cylinder of radius R. Find the force with which the particle acts on the cylinder wall if at the initial moment of time its velocity equals v_0 and forms an angle α with the horizontal.

1.95. Find the magnitude and direction of the force acting on the particle of mass m during its motion in the plane xy according to the law $x = a \sin \omega t$, $y = b \cos \omega t$, where a, b, and ω are constants.

1.96. A body of mass m is thrown at an angle to the horizontal with the initial velocity $\mathbf{v}_0$. Assuming the air drag to be negligible, find:

(a) the momentum increment $\Delta\mathbf{p}$ that the body acquires over the first t seconds of motion;

(b) the modulus of the momentum increment $\Delta\mathbf{p}$ during the total time of motion.

1.97. At the moment $t = 0$ a stationary particle of mass m experiences a time-dependent force $\mathbf{F} = \mathbf{a}t(\tau - t)$, where $\mathbf{a}$ is a constant vector, τ is the time during which the given force acts. Find:

(a) the momentum of the particle when the action of the force discontinued;

(b) the distance covered by the particle while the force acted.

1.98. At the moment $t = 0$ a particle of mass m starts moving due to a force $\mathbf{F} = \mathbf{F}_0 \sin \omega t$, where $\mathbf{F}_0$ and ω are constants. Find the distance covered by the particle as a function of t. Draw the approximate plot of this function.

1.99. At the moment $t = 0$ a particle of mass m starts moving due to a force $\mathbf{F} = \mathbf{F}_0 \cos \omega t$, where $\mathbf{F}_0$ and ω are constants. How long will it be moving until it stops for the first time? What distance will it traverse during that time? What is the maximum velocity of the particle over this distance?

1.100. A motorboat of mass m moves along a lake with velocity v_0. At the moment $t = 0$ the engine of the boat is shut down. Assuming the resistance of water to be proportional to the velocity of the boat $\mathbf{F} = -r\mathbf{v}$, find:

(a) how long the motorboat moved with the shutdown engine;

(b) the velocity of the motorboat as a function of the distance covered with the shutdown engine, as well as the total distance covered till the complete stop;

(c) the mean velocity of the motorboat over the time interval (beginning with the moment $t = 0$), during which its velocity decreases η times.

1.101. Having gone through a plank of thickness h, a bullet changed its velocity from v_0 to v. Find the time of motion of the bullet in the plank, assuming the resistance force to be proportional to the square of the velocity.

1.102. A small bar starts sliding down an inclined plane forming an angle α with the horizontal. The friction coefficient depends on the distance x covered as $k = ax$, where a is a constant. Find the distance covered by the bar till it stops, and its maximum velocity over this distance.

1.103. A body of mass m rests on a horizontal plane with the friction coefficient k. At the moment $t = 0$ a horizontal force is applied to it, which varies with time as $\mathbf{F} = \mathbf{a}t$, where $\mathbf{a}$ is a constant vector.

Find the distance traversed by the body during the first t second after the force action began.

1.104. A body of mass m is thrown straight up with velocity v_0. Find the velocity v' with which the body comes down if the air drag equal kv^2, where k is a constant and v is the velocity of the body.

1.105. A particle of mass m moves in a certain plane P due to a force F whose magnitude is constant and whose vector rotates in that plane with a constant angular velocity ω. Assuming the particle to be stationary at the moment $t = 0$, find:

(a) its velocity as a function of time;

(b) the distance covered by the particle between two successive stops, and the mean velocity over this time.

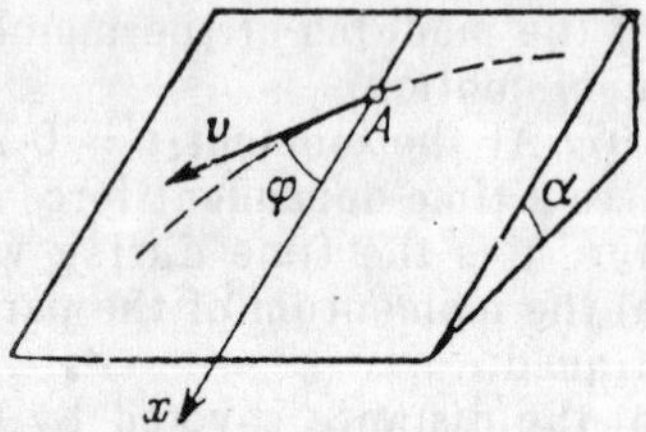

Fig. 1.27

1.106. A small disc A is placed on a inclined plane forming an angle α with the horizontal (Fig. 1.27) and is imparted an initial velocity v_0. Find how the velocity of the disc depends on the angle φ if the friction coefficient $k = \tan\alpha$ and at the initial moment $\varphi_0 = \pi/2$.

1.107. A chain a length l is placed on a smooth spherical surface of radius R with one of its ends fixed at the top of the sphere. What will be the acceleration w of each element of the chain when its upper end is released? It is assumed that the length of the chain $1 < \frac{1}{2}\pi R$.

1.108. A small body is placed on the top of a smooth sphere of radius R. Then the sphere is imparted a constant acceleration w_0 in the horizontal direction and the body begins sliding down. Find:

(a) the velocity of the body relative to the sphere at the moment of break-off;

(b) the angle θ_0 between the vertical and the radius vector drawn from the centre of the sphere to the break-off point; calculate θ_0 for $w_0 = g$.

1.109. A particle moves in a plane under the action of a force which is always perpendicular to the particle's velocity and depends on a distance to a certain point on the plane as $1/r^n$, where n is a constant. At what value of n will the motion of the particle along the circle be *steady*?

1.110. A sleeve A can slide freely along a smooth rod bent in the shape of a half-circle of radius R (Fig. 1.28). The system is set in rotation with a constant angular velocity ω about a vertical exist OO'. Find the angle θ corresponding to the steady position of the sleeve.

1.111. A rifle was aimed at the vertical line on the target located precisely in the northern direction, and then fired. Assuming the air drag to be negligible, find how much off the line, and in what direction, will the bullet hit the target. The shot was fired in the horizontal direction at the latitude $\varphi = 60°$, the bullet velocity $v = 900$ m/s, and the distance from the target equals $s = 1.0$ km.

1.112. A horizontal disc rotates with a constant angular velocity $\omega = 6.0$ rad/s about a vertical axis passing through its centre. A small body of mass $m = 0.50$ kg moves along a diameter of the disc with a velocity $v' = 50$ cm/s which is constant relative to the disc. Find the force that the disc exerts on the body at the moment when it is located at the distance $r = 30$ cm from the rotation axis.

1.113. A horizontal smooth rod *AB* rotates with a constant angular velocity $\omega = 2.00$ rad/s about a vertical axis passing through its end *A*. A freely sliding sleeve of mass $m = 0.50$ kg moves along the rod from the point *A* with the initial velocity $v_0 = 1.00$ m/s. Find the Coriolis force acting on the sleeve (in the reference frame fixed to the rotating rod) at the moment when the sleeve is located at the distance $r = 50$ cm from the rotation axis.

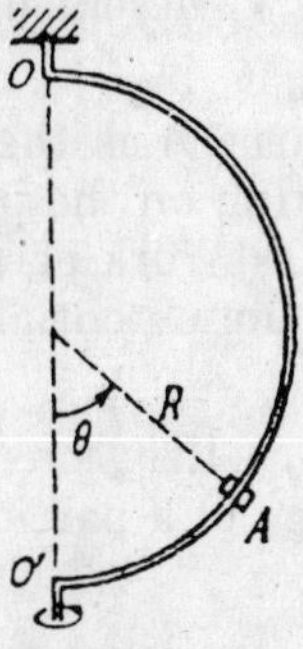

Fig. 1.28

1.114. A horizontal disc of radius R rotates with a constant angular velocity ω about a stationary vertical axis passing through its edge. Along the circumference of the disc a particle of mass m moves with a velocity that is constant relative to the disc. At the moment when the particle is at the maximum distance from the rotation axis, the resultant of the inertial force F_{in} acting on the particle in the reference frame fixed to the disc turns into zero. Find:

(a) the acceleration ω' of the particle relative to the disc;

(b) the dependence of F_{in} on the distance from the rotation axis.

1.115. A small body of mass $m = 0.30$ kg starts sliding down from the top of a smooth sphere of radius $R = 1.00$ m. The sphere rotates with a constant angular velocity $\omega = 6.0$ rad/s about a vertical axis passing through its centre. Find the centrifugal force of inertia and the Coriolis force at the moment when the body breaks off the surface of the sphere in the reference frame fixed to the sphere.

1.116. A train of mass $m = 2000$ tons moves in the latitude $\varphi = 60°$ North. Find:

(a) the magnitude and direction of the lateral force that the train exerts on the rails if it moves along a meridian with a velocity $v = 54$ km per hour;

(b) in what direction and with what velocity the train should move for the resultant of the inertial forces acting on the train in the reference frame fixed to the Earth to the equal to zero.

1.117. At the equator a stationary (relative to the Earth) body falls down from the height $h = 500$ m. Assuming the air drag to be negligible, find how much off the vertical, and in what direction, the body will deviate when it hits the ground.

1.3. LAWS OF CONSERVATION OF ENERGY, MOMENTUM, AND ANGULAR MOMENTUM

• Work and power of the force F:

$$A = \int \mathbf{F}\, d\mathbf{r} = \int F_s\, ds, \quad P = \mathbf{F}\mathbf{v}. \tag{1.3a}$$

• Increment of the kinetic energy of a particle:

$$T_2 - T_1 = A, \tag{1.3b}$$

where A is the work performed by the resultant of *all* the forces acting on the particle.

• Work performed by the forces of a field is equal to the decrease of the potential energy of a particle in the given field:

$$A = U_1 - U_2 \tag{1.3c}$$

• Relationship between the force of a field and the potential energy of a particle in the field:

$$F = -\nabla U, \tag{1.3d}$$

i.e. the force is equal to the antigradient of the potential energy.

• Increment of the total mechanical energy of a particle in a given potential field:

$$E_2 - E_1 = A_{ext}, \tag{1.3e}$$

where A_{ext} is the algebraic sum of works performed by all *extraneous* forces not belonging to those of the given field.

• Increment of the total mechanical energy of a system:

$$E_2 - E_1 = A_{ext} + A_{int}^{noncons}, \tag{1.3f}$$

where $E = T + U$, and U is the *inherent* potential energy of the system.

• Law of momentum variation of a system:

$$dp/dt = F, \tag{1.3g}$$

where F is the resultant of all external forces.

• Equation of motion of the system's centre of inertia:

$$m\frac{dv_C}{dt} = F, \tag{1.3h}$$

where F is the resultant of all external forces.

• Kinetic energy of a system

$$T = \tilde{T} + \frac{mv_C^2}{2} \tag{1.3i}$$

where $\tilde{T}$ is the kinetic energy in the system of centre of inertia.

• Equation of dynamics of a body with variable mass:

$$m\frac{dv}{dt} = F + \frac{dm}{dt}u, \tag{1.3j}$$

where u is the velocity of the separated (gained) substance relative to the body considered.

• Law of angular momentum variation of a system:

$$\frac{d\mathbf{M}}{dt}=\mathbf{N}, \qquad (1.3k)$$

where **M** is the angular momentum of the system, and **N** is the total moment of all *external* forces.

• Angular momentum of a system:

$$\mathbf{M}=\widetilde{\mathbf{M}}+[\mathbf{r}_C\mathbf{p}], \qquad (1.3l)$$

where $\widetilde{\mathbf{M}}$ is its angular momentum in the system of the centre of inertia, $\mathbf{r}_C$ is the radius vector of the centre of inertia, and **p** is the momentum of the system.

1.118. A particle has shifted along some trajectory in the plane xy from point *1* whose radius vector $\mathbf{r}_1 = \mathbf{i} + 2\mathbf{j}$ to point *2* with the radius vector $\mathbf{r}_2 = 2\mathbf{i} - 3\mathbf{j}$. During that time the particle experienced the action of certain forces, one of which being $\mathbf{F} = 3\mathbf{i} + 4\mathbf{j}$. Find the work performed by the force **F**. (Here r_1, r_2, and F are given in SI units).

1.119. A locomotive of mass m starts moving so that its velocity varies according to the law $v = a\sqrt{s}$, where a is a constant, and s is the distance covered. Find the total work performed by all the forces which are acting on the locomotive during the first t seconds after the beginning of motion.

1.120. The kinetic energy of a particle moving along a circle of radius R depends on the distance covered s as $T = as^2$, where a is a constant. Find the force acting on the particle as a function of s.

1.121. A body of mass m was slowly hauled up the hill (Fig. 1.29) by a force **F** which at each point was directed along a tangent to the trajectory. Find the work performed by this force, if the height of the hill is h, the length of its base l, and the coefficient of friction k.

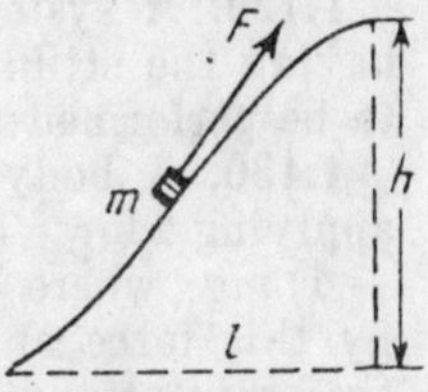

Fig. 1.29.

1.122. A disc of mass $m = 50$ g slides with the zero initial velocity down an inclined plane set at an angle $\alpha = 30°$ to the horizontal; having traversed the distance $l = 50$ cm along the horizontal plane, the disc stops. Find the work performed by the friction forces over the whole distance, assuming the friction coefficient $k = 0.15$ for both inclined and horizontal planes.

1.123. Two bars of masses m_1 and m_2 connected by a non-deformed light spring rest on a horizontal plane. The coefficient of friction between the bars and the surface is equal to k. What minimum constant force has to be applied in the horizontal direction to the bar of mass m_1 in order to shift the other bar?

1.124. A chain of mass $m = 0.80$ kg and length $l = 1.5$ m rests on a rough-surfaced table so that one of its ends hangs over the edge. The chain starts sliding off the table all by itself provided the overhanging part equals $\eta = 1/3$ of the chain length. What will be the total work performed by the friction forces acting on the chain by the moment it slides completely off the table?

1.125. A body of mass m is thrown at an angle α to the horizontal with the initial velocity v_0. Find the mean power developed by gravity over the whole time of motion of the body, and the instantaneous power of gravity as a function of time.

1.126. A particle of mass m moves along a circle of radius R with a normal acceleration varying with time as $w_n = at^2$, where a is a constant. Find the time dependence of the power developed by all the forces acting on the particle, and the mean value of this power averaged over the first t seconds after the beginning of motion.

1.127. A small body of mass m is located on a horizontal plane at the point O. The body acquires a horizontal velocity v_0. Find:

(a) the mean power developed by the friction force during the whole time of motion, if the friction coefficient $k = 0.27$, $m = 1.0$ kg, and $v_0 = 1.5$ m/s;

(b) the maximum instantaneous power developed by the friction force, if the friction coefficient varies as $k = \alpha x$, where α is a constant, and x is the distance from the point O.

1.128. A small body of mass $m = 0.10$ kg moves in the reference frame rotating about a stationary axis with a constant angular velocity $\omega = 5.0$ rad/s. What work does the centrifugal force of inertia perform during the transfer of this body along an arbitrary path from point *1* to point *2* which are located at the distances $r_1 = 30$ cm and $r_2 = 50$ cm from the rotation axis?

1.129. A system consists of two springs connected in series and having the stiffness coefficients k_1 and k_2. Find the minimum work to be performed in order to stretch this system by Δl.

1.130. A body of mass m is hauled from the Earth's surface by applying a force **F** varying with the height of ascent y as $\mathbf{F} = 2(ay - 1)m\mathbf{g}$, where a is a positive constant. Find the work performed by this force and the increment of the body's potential energy in the gravitational field of the Earth over the first half of the ascent.

1.131. The potential energy of a particle in a certain field has the form $U = a/r^2 - b/r$, where a and b are positive constants, r is the distance from the centre of the field. Find:

(a) the value of r_0 corresponding to the equilibrium position of the particle; examine whether this position is steady;

(b) the maximum magnitude of the attraction force; draw the plots $U(r)$ and $F_r(r)$ (the projections of the force on the radius vector **r**).

1.132. In a certain two-dimensional field of force the potential energy of a particle has the form $U = \alpha x^2 + \beta y^2$, where α and β are positive constants whose magnitudes are different. Find out:

(a) whether this field is central;

(b) what is the shape of the equipotential surfaces and also of the surfaces for which the magnitude of the vector of force $F = \text{const}$.

1.133. There are two stationary fields of force $\mathbf{F} = ay\mathbf{i}$ and $\mathbf{F} =$

$= ax\mathbf{i} + by\mathbf{j}$, where $\mathbf{i}$ and $\mathbf{j}$ are the unit vectors of the x and y axes, and a and b are constants. Find out whether these fields are potential.

1.134. A body of mass m is pushed with the initial velocity v_0 up an inclined plane set at an angle α to the horizontal. The friction coefficient is equal to k. What distance will the body cover before it stops and what work do the friction forces perform over this distance?

1.135. A small disc A slides down with initial velocity equal to zero from the top of a smooth hill of height H having a horizontal portion (Fig. 1.30). What must be the height of the horizontal portion h to ensure the maximum distance s covered by the disc? What is it equal to?

1.136. A small body A starts sliding from the height h down an inclined groove passing into a half-circle of radius $h/2$ (Fig. 1.31). Assuming the friction to be negligible, find the velocity of the body at the

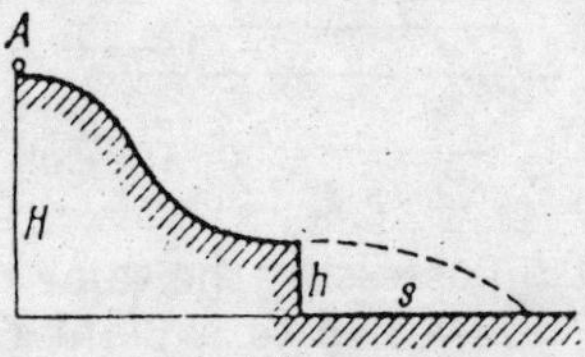

Fig. 1.30

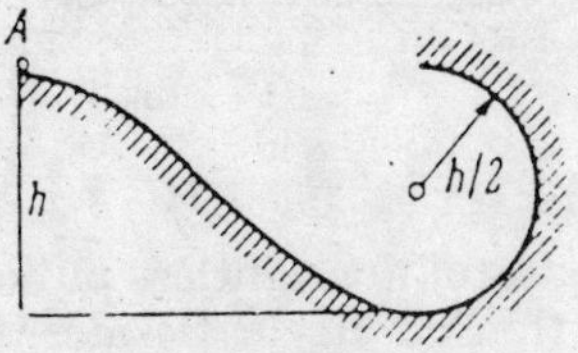

Fig. 1.31

highest point of its trajectory (after breaking off the groove).

1.137. A ball of mass m is suspended by a thread of length l. With what minimum velocity has the point of suspension to be shifted in the horizontal direction for the ball to move along the circle about that point? What will be the tension of the thread at the moment it will be passing the horizontal position?

1.138. A horizontal plane supports a stationary vertical cylinder of radius R and a disc A attached to the cylinder by horizontal thread AB of length l_0 (Fig. 1.32, top view). An initial velocity v_0 is imparted to the disc as shown in the figure. How long will it move along the plane

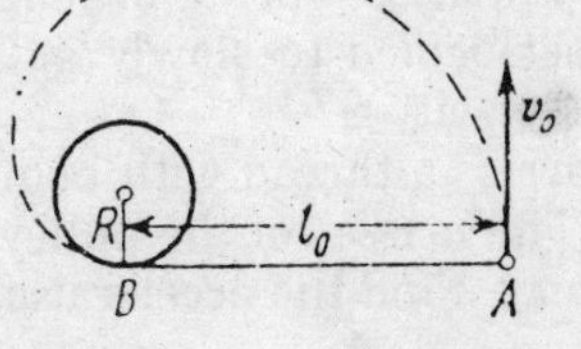

Fig. 1.32

Fig. 1.33

until it strikes against the cylinder? The friction is assumed to be absent.

1.139. A smooth rubber cord of length l whose coefficient of elasticity is k is suspended by one end from the point O (Fig. 1.33). The other end is fitted with a catch B. A small sleeve A of mass m starts falling from the point O. Neglecting the masses of the thread and the catch, find the maximum elongation of the cord.

1.140. A small bar A resting on a smooth horizontal plane is attached by threads to a point P (Fig. 1.34) and, by

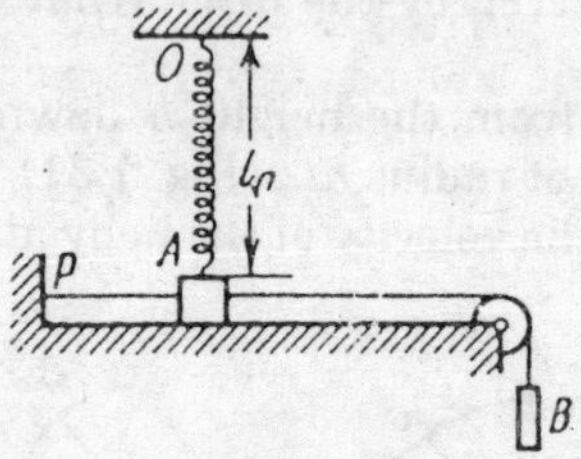

Fig. 1.34

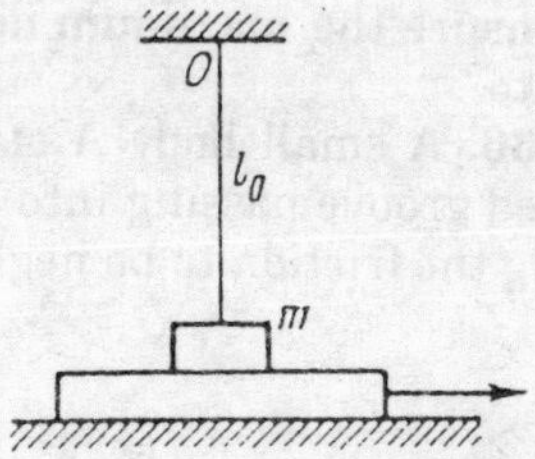

Fig. 1.35

means of a weightless pulley, to a weight B possessing the same mass as the bar itself. Besides, the bar is also attached to a point O by means of a light nondeformed spring of length $l_0 = 50$ cm and stiffness $x = 5\ mg/l_0$, where m is the mass of the bar. The thread PA having been burned, the bar starts moving. Find its velocity at the moment when it is breaking off the plane.

1.141. A horizontal plane supports a plank with a bar of mass m = 1.0 kg placed on it and attache by a light elastic non-deformed cord of length l_0 = 40 cm to a point O (Fig. 1.35). The coefficient of friction between the bar and the plank equals k = 0.20. The plank is slowly shifted to the right until the bar starts sliding over it. It occurs at the moment when the cord deviates from the vertical by an angle $\theta = 30°$. Find the work that has been performed by that moment by the friction force acting on the bar in the reference frame fixed to the plane.

1.142. A smooth light horizontal rod AB can rotate about a vertical axis passing through its end A. The rod is fitted with a small sleeve of mass m attached to the end A by a weightless spring of length l_0 and stiffness x. What work must be performed to slowly get this system going and reaching the angular velocity ω?

1.143. A pulley fixed to the ceiling carries a thread with bodies of masses m_1 and m_2 attached to its ends. The masses of the pulley and the thread are negligible, friction is absent. Find the acceleration w_C of the centre of inertia of this system.

1.144. Two interacting particles form a closed system whose centre of inertia is at rest. Fig 1.36 illustrates the positions of both particles at a certain moment and the trajectory of the particle of mass m_1. Draw the trajectory of the particle of mass m_2 if $m_2 = m_1/2$.

1.145. A closed chain A of mass $m = 0.36$ kg is attached to a vertical rotating shaft by means of a thread (Fig. 1.37), and rotates with a constant angular velocity $\omega = 35$ rad/s. The thread forms an angle $\theta = 45°$ with the vertical. Find the distance between the chain's centre of gravity and the rotation axis, and the tension of the thread.

1.146. A round cone A of mass $m = 3.2$ kg and half-angle $\alpha = 10°$ rolls uniformly and without slipping along a round conical surface B so that its apex O remains stationary (Fig. 1.38). The centre of gravity of the cone A is at the same level as the point O and at a distance $l = 17$ cm from it. The cone's axis moves with angular velocity ω. Find:

Fig. 1.36.

(a) the static friction force acting on the cone A, if $\omega = 1.0$ rad/s;

(b) at what values of ω the cone A will roll without sliding, if the coefficient of friction between the surfaces is equal to $k = 0.25$.

1.147. In the reference frame K two particles travel along the x axis, one of mass m_1 with velocity $\mathbf{v}_1$, and the other of mass m_2 with velocity $\mathbf{v}_2$. Find:

(a) the velocity $\mathbf{V}$ of the reference frame K' in which the cumulative kinetic energy of these particles is minimum;

(b) the cumulative kinetic energy of these particles in the K' frame.

1.148. The reference frame, in which the centre of inertia of a given system of particles is at rest, translates with a velocity $\mathbf{V}$ relative

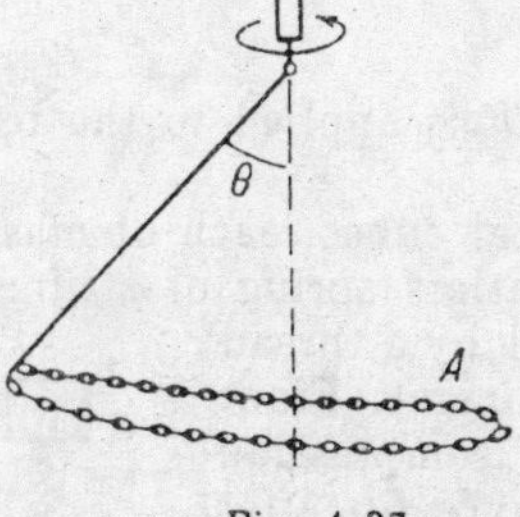

Fig. 1.37.

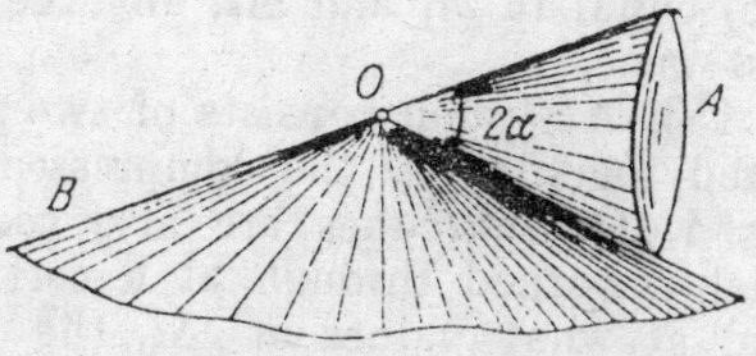

Fig. 1.38.

to an inertial reference frame K. The mass of the system of particles equals m, and the total energy of the system in the frame of the centre of inertia is equal to $\tilde{E}$. Find the total energy E of this system of particles in the reference frame K.

1.149. Two small discs of masses m_1 and m_2 interconnected by a weightless spring rest on a smooth horizontal plane. The discs are set in motion with initial velocities v_1 and v_2 whose directions are mutually perpendicular and lie in a horizontal plane. Find the total energy $\tilde{E}$ of this system in the frame of the centre of inertia.

1.150. A system consists of two small spheres of masses m_1 and m_2 interconnected by a weightless spring. At the moment $t = 0$ the spheres are set in motion with the initial velocities $\mathbf{v}_1$ and $\mathbf{v}_2$ after which the system starts moving in the Earth's uniform gravitational field. Neglecting the air drag, find the time dependence of the total momentum of this system in the process of motion and of the radius vector of its centre of inertia relative to the initial position of the centre.

1.151. Two bars of masses m_1 and m_2 connected by a weightless spring of stiffness $\varkappa$ (Fig. 1.39) rest on a smooth horizontal plane.

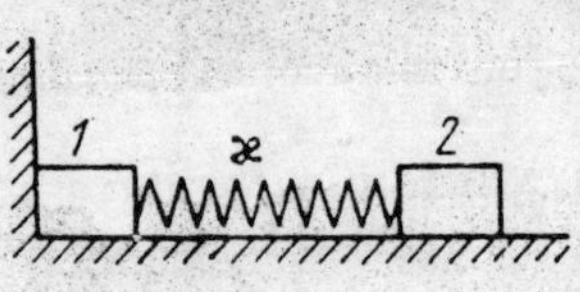

Fig. 1.39.

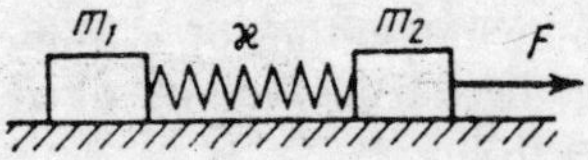

Fig. 1.40.

Bar *2* is shifted a small distance x to the left and then released. Find the velocity of the centre of inertia of the system after bar *1* breaks off the wall.

1.152. Two bars connected by a weightless spring of stiffness $\varkappa$ and length (in the non-deformed state) l_0 rest on a horizontal plane. A constant horizontal force F starts acting on one of the bars as shown in Fig. 1.40. Find the maximum and minimum distances between the bars during the subsequent motion of the system, if the masses of the bars are:

(a) equal;

(b) equal to m_1 and m_2, and the force F is applied to the bar of mass m_2.

1.153. A system consists of two identical cubes, each of mass m, linked together by the compressed weightless spring of stiffness $\varkappa$ (Fig. 1.41). The cubes are also connected by a thread which is burned through at a certain moment. Find:

(a) at what values of Δl, the initial compression of the spring, the lower cube will bounce up after the thread has been burned through;

(b) to what height h the centre of gravity of this system will rise if the initial compression of the spring $\Delta l = 7\ mg/\varkappa$.

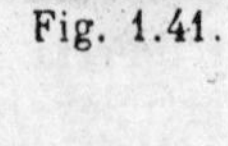

Fig. 1.41.

1.154. Two identical buggies *1* and *2* with one man in each move without friction due to inertia along the parallel rails toward each other. When the buggies get opposite each other, the men exchange their places by jumping in the direction perpendicular to the motion direction. As a consequence, buggy

1 stops and buggy *2* keeps moving in the same direction, with its velocity becoming equal to **v**. Find the initial velocities of the buggies $\mathbf{v}_1$ and $\mathbf{v}_2$ if the mass of each buggy (without a man) equals M and the mass of each man m.

1.155. Two identical buggies move one after the other due to inertia (without friction) with the same velocity $\mathbf{v}_0$. A man of mass m rides the rear buggy. At a certain moment the man jumps into the front buggy with a velocity **u** relative to his buggy. Knowing that the mass of each buggy is equal to M, find the velocities with which the buggies will move after that.

1.156. Two men, each of mass m, stand on the edge of a stationary buggy of mass M. Assuming the friction to be negligible, find the velocity of the buggy after both men jump off with the same horizontal velocity **u** relative to the buggy: (1) simultaneously; (2) one after the other. In what case will the velocity of the buggy be greater and how many times?

1.157. A chain hangs on a thread and touches the surface of a table by its lower end. Show that after the thread has been burned through, the force exerted on the table by the falling part of the chain at any moment is twice as great as the force of pressure exerted by the part already resting on the table.

1.158. A steel ball of mass $m = 50$ g falls from the height $h = 1.0$ m on the horizontal surface of a massive slab. Find the cumulative momentum that the ball imparts to the slab after numerous bounces, if every impact decreases the velocity of the ball $\eta = 1.25$ times.

1.159. A raft of mass M with a man of mass m aboard stays motionless on the surface of a lake. The man moves a distance $\mathbf{l}'$ relative to the raft with velocity $\mathbf{v}'(t)$ and then stops. Assuming the water resistance to be negligible, find:

(a) the displacement of the raft **l** relative to the shore;

(b) the horizontal component of the force with which the man acted on the raft during the motion.

1.160. A stationary pulley carries a rope whose one end supports a ladder with a man and the other end the counterweight of mass M. The man of mass m climbs up a distance $\mathbf{l}'$ with respect to the ladder and then stops. Neglecting the mass of the rope and the friction in the pulley axle, find the displacement **l** of the centre of inertia of this system.

1.161. A cannon of mass M starts sliding freely down a smooth inclined plane at an angle α to the horizontal. After the cannon covered the distance l, a shot was fired, the shell leaving the cannon in the horizontal direction with a momentum **p**. As a consequence, the cannon stopped. Assuming the mass of the shell to be negligible, as compared to that of the cannon, determine the duration of the shot.

1.162. A horizontally flying bullet of mass m gets stuck in a body of mass M suspended by two identical threads of length l (Fig. 1.42).

As a result, the threads swerve through an angle θ. Assuming $m \ll M$, find:

(a) the velocity of the bullet before striking the body;

(b) the fraction of the bullet's initial kinetic energy that turned into heat.

1.163. A body of mass M (Fig. 1.43) with a small disc of mass m placed on it rests on a smooth horizontal plane. The disc is set in

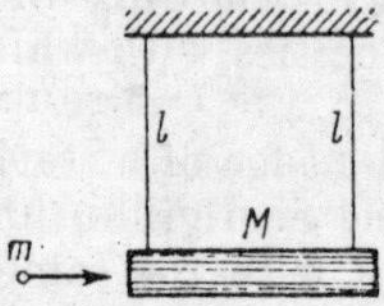

Fig. 1.42.

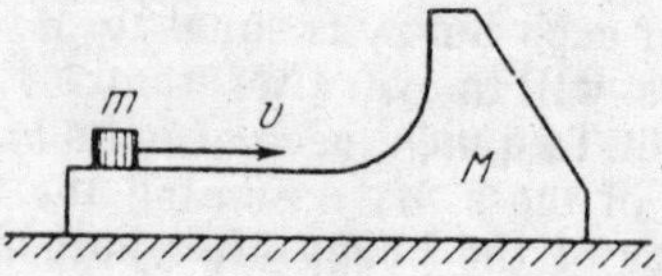

Fig. 1.43.

motion in the horizontal direction with velocity v. To what height (relative to the initial level) will the disc rise after breaking off the body M? The friction is assumed to be absent.

1.164. A small disc of mass m slides down a smooth hill of height h without initial velocity and gets onto a plank of mass M lying on

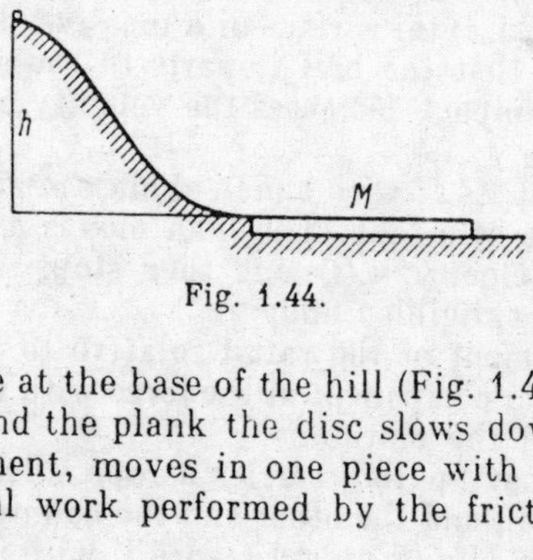

Fig. 1.44.

the horizontal plane at the base of the hill (Fig. 1.44). Due to friction between the disc and the plank the disc slows down and, beginning with a certain moment, moves in one piece with the plank.

(1) Find the total work performed by the friction forces in this process.

(2) Can it be stated that the result obtained does not depend on the choice of the reference frame?

1.165. A stone falls down without initial velocity from a height h onto the Earth's surface. The air drag assumed to be negligible, the stone hits the ground with velocity $v_0 = \sqrt{2gh}$ relative to the Earth. Obtain the same formula in terms of the reference frame "falling" to the Earth with a constant velocity v_0.

1.166. A particle of mass 1.0 g moving with velocity $\mathbf{v}_1 = 3.0\mathbf{i} - 2.0\mathbf{j}$ experiences a perfectly inelastic collision with another particle of mass 2.0 g and velocity $\mathbf{v}_2 = 4.0\mathbf{j} - 6.0\mathbf{k}$. Find the velocity of the formed particle (both the vector $\mathbf{v}$ and its modulus), if the components of the vectors $\mathbf{v}_1$ and $\mathbf{v}_2$ are given in the SI units.

1.167. Find the increment of the kinetic energy of the closed system omprising two spheres of masses m_1 and m_2 due to their perfectly ielastic collision, if the initial velocities of the spheres were equal o v_1 and v_2.

1.168. A particle of mass m_1 experienced a perfectly elastic collision with a stationary particle of mass m_2. What fraction of the kinetic energy does the striking particle lose, if

(a) it recoils at right angles to its original motion direction;

(b) the collision is a head-on one?

1.169. Particle 1 experiences a perfectly elastic collision with a stationary particle 2. Determine their mass ratio, if

(a) after a head-on collision the particles fly apart in the opposite directions with equal velocities;

(b) the particles fly apart symmetrically relative to the initial motion direction of particle 1 with the angle of divergence $\theta = 60°$.

1.170. A ball moving translationally collides elastically with another, stationary, ball of the same mass. At the moment of impact the angle between the straight line passing through the centres of the balls and the direction of the initial motion of the striking ball is equal to $\alpha = 45°$. Assuming the balls to be smooth, find the fraction η of the kinetic energy of the striking ball that turned into potential energy at the moment of the maximum deformation.

1.171. A shell flying with velocity $v = 500$ m/s bursts into three identical fragments so that the kinetic energy of the system increases $\eta = 1.5$ times. What maximum velocity can one of the fragments obtain?

1.172. Particle *1* moving with velocity $v = 10$ m/s experienced a head-on collision with a stationary particle *2* of the same mass. As a result of the collision, the kinetic energy of the system decreased by $\eta = 1.0\%$. Find the magnitude and direction of the velocity of particle 1 after the collision.

1.173. A particle of mass m having collided with a stationary particle of mass M deviated by an angle $\pi/2$ whereas the particle M recoiled at an angle $\theta = 30°$ to the direction of the initial motion of the particle m. How much (in per cent) and in what way has the kinetic energy of this system changed after the collision, if $M/m = 5.0$?

1.174. A closed system consists of two particles of masses m_1 and m_2 which move at right angles to each other with velocities v_1 and v_2. Find:

(a) the momentum of each particle and

(b) the total kinetic energy of the two particles in the reference frame fixed to their centre of inertia.

1.175. A particle of mass m1 collides elastically with a stationary particle of mass m_2 ($m_1 > m_2$). Find the maximum angle through which the striking particle may deviated as a result of the collision.

1.176. Three identical discs A, B, and C (Fig. 1.45) rest on a smooth horizontal plane. The disc A is get in motion with velocity v after which it experiences an elastic collision simultaneously with the discs B and C. The distance between the centres of the latter discs prior to the collision is η times greater than the diameter of each disc. Find the velocity of the disc A after the collision. At what value of η will the disc A recoil after the collision; stop; move on?

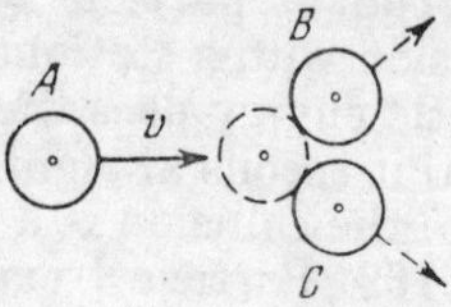

Fig. 1.45.

1.177. A molecule collides with another, stationary, molecule of the same mass. Demonstrate that the angle of divergence

(a) equals 90° when the collision is ideally elastic;

(b) differs from 90° when the collision is inelastic.

1.178. A rocket ejects a steady jet whose velocity is equal to **u** relative to the rocket. The gas discharge rate equals μ kg/s. Demonstrate that the rocket motion equation in this case takes the form

$$m\mathbf{w} = \mathbf{F} - \mu\mathbf{u},$$

where m is the mass of the rocket at a given moment, **w** is its acceleration, and **F** is the external force.

1.179. A rocket moves in the absence of external forces by ejecting a steady jet with velocity **u** constant relative to the rocket. Find the velocity **v** of the rocket at the moment when its mass is equal to m, if at the initial moment it possessed the mass m_0 and its velocity was equal to zero. Make use of the formula given in the foregoing problem.

1.180. Find the law according to which the mass of the rocket varies with time, when the rocket moves with a constant acceleration w, the external forces are absent, the gas escapes with a constant velocity u relative to the rocket, and its mass at the initial moment equals m_0.

1.181. A spaceship of mass m_0 moves in the absence of external forces with a constant velocity $\mathbf{v}_0$. To change the motion direction, a jet engine is switched on. It starts ejecting a gas jet with velocity u which is constant relative to the spaceship and directed at right angles to the spaceship motion. The engine is shut down when the mass of the spaceship decreases to m. Through what angle α did the motion direction of the spaceship deviate due to the jet engine operation?

1.182. A cart loaded with sand moves along a horizontal plane due to a constant force **F** coinciding in direction with the cart's velocity vector. In the process, sand spills through a hole in the bottom with a constant velocity μ kg/s. Find the acceleration and the velocity of the cart at the moment t, if at the initial moment $t = 0$ the cart with loaded sand had the mass m_0 and its velocity was equal to zero. The friction is to be neglected.

1.183. A flatcar of mass m_0 starts moving to the right due to a constant horizontal force **F** (Fig. 1.46). Sand spills on the flatcar from a stationary hopper. The velocity of loading is constant and equal to μ kg/s. Find the time dependence of the velocity and the acceleration of the flatcar in the process of loading. The friction is negligibly small.

1.184. A chain AB of length l is located in a smooth horizontal tube so that its fraction of length h hangs freely and touches the surface of the table with its end B (Fig. 1.47). At a certain moment

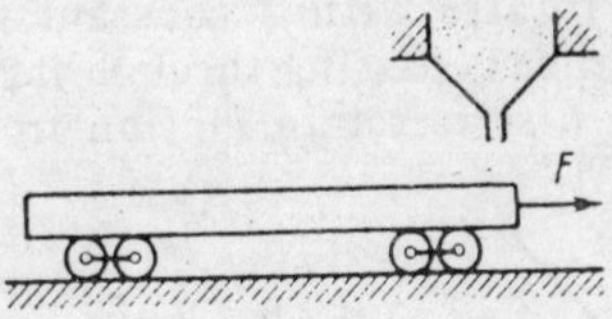

Fig. 1.46.

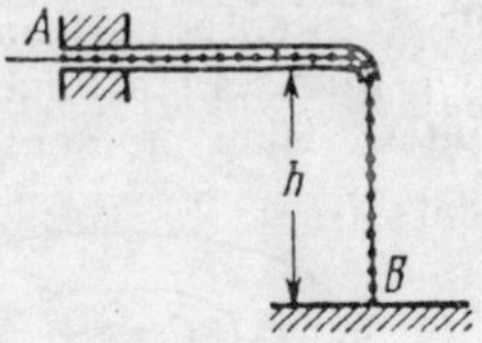

Fig. 1.47.

the end A of the chain is set free. With what velocity will this end of the chain slip out of the tube?

1.185. The angular momentum of a particle relative to a certain point O varies with time as $\mathbf{M} = \mathbf{a} + \mathbf{b}t^2$, where **a** and **b** are constant vectors, with $\mathbf{a} \perp \mathbf{b}$. Find the force moment **N** relative to the point O acting on the particle when the angle between the vectors **N** and **M** equals 45°.

1.186. A ball of mass m is thrown at an angle α to the horizontal with the initial velocity v_0. Find the time dependence of the magnitude of the ball's angular momentum vector relative to the point from which the ball is thrown. Find the angular momentum M at the highest point of the trajectory if $m = 130$ g, $\alpha = 45°$, and $v_0 = 25$ m/s. The air drag is to be neglected.

1.187. A disc A of mass m sliding over a smooth horizontal surface with velocity v experiences a perfectly elastic collision with a smooth stationary wall at a point O (Fig. 1.48). The angle between the motion direction of the disc and the normal of the wall is equal to α. Find:

(a) the points relative to which the angular momentum **M** of the disc remains constant in this process;

(b) the magnitude of the increment of the vector of the disc's angular momentum relative to the point O' which is located in the plane of the disc's motion at the distance l from the point O.

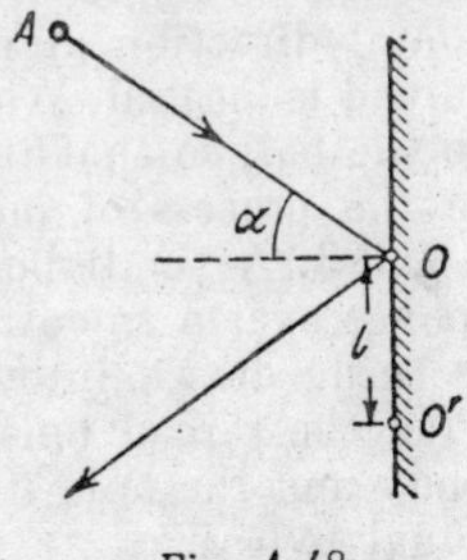

Fig. 1.48.

1.188. A small ball of mass m suspended from the ceiling at a point O by a thread of length l moves along a horizontal circle with a constant angular velocity ω. Relative to which points does the angular momentum **M** of the ball remain constant? Find the magnitude of the increment of the vector of the ball's angular momentum relative to the point O picked up during half a revolution.

1.189. A ball of mass m falls down without initial velocity from a height h over the Earth's surface. Find the increment of the ball's angular momentum vector picked up during the time of falling (relative to the point O of the reference frame moving translationally in a horizontal direction with a velocity V). The ball starts falling from the point O. The air drag is to be neglected.

1.190. A smooth horizontal disc rotates with a constant angular velocity ω about a stationary vertical a. is passing through its centre, the point O. At a moment $t = 0$ a disc is set in motion from that

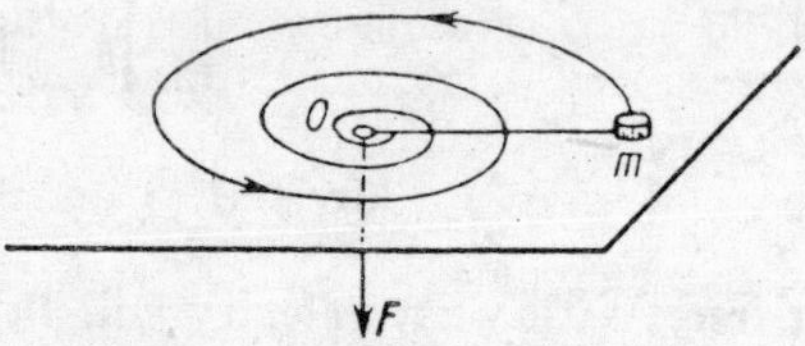

Fig. 1.49.

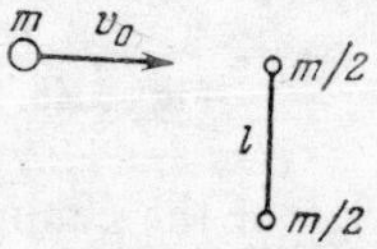

Fig. 1.50.

point with velocity v_0. Find the angular momentum $M(t)$ of the disc relative to the point O in the reference frame fixed to the disc. Make sure that this angular momentum is caused by the Coriolis force.

1.191. A particle moves along a closed trajectory in a central field of force where the particle's potential energy $U = kr^2$ (k is a positive constant, r is the distance of the particle from the centre O of the field). Find the mass of the particle if its minimum distance from the point O equals r_1 and its velocity at the point farthest from O equals v_2.

1.192. A small ball is suspended from a point O by a light thread of length l. Then the ball is drawn aside so that the thread deviates through an angle θ from the vertical and set in motion in a horizontal direction at right angles to the vertical plane in which the thread is located. What is the initial velocity that has to be imparted to the ball so that it could deviate through the maximum angle $\pi/2$ in the process of motion?

1.193. A small body of mass m tied to a non-stretchable thread moves over a smooth horizontal plane. The other end of the thread is being drawn into a hole O (Fig. 1.49) with a constant velocity. Find the thread tension as a function of the distance r between the body and the hole if at $r = r_0$ the angular velocity of the thread is equal to ω_0.

1.194. A light non-stretchable thread is wound on a massive fixed pulley of radius R. A small body of mass m is tied to the free end of the thread. At a moment $t = 0$ the system is released and starts moving. Find its angular momentum relative to the pulley axle as a function of time t.

1.195. A uniform sphere of mass m and radius R starts rolling without slipping down an inclined plane at an angle α to the horizontal. Find the time dependence of the angular momentum of the sphere relative to the point of contact at the initial moment. How will the obtained result change in the case of a perfectly smooth inclined plane?

1.196. A certain system of particles possesses a total momentum $\mathbf{p}$ and an angular momentum $\mathbf{M}$ relative to a point O. Find its angular momentum $\mathbf{M}'$ relative to a point O' whose position with respect to the point O is determined by the radius vector $\mathbf{r}_0$. Find out when the angular momentum of the system of particles does not depend on the choice of the point O.

1.197. Demonstrate that the angular momentum $\mathbf{M}$ of the system of particles relative to a point O of the reference frame K can be represented as

$$\mathbf{M} = \widetilde{\mathbf{M}} + [\mathbf{r}_C \mathbf{p}],$$

where $\widetilde{\mathbf{M}}$ is its proper angular momentum (in the reference frame moving translationally and fixed to the centre of inertia), $\mathbf{r}_C$ is the radius vector of the centre of inertia relative to the point O, $\mathbf{p}$ is the total momentum of the system of particles in the reference frame K.

1.198. A ball of mass m moving with velocity v_0 experiences a head-on elastic collision with one of the spheres of a stationary rigid dumbbell as whown in Fig. 1.50. The mass of each sphere equals $m/2$, and the distance between them is l. Disregarding the size of the spheres, find the proper angular momentum $\widetilde{M}$ of the dumbbell after the collision, i.e. the angular momentum in the reference frame moving translationally and fixed to the dumbbell's centre of inertia.

1.199. Two small identical discs, each of mass m, lie on a smooth horizontal plane. The discs are interconnected by a light non-deformed spring of length l_0 and stiffness $\varkappa$. At a certain moment one of the discs is set in motion in a horizontal direction perpendicular to the spring with velocity v_0. Find the maximum elongation of the spring in the process of motion, if it is known to be considerably less than unity.

1.4. UNIVERSAL GRAVITATION

- Universal gravitation law

$$F = \gamma \frac{m_1 m_2}{r^2}. \tag{1.4a}$$

- The squares of the periods of revolution of any two planets around the Sun are proportional to the cubes of the major semiaxes of their orbits (Kepler):

$$T^2 \propto a^3. \tag{1.4b}$$

- Strength $\mathbf{G}$ and potential φ of the gravitational field of a mass point:

$$\mathbf{G} = -\gamma \frac{m}{r^3}\mathbf{r}, \quad \varphi = -\gamma \frac{m}{r}. \tag{1.4c}$$

- Orbital and escape velocities:

$$v_1 = \sqrt{gR}, \quad v_2 = \sqrt{2}\, v_1. \tag{1.4d}$$

1.200. A planet of mass M moves along a circle around the Sun with velocity $v = 34.9$ km/s (relative to the heliocentric reference frame). Find the period of revolution of this planet around the Sun.

1.201. The Jupiter's period of revolution around the Sun is 12 times that of the Earth. Assuming the planetary orbits to be circular, find:

(a) how many times the distance between the Jupiter and the Sun exceeds that between the Earth and the Sun;

(b) the velocity and the acceleration of Jupiter in the heliocentric reference frame.

1.202. A planet of mass M moves around the Sun along an ellipse so that its minimum distance from the Sun is equal to r and the maximum distance to R. Making use of Kepler's laws, find its period of revolution around the Sun.

1.203. A small body starts falling onto the Sun from a distance equal to the radius of the Earth's orbit. The initial velocity of the body is equal to zero in the heliocentric reference frame. Making use of Kepler's laws, find how long the body will be falling.

1.204. Suppose we have made a model of the Solar system scaled down in the ratio η but of materials of the same mean density as the actual materials of the planets and the Sun. How will the orbital periods of revolution of planetary models change in this case?

1.205. A double star is a system of two stars moving around the centre of inertia of the system due to gravitation. Find the distance between the components of the double star, if its total mass equals M and the period of revolution T.

1.206. Find the potential energy of the gravitational interaction

(a) of two mass points of masses m_1 and m_2 located at a distance r from each other;

(b) of a mass point of mass m and a thin uniform rod of mass M and length l, if they are located along a straight line at a distance a from each other; also find the force of their interaction.

1.207. A planet of mass m moves along an ellipse around the Sun so that its maximum and minimum distances from the Sun are equal to r_1 and r_2 respectively. Find the angular momentum M of this planet relative to the centre of the Sun.

1.208. Using the conservation laws, demonstrate that the total mechanical energy of a planet of mass m moving around the Sun along an ellipse depends only on its semi-major axis a. Find this energy as a function of a.

1.209. A planet A moves along an elliptical orbit around the Sun. At the moment when it was at the distance r_0 from the Sun its velocity was equal to v_0 and the angle between the radius vector $\mathbf{r}_0$ and the velocity vector $\mathbf{v}_0$ was equal to α. Find the maximum and minimum distances that will separate this planet from the Sun during its orbital motion.

1.210. A cosmic body A moves to the Sun with velocity v_0 (when far from the Sun) and aiming parameter l the arm of the vector $\mathbf{v}_0$

relative to the centre of the Sun (Fig. 1.51). Find the minimum distance by which this body will get to the Sun.

1.211. A particle of mass m is located outside a uniform sphere of mass M at a distance r from its centre. Find:

(a) the potential energy of gravitational interaction of the particle and the sphere;

(b) the gravitational force which the sphere exerts on the particle.

1.212. Demonstrate that the gravitational force acting on a particle A inside a uniform spherical layer of matter is equal to zero.

1.213. A particle of mass m was transferred from the centre of the base of a uniform hemisphere of mass M and radius R into infinity.

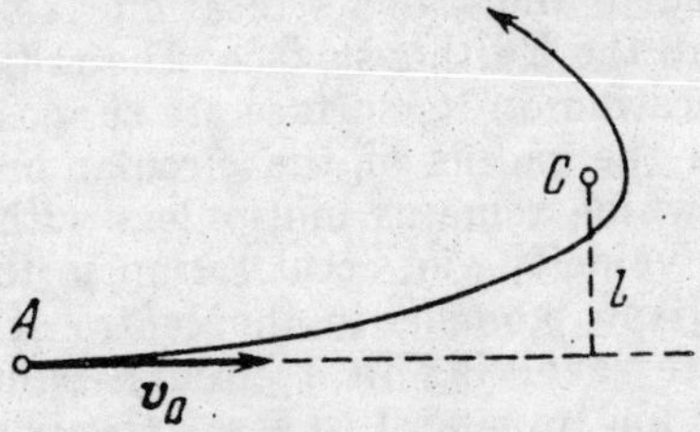

Fig. 1.51.

What work was performed in the process by the gravitational force exerted on the particle by the hemisphere?

1.214. There is a uniform sphere of mass M and radius R. Find the strength $\mathbf{G}$ and the potential φ of the gravitational field of this sphere as a function of the distance r from its centre (with $r < R$ and $r > R$). Draw the approximate plots of the functions $G(r)$ and $\varphi(r)$.

1.215. Inside a uniform sphere of density ρ there is a spherical cavity whose centre is at a distance $\mathbf{l}$ from the centre of the sphere. Find the strength $\mathbf{G}$ of the gravitational field inside the cavity.

1.216. A uniform sphere has a mass M and radius R. Find the pressure p inside the sphere, caused by gravitational compression, as a function of the distance r from its centre. Evaluate p at the centre of the Earth, assuming it to be a uniform sphere.

1.217. Find the proper potential energy of gravitational interaction of matter forming

(a) a thin uniform spherical layer of mass m and radius R;

(b) a uniform sphere of mass m and radius R (make use of the answer to Problem 1.214).

1.218. Two Earth's satellites move in a common plane along circular orbits. The orbital radius of one satellite $r = 7000$ km while that of the other satellite is $\Delta r = 70$ km less. What time interval separates the periodic approaches of the satellites to each other over the minimum distance?

1.219. Calculate the ratios of the following accelerations: the acceleration w_1 due to the gravitational force on the Earth's surface, the acceleration w_2 due to the centrifugal force of inertia on the Earth's equator, and the acceleration w_3 caused by the Sun to the bodies on the Earth.

1.220. At what height over the Earth's pole the free-fall acceleration decreases by one per cent; by half?

1.221. On the pole of the Earth a body is imparted velocity v_0 directed vertically up. Knowing the radius of the Earth and the free-fall acceleration on its surface, find the height to which the body will ascend. The air drag is to be neglected.

1.222. An artificial satellite is launched into a circular orbit around the Earth with velocity v relative to the reference frame moving translationally and fixed to the Earth's rotation axis. Find the distance from the satellite to the Earth's surface. The radius of the Earth and the free-fall acceleration on its surface are supposed to be known.

1.223. Calculate the radius of the circular orbit of a stationary Earth's satellite, which remains motionless with respect to its surface. What are its velocity and acceleration in the inertial reference frame fixed at a given moment to the centre of the Earth?

1.224. A satellite revolving in a circular equatorial orbit of radius $R = 2.00 \cdot 10^4$ km from west to east appears over a certain point at the equator every $\tau = 11.6$ hours. Using these data, calculate the mass of the Earth. The gravitational constant is supposed to be known.

1.225. A satellite revolves from east to west in a circular equatorial orbit of radius $R = 1.00 \cdot 10^4$ km around the Earth. Find the velocity and the acceleration of the satellite in the reference frame fixed to the Earth.

1.226. A satellite must move in the equatorial plane of the Earth close to its surface either in the Earth's rotation direction or against it. Find how many times the kinetic energy of the satellite in the latter case exceeds that in the former case (in the reference frame fixed to the Earth).

1.227. An artificial satellite of the Moon revolves in a circular orbit whose radius exceeds the radius of the Moon η times. In the process of motion the satellite experiences a slight resistance due to cosmic dust. Assuming the resistance force to depend on the velocity of the satellite as $F = \alpha v^2$, where α is a constant, find how long the satellite will stay in orbit until it falls onto the Moon's surface.

1.228. Calculate the orbital and escape velocities for the Moon. Compare the results obtained with the corresponding velocities for the Earth.

1.229. A spaceship approaches the Moon along a parabolic trajectory which is almost tangent to the Moon's surface. At the moment of the maximum approach the brake rocket was fired for a short time interval, and the spaceship was transferred into a circular orbit of a Moon satellite. Find how the spaceship velocity modulus increased in the process of braking.

1.230. A spaceship is launched into a circular orbit close to the

Earth's surface. What additional velocity has to be imparted to the spaceship to overcome the gravitational pull?

1.231. At what distance from the centre of the Moon is the point at which the strength of the resultant of the Earth's and Moon's gravitational fields is equal to zero? The Earth's mass is assumed to be $\eta = 81$ times that of the Moon, and the distance between the centres of these planets $n = 60$ times greater than the radius of the Earth R.

1.232. What is the minimum work that has to be performed to bring a spaceship of mass $m = 2.0 \cdot 10^3$ kg from the surface of the Earth to the Moon?

1.233. Find approximately the third cosmic velocity v_3, i.e. the minimum velocity that has to be imparted to a body relative to the Earth's surface to drive it out of the Solar system. The rotation of the Earth about its own axis is to be neglected.

1.5. DYNAMICS OF A SOLID BODY

• Equation of dynamics of a solid body rotating about a stationary axis z:

$$I\beta_z = N_z, \tag{1.5a}$$

where N_z is the algebraic sum of the moments of external forces relative to the x axis.

• According to Stainer's theorem:

$$I = I_C + ma^2. \tag{1.5b}$$

• Kinetic energy of a solid body rotating about a stationary axis.

$$T = \frac{1}{2} I\omega^2. \tag{1.5c}$$

• Work performed by external forces during the rotation of a solid body about a stationary axis:

$$A = \int N_z \, d\varphi. \tag{1.5d}$$

• Kinetic energy of a solid body in plane motion:

$$T = \frac{I_C\omega^2}{2} + \frac{mv_C^2}{2} \tag{1.5e}$$

• Relationship between the angular velocity ω' of gyroscope precession, its angular momentum **M** equal to $I\omega$, and the moment **N** of the external forces:

$$|\omega' \mathbf{M}| = \mathbf{N}. \tag{1.5f}$$

1.234. A thin uniform rod AB of mass $m = 1.0$ kg moves translationally with acceleration $w = 2.0$ m/s^2 due to two antiparallel forces $\mathbf{F}_1$ and $\mathbf{F}_2$ (Fig. 1.52). The distance between the points at which these forces are applied is equal to $a = 20$ cm. Besides, it is known that $F_2 = 5.0$ N. Find the length of the rod.

1.235. A force $\mathbf{F} = A\mathbf{i} + B\mathbf{j}$ is applied to a point whose radius vector relative to the origin of coordinates O is equal to $\mathbf{r} = a\mathbf{i} + b\mathbf{j}$, where a, b, A, B are constants, and $\mathbf{i}$, $\mathbf{j}$ are the unit vectors of the x and y axes. Find the moment **N** and the arm l of the force **F** relative to the point O.

1.236. A force $\mathbf{F}_1 = A\mathbf{j}$ is applied to a point whose radius vector $\mathbf{r}_1 = a\mathbf{i}$, while a force $\mathbf{F}_2 = B\mathbf{i}$ is applied to the point whose radius vector $\mathbf{r}_2 = b\mathbf{j}$. Both radius vectors are determined relative to the origin of coordinates O, **i** and **j** are the unit vectors of the x and y

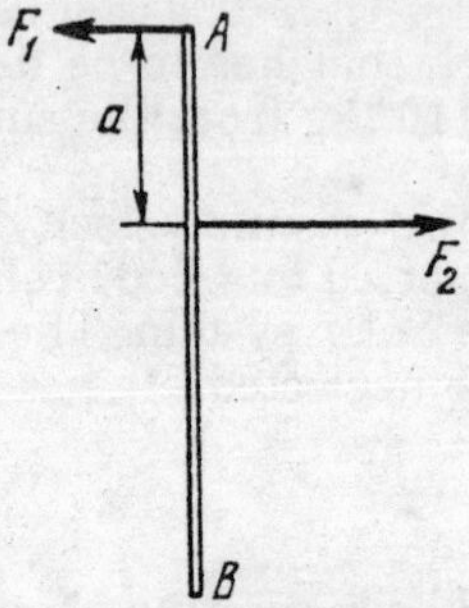

Fig. 1.52.

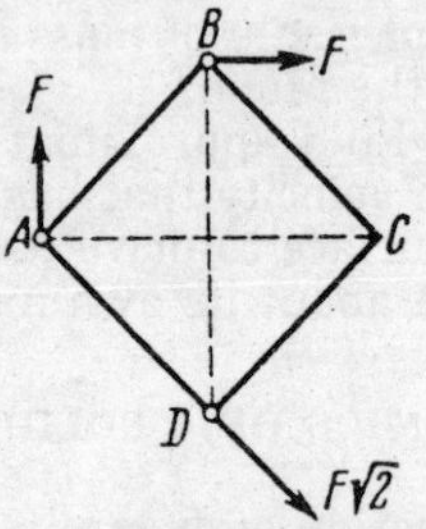

Fig. 1.53.

axes, a, b, A, B are constants. Find the arm l of the resultant force relative to the point O.

1.237. Three forces are applied to a square plate as shown in Fig. 1.53. Find the modulus, direction, and the point of application of the resultant force, if this point is taken on the side BC.

1.238. Find the moment of inertia

(a) of a thin uniform rod relative to the axis which is perpendicular to the rod and passes through its end, if the mass of the rod is m and its length l;

(b) of a thin uniform rectangular plate relative to the axis passing perpendicular to the plane of the plate through one of its vertices, if the sides of the plate are equal to a and b, and its mass is m.

1.239. Calculate the moment of inertia

(a) of a copper uniform disc relative to the symmetry axis perpendicular to the plane of the disc, if its thickness is equal to $b = 2.0$ mm and its radius to $R = 100$ mm;

(b) of a uniform solid cone relative to its symmetry axis, if the mass of the cone is equal to m and the radius of its base to R.

1.240. Demonstrate that in the case of a thin plate of arbitrary shape there is the following relationship between the moments of inertia: $I_1 + I_2 = I_3$, where subindices 1, 2, and 3 define three mutually perpendicular axes passing through one point, with axes 1 and 2 lying in the plane of the plate. Using this relationship, find the moment of inertia of a thin uniform round disc of radius R and mass m relative to the axis coinciding with one of its diameters.

1.241. A uniform disc of radius $R = 20$ cm has a round cut as shown in Fig. 1.54. The mass of the remaining (shaded) portion of the disc equals $m = 7.3$ kg. Find the moment of inertia of such a disc relative to the axis passing through its centre of inertia and perpendicular to the plane of the disc.

1.242. Using the formula for the moment of inertia of a uniform sphere, find the moment of inertia of a thin spherical layer of mass m and radius R relative to the axis passing through its centre.

1.243. A light thread with a body of mass m tied to its end is wound on a uniform solid cylinder of mass M and radius R (Fig. 1.55). At a moment $t = 0$ the system is set in motion. Assuming the friction in the axle of the cylinder to be negligible, find the time dependence of

(a) the angular velocity of the cylinder;

(b) the kinetic energy of the whole system.

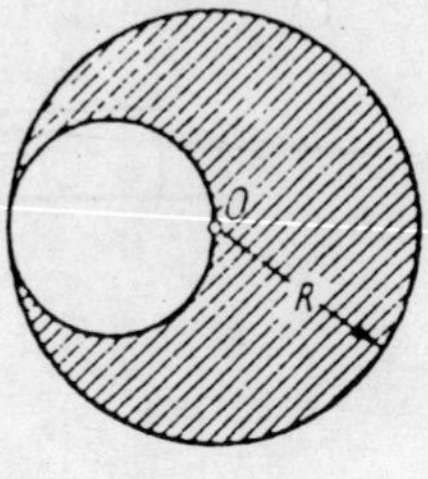

Fig. 1.54.

1.244. The ends of thin threads tightly wound on the axle of radius r of the Maxwell disc are attached to a horizontal bar. When the disc unwinds, the bar is raised to keep the disc at the same height. The mass of the disc with the axle is equal to m, the moment of inertia of the arrangement relative to its axis is I. Find the tension of each thread and the acceleration of the bar.

1.245. A thin horizontal uniform rod AB of mass m and length l can rotate freely about a vertical axis passing through its end A. At a certain moment the end B starts experiencing a constant force F

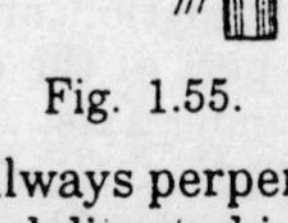

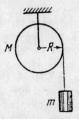

Fig. 1.55.

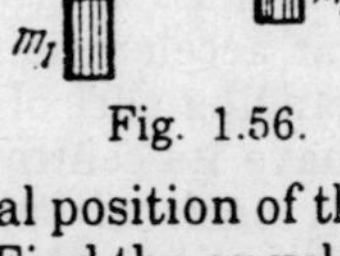

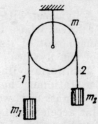

Fig. 1.56.

which is always perpendicular to the original position of the stationary rod and directed in a horizontal plane. Find the angular velocity of the rod as a function of its rotation angle φ counted relative to the initial position.

1.246. In the arrangement shown in Fig. 1.56 the mass of the uniform solid cylinder of radius R is equal to m and the masses of two bodies are equal to m_1 and m_2. The thread slipping and the friction in the axle of the cylinder are supposed to be absent. Find the angular acceleration of the cylinder and the ratio of tensions T_1/T_2 of the vertical sections of the thread in the process of motion.

1.247. In the system shown in Fig. 1.57 the masses of the bodies are known to be m_1 and m_2, the coefficient of friction between the body m_1 and the horizontal plane is equal to k, and a pulley of mass m is assumed to be a uniform disc. The thread does not slip over the pulley. At the moment $t = 0$ the body m_2 starts descending. Assuming the mass of the thread and the friction in the axle of the pulley to be negligible, find the work performed by the friction forces acting on the body m_1 over the first t seconds after the beginning of motion.

1.248. A uniform cylinder of radius R is spinned about its axis to the angular velocity ω_0 and then placed into a corner (Fig. 1.58).

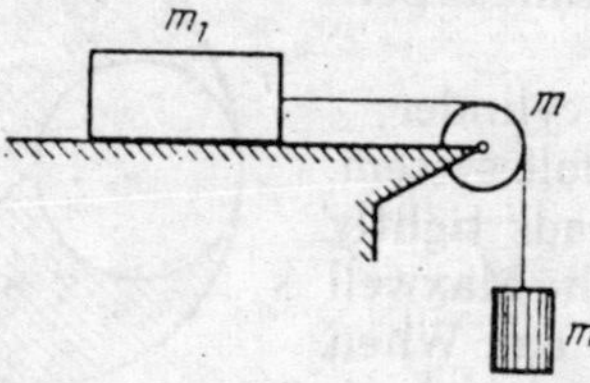

Fig. 1.57.

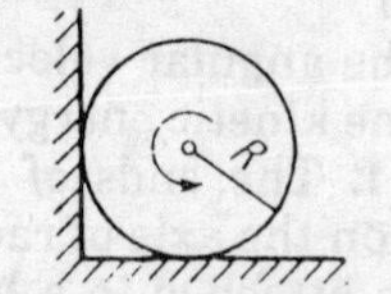

Fig. 1.58.

The coefficient of friction between the corner walls and the cylinder is equal to k. How many turns will the cylinder accomplish before it stops?

1.249. A uniform disc of radius R is spinned to the angular velocity ω and then carefully placed on a horizontal surface. How long will the disc be rotating on the surface if the friction coefficient is equal to k? The pressure exerted by the disc on the surface can be regarded as uniform.

1.250. A flywheel with the initial angular velocity ω_0 decelerates due to the forces whose moment relative to the axis is proportional to the square root of its angular velocity. Find the mean angular velocity of the flywheel averaged over the total deceleration time.

1.251. A uniform cylinder of radius R and mass M can rotate freely about a stationary horizontal axis O (Fig. 1.59). A thin cord of length l and mass m is wound on the cylinder in a single layer. Find the angular acceleration of the cylinder as a function of the length x of the hanging part of the cord. The wound part of the cord is supposed to have its centre of gravity on the cylinder axis.

1.252. A uniform sphere of mass m and radius R rolls without slipping down an inclined plane set at an angle α to the horizontal. Find:

(a) the magnitudes of the friction coefficient at which slipping is absent;

(b) the kinetic energy of the sphere t seconds after the beginning of motion.

1.253. A uniform cylinder of mass $m = 8.0$ kg and radius $R = 1.3$ cm (Fig. 1.60) starts descending at a moment $t = 0$ due to gravity. Neglecting the mass of the thread, find:

(a) the tension of each thread and the angular acceleration of the cylinder;

(b) the time dependence of the instantaneous power developed by the gravitational force.

1.254. Thin threads are tightly wound on the ends of a uniform solid cylinder of mass m. The free ends of the threads are attached

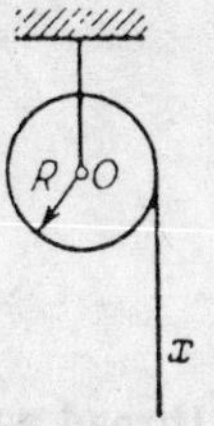

Fig. 1.59.

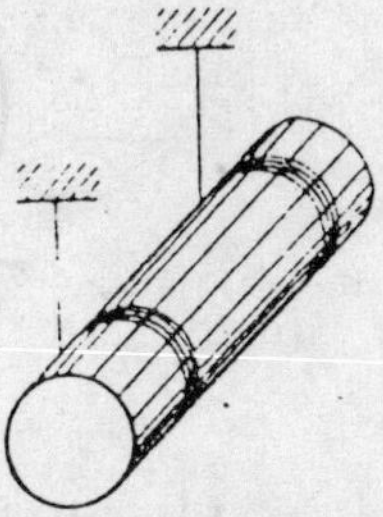
Fig. 1.60.

to the ceiling of an elevator car. The car starts going up with an acceleration w_0. Find the acceleration w' of the cylinder relative to the car and the force **F** exerted by the cylinder on the ceiling (through the threads).

1.255. A spool with a thread wound on it is placed on an inclined smooth plane set at an angle $\alpha = 30°$ to the horizontal. The free end of the thread is attached to the wall as shown in Fig. 1.61. The mass of the spool is $m = 200$ g, its moment of inertia relative to its own axis $I = 0.45$ g · m^2, the radius of the wound thread layer $r = 3.0$ cm. Find the acceleration of the spool axis.

1.256. A uniform solid cylinder of mass m rests on two horizontal planks. A thread is wound to the cylinder. The hanging end of the thread is pulled vertically down with a constant force F (Fig. 1.62).

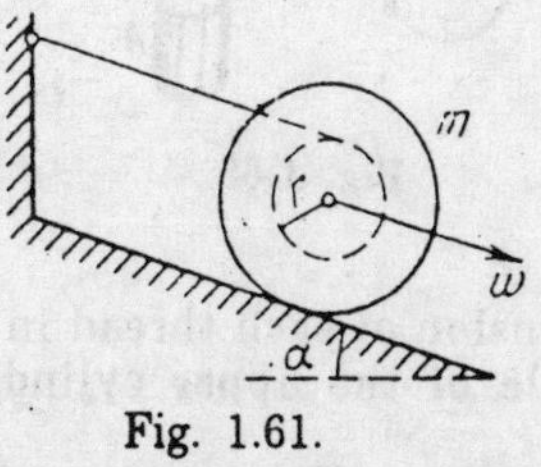

Fig. 1.61.

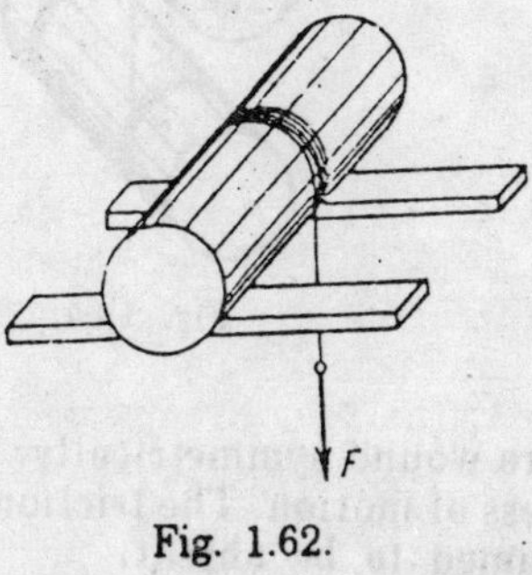

Fig. 1.62.

Find the maximum magnitude of the force F which still does not bring about any sliding of the cylinder, if the coefficient of friction between the cylinder and the planks is equal to k. What is the acceleration w_{max} of the axis of the cylinder rolling down the inclined plane?

1.257. A spool with thread wound on it, of mass m, rests on a rough horizontal surface. Its moment of inertia relative to its own axis is equal to $I = \gamma m R^2$, where γ is a numerical factor, and R is the outside radius of the spool. The radius of the wound thread layer is equal

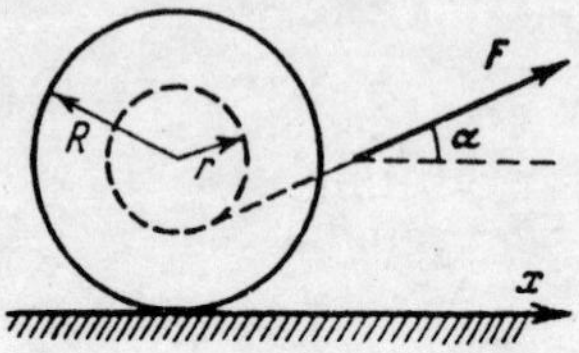

Fig. 1.63.

to r. The spool is pulled without sliding by the thread with a constant force F directed at an angle α to the horizontal (Fig. 1.63). Find:

(a) the projection of the acceleration vector of the spool axis on the x-axis;

(b) the work performed by the force F during the first t seconds after the beginning of motion.

1.258. The arrangement shown in Fig. 1.64 consists of two identical uniform solid cylinders, each of mass m, on which two light threads

Fig. 1.64.

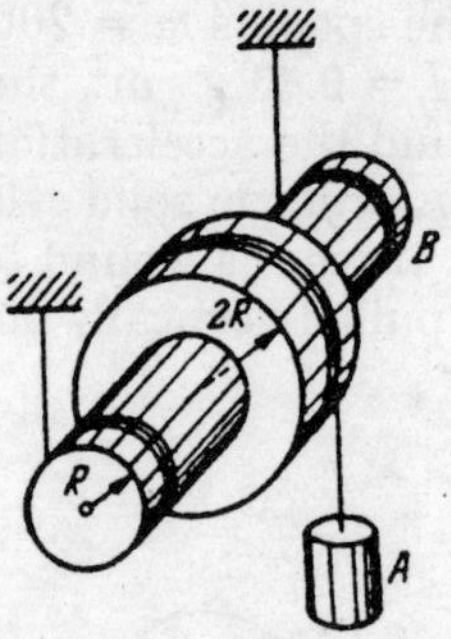

Fig. 1.65.

are wound symmetrically. Find the tension of each thread in the process of motion. The friction in the axle of the upper cylinder is assumed to be absent.

1.259. In the arrangement shown in Fig. 1.65 a weight A possesses mass m, a pulley B possesses mass M. Also known are the moment of inertia I of the pulley relative to its axis and the radii of the pulley

R and $2R$. The mass of the threads is negligible. Find the acceleration of the weight A after the system is set free.

1.260. A uniform solid cylinder A of mass m_1 can freely rotate about a horizontal axis fixed to a mount B of mass m_2 (Fig. 1.66). A constant horizontal force F is applied to the end K of a light thread tightly wound on the cylinder. The friction between the mount and the supporting horizontal plane is assumed to be absent. Find:

(a) the acceleration of the point K;

(b) the kinetic energy of this system t seconds after the beginning of motion.

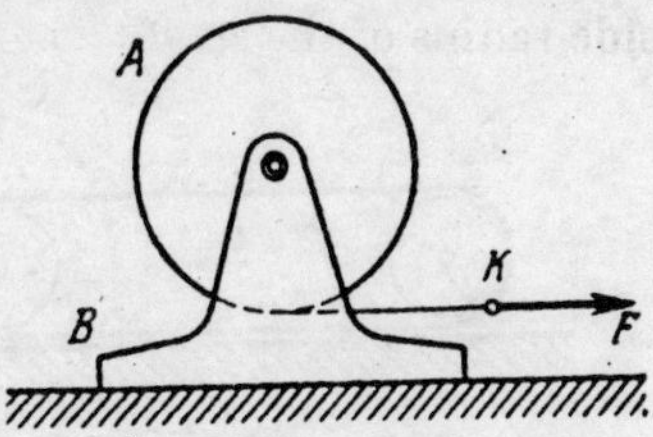

Fig. 1.66.

1.261. A plank of mass m_1 with a uniform sphere of mass m_2 placed on it rests on a smooth horizontal plane. A constant horizontal force F is applied to the plank. With what accelerations will the plank and the centre of the sphere move provided there is no sliding between the plank and the sphere?

1.262. A uniform solid cylinder of mass m and radius R is set in rotation about its axis with an angular velocity ω_0, then lowered with its lateral surface onto a horizontal plane and released. The coefficient of friction between the cylinder and the plane is equal to k. Find:

(a) how long the cylinder will move with sliding;

(b) the total work performed by the sliding friction force acting on the cylinder.

1.263. A uniform ball of radius r rolls without slipping down from the top of a sphere of radius R. Find the angular velocity of the ball at the moment it breaks off the sphere. The initial velocity of the ball is negligible.

1.264. A uniform solid cylinder of radius $R = 15$ cm rolls over a horizontal plane passing into an inclined plane forming an angle

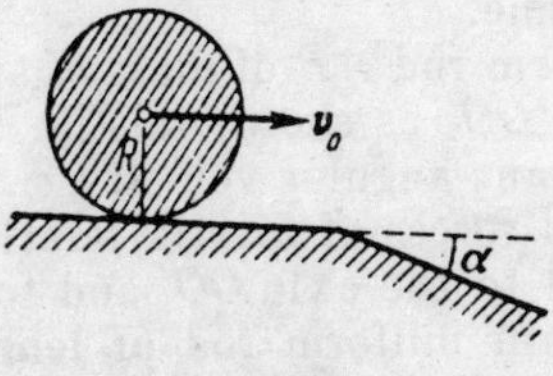

Fig. 1.67.

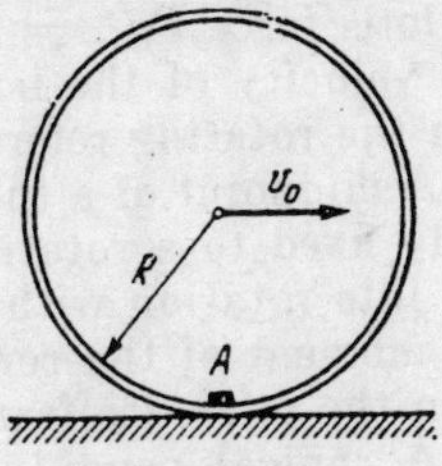

Fig. 1.68.

$\alpha = 30°$ with the horizontal (Fig. 1.67). Find the maximum value of the velocity v_0 which still permits the cylinder to roll onto the inclined plane section without a jump. The sliding is assumed to be absent.

1.265. A small body A is fixed to the inside of a thin rigid hoop of radius R and mass equal to that of the body A. The hoop rolls without slipping over a horizontal plane; at the moments when the body A gets into the lower position, the centre of the hoop moves with velocity

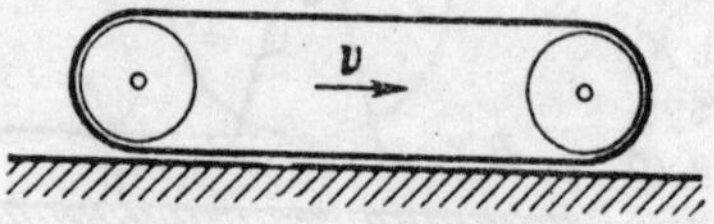

Fig. 1.69.

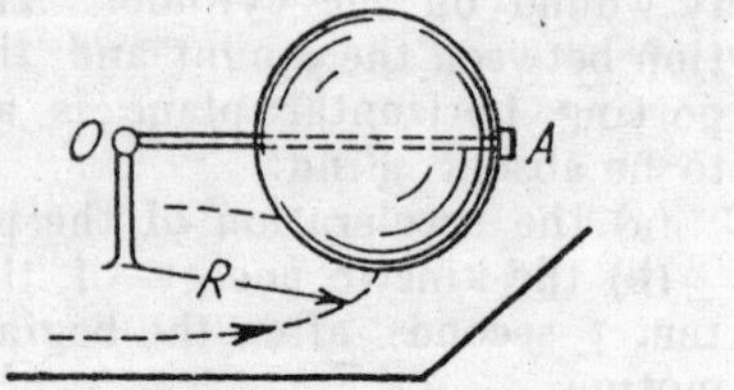

Fig. 1.70.

v_0 (Fig. 1.68). At what values of v_0 will the hoop move without bouncing?

1.266. Determine the kinetic energy of a tractor crawler belt of mass m if the tractor moves with velocity v (Fig. 1.69).

1.267. A uniform sphere of mass m and radius r rolls without sliding over a horizontal plane, rotating about a horizontal axle OA (Fig. 1.70). In the process, the centre of the sphere moves with velocity v along a circle of radius R Find the kinetic energy of the sphere.

1.268. Demonstrate that in the reference frame rotating with a constant angular velocity ω about a stationary axis a body of mass m experiences the resultant

(a) centrifugal force of inertia $\mathbf{F}_{cf} = m\omega^2\mathbf{R}_C$, where $\mathbf{R}_C$ is the radius vector of the body's centre of inertia relative to the rotation axis;

(b) Coriolis force $\mathbf{F}_{cor} = 2m[\mathbf{v}'_C\boldsymbol{\omega}]$, where $\mathbf{v}'_C$ is the velocity of the body's centre of inertia in the rotating reference frame.

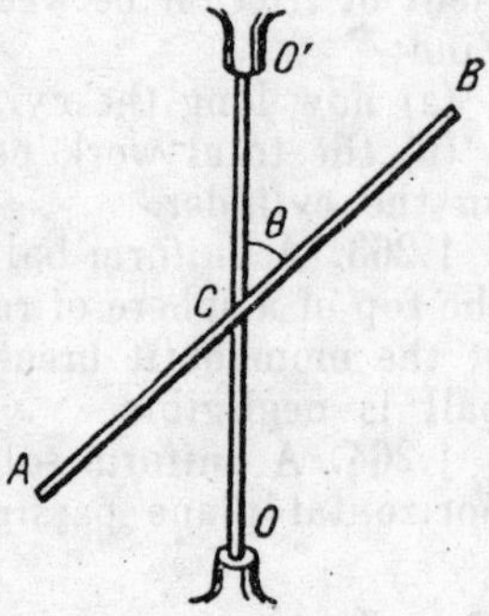

Fig. 1.71.

1.269. A midpoint of a thin uniform rod AB of mass m and length l is rigidly fixed to a rotation axle OO' as shown in Fig. 1.71. The rod is set into rotation with a constant angular velocity ω. Find the resultant moment of the centrifugal forces of inertia relative to the point C in the reference frame fixed to the axle OO' and to the rod.

1.270. A conical pendulum, a thin uniform rod of length l and mass m, rotates uniformly about a vertical axis with angular velocity ω (the upper end of the rod is hinged). Find the angle θ between the rod and the vertical.

1.271. A uniform cube with edge a rests on a horizontal plane whose friction coefficient equals k. The cube is set in motion with an initial velocity, travels some distance over the plane and comes to a standstill. Explain the disappearance of the angular momentum of the cube relative to the axis lying in the plane at right angles to the cube's motion direction. Find the distance between the resultants of gravitational forces and the reaction forces exerted by the supporting plane.

1.272. A smooth uniform rod AB of mass M and length l rotates freely with an angular velocity ω_0 in a horizontal plane about a stationary vertical axis passing through its end A. A small sleeve of mass m starts sliding along the rod from the point A. Find the velocity v' of the sleeve relative to the rod at the moment it reaches its other end B.

1.273. A uniform rod of mass $m = 5.0$ kg and length $l = 90$ cm rests on a smooth horizontal surface. One of the ends of the rod is struck with the impulse $J = 3.0$ N·s in a horizontal direction perpendicular to the rod. As a result, the rod obtains the momentum $p = 3.0$ N·s. Find the force with which one half of the rod will act on the other in the process of motion.

1.274. A thin uniform square plate with side l and mass M can rotate freely about a stationary vertical axis coinciding with one of its sides. A small ball of mass m flying with velocity $\mathbf{v}$ at right angles to the plate strikes elastically the centre of it. Find:

(a) the velocity of the ball $\mathbf{v}'$ after the impact;

(b) the horizontal component of the resultant force which the axis will exert on the plate after the impact.

1.275. A vertically oriented uniform rod of mass M and length l can rotate about its upper end. A horizontally flying bullet of mass m strikes the lower end of the rod and gets stuck in it; as a result, the rod swings through an angle α. Assuming that $m \ll M$, find:

(a) the velocity of the flying bullet;

(b) the momentum increment in the system "bullet-rod" during the impact; what causes the change of that momentum;

(c) at what distance x from the upper end of the rod the bullet must strike for the momentum of the system "bullet-rod" to remain constant during the impact.

1.276. A horizontally oriented uniform disc of mass M and radius R rotates freely about a stationary vertical axis passing through its centre. The disc has a radial guide along which can slide without friction a small body of mass m. A light thread running down through the hollow axle of the disc is tied to the body. Initially the body was located at the edge of the disc and the whole system rotated with an angular velocity ω_0. Then by means of a force F applied to the lower end of the thread the body was slowly pulled to the rotation axis. Find:

(a) the angular velocity of the system in its final state;

(b) the work performed by the force F.

1.277. A man of mass m_1 stands on the edge of a horizontal uniform disc of mass m_2 and radius R which is capable of rotating freely about a stationary vertical axis passing through its centre. At a certain moment the man starts moving along the edge of the disc; he shifts over an angle φ' relative to the disc and then stops. In the process of motion the velocity of the man varies with time as $v'(t)$. Assuming the dimensions of the man to be negligible, find:

(a) the angle through which the disc had turned by the moment the man stopped:

(b) the force moment (relative to the rotation axis) with which the man acted on the disc in the process of motion.

1.278. Two horizontal discs rotate freely about a vertical axis passing through their centres. The moments of inertia of the discs relative to the axis are equal to I_1 and I_2, and the angular velocities to ω_1 and ω_2. When the upper disc fell on the lower one, both discs began rotating, after some time, as a single whole (due to friction). Find:

(a) the steady-state angular rotation velocity of the discs;

(b) the work performed by the friction forces in this process

1.279. A small disc and a thin uniform rod of length l, whose mass is η times greater than the mass of the disc, lie on a smooth horizontal plane. The disc is set in motion, in horizontal direction and perpendicular to the rod, with velocity v, after which it elastically collides with the end of the rod. Find the velocity of the disc and the angular velocity of the rod after the collision. At what value of η will the velocity of the disc after the collision be equal to zero? Reverse its direction?

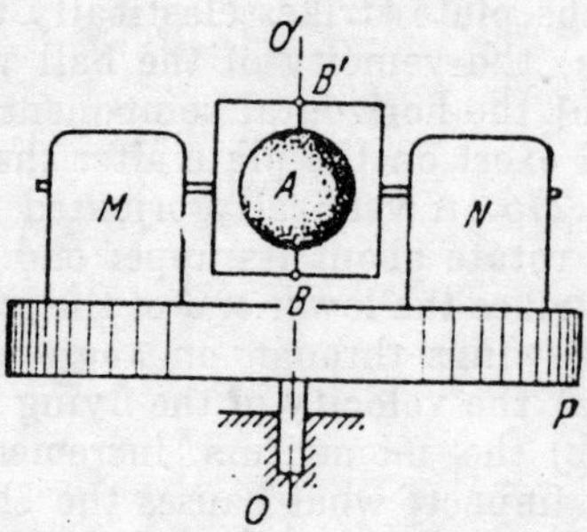

Fig. 1.72.

1.280. A stationary platform P which can rotate freely about a vertical axis (Fig. 1.72) supports a motor M and a balance weight N. The moment of inertia of the platform with the motor and the balance weight relative to this axis is equal to I. A light frame is fixed to the motor's shaft with a uniform sphere A rotating freely with an angular velocity ω_0 about a shaft BB' coinciding with the axis OO'. The moment of inertia of the sphere relative to the rotation axis is equal to I_0. Find:

(a) the work performed by the motor in turning the shaft BB' through 90°; through 180°;

(b) the moment of external forces which maintains the axis of the arrangement in the vertical position after the motor turns the shaft BB' through 90°.

1.281. A horizontally oriented uniform rod AB of mass $m = 1.40$ kg and length $l_0 = 100$ cm rotates freely about a stationary vertical axis OO' passing through its end A. The point A is located at the middle of the axis OO' whose length is equal to $l = 55$ cm. At what angular velocity of the rod of the horizontal component of the force acting on the lower end of the axis OO' is equal to zero? What is in this case the horizontal component of the force acting on the upper end of the axis?

1.282. The middle of a uniform rod of mass m and length l is rigidly fixed to a vertical axis OO' so that the angle between the rod and the axis is equal to θ (see Fig. 1.71). The ends of the axis OO' are provided with bearings. The system rotates without friction with an angular velocity ω. Find:

(a) the magnitude and direction of the rod's angular momentum **M** relative to the point C, as well as its angular momentum relative to the rotation axis:

(b) how much the modulus of the vector **M** relative to the point C increases during a half-turn;

(c) the moment of external forces N acting on the axle OO' in the process of rotation.

1.283. A top of mass $m = 0.50$ kg, whose axis is tilted by an angle $\theta = 30°$ to the vertical, precesses due to gravity. The moment of inertia of the top relative to its symmetry axis is equal to $I = 2.0$ g · m^2, the angular velocity of rotation about that axis is equal to $\omega = 350$ rad/s, the distance from the point of rest to the centre of inertia of the top is $l = 10$ cm. Find:

(a) the angular velocity of the top's precession;

(b) the magnitude and direction of the horizontal component of the reaction force acting on the top at the point of rest.

1.284. A gyroscope, a uniform disc of radius $R = 5.0$ cm at the end of a rod of length $l = 10$ cm (Fig. 1.73), is mounted on the floor of an elevator car going up with a constant acceleration $w = 2.0$ m/s^2. The other end of the rod is hinged at the point O. The gyroscope precesses with an angular velocity $n = 0.5$ rps. Neglecting the friction and the mass of the rod, find the proper angular velocity of the disc.

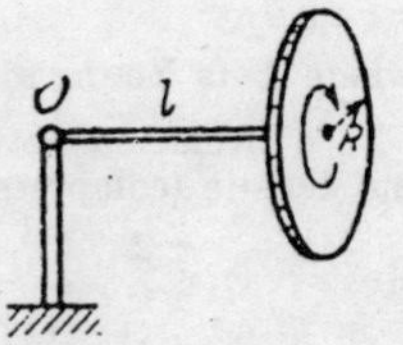

Fig. 1.73.

1.285. A top of mass $m = 1.0$ kg and moment of inertia relative to its own axis $I = 4.0$ g · m^2 spins with an angular velocity $\omega = 310$ rad/s. Its point of rest is located on a block which is shifted in a horizontal direction with a constant acceleration $w = 1.0$ m/s^2. The distance between the point of rest and the centre of inertia of the top equals $l = 10$ cm. Find the magnitude and direction of the angular velocity of precession ω'.

1.286. A uniform sphere of mass $m = 5.0$ kg and radius $R = 6.0$ cm rotates with an angular velocity $\omega = 1250$ rad/s about a horizontal axle passing through its centre and fixed on the mounting base by means of bearings. The distance between the bearings equals $l =$ 15 cm. The base is set in rotation about a vertical axis with an angular velocity $\omega' = 5.0$ rad/s. Find the modulus and direction of the gyroscopic forces.

1.287. A cylindrical disc of a gyroscope of mass $m = 15$ kg and radius $r = 5.0$ cm spins with an angular velocity $\omega = 330$ rad/s.

The distance between the bearings in which the axle of the disc is mounted is equal to $l = 15$ cm. The axle is forced to oscillate about a horizontal axis with a period $T = 1.0$ s and amplitude $\varphi_m = 20°$. Find the maximum value of the gyroscopic forces exerted by the axle on the bearings.

1.288. A ship moves with velocity $v = 36$ km per hour along an arc of a circle of radius $R = 200$ m. Find the moment of the gyroscopic forces exerted on the bearings by the shaft with a flywheel whose moment of inertia relative to the rotation axis equals $I = 3.8 \cdot 10^3$ kg·m² and whose rotation velocity $n = 300$ rpm. The rotation axis is oriented along the length of the ship.

1.289. A locomotive is propelled by a turbine whose axle is parallel to the axes of wheels. The turbine's rotation direction coincides with that of wheels. The moment of inertia of the turbine rotor relative to its own axis is equal to $I = 240$ kg·m². Find the additional force exerted by the gyroscopic forces on the rails when the locomotive moves along a circle of radius $R = 250$ m with velocity $v = 50$ km per hour. The gauge is equal to $l = 1.5$ m. The angular velocity of the turbine equals $n = 1500$ rpm.

1.6. ELASTIC DEFORMATIONS OF A SOLID BODY

• Relation between tensile (compressive) strain ε and stress σ:

$$\varepsilon = \sigma/E, \tag{1.6a}$$

where E is Young's modulus.

• Relation between lateral compressive (tensile) strain ε' and longitudinal tensile (compressive) strain ε:

$$\varepsilon' = -\mu\varepsilon, \tag{1.6b}$$

where μ is Poisson's ratio.

• Relation between shear strain γ and tangential stress τ:

$$\gamma = \tau/G, \tag{1.6c}$$

where G is shear modulus.

• Compressibility:

$$\beta = -\frac{1}{V}\frac{dV}{dp}. \tag{1.6d}$$

• Volume density of elastic strain energy:

$$u = E\varepsilon^2/2, \quad u = G\gamma^2/2. \tag{1.6e}$$

1.290. What pressure has to be applied to the ends of a steel cylinder to keep its length constant on raising its temperature by 100 °C?

1.291. What internal pressure (in the absence of an external pressure) can be sustained

(a) by a glass tube; (b) by a glass spherical flask, if in both cases the wall thickness is equal to $\Delta r = 1.0$ mm and the radius of the tube and the flask equals $r = 25$ mm?

1.292. A horizontally oriented copper rod of length $l = 1.0$ m is rotated about a vertical axis passing through its middle. What is the number of rps at which this rod ruptures?

1.293. A ring of radius $r = 25$ cm made of lead wire is rotated about a stationary vertical axis passing through its centre and perpendicular to the plane of the ring. What is the number of rps at which the ring ruptures?

1.294. A steel wire of diameter $d = 1.0$ mm is stretched horizontally between two clamps located at the distance $l = 2.0$ m from each other. A weight of mass $m = 0.25$ kg is suspended from the midpoint O of the wire. What will the resulting descent of the point O be in centimetres?

1.295. A uniform elastic plank moves over a smooth horizontal plane due to a constant force F_0 distributed uniformly over the end face. The surface of the end face is equal to S, and Young's modulus of the material to E. Find the compressive strain of the plank in the direction of the acting force.

1.296. A thin uniform copper rod of length l and mass m rotates uniformly with an angular velocity ω in a horizontal plane about a vertical axis passing through one of its ends. Determine the tension in the rod as a function of the distance r from the rotation axis. Find the elongation of the rod.

1.297. A solid copper cylinder of length $l = 65$ cm is placed on a horizontal surface and subjected to a vertical compressive force $F = 1000$ N directed downward and distributed uniformly over the end face. What will be the resulting change of the volume of the cylinder in cubic millimetres?

1.298. A copper rod of length l is suspended from the ceiling by one of its ends. Find:

(a) the elongation Δl of the rod due to its own weight;

(b) the relative increment of its volume $\Delta V/V$.

1.299. A bar made of material whose Young's modulus is equal to E and Poisson's ratio to μ is subjected to the hydrostatic pressure p. Find:

(a) the fractional decrement of its volume;

(b) the relationship between the compressibility β and the elastic constants E and μ.

Show that Poisson's ratio μ cannot exceed 1/2.

1.300. One end of a steel rectangular girder is embedded into a wall (Fig. 1.74). Due to gravity it sags slightly. Find the radius of curvature of the neutral layer (see the dotted line in the figure) in the vicinity of the point O if the length of the protruding section of

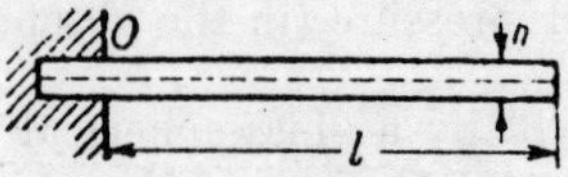

Fig. 1.74.

the girder is equal to $l = 6.0$ m and the thickness of the girder equals $h = 10$ cm.

1.301. The bending of an elastic rod is described by the *elastic curve* passing through centres of gravity of rod's cross-sections. At small bendings the equation of this curve takes the form

$$N(x) = EI \frac{d^2y}{dx^2},$$

where $N(x)$ is the bending moment of the elastic forces in the cross-section corresponding to the x coordinate, E is Young's modulus, I is the *moment of inertia* of the cross-section relative to the axis passing through the neutral layer ($I = \int z^2 dS$, Fig. 1.75).

Suppose one end of a steel rod of a square cross-section with side a is embedded into a wall, the protruding section being of length l

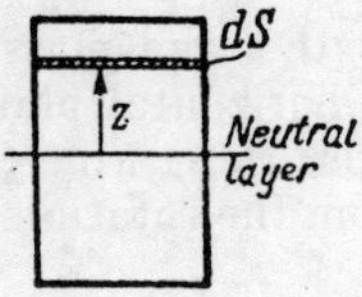

Fig. 1.75.

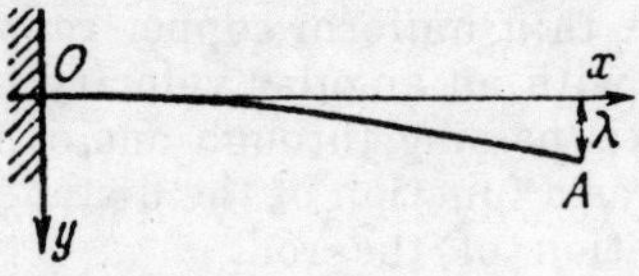

Fig. 1.76.

(Fig. 1.76). Assuming the mass of the rod to be negligible, find the shape of the elastic curve and the deflection of the rod λ, if its end A experiences

(a) the bending moment of the couple N_0;

(b) a force F oriented along the y axis.

1.302. A steel girder of length l rests freely on two supports (Fig. 1.77). The moment of inertia of its cross-section is equal to I (see the foregoing problem). Neglecting the mass of the girder and assuming the sagging to be slight, find the deflection λ due to the force F applied to the middle of the girder.

1.303. The thickness of a rectangular steel girder equals h. Using the equation of Problem 1.301, find the deflection λ caused by the weight of the girder in two cases:

(a) one end of the girder is embedded into a wall with the length of the protruding section being equal to l (Fig. 1.78*a*);

(b) the girder of length $2l$ rests freely on two supports (Fig. 1.78*b*).

1.304. A steel plate of thickness h has the shape of a square whose side equals l, with $h \ll l$. The plate is rigidly fixed to a vertical axle

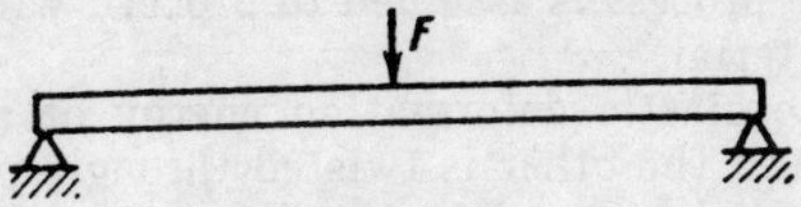

Fig. 1.77.

OO which is rotated with a constant angular acceleration β (Fig. 1.79). Find the deflection λ, assuming the sagging to be small.

1.305. Determine the relationship between the torque N and the torsion angle φ for

(a) the tube whose wall thickness Δr is considerably less than the tube radius;

(b) for the solid rod of circular cross-section. Their length l, radius r, and shear modulus G are supposed to be known.

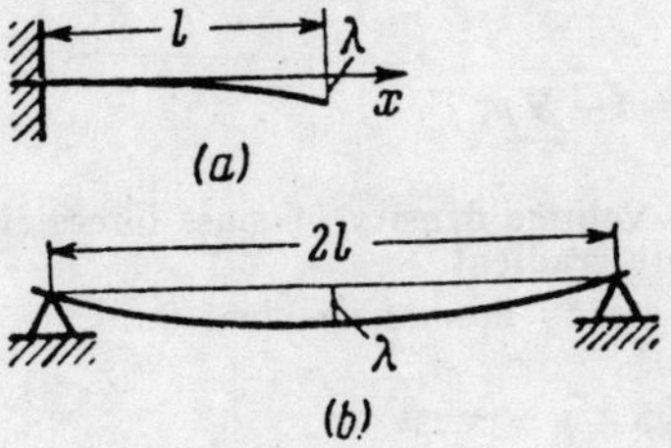

Fig. 1.78.

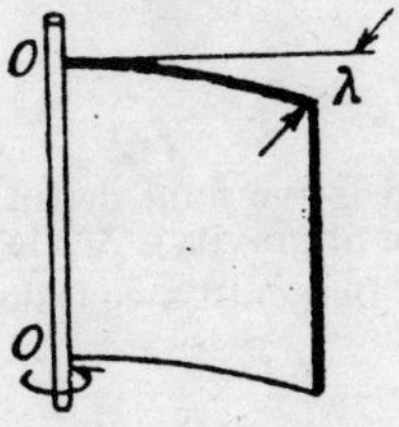

Fig. 1.79.

1.306. Calculate the torque N twisting a steel tube of length $l = 3.0$ m through an angle $\varphi = 2.0°$ about its axis, if the inside and outside diameters of the tube are equal to $d_1 = 30$ mm and $d_2 = 50$ mm.

1.307. Find the maximum power which can be transmitted by means of a steel shaft rotating about its axis with an angular velocity $\omega = 120$ rad/s, if its length $l = 200$ cm, radius $r = 1.50$ cm, and the permissible torsion angle $\varphi = 2.5°$.

1.308. A uniform ring of mass m, with the outside radius r_2, is fitted tightly on a shaft of radius r_1. The shaft is rotated about its axis with a constant angular acceleration β. Find the moment of elastic forces in the ring as a function of the distance r from the rotation axis.

1.309. Find the elastic deformation energy of a steel rod of mass $m = 3.1$ kg stretched to a tensile strain $\varepsilon = 1.0 \cdot 10^{-3}$.

1.310. A steel cylindrical rod of length l and radius r is suspended by its end from the ceiling.

(a) Find the elastic deformation energy U of the rod.

(b) Define U in terms of tensile strain $\Delta l/l$ of the rod.

1.311. What work has to be performed to make a hoop out of a steel band of length $l = 2.0$ m, width $h = 6.0$ cm, and thickness $\delta = 2.0$ mm? The process is assumed to proceed within the elasticity range of the material.

1.312. Find the elastic deformation energy of a steel rod whose one end is fixed and the other is twisted through an angle $\varphi = 6.0°$. The length of the rod is equal to $l = 1.0$ m, and the radius to $r = 10$ mm.

1.313. Find how the volume density of the elastic deformation energy is distributed in a steel rod depending on the distance r from its axis. The length of the rod is equal to l, the torsion angle to φ.

1.314. Find the volume density of the elastic deformation energy in fresh water at the depth of $h = 1000$ m.

1.7. HYDRODYNAMICS

• The fundamental equation of hydrodynamics of ideal fluid (Eulerian equation):

$$\rho \frac{d\mathbf{v}}{dt} = \mathbf{f} - \nabla p, \qquad (1.7a)$$

where ρ is the fluid density, $\mathbf{f}$ is the volume density of mass forces ($\mathbf{f} = \rho\mathbf{g}$ in the case of gravity), ∇p is the pressure gradient.

• Bernoulli's equation. In the steady flow of an ideal fluid

$$\frac{\rho v^2}{2} + \rho g h + p = \text{const} \qquad (1.7b)$$

along any streamline.

• Reynolds number defining the flow pattern of a viscous fluid:

$$\text{Re} = \rho v l/\eta, \qquad (1.7c)$$

where l is a characteristic length, η is the fluid viscosity.

• Poiseuille's law. The volume of liquid flowing through a circular tube (in m³/s):

$$Q = \frac{\pi R^4}{8\eta} \frac{p_1 - p_2}{l}, \qquad (1.7d)$$

where R and l are the tube's radius and length, $p_1 - p_2$ is the pressure difference between the ends of the tube.

• Stokes' law. The friction force on the sphere of radius r moving through a viscous fluid:

$$F = 6\pi\eta r v. \qquad (1.7e)$$

1.315. Ideal fluid flows along a flat tube of constant cross-section, located in a horizontal plane and bent as shown in Fig. 1.80 (top view). The flow is steady. Are the pressures and velocities of the fluid equal at points *1* and *2*? What is the shape of the streamlines?

1.316. Two manometric tubes are mounted on a horizontal pipe of varying cross-section at the sections S_1 and S_2 (Fig. 1.81). Find the volume of water flowing across the pipe's section per unit time if the difference in water columns is equal to Δh.

1.317. A Pitot tube (Fig. 1.82) is mounted along the axis of a gas pipeline whose cross-sectional area is equal to S. Assuming the viscosity to be negligible, find the volume of gas flowing across the

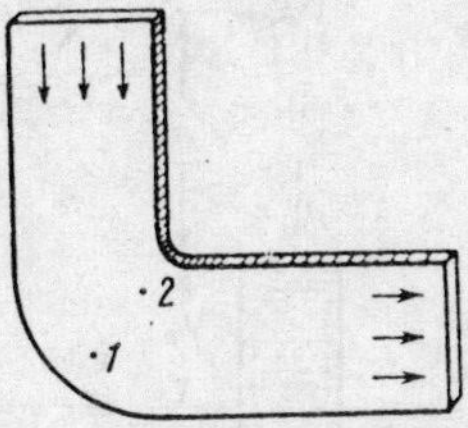

Fig. 1.80.

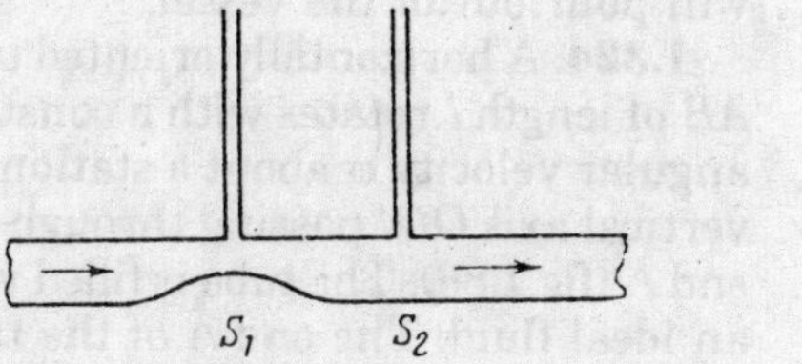

Fig. 1.81.

section of the pipe per unit time, if the difference in the liquid columns is equal to Δh, and the densities of the liquid and the gas are ρ_0 and ρ respectively.

1.318. A wide vessel with a small hole in the bottom is filled with water and kerosene. Neglecting the viscosity, find the velocity of the water flow, if the thickness of the water layer is equal to $h_1 = 30$ cm and that of the kerosene layer to $h_2 = 20$ cm.

1.319. A wide cylindrical vessel 50 cm in height is filled with water and rests on a table. Assuming the viscosity to be negligible, find at what height from the bottom of the vessel a small hole should be perforated for the water jet coming out of it to hit the surface of the table at the maximum distance l_{max} from the vessel. Find l_{max}.

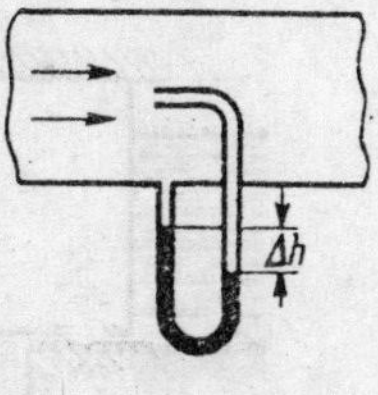

Fig. 1.82.

1.320. A bent tube is lowered into a water stream as shown in Fig. 1.83. The velocity of the stream relative to the tube is equal to $v = 2.5$ m/s. The closed upper end of the tube located at the height $h_0 = 12$ cm has a small orifice. To what height h will the water jet spurt?

1.321. The horizontal bottom of a wide vessel with an ideal fluid has a round orifice of radius R_1 over which a round closed cylinder is mounted, whose radius $R_2 > R_1$ (Fig. 1.84). The clearance between the cylinder and the bottom of the vessel is very small, the fluid density is ρ. Find the static pressure of the fluid in the clearance as a function of the distance r from the axis of the orifice (and the cylinder), if the height of the fluid is equal to h.

1.322. What work should be done in order to squeeze all water from a horizontally located cylinder (Fig. 1.85) during the time t by means of a constant force acting on the piston? The volume of water in the cylinder is equal to V, the cross-sectional area of the orifice to s, with s being considerably less than the piston area. The friction and viscosity are negligibly small.

1.323. A cylindrical vessel of height h and base are S is filled with water. An orifice of area $s \ll S$ is opened in the bottom of the vessel. Neglecting the viscosity of water, determine how soon all the water will pour out of the vessel.

1.324. A horizontally oriented tube AB of length l rotates with a constant angular velocity ω about a stationary vertical axis OO' passing through the end A (fig.1.86). The tube is filled with an ideal fluid. The end A of the tube is open, the closed end B has a very small orifice. Find the velocity of the fluid relative to the tube as a function of the column "height" h.

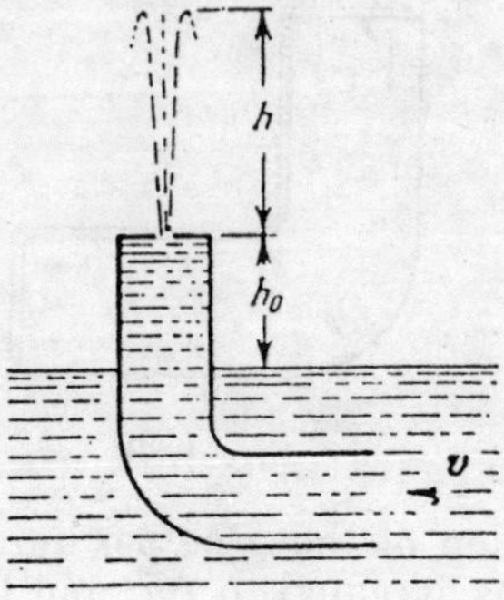

Fig. 1.83.

1.325. Demonstrate that in the case of a steady flow of an ideal fluid Eq. (1.7a) turns into Beroulli equation.

1.326. On the opposite sides of a wide vertical vessel filled with

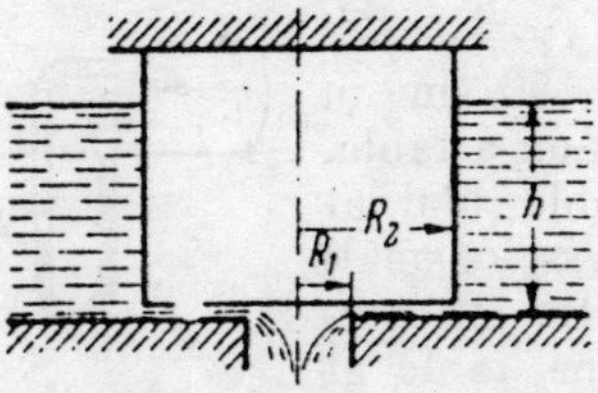

Fig. 1.84.

Fig. 1.85.

water two identical holes are opened, each having the cross-sectional are $S = 0.50\ \text{cm}^2$. The height difference between them is equal to $\Delta h = 51$ cm. Find the resultant force of reaction of the water flowing out of the vessel.

1.327. The side wall of a wide vertical cylindrical vessel of height $h = 75$ cm has a narrow vertical slit running all the way down to the bottom of the vessel. The length of the slit is $l = 50$ cm and the width $b = 1.0$ mm. With the slit closed, the vessel is filled with water. Find the resultant force of reaction of the water flowing out of the vessel immediately after the slit is opened.

1.328. Water flows out of a big tank along a tube bent at right angles: the inside radius of the tube is equal to $r = 0.50$ cm (Fig. 1.87). The length of the horizontal section of the tube is equal to $l = 22$ cm. The water flow rate is $Q = 0.50$ litres per second. Find the moment of reaction forces of flowing water, acting on the tube's walls, relative to the point O.

1.329. A side wall of a wide open tank is provided with a narrowing tube (Fig. 1.88) through which water flows out. The cross-sectional area of the tube decreases from $S = 3.0\ \text{cm}^2$ to $s = 1.0\ \text{cm}^2$. The water level in the tank is $h = 4.6$ m higher than that in the tube.

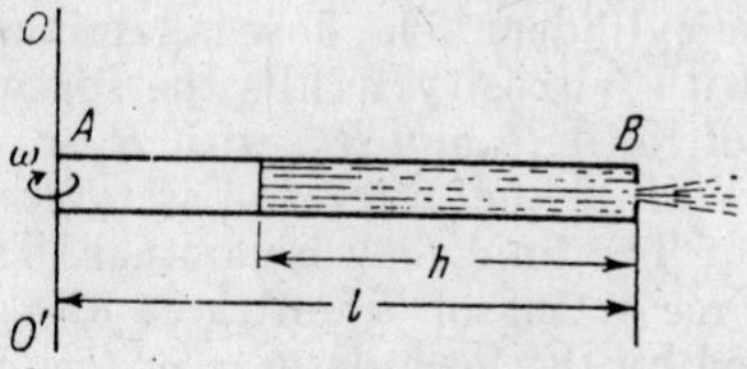

Fig. 1.86.

Neglecting the viscosity of the water, find the horizontal component of the force tending to pull the tube out of the tank.

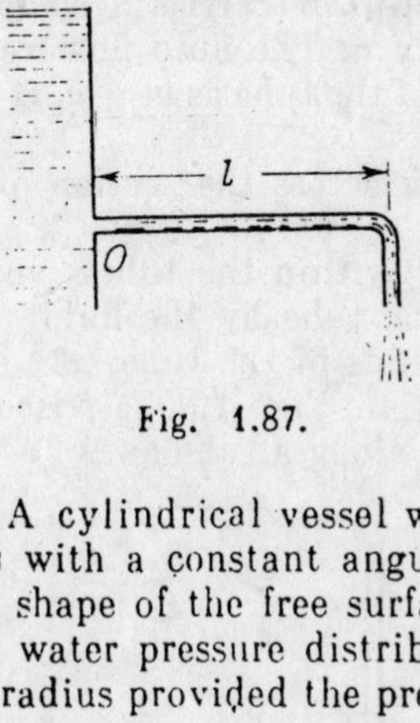

Fig. 1.87.

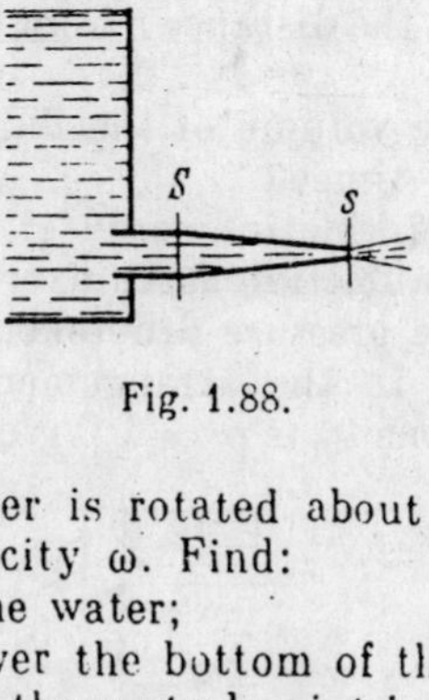

Fig. 1.88.

1.330. A cylindrical vessel with water is rotated about its vertical axis with a constant angular velocity ω. Find:

(a) the shape of the free surface of the water;

(b) the water pressure distribution over the bottom of the vessel along its radius provided the pressure at the central point is equal to p_0.

1.331. A thin horizontal disc of radius $R = 10$ cm is located within a cylindrical cavity filled with oil whose viscosity $\eta = 0.08$ P (Fig. 1.89). The clearance between the disc and the horizontal planes

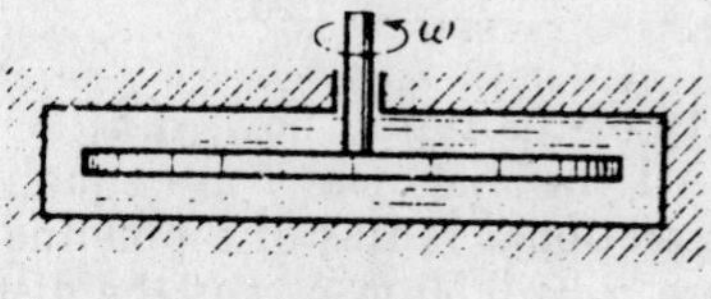

Fig. 1.89.

of the cavity is equal to $h = 1.0$ mm. Find the power developed by the viscous forces acting on the disc when it rotates with the angular velocity $\omega = 60$ rad/s. The end effects are to be neglected.

1.332. A long cylinder of radius R_1 is displaced along its axis with a constant velocity v_0 inside a stationary co-axial cylinder of radius R_2. The space between the cylinders is filled with viscous liquid. Find the velocity of the liquid as a function of the distance r from the axis of the cylinders. The flow is laminar.

1.333. A fluid with viscosity η fills the space between two long co-axial cylinders of radii R_1 and R_2, with $R_1 < R_2$. The inner cylinder is stationary while the outer one is rotated with a constant angular velocity ω_2. The fluid flow is laminar. Taking into account that the friction force acting on a unit area of a cylindrical surface of radius r is defined by the formula $\sigma = \eta r\,(\partial\omega/\partial r)$, find:

(a) the angular velocity of the rotating fluid as a function of radius r;

(b) the moment of the friction forces acting on a unit length of the outer cylinder.

1.334. A tube of length l and radius R carries a steady flow of fluid whose density is ρ and viscosity η. The fluid flow velocity depends on the distance r from the axis of the tube as $v = v_0\,(1 - r^2/R^2)$. Find:

(a) the volume of the fluid flowing across the section of the tube per unit time;

(b) the kinetic energy of the fluid within the tube's volume;

(c) the friction force exerted on the tube by the fluid;

(d) the pressure difference at the ends of the tube.

1.335. In the arrangement shown in Fig. 1.90 a viscous liquid whose density is $\rho = 1.0$ g/cm³ flows along a tube out of a wide tank

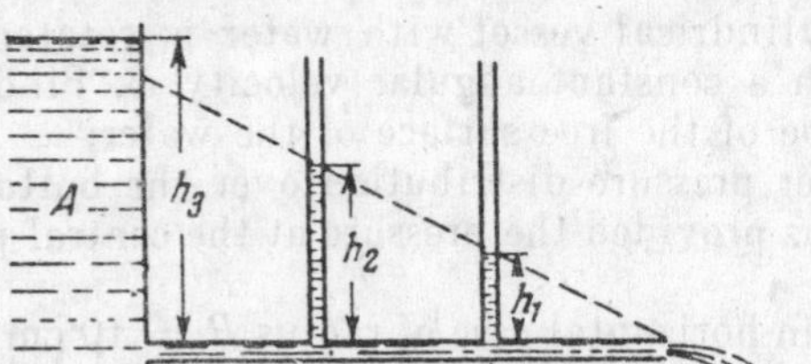

Fig. 1.90.

A. Find the velocity of the liquid flow, if $h_1 = 10$ cm, $h_2 = 20$ cm, and $h_3 = 35$ cm. All the distances l are equal.

1.336. The cross-sectional radius of a pipeline decreases gradually as $r = r_0 e^{-\alpha x}$, where $\alpha = 0.50\ \text{m}^{-1}$, x is the distance from the pipeline inlet. Find the ratio of Reynolds numbers for two cross-sections separated by $\Delta x = 3.2$ m.

1.337. When a sphere of radius $r_1 = 1.2$ mm moves in glycerin, the laminar flow is observed if the velocity of the sphere does not exceed $v_1 = 23$ cm/s. At what minimum velocity v_2 of a sphere of radius $r_2 = 5.5$ cm will the flow in water become turbulent? The viscosities of glycerin and water are equal to $\eta_1 = 13.9$ P and $\eta_2 = 0.011$ P respectively.

1.338. A lead sphere is steadily sinking in glycerin whose viscosity is equal to $\eta = 13.9$ P. What is the maximum diameter of the sphere at which the flow around that sphere still remains laminar? It is known that the transition to the turbulent flow corresponds to Reynolds number Re = 0.5. (Here the characteristic length is taken to be the sphere diameter.)

1.339. A steel ball of diameter $d = 3.0$ mm starts sinking with zero initial velocity in olive oil whose viscosity is $\eta = 0.90$ P. How soon after the beginning of motion will the velocity of the ball differ from the steady-state velocity by $n = 1.0\%$?

1.8. RELATIVISTIC MECHANICS

• Lorentz contraction of length and slowing of a moving clock:

$$l = l_0 \sqrt{1-(v/c)^2}, \qquad \Delta t = \frac{\Delta t_0}{\sqrt{1-(v/c)^2}}, \tag{1.8a}$$

where l_0 is the proper length and Δt_0 is the proper time of the moving clock.

• Lorentz transformation*:

$$x' = \frac{x - Vt}{\sqrt{1-(V/c)^2}}, \qquad y' = y, \qquad t' = \frac{t - xV/c^2}{1-(V/c)^2}. \tag{1.8b}$$

• Interval s_{12} is an invariant:

$$s_{12}^2 = c^2 t_{12}^2 - l_{12}^2 = \text{inv}, \tag{1.8c}$$

where t_{12} is the time interval between events 1 and 2, l_{12} is the distance between the points at which these events occurred.

• Transformation of velocity*:

$$v'_x = \frac{v_x - V}{1 - v_x V/c^2}, \qquad v'_y = \frac{v_y \sqrt{1-(V/c)^2}}{1 - v_x V/c^2}. \tag{1.8d}$$

• Relativistic mass and relativistic momentum:

$$m = \frac{m_0}{\sqrt{1-(v/c)^2}}, \qquad \mathbf{p} = m\mathbf{v} = \frac{m_0 \mathbf{v}}{\sqrt{1-(v/c)^2}}, \tag{1.8e}$$

where m_0 is the rest mass, or, simply, the mass.

• Relativistic equation of dynamics for a particle:

$$\frac{d\mathbf{p}}{dt} = \mathbf{F}, \tag{1.8f}$$

where $\mathbf{p}$ is the relativistic momentum of the particle.

• Total and kinetic energies of a relativistic particle:

$$E = mc^2 = m_0 c^2 + T, \qquad T = (m - m_0)\, c^2. \tag{1.8g}$$

---

* The reference frame K' is assumed to move with a velocity V in the positive direction of the x axis of the frame K, with the x' and x axes coinciding and the y' and y axes parallel.

• **Relationship between the energy and momentum of a relativistic particle**

$$E^2 - p^2c^2 = m_0^2c^4, \qquad pc = \sqrt{T(T + 2m_0c^2)}. \tag{1.8h}$$

• **When considering the collisions of particles it helps to use the following invariant quantity:**

$$E^2 - p^2c^2 = m_0^2c^4, \tag{1.8i}$$

where E and p are the total energy and momentum of the system prior to the collision, and m_0 is the rest mass of the particle (or the system) formed.

1.340. A rod moves lengthwise with a constant velocity v relative to the inertial reference frame K. At what value of v will the length of the rod in this frame be $\eta = 0.5\%$ less than its proper length?

1.341. In a triangle the proper length of each side equals a. Find the perimeter of this triangle in the reference frame moving relative to it with a constant velocity V along one of its

(a) bisectors; (b) sides.

Investigate the results obtained at $V \ll c$ and $V \to c$, where c is the velocity of light.

1.342. Find the proper length of a rod if in the laboratory frame of reference its velocity is $v = c/2$, the length $l = 1.00$ m, and the angle between the rod and its direction of motion is $\theta = 45°$.

1.343. A stationary upright cone has a taper angle $\theta = 45°$, and the area of the lateral surface $S_0 = 4.0\ \text{m}^2$. Find: (a) its taper angle; (b) its lateral surface area, in the reference frame moving with a velocity $v = (4/5)c$ along the axis of the cone.

1.344. With what velocity (relative to the reference frame K) did the clock move, if during the time interval $t = 5.0$ s, measured by the clock of the frame K, it became slow by $\Delta t = 0.10$ s?

1.345. A rod flies with constant velocity past a mark which is stationary in the reference frame K. In the frame K it takes $\Delta t = 20$ ns for the rod to fly past the mark. In the reference frame fixed to the rod the mark moves past the rod for $\Delta t' = 25$ ns. Find the proper length of the rod.

1.346. The proper lifetime of an unstable particle is equal to $\Delta t_0 = 10$ ns. Find the distance this particle will traverse till its decay in the laboratory frame of reference, where its lifetime is equal to $\Delta t = 20$ ns.

1.347. In the reference frame K a muon moving with a velocity $v = 0.990c$ travelled a distance $l = 3.0$ km from its birthplace to the point where it decayed. Find:

(a) the proper lifetime of this muon;

(b) the distance travelled by the muon in the frame K "from the muon's standpoint".

•1.348. Two particles moving in a laboratory frame of reference along the same straight line with the same velocity $v = (3/4)c$ strike against a stationary target with the time interval $\Delta t = 50$ ns. Find the proper distance between the particles prior to their hitting the target.

1.349. A rod moves along a ruler with a constant velocity. When the positions of both ends of the rod are marked simultaneously in the reference frame fixed to the ruler, the difference of readings on the ruler is equal to $\Delta x_1 = 4.0$ m. But when the positions of the rod's ends are marked simultaneously in the reference frame fixed to the rod, the difference of readings on the same ruler is equal to $\Delta x_2 = 9.0$ m. Find the proper length of the rod and its velocity relative to the ruler.

1.350. Two rods of the same proper length l_0 move toward each other parallel to a common horizontal axis. In the reference frame fixed to one of the rods the time interval between the moments, when the right and left ends of the rods coincide, is equal to Δt. What is the velocity of one rod relative to the other?

1.351. Two unstable particles move in the reference frame K along a straight line in the same direction with a velocity $v = 0.990c$. The distance between them in this reference frame is equal to $l = 120$ m. At a certain moment both particles decay simultaneously in the reference frame fixed to them. What time interval between the moments of decay of the two particles will be observed in the frame K? Which particle decays later in the frame K?

1.352. A rod AB oriented along the x axis of the reference frame K moves in the positive direction of the x axis with a constant velocity v. The point A is the forward end of the rod, and the point B its rear end. Find:

(a) the proper length of the rod, if at the moment t_A the coordinate of the point A is equal to x_A, and at the moment t_B the coordinate of the point B is equal to x_B;

(b) what time interval should separate the markings of coordinates of the rod's ends in the frame K for the difference of coordinates to become equal to the proper length of the rod.

1.353. The rod $A'B'$ moves with a constant velocity v relative to the rod AB (Fig. 1.91). Both rods have the same proper length l_0 and

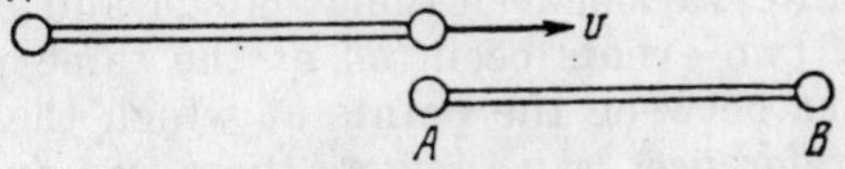

Fig. 1.91.

at the ends of each of them clocks are mounted, which are synchronized pairwise: A with B and A' with B'. Suppose the moment when the clock B' gets opposite the clock A is taken for the beginning of the time count in the reference frames fixed to each of the rods. Determine:

(a) the readings of the clocks B and B' at the moment when they are opposite each other;

(b) the same for the clocks A and A'.

1.354. There are two groups of mutually synchronized clocks K and K' moving relative to each other with a velocity v as shown in Fig. 1.92. The moment when the clock A' gets opposite the clock A

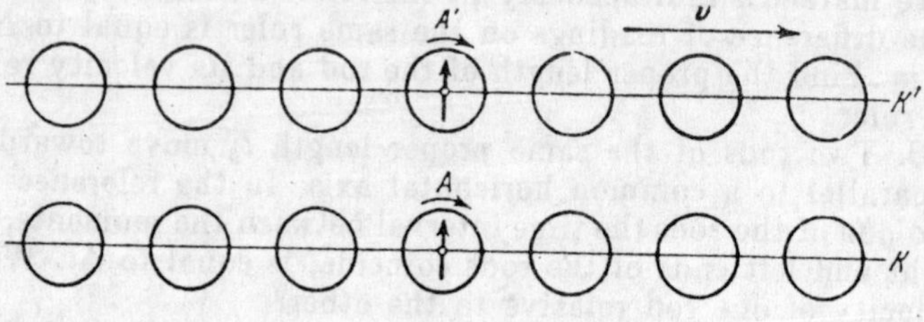

Fig. 1.92.

is taken for the beginning of the time count. Draw the approximate position of hands of all the clocks at this moment "in terms of the K clocks"; "in terms of the K' clocks".

1.355. The reference frame K' moves in the positive direction of the x axis of the frame K with a relative velocity V. Suppose that at the moment when the origins of coordinates O and O' coincide, the clock readings at these points are equal to zero in both frames. Find the displacement velocity $\dot{x}$ of the point (in the frame K) at which the readings of the clocks of both reference frames will be permanently identical. Demonstrate that $\dot{x} < V$.

1.356. At two points of the reference frame K two events occurred separated by a time interval Δt. Demonstrate that if these events obey the cause-and-effect relationship in the frame K (e.g. a shot fired and a bullet hitting a target), they obey that relationship in any other inertial reference frame K'.

1.357. The space-time diagram of Fig. 1.93 shows three events A, B, and C which occurred on the x axis of some inertial reference frame. Find:

(a) the time interval between the events A and B in the reference frame where the two events occurred at the same point;

(b) the distance between the points at which the events A and C occurred in the reference frame where these two events are simultaneous.

1.358. The velocity components of a particle moving in the xy plane of the reference frame K are equal to v_x and v_y. Find the velocity v' of this particle in the frame K' which moves with the velocity V relative to the frame K in the positive direction of its x axis.

1.359. Two particles move toward each other with velocities $v_1 = 0.50c$ and $v_2 = 0.75c$ relative to a laboratory frame of reference. Find:

(a) the approach velocity of the particles in the laboratory frame of reference;

(b) their relative velocity.

1.360. Two rods having the same proper length l_0 move lengthwise toward each other parallel to a common axis with the same velocity

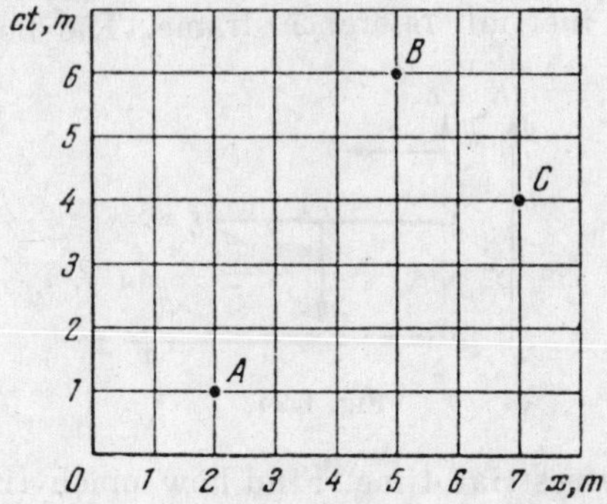

Fig. 1.93.

v relative to the laboratory frame of reference. What is the length of each rod in the reference frame fixed to the other rod?

1.361. Two relativistic particles move at right angles to each other in a laboratory frame of reference, one with the velocity v_1 and the other with the velocity v_2. Find their relative velocity.

1.362. An unstable particle moves in the reference frame K' along its y' axis with a velocity v'. In its turn, the frame K' moves relative to the frame K in the positive direction of its x axis with a velocity V. The x' and x axes of the two reference frames coincide, the y' and y axes are parallel. Find the distance which the particle traverses in the frame K, if its proper lifetime is equal to Δt_0.

1.363. A particle moves in the frame K with a velocity v at an angle θ to the x axis. Find the corresponding angle in the frame K' moving with a velocity V relative to the frame K in the positive direction of its x axis, if the x and x' axes of the two frames coincide.

1.364. The rod AB oriented parallel to the x' axis of the reference frame K' moves in this frame with a velocity v' along its y' axis. In its turn, the frame K' moves with a velocity V relative to the frame K as shown in Fig. 1.94. Find the angle θ between the rod and the x axis in the frame K.

1.365. The frame K' moves with a constant velocity $\mathbf{V}$ relative to the frame K. Find the acceleration w' of a particle in the frame K', if in the frame K this particle moves with a velocity v and acceleration w along a straight line

(a) in the direction of the vector **V**;

(b) perpendicular to the vector **V**.

1.366. An imaginary space rocket launched from the Earth moves with an acceleration $w' = 10g$ which is the same in every instantaneous co-moving inertial reference frame. The boost stage lasted

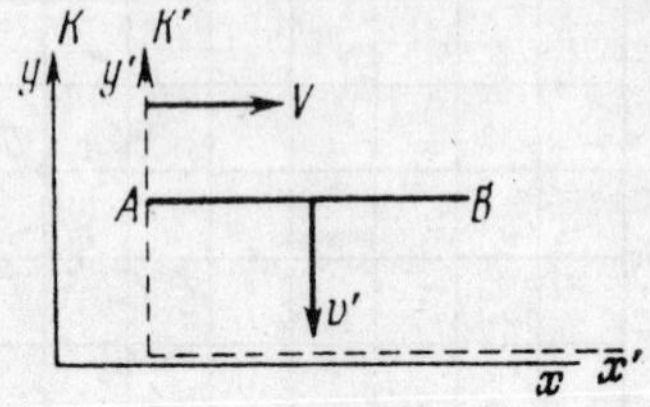

Fig. 1.94.

$\tau = 1.0$ year of terrestrial time. Find how much (in per cent) does the rocket velocity differ from the velocity of light at the end of the boost stage. What distance does the rocket cover by that moment?

1.367. From the conditions of the foregoing problem determine the boost time τ_0 in the reference frame fixed to the rocket. Remember that this time is defined by the formula

$$\tau_0 = \int_0^{\tau} \sqrt{1-(v/c)^2}\, dt,$$

where dt is the time in the geocentric reference frame.

1.368. How many times does the relativistic mass of a particle whose velocity differs from the velocity of light by 0.010% exceed its rest mass?

1.369. The density of a stationary body is equal to ρ_0. Find the velocity (relative to the body) of the reference frame in which the density of the body is $\eta = 25\%$ greater than ρ_0.

1.370. A proton moves with a momentum $p = 10.0$ GeV/c, where c is the velocity of light. How much (in per cent) does the proton velocity differ from the velocity of light?

1.371. Find the velocity at which the relativistic momentum of a particle exceeds its Newtonian momentum $\eta = 2$ times.

1.372. What work has to be performed in order to increase the velocity of a particle of rest mass m_0 from $0.60\,c$ to $0.80\,c$? Compare the result obtained with the value calculated from the classical formula.

1.373. Find the velocity at which the kinetic energy of a particle equals its rest energy.

1.374. At what values of the ratio of the kinetic energy to rest energy can the velocity of a particle be calculated from the classical formula with the relative error less than $\varepsilon = 0.010$?

1.375. Find how the momentum of a particle of rest mass m_0 depends on its kinetic energy. Calculate the momentum of a proton whose kinetic energy equals 500 MeV.

1.376. A beam of relativistic particles with kinetic energy T strikes against an absorbing target. The beam current equals I, the charge and rest mass of each particle are equal to e and m_0 respectively. Find the pressure developed by the beam on the target surface, and the power liberated there.

1.377. A sphere moves with a relativistic velocity v through a gas whose unit volume contains n slowly moving particles, each of mass m. Find the pressure p exerted by the gas on a spherical surface element perpendicular to the velocity of the sphere, provided that the particles scatter elastically. Show that the pressure is the same both in the reference frame fixed to the sphere and in the reference frame fixed to the gas.

1.378. A particle of rest mass m_0 starts moving at a moment $t = 0$ due to a constant force **F**. Find the time dependence of the particle's velocity and of the distance covered.

1.379. A particle of rest mass m_0 moves along the x axis of the frame K in accordance with the law $x = \sqrt{a^2 + c^2t^2}$, where a is a constant, c is the velocity of light, and t is time. Find the force acting on the particle in this reference frame.

1.380. Proceeding from the fundamental equation of relativistic dynamics, find:

(a) under what circumstances the acceleration of a particle coincides in direction with the force **F** acting on it;

(b) the proportionality factors relating the force **F** and the acceleration **w** in the cases when $\mathbf{F} \perp \mathbf{v}$ and $\mathbf{F} \parallel \mathbf{v}$, where **v** is the velocity of the particle.

1.381. A relativistic particle with momentum p and total energy E moves along the x axis of the frame K. Demonstrate that in the frame K' moving with a constant velocity V relative to the frame K in the positive direction of its axis x the momentum and the total energy of the given particle are defined by the formulas:

$$p'_x = \frac{p_x - EV/c^2}{\sqrt{1-\beta^2}}, \qquad E' = \frac{E - p_x V}{\sqrt{1-\beta^2}}$$

where $\beta = V/c$.

1.382. The photon energy in the frame K is equal to ε. Making use of the transformation formulas cited in the foregoing problem, find the energy ε' of this photon in the frame K' moving with a velocity V relative to the frame K in the photon's motion direction. At what value of V is the energy of the photon equal to $\varepsilon' = \varepsilon/2$?

1.383. Demonstrate that the quantity $E^2 - p^2c^2$ for a particle is an invariant, i.e. it has the same magnitude in all inertial reference frames. What is the magnitude of this invariant?

1.384. A neutron with kinetic energy $T = 2m_0c^2$, where m_0 is its rest mass, strikes another, stationary, neutron. Determine:

(a) the combined kinetic energy $\widetilde{T}$ of both neutrons in the frame of their centre of inertia and the momentum $\widetilde{p}$ of each neutron in that frame;

(b) the velocity of the centre of inertia of this system of particles.

Instruction. Make use of the invariant $E^2 - p^2c^2$ remaining constant on transition from one inertial reference frame to another (E is the total energy of the system, p is its composite momentum).

1.385. A particle of rest mass m_0 with kinetic energy T strikes a stationary particle of the same rest mass. Find the rest mass and the velocity of the compound particle formed as a result of the collision.

1.386. How high must be the kinetic energy of a proton striking another, stationary, proton for their combined kinetic energy in the frame of the centre of inertia to be equal to the total kinetic energy of two protons moving toward each other with individual kinetic energies $T = 25.0$ GeV?

1.387. A stationary particle of rest mass m_0 disintegrates into three particles with rest masses m_1, m_2, and m_3. Find the maximum total energy that, for example, the particle m_1 may possess.

1.388. A relativistic rocket emits a gas jet with non-relativistic velocity $\mathbf{u}$ constant relative to the rocket. Find how the velocity v of the rocket depends on its rest mass m if the initial rest mass of the rocket equals m_0.

2

THERMODYNAMICS AND MOLECULAR PHYSICS

2.1. EQUATION OF THE GAS STATE. PROCESSES

- Ideal gas law;

$$pV = \frac{m}{M} RT, \tag{2.1a}$$

where M is the molar mass.

- Barometric formula:

$$p = p_0 e^{-mgh/RT}, \tag{2.1b}$$

where p_0 is the pressure at the height $h = 0$

- Van der Waals equation of gas state (for a mole):

$$\left(p + \frac{a}{V_M^2}\right)(V_M - b) = RT, \tag{2.1c}$$

where V_M is the molar volume under given p and T.

2.1. A vessel of volume V = 30. 1 contains ideal gas at the temperature 0°C. After a portion of the gas has been let out, the pressure in the vessel decreased by Δp = 0.78 atm (the temperature remaining constant). Find the mass of the released gas. The gas density under the normal conditions ρ = 1.3 g/l.

2.2. Two identical vessels are connected by a tube with a value letting the gas passint from one vessel into the other if the pressure difference $\Delta p \geq 1.10$ atm. Initially there was a vacuum in one vessel while the other contained ideal gas at a temperature t_1 = 27°C and pressure p_1 = 1.00 atm. Then both vessels were heated to a temperature t_2 = 107 °C. Up to what value will the pressure in the first vessel (which had vacuum initially) increase?

2.3. A vessel of volume V = 20. 1 contains a mixture of hydrogen and helium at a temperature t = 20 °C and pressure p = 2.0 atm. The mass of the mixture is equal to m = 5.0 g. Find the ratio of the mass of hydrogen to that of helium in the gien mixture.

2.4. A vessel contains a mixture of nitrogen (m_1 = 7.0 g) and carbon dioxide (m_2 = 11g) at a temperature T = 290 K and pressure p_0 = 1.0 atm. Find the density of this mixture, assuming the gases to be ideal.

2.5. A vessel of volume V = 7.5 1 contains a mixture of ideal gases at a temperature T = 300 K: V_1 = 0.10 mole of oxygen, V_2 = 0.20 mole of nitrogen, and V_3 = 0.30 mole of carbon dioxide. Assuming the gases to be ideal, find:

(a) the pressure of the mixture;

(b) the mean molar mass M of the given mixture which enters its equation of state $pV = (m/M)\,RT$, where m is the mass of the mixture.

2.6. A vertical cylinder closed from both ends is equipped with an easily moving piston dividing the volume into two parts, each containing one mole of air. In equilibrium at $T_0 = 300$ K the volume of the upper part is $\eta = 4.0$ times greater than that of the lower part. At what temperature will the ratio of these volumes be equal to $\eta' = 3.0$?

2.7. A vessel of volume V is evacuated by means of a piston air pump. One piston stroke captures the volume ΔV. How many strokes are needed to reduce the pressure in the vessel η times? The process is assumed to be isothermal, and the gas ideal.

2.8. Find the pressure of air in a vessel being evacuated as a function of evacuation time t. The vessel volume is V, the initial pressure is p_0. The process is assumed to be isothermal, and the evacuation rate equal to C and independent of pressure.

Note. The evacuation rate is the gas volume being evacuated per unit time, with that volume being measured under the gas pressure attained by that moment.

2.9. A chamber of volume $V = 87$ l is evacuated by a pump whose evacuation rate (see Note to the foregoing problem) equals $C = 10$ l/s. How soon will the pressure in the chamber decrease by $\eta = 1000$ times?

2.10. A smooth vertical tube having two different sections is open from both ends and equipped with two pistons of different areas (Fig. 2.1). Each piston slides within a respective tube section. One mole of ideal gas is enclosed between the pistons tied with a non-stretchable thread. The cross-sectional area of the upper piston is $\Delta S = 10$ cm² greater than that of the lower one. The combined mass of the two pistons is equal to $m = 5.0$ kg. The outside air pressure is $p_0 = 1.0$ atm. By how many kelvins must the gas between the pistons be heated to shift the pistons through $l = 5.0$ cm?

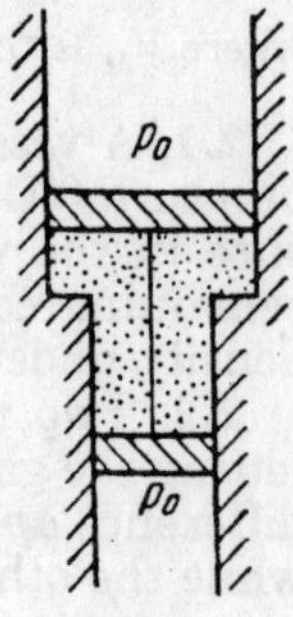

Fig. 2.1.

2.11. Find the maximum attainable temperature of ideal gas in each of the following processes:

(a) $p = p_0 - \alpha V^2$; (b) $p = p_0 e^{-\beta V}$,

where p_0, α and β are positive constants, and V is the volume of one mole of gas.

2.12. Find the minimum attainable pressure of ideal gas in the process $T = T_0 + \alpha V^2$, where T_0 and α are positive constants, and V is the volume of one mole of gas. Draw the approximate p vs V plot of this process.

2.13. A tall cylindrical vessel with gaseous nitrogen is located in a uniform gravitational field in which the free-fall acceleration is equal to g. The temperature of the nitrogen varies along the height

h so that its density is the same throughout the volume. Find the temperature gradient dT/dh.

2.14. Suppose the pressure p and the density ρ of air are related as p/ρ^n = const regardless of height (n is a constant here). Find the corresponding temperature gradient.

2.15. Let us assume that air is under standard conditions close to the Earth's surface. Presuming that the temperature and the molar mass of air are independent of height, find the air pressure at the height 5.0 km over the surface and in a mine at the depth 5.0 km below the surface.

2.16. Assuming the temperature and the molar mass of air, as well as the free-fall acceleration, to be independent of the height, find the difference in heights at which the air densities at the temperature 0 °C differ

(a) e times; (b) by $\eta = 1.0\%$.

2.17. An ideal gas of molar mass M is contained in a tall vertical cylindrical vessel whose base area is S and height h. The temperature of the gas is T, its pressure on the bottom base is p_0. Assuming the temperature and the free-fall acceleration g to be independent of the height, find the mass of gas in the vessel.

2.18. An ideal gas of molar mass M is contained in a very tall vertical cylindrical vessel in the uniform gravitational field in which the free-fall acceleration equals g. Assuming the gas temperature to be the same and equal to T, find the height at which the centre of gravity of the gas is located.

2.19. An ideal gas of molar mass M is located in the uniform gravitational field in which the free-fall acceleration is equal to g. Find the gas pressure as a function of height h, if $p = p_0$ at $h = 0$, and the temperature varies with height as

(a) $T = T_0(1 - ah)$; (b) $T = T_0(1 + ah)$,

where a is a positive constant.

2.20. A horizontal cylinder closed from one end is rotated with a constant angular velocity ω about a vertical axis passing through the open end of the cylinder. The outside air pressure is equal to p_0, the temperature to T, and the molar mass of air to M. Find the air pressure as a function of the distance r from the rotation axis. The molar mass is assumed to be independent of r.

2.21. Under what pressure will carbon dioxide have the density $\rho = 500$ g/l at the temperature $T = 300$ K? Carry out the calculations both for an ideal and for a Van der Waals gas.

2.22. One mole of nitrogen is contained in a vessel of volume $V = 1.00$ l. Find:

(a) the temperature of the nitrogen at which the pressure can be calculated from an ideal gas law with an error $\eta = 10\%$ (as compared with the pressure calculated from the Van der Waals equation of state);

(b) the gas pressure at this temperature.

2.23. One mole of a certain gas is contained in a vessel of volume $V = 0.250$ l. At a temperature $T_1 = 300$ K the gas pressure is $p_1 =$

$= 90$ atm, and at a temperature $T_2 = 350$ K the pressure is $p_2 = 110$ atm. Find the Van der Waals parameters for this gas.

2.24. Find the isothermal compressibility $\varkappa$ of a Van der Waals gas as a function of volume V at temperature T.

Note. By definition, $\varkappa = -\frac{1}{V}\frac{\partial V}{\partial p}$.

2.25. Making use of the result obtained in the foregoing problem, find at what temperature the isothermal compressibility $\varkappa$ of a Van der Waals gas is greater than that of an ideal gas. Examine the case when the molar volume is much greater than the parameter b.

2.2. THE FIRST LAW OF THERMODYNAMICS. HEAT CAPACITY

- The first law of thermodynamics:

$$Q = \Delta U + A, \tag{2.2a}$$

where ΔU is the increment of the internal energy of the system.

- Work performed by gas:

$$A = \int p\, dV. \tag{2.2b}$$

- Internal energy of an ideal gas:

$$U = \frac{m}{M} C_V T = \frac{m}{M} \frac{RT}{\gamma - 1} = \frac{pV}{\gamma - 1}. \tag{2.2c}$$

- Molar heat capacity in a polytropic process ($pV^n = \text{const}$):

$$C = \frac{R}{\gamma - 1} - \frac{R}{n - 1} = \frac{(n-\gamma)R}{(n-1)(\gamma-1)}. \tag{2.2d}$$

- Internal energy of one mole of a Van der Waals gas:

$$U = C_V T - \frac{a}{V_M}. \tag{2.2e}$$

2.26. Demonstrate that the interval energy U of the air in a room is independent of temperature provided the outside pressure p is constant. Calculate U, if p is equal to the normal atmospheric pressure and the room's volume is equal to $V = 40$ m³.

2.27. A thermally insulated vessel containing a gas whose molar mass is equal to M and the ratio of specific heats $C_p/C_V = \gamma$ moves with a velocity v. Find the gas temperature increment resulting from the sudden stoppage of the vessel.

2.28. Two thermally insulated vessels *1* and *2* are filled with air and connected by a short tube equipped with a valve. The volumes of the vessels, the pressures and temperatures of air in them are known (V_1, p_1, T_1 and V_2, p_2, T_2). Find the air temperature and pressure established after the opening of the valve.

2.29. Gaseous hydrogen contained initially under standard conditions in a sealed vessel of volume $V = 5.0$ l was cooled by $\Delta T =$

= 55 K. Find how much the internal energy of the gas will change and what amount of heat will be lost by the gas.

2.30. What amount of heat is to be transferred to nitrogen in the isobaric heating process for that gas to perform the work $A = 2.0$ J?

2.31. As a result of the isobaric heating by $\Delta T = 72$ K one mole of a certain ideal gas obtains an amount of heat $Q = 1.60$ kJ. Find the work performed by the gas, the increment of its internal energy, and the value of $\gamma = C_p/C_V$.

2.32. Two moles of a certain ideal gas at a temperature $T_0 = 300$ K were cooled isochorically so that the gas pressure reduced $n = 2.0$ times. Then, as a result of the isobaric process, the gas expanded till its temperature got back to the initial value. Find the total amount of heat absorbed by the gas in this process.

2.33. Calculate the value of $\gamma = C_p/C_V$ for a gaseous mixture consisting of $\nu_1 = 2.0$ moles of oxygen and $\nu_2 = 3.0$ moles of carbon dioxide. The gases are assumed to be ideal.

2.34. Find the specific heat capacities c_V and c_p for a gaseous mixture consisting of 7.0 g of nitrogen and 20 g of argon. The gases are assumed to be ideal.

2.35. One mole of a certain ideal gas is contained under a weightless piston of a vertical cylinder at a temperature T. The space over the piston opens into the atmosphere. What work has to be performed in order to increase isothermally the gas volume under the piston n times by slowly raising the piston? The friction of the piston against the cylinder walls is negligibly small.

2.36. A piston can freely move inside a horizontal cylinder closed from both ends. Initially, the piston separates the inside space of the cylinder into two equal parts each of volume V_0, in which an ideal gas is contained under the same pressure p_0 and at the same temperature. What work has to be performed in order to increase isothermally the volume of one part of gas η times compared to that of the other by slowly moving the piston?

2.37. Three moles of an ideal gas being initially at a temperature $T_0 = 273$ K were isothermally expanded $n = 5.0$ times its initial volume and then isochorically heated so that the pressure in the final state became equal to that in the initial state. The total amount of heat transferred to the gas during the process equals $Q = 80$ kJ. Find the ratio $\gamma = C_p/C_V$ for this gas.

2.38. Draw the approximate plots of isochoric, isobaric, isothermal, and adiabatic processes for the case of an ideal gas, using the following variables:

(a) p, T; (b) V, T.

2.39. One mole of oxygen being initially at a temperature $T_0 = 290$ K is adiabatically compressed to increase its pressure $\eta = 10.0$ times. Find:

(a) the gas temperature after the compression;

(b) the work that has been performed on the gas.

2.40. A certain mass of nitrogen was compressed $\eta = 5.0$ times (in terms of volume), first adiabatically, and then isothermally. In both cases the initial state of the gas was the same. Find the ratio of the respective works expended in each compression.

2.41. A heat-conducting piston can freely move inside a closed thermally insulated cylinder with an ideal gas. In equilibrium the piston divides the cylinder into two equal parts, the gas temperature being equal to T_0. The piston is slowly displaced. Find the gas temperature as a function of the ratio η of the volumes of the greater and smaller sections. The adiabatic exponent of the gas is equal to γ.

2.42. Find the rate v with which helium flows out of a thermally insulated vessel into vacuum through a small hole. The flow rate of the gas inside the vessel is assumed to be negligible under these conditions. The temperature of helium in the vessel is $T = 1{,}000$ K.

2.43. The volume of one mole of an ideal gas with the adiabatic exponent γ is varied according to the law $V = a/T$, where a is a constant. Find the amount of heat obtained by the gas in this process if the gas temperature increased by ΔT.

2.44. Demonstrate that the process in which the work performed by an ideal gas is proportional to the corresponding increment of its internal energy is describ^d by the equation $pV^n =$ const, where n is a constant.

2.45. Find the molar heat capacity of an ideal gas in a polytropic process $pV^n =$ const if the adiabatic exponent of the gas is equal to γ. At what values of the polytropic constant n will the heat capacity of the gas be negative?

2.46. In a certain polytropic process the volume of argon was increased $\alpha = 4.0$ times. Simultaneously, the pressure decreased $\beta = 8.0$ times. Find the molar heat capacity of argon in this process, assuming the gas to be ideal.

2.47. One mole of argon is expanded polytropically, the polytropic constant being $n = 1.50$. In the process, the gas temperature changes by $\Delta T = -26$ K. Find:

(a) the amount of heat obtained by the gas;

(b) the work performed by the gas.

2.48. An ideal gas whose adiabatic exponent equals γ is expanded according to the law $p = \alpha V$, where α is a constant. The initial volume of the gas is equal to V_0. As a result of expansion the volume increases η times. Find:

(a) the increment of the internal energy of the gas;

(b) the work performed by the gas;

(c) the molar heat capacity of the gas in the process.

2.49. An ideal gas whose adiabatic exponent equals γ is expanded so that the amount of heat transferred to the gas is equal to the decrease of its internal energy. Find:

(a) the molar heat capacity of the gas in this process;

(b) the equation of the process in the variables T, V;

(c) the work performed by one mole of the gas when its volume increases η times if the initial temperature of the gas is T_0.

2.50. One mole of an ideal gas whose adiabatic exponent equals γ undergoes a process in which the gas pressure relates to the temperature as $p = aT^\alpha$, where a and α are constants. Find:

(a) the work performed by the gas if its temperature gets an increment ΔT;

(b) the molar heat capacity of the gas in this process; at what value of α will the heat capacity be negative?

2.51. An ideal gas with the adiabatic exponent γ undergoes a process in which its internal energy relates to the volume as $U = aV^\alpha$, where a and α are constants. Find:

(a) the work performed by the gas and the amount of heat to be transferred to this gas to increase its internal energy by ΔU;

(b) the molar heat capacity of the gas in this process.

2.52. An ideal gas has a molar heat capacity C_V at constant volume. Find the molar heat capacity of this gas as a function of its volume V, if the gas undergoes the following process:

(a) $T = T_0 e^{\alpha V}$; (b) $p = p_0 e^{\alpha V}$,

where T_0, p_0, and α are constants.

2.53. One mole of an ideal gas whose adiabatic exponent equals γ undergoes a process $p = p_0 + \alpha/V$, where p_0 and α are positive constants. Find:

(a) heat capacity of the gas as a function of its volume;

(b) the internal energy increment of the gas, the work performed by it, and the amount of heat transferred to the gas, if its volume increased from V_1 to V_2.

2.54. One mole of an ideal gas with heat capacity at constant pressure C_p undergoes the process $T = T_0 + \alpha V$, where T_0 and α are constants. Find:

(a) heat capacity of the gas as a function of its volume;

(b) the amount of heat transferred to the gas, if its volume increased from V_1 to V_2.

2.55. For the case of an ideal gas find the equation of the process (in the variables T, V) in which the molar heat capacity varies as:

(a) $C = C_V + \alpha T$; (b) $C = C_V + \beta V$; (c) $C = C_V + ap$,

where α, β, and a are constants.

2.56. An ideal gas has an adiabatic exponent γ. In some process its molar heat capacity varies as $C = \alpha/T$, where α is a constant. Find:

(a) the work performed by one mole of the gas during its heating from the temperature T_0 to the temperature η times higher;

(b) the equation of the process in the variables p, V.

2.57. Find the work performed by one mole of a Van der Waals gas during its isothermal expansion from the volume V_1 to V_2 at a temperature T.

2.58. One mole of oxygen is expanded from a volume $V_1 = 1.00$ l to $V_2 = 5.0$ l at a constant temperature $T = 280$ K. Calculate:

(a) the increment of the internal energy of the gas:

(b) the amount of the absorbed heat.
The gas is assumed to be a Van der Waals gas.

2.59. For a Van der Waals gas find:
(a) the equation of the adiabatic curve in the variables T, V;
(b) the difference of the molar heat capacities $C_p - C_V$ as a function of T and V.

2.60. Two thermally insulated vessels are interconnected by a tube equipped with a valve. One vessel of volume $V_1 = 10$ l contains $\nu = 2.5$ moles of carbon dioxide. The other vessel of volume $V_2 = 100$ l is evacuated. The valve having been opened, the gas adiabatically expanded. Assuming the gas to obey the Van der Waals equation, find its temperature change accompanying the expansion.

2.61. What amount of heat has to be transferred to $\nu = 3.0$ moles of carbon dioxide to keep its temperature constant while it expands into vacuum from the volume $V_1 = 5.0$ l to $V_2 = 10$ l? The gas is assumed to be a Van der Waals gas.

2.3. KINETIC THEORY OF GASES. BOLTZMANN'S LAW AND MAXWELL'S DISTRIBUTION

• Number of collisions exercised by gas molecules on a unit area of the wall surface per unit time:

$$\nu = \frac{1}{4} n \langle v \rangle, \tag{2.3a}$$

where n is the concentration of molecules, and $\langle v \rangle$ is their mean velocity.

• Equation of an ideal gas state:

$$p = nkT. \tag{2.3b}$$

• Mean energy of molecules:

$$\langle \varepsilon \rangle = \frac{i}{2} kT, \tag{2.3c}$$

where i is the sum of translational, rotational, and the double number of vibrational degrees of freedom.

• Maxwellian distribution:

$$dN(v_x) = N \left(\frac{m}{2\pi kT} \right)^{1/2} e^{-mv_x^2/2kT} \, dv_x, \tag{2.3d}$$

$$dN(v) = N \left(\frac{m}{2\pi kT} \right)^{3/2} e^{-mv^2/2kT} \, 4\pi v^2 \, dv. \tag{2.3e}$$

• Maxwellian distribution in a reduced form:

$$dN(u) = N \frac{4}{\sqrt{\pi}} e^{-u^2} u^2 \, du, \tag{2.3f}$$

where $u = v/v_p$, v_p is the most probable velocity.

• The most probable, the mean, and the root mean square velocities of molecules:

$$v_p = \sqrt{2 \frac{kT}{m}}, \quad \langle v \rangle = \sqrt{\frac{8}{\pi} \frac{kT}{m}}, \quad v_{sq} = \sqrt{3 \frac{kT}{m}} \tag{2.3g}$$

• Boltzmann's formula:

$$n = n_0 e^{-(U-U_0)/kT}, \tag{2.3h}$$

where U is the potential energy of a molecule.

2.62. Modern vacuum pumps permit the pressures down to $p = 4 \cdot 10^{-15}$ atm to be reached at room temperatures. Assuming that the gas exhausted is nitrogen, find the number of its molecules per 1 cm^3 and the mean distance between them at this pressure.

2.63. A vessel of volume $V = 5.0$ l contains $m = 1.4$ g of nitrogen at a temperature $T = 1800$ K. Find the gas pressure, taking into account that $\eta = 30\%$ of molecules are disassociated into atoms at this temperature.

2.64. Under standard conditions the density of the helium and nitrogen mixture equals $\rho = 0.60$ g/l. Find the concentration of helium atoms in the given mixture.

2.65. A parallel beam of nitrogen molecules moving with velocity $v = 400$ m/s impinges on a wall at an angle $\theta = 30°$ to its normal. The concentration of molecules in the beam $n = 0.9 \cdot 10^{19}$ cm^{-3}. Find the pressure exerted by the beam on the wall assuming the molecules to scatter in accordance with the perfectly elastic collision law.

2.66. How many degrees of freedom have the gas molecules, if under standard conditions the gas density is $\rho = 1.3$ mg/cm^3 and the velocity of sound propagation in it is $v = 330$ m/s.

2.67. Determine the ratio of the sonic velocity v in a gas to the root mean square velocity of molecules of this gas, if the molecules are

(a) monatomic; (b) rigid diatomic.

2.68. A gas consisting of N-atomic molecules has the temperature T at which all degrees of freedom (translational, rotational, and vibrational) are excited. Find the mean energy of molecules in such a gas. What fraction of this energy corresponds to that of translational motion?

2.69. Suppose a gas is heated up to a temperature at which all degrees of freedom (translational, rotational, and vibrational) of its molecules are excited. Find the molar heat capacity of such a gas in the isochoric process, as well as the adiabatic exponent γ, if the gas consists of

(a) diatomic;

(b) linear N-atomic;

(c) network N-atomic

molecules.

2.70. An ideal gas consisting of N-atomic molecules is expanded isobarically. Assuming that all degrees of freedom (translational, rotational, and vibrational) of the molecules are excited, find what fraction of heat transferred to the gas in this process is spent to perform the work of expansion. How high is this fraction in the case of a monatomic gas?

2.71. Find the molar mass and the number of degrees of freedom of molecules in a gas if its heat capacities are known: $c_V = 0.65$ J/(g·K) and $c_p = 0.91$ J/(g·K).

2.72. Find the number of degrees of freedom of molecules in a gas whose molar heat capacity

(a) at constant pressure is equal to $C_p = 29$ J/(mol·K);

(b) is equal to $C = 29$ J/(mol·K) in the process $pT = \text{const}$.

2.73. Find the adiabatic exponent γ for a mixture consisting of ν_1 moles of a monatomic gas and ν_2 moles of gas of rigid diatomic molecules.

2.74. A thermally insulated vessel with gaseous nitrogen at a temperature $t = 27$ °C moves with velocity $v = 100$ m/s. How much (in per cent) and in what way will the gas pressure change on a sudden stoppage of the vessel?

2.75. Calculate at the temperature $t = 17$ °C:

(a) the root mean square velocity and the mean kinetic energy of an oxygen molecule in the process of translational motion;

(b) the root mean square velocity of a water droplet of diameter $d = 0.10$ μm suspended in the air.

2.76. A gas consisting of rigid diatomic molecules is expanded adiabatically. How many times has the gas to be expanded to reduce the root mean square velocity of the molecules $\eta = 1.50$ times?

2.77. The mass $m = 15$ g of nitrogen is enclosed in a vessel at a temperature $T = 300$ K. What amount of heat has to be transferred to the gas to increase the root mean square velocity of its molecules $\eta = 2.0$ times?

2.78. The temperature of a gas consisting of rigid diatomic molecules is $T = 300$ K. Calculate the angular root mean square velocity of a rotating molecule if its moment of inertia is equal to $I = 2.1 \cdot 10^{-39}$ g·cm².

2.79. A gas consisting of rigid diatomic molecules was initially under standard conditions. Then the gas was compressed adiabatically $\eta = 5.0$ times. Find the mean kinetic energy of a rotating molecule in the final state.

2.80. How will the rate of collisions of rigid diatomic molecules against the vessel's wall change, if the gas is expanded adiabatically η times?

2.81. The volume of gas consisting of rigid diatomic molecules was increased $\eta = 2.0$ times in a polytropic process with the molar heat capacity $C = R$. How many times will the rate of collisions of molecules against a vessel's wall be reduced as a result of this process?

2.82. A gas consisting of rigid diatomic molecules was expanded in a polytropic process so that the rate of collisions of the molecules against the vessel's wall did not change. Find the molar heat capacity of the gas in this process.

2.83. Calculate the most probable, the mean, and the root mean square velocities of a molecule of a gas whose density under standard atmospheric pressure is equal to $\rho = 1.00$ g/l.

2.84. Find the fraction of gas molecules whose velocities differ by less than $\delta\eta = 1.00\%$ from the value of

(a) the most probable velocity;

(b) the root mean square velocity.

2.85. Determine the gas temperature at which

(a) the root mean square velocity of hydrogen molecules exceeds their most probable velocity by $\Delta v = 400$ m/s;

(b) the velocity distribution function $F(v)$ for the oxygen molecules will have the maximum value at the velocity $v = 420$ m/s.

2.86. In the case of gaseous nitrogen find:

(a) the temperature at which the velocities of the molecules $v_1 = 300$ m/s and $v_2 = 600$ m/s are associated with equal values of the Maxwell distribution function $F(v)$;

(b) the velocity of the molecules v at which the value of the Maxwell distribution function $F(v)$ for the temperature T_0 will be the same as that for the temperature η times higher.

2.87. At what temperature of a nitrogen and oxygen mixture do the most probable velocities of nitrogen and oxygen molecules differ by $\Delta v = 30$ m/s?

2.88. The temperature of a hydrogen and helium mixture is $T = 300$ K. At what value of the molecular velocity v will the Maxwell distribution function $F(v)$ yield the same magnitude for both gases?

2.89. At what temperature of a gas will the number of molecules, whose velocities fall within the given interval from v to $v + dv$, be the greatest? The mass of each molecule is equal to m.

2.90. Find the fraction of molecules whose velocity projections on the x axis fall within the interval from v_x to $v_x + dv_x$, while the moduli of perpendicular velocity components fall within the interval from $v_\perp$ to $v_\perp + dv_\perp$. The mass of each molecule is m, and the temperature is T.

2.91. Using the Maxwell distribution function, calculate the mean velocity projection $\langle v_x \rangle$ and the mean value of the modulus of this projection $\langle | v_x | \rangle$ if the mass of each molecule is equal to m and the gas temperature is T.

2.92. From the Maxwell distribution function find $\langle v_x^2 \rangle$, the mean value of the squared v_x projection of the molecular velocity in a gas at a temperature T. The mass of each molecule is equal to m.

2.93. Making use of the Maxwell distribution function, calculate the number ν of gas molecules reaching a unit area of a wall per unit time, if the concentration of molecules is equal to n, the temperature to T, and the mass of each molecule is m.

2.94. Using the Maxwell distribution function, determine the pressure exerted by gas on a wall, if the gas temperature is T and the concentration of molecules is n.

2.95. Making use of the Maxwell distribution function, find $\langle 1/v \rangle$, the mean value of the reciprocal of the velocity of molecules in an ideal gas at a temperature T, if the mass of each molecule is equal to m. Compare the value obtained with the reciprocal of the mean velocity.

2.96. A gas consists of molecules of mass m and is at a temperature T. Making use of the Maxwell velocity distribution function, find the corresponding distribution of the molecules over the kinetic energies ε. Determine the most probable value of the kinetic energy ε_p. Does ε_p correspond to the most probable velocity?

2.97. What fraction of monatomic molecules of a gas in a thermal equilibrium possesses kinetic energies differing from the mean value by $\delta\eta = 1.0\ \%$ and less?

2.98. What fraction of molecules in a gas at a temperature T has the kinetic energy of translational motion exceeding ε_0 if $\varepsilon_0 \gg kT$?

2.99. The velocity distribution of molecules in a beam coming out of a hole in a vessel is described by the function $F(v) = Av^3e^{-mv^2/2kT}$, where T is the temperature of the gas in the vessel. Find the most probable values of

(a) the velocity of the molecules in the beam; compare the result obtained with the most probable velocity of the molecules in the vessel;

(b) the kinetic energy of the molecules in the beam.

2.100. An ideal gas consisting of molecules of mass m with concentration n has a temperature T. Using the Maxwell distribution function, find the number of molecules reaching a unit area of a wall at the angles between θ and $\theta + d\theta$ to its normal per unit time.

2.101. From the conditions of the foregoing problem find the number of molecules reaching a unit area of a wall with the velocities in the interval from v to $v + dv$ per unit time.

2.102. Find the force exerted on a particle by a uniform field if the concentrations of these particles at two levels separated by the distance $\Delta h = 3.0$ cm (along the field) differ by $\eta = 2.0$ times. The temperature of the system is equal to $T = 280$ K.

2.103. When examining the suspended gamboge droplets under a microscope, their average numbers in the layers separated by the distance $h = 40\ \mu$m were found to differ by $\eta = 2.0$ times. The environmental temperature is equal to $T = 290$ K. The diameter of the droplets is $d = 0.40\ \mu$m, and their density exceeds that of the surrounding fluid by $\Delta\rho = 0.20$ g/cm^3. Find Avogadro's number from these data.

2.104. Suppose that η_0 is the ratio of the molecular concentration of hydrogen to that of nitrogen at the Earth's surface, while η is the corresponding ratio at the height $h = 3000$ m. Find the ratio η/η_0 at the temperature $T = 280$ K, assuming that the temperature and the free fall acceleration are independent of the height.

2.105. A tall vertical vessel contains a gas composed of two kinds of molecules of masses m_1 and m_2, with $m_2 > m_1$. The concentrations of these molecules at the bottom of the vessel are equal to n_1 and n_2

respectively, with $n_2 > n_1$. Assuming the temperature T and the free-fall acceleration g to be independent of the height, find the height at which the concentrations of these kinds of molecules are equal.

2.106. A very tall vertical cylinder contains carbon dioxide at a certain temperature T. Assuming the gravitational field to be uniform, find how the gas pressure on the bottom of the vessel will change when the gas temperature increases η times.

2.107. A very tall vertical cylinder contains a gas at a temperature T. Assuming the gravitational field to be uniform, find the mean value of the potential energy of the gas molecules. Does this value depend on whether the gas consists of one kind of molecules or of several kinds?

2.108. A horizontal tube of length $l = 100$ cm closed from both ends is displaced lengthwise with a constant acceleration w. The tube contains argon at a temperature $T = 330$ K. At what value of w will the argon concentrations at the tube's ends differ by $\eta = 1.0\%$?

2.109. Find the mass of a mole of colloid particles if during their centrifuging with an angular velocity ω about a vertical axis the concentration of the particles at the distance r_2 from the rotation axis is η times greater than that at the distance r_1 (in the same horizontal plane). The densities of the particles and the solvent are equal to ρ and to ρ_0 respectively.

2.110. A horizontal tube with closed ends is rotated with a constant angular velocity ω about a vertical axis passing through one of its ends. The tube contains carbon dioxide at a temperature $T = 300$ K. The length of the tube is $l = 100$ cm. Find the value ω at which the ratio of molecular concentrations at the opposite ends of the tube is equal to $\eta = 2.0$.

2.111. The potential energy of gas molecules in a certain central field depends on the distance r from the field's centre as $U(r) = ar^2$, where a is a positive constant. The gas temperature is T, the concentration of molecules at the centre of the field is n_0. Find:

(a) the number of molecules located at the distances between r and $r + dr$ from the centre of the field;

(b) the most probable distance separating the molecules from the centre of the field;

(c) the fraction of molecules located in the spherical layer between r and $r + dr$;

(d) how many times the concentration of molecules in the centre of the field will change if the temperature decreases η times.

2.112. From the conditions of the foregoing problem find:

(a) the number of molecules whose potential energy lies within the interval from U to $U + dU$;

(b) the most probable value of the potential energy of a molecule; compare this value with the potential energy of a molecule located at its most probable distance from the centre of the field.

2.4. THE SECOND LAW OF THERMODYNAMICS ENTROPY

• Heat engine efficiency:

$$\eta = \frac{A}{Q_1} = 1 - \frac{Q_2'}{Q_1}, \tag{2.4a}$$

where Q_1 is the heat obtained by the working substance, Q_2' is the heat released by the working substance.

• Efficiency of a Carnot cycle:

$$\eta = \frac{T_1 - T_2}{T_1}, \tag{2.4b}$$

where T_1 and T_2 are the temperatures of the hot and cold bodies respectively.

• Clausius inequality:

$$\oint \frac{\delta Q}{T} \leq 0, \tag{2.4c}$$

where δQ is the elementary amount of heat transferred to the system (δQ is an algebraic quantity).

• Entropy increment of a system:

$$\Delta S \geq \int \frac{\delta Q}{T}. \tag{2.4d}$$

• Fundamental relation of thermodynamics:

$$T\,dS \geq dU + p\,dV. \tag{2.4e}$$

• Relation between the entropy and the statistical weight Ω (the thermodynamic prohability):

$$S = k \ln \Omega. \tag{2.4f}$$

where k is the Boltzmann constant.

2.113. In which case will the efficiency of a Carnot cycle be higher: when the hot body temperature is increased by ΔT, or when the cold body temperature is decreased by the same magnitude?

2.114. Hydrogen is used in a Carnot cycle as a working substance. Find the efficiency of the cycle, if as a result of an adiabatic expansion.
(a) the gas volume increases $n = 2.0$ times;
(b) the pressure decreases $n = 2.0$ times.

2.115. A heat engine employing a Carnot cycle with an efficiency of $\eta = 10\%$ is used as a refrigerating machine, the thermal reservoirs being the same. Find its refrigerating efficiency ε.

2.116. An ideal gas goes through a cycle consisting of alternate isothermal and adiabatic curves (Fig. 2.2). The isothermal processes proceed at the temperatures T_1, T_2, and T_3. Find the efficiency of such a cycle, if in each isothermal expansion the gas volume increase in the same proportion.

2.117. Find the efficiency of a cycle consisting of two isochoric and two adiabatic lines, if the volume of the ideal gas changes $n = 10$ times within the cycle. The working substance is nitrogen.

2.118. Find the efficiency of a cycle consisting of two isobaric and two adiabatic lines, if the pressure changes n times within the cycle. The working substance is an ideal gas whose adiabatic exponent is equal to γ.

2.119. An ideal gas whose adiabatic exponent equals γ goes through a cycle consisting of two isochoric and two isobaric lines. Find the efficiency of such a cycle, if the absolute temperature of the gas rises n times both in the isochoric heating and in the isobaric expansion.

2.120. An ideal gas goes through a cycle consisting of

(a) isochoric, adiabatic, and isothermal lines;

(b) isobaric, adiabatic, and isothermal lines,

with the isothermal process proceeding at the *minimum* temperature of the whole cycle. Find the efficiency of each cycle if the absolute temperature varies n-fold within the cycle.

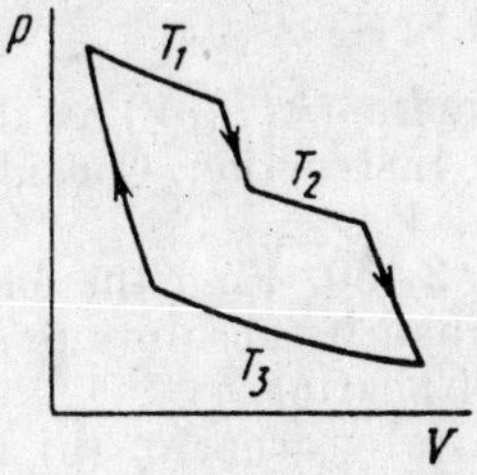

Fig. 2.2.

2.121. The conditions are the same as in the foregoing problem with the exception that the isothermal process proceeds at the *maximum* temperature of the whole cycle.

2.122. An ideal gas goes through a cycle consisting of isothermal, polytropic, and adiabatic lines, with the isothermal process proceeding at the *maximum* temperature of the whole cycle. Find the efficiency of such a cycle if the absolute temperature varies n-fold within the cycle.

2.123. An ideal gas with the adiabatic exponent γ goes through a direct (clockwise) cycle consisting of adiabatic, isobaric, and isochoric lines. Find the efficiency of the cycle if in the adiabatic process the volume of the ideal gas

(a) increases n-fold; (b) decreases n-fold.

2.124. Calculate the efficiency of a cycle consisting of isothermal, isobaric, and isochoric lines, if in the isothermal process the volume of the ideal gas with the adiabatic exponent γ

(a) increases n-fold; (b) decreases n-fold.

2.125. Find the efficiency of a cycle consisting of two isochoric and two isothermal lines if the volume varies ν-fold and the absolute temperature τ-fold within the cycle. The working substance is an ideal gas with the adiabatic exponent γ.

2.126. Find the efficiency of a cycle consisting of two isobaric and two isothermal lines if the pressure varies n-fold and the absolute temperature τ-fold within the cycle. The working substance is an ideal gas with the adiabatic exponent γ.

2.127. An ideal gas with the adiabatic exponent γ goes through a cycle (Fig. 2.3) within which the absolute temperature varies τ-fold. Find the efficiency of this cycle.

2.128. Making use of the Clausius inequality, demonstrate that all cycles having the same maximum temperature T_{max} and the same minimum temperature T_{min} are less efficient compared to the Carnot cycle with the same T_{max} and T_{min}.

2.129. Making use of the Carnot theorem, show that in the case of a physically uniform substance whose state is defined by the parameters T and V

$$(\partial U/\partial V)_T = T\,(\partial p/\partial T)_V - p,$$

where $U\,(T,\ V)$ is the internal energy of the substance.

Instruction. Consider the infinitesimal Carnot cycle in the variables p, V.

2.130. Find the entropy increment of one mole of carbon dioxide when its absolute temperature increases $n = 2.0$ times if the process of heating is

(a) isochoric; (b) isobaric.

The gas is to be regarded as ideal.

2.131. The entropy of $\nu = 4.0$ moles of an ideal gas increases by $\Delta S = 23$ J/K due to the isothermal expansion. How many times should the volume $\nu = 4.0$ moles of the gas be increased?

2.132. Two moles of an ideal gas are cooled isochorically and then expanded isobarically to lower the gas temperature back to the initial value. Find the entropy increment of the gas if in this process the gas pressure changed $n = 3.3$ times.

2.133. Helium of mass $m = 1.7$ g is expanded adiabatically $n = 3.0$ times and then compressed isobarically down to the initial volume. Find the entropy increment of the gas in this process.

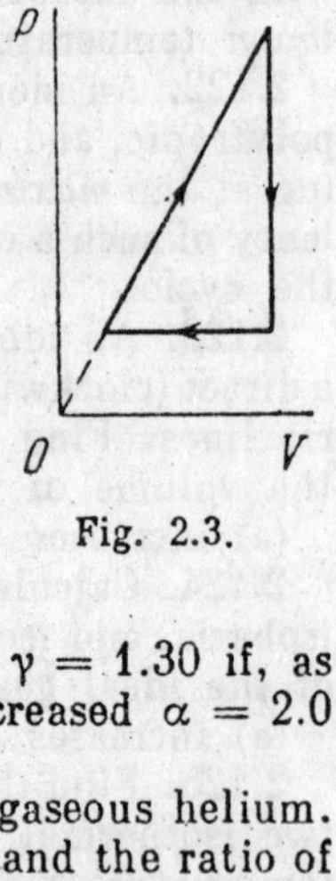

Fig. 2.3.

2.134. Find the entropy increment of $\nu = 2.0$ moles of an ideal gas whose adiabatic exponent $\gamma = 1.30$ if, as a result of a certain process, the gas volume increased $\alpha = 2.0$ times while the pressure dropped $\beta = 3.0$ times.

2.135. Vessels *1* and *2* contain $\nu = 1.2$ moles of gaseous helium. The ratio of the vessels' volumes $V_2/V_1 = \alpha = 2.0$, and the ratio of the absolute temperatures of helium in them $T_1/T_2 = \beta = 1.5$. Assuming the gas to be ideal, find the difference of gas entropies in these vessels, $S_2 - S_1$.

2.136. One mole of an ideal gas with the adiabatic exponent γ goes through a polytropic process as a result of which the absolute temperature of the gas increases τ-fold. The polytropic constant equals n. Find the entropy increment of the gas in this process.

2.137. The expansion process of $\nu = 2.0$ moles of argon proceeds so that the gas pressure increases in direct proportion to its volume.

Find the entropy increment of the gas in this process provided its volume increases $\alpha = 2.0$ times.

2.138. An ideal gas with the adiabatic exponent γ goes through a process $p = p_0 - \alpha V$, where p_0 and α are positive constants, and V is the volume. At what volume will the gas entropy have the maximum value?

2.139. One mole of an ideal gas goes through a process in which the entropy of the gas changes with temperature T as $S = aT + C_V \ln T$, where a is a positive constant, C_V is the molar heat capacity of this gas at constant volume. Find the volume dependence of the gas temperature in this process if $T = T_0$ at $V = V_0$.

2.140. Find the entropy increment of one mole of a Van der Waals gas due to the isothermal variation of volume from V_1 to V_2. The Van der Waals corrections are assumed to be known.

2.141. One mole of a Van der Waals gas which had initially the volume V_1 and the temperature T_1 was transferred to the state with the volume V_2 and the temperature T_2. Find the corresponding entropy increment of the gas, assuming its molar heat capacity C_V to be known.

2.142. At very low temperatures the heat capacity of crystals is equal to $C = aT^3$, where a is a constant. Find the entropy of a crystal as a function of temperature in this temperature interval.

2.143. Find the entropy increment of an aluminum bar of mass $m = 3.0$ kg on its heating from the temperature $T_1 = 300$ K up to $T_2 = 600$ K if in this temperature interval the specific heat capacity of aluminum varies as $c = a + bT$, where $a = 0.77$ J/(g·K), $b = 0.46$ mJ/(g·K²).

2.144. In some process the temperature of a substance depends on its entropy S as $T = aS^n$, where a and n are constants. Find the corresponding heat capacity C of the substance as a function of S. At what condition is $C < 0$?

2.145. Find the temperature T as a function of the entropy S of a substance for a polytropic process in which the heat capacity of the substance equals C. The entropy of the substance is known to be equal to S_0 at the temperature T_0. Draw the approximate plots $T(S)$ for $C > 0$ and $C < 0$.

2.146. One mole of an ideal gas with heat capacity C_V goes through a process in which its entropy S depends on T as $S = \alpha/T$, where α is a constant. The gas temperature varies from T_1 to T_2. Find:

(a) the molar heat capacity of the gas as a function of its temperature;

(b) the amount of heat transferred to the gas;

(c) the work performed by the gas.

2.147. A working substance goes through a cycle within which the absolute temperature varies n-fold, and the shape of the cycle is shown in (a) Fig. 2.4*a*; (b) Fig. 2.4*b*, where T is the absolute temperature, and S the entropy. Find the efficiency of each cycle.

2.148. One of the two thermally insulated vessels interconnected by a tube with a valve contains $\nu = 2.2$ moles of an ideal gas. The other vessel is evacuated. The valve having been opened, the gas increased its volume $n = 3.0$ times. Find the entropy increment of the gas.

2.149. A weightless piston divides a thermally insulated cylinder into two equal parts. One part contains one mole of an ideal gas with adiabatic exponent γ, the other is evacuated. The initial gas temperature is T_0. The piston is released and the gas fills the whole

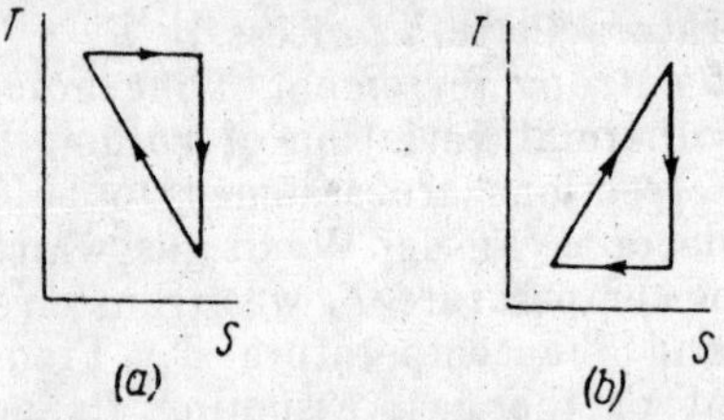

Fig. 2.4.

volume of the cylinder. Then the piston is slowly displaced back to the initial position. Find the increment of the internal energy and the entropy of the gas resulting from these two processes.

2.150. An ideal gas was expanded from the initial state to the volume V without any heat exchange with the surrounding bodies. Will the final gas pressure be the same in the case of (a) a fast and in the case of (b) a very slow expansion process?

2.151. A thermally insulated vessel is partitioned into two parts so that the volume of one part is $n = 2.0$ times greater than that of the other. The smaller part contains $\nu_1 = 0.30$ mole of nitrogen, and the greater one $\nu_2 = 0.70$ mole of oxygen. The temperature of the gases is the same. A hole is punctured in the partition and the gases are mixed. Find the corresponding increment of the system's entropy, assuming the gases to be ideal.

2.152. A piece of copper of mass $m_1 = 300$ g with initial temperature $t_1 = 97°C$ is placed into a calorimeter in which the water of mass $m_2 = 100$ g is at a temperature $t_2 = 7°C$. Find the entropy increment of the system by the moment the temperatures equalize. The heat capacity of the calorimeter itself is negligibly small.

2.153. Two identical thermally insulated vessels interconnected by a tube with a valve contain one mole of the same ideal gas each. The gas temperature in one vessel is equal to T_1 and in the other T_2. The molar heat capacity of the gas of constant volume equals C_V. The valve having been opened, the gas comes to a new equilibrium state. Find the entropy increment ΔS of the gas. Demonstrate that $\Delta S > 0$.

2.154. N atoms of gaseous helium are enclosed in a cubic vessel of volume 1.0 cm^3 at room temperature. Find:

(a) the probability of atoms gathering in one half of the vessel;

(b) the approximate numerical value of N ensuring the occurrence of this event within the time interval $t \approx 10^{10}$ years (the age of the Universe).

2.155. Find the statistical weight of the most probable distribution of $N = 10$ identical molecules over two halves of the cylinder's volume. Find also the probability of such a distribution.

2.156. A vessel contains N molecules of an ideal gas. Dividing mentally the vessel into two halves A and B, find the probability that the half A contains n molecules. Consider the cases when $N = 5$ and $n = 0, 1, 2, 3, 4, 5$.

2.157. A vessel of volume V_0 contains N molecules of an ideal gas. Find the probability of n molecules getting into a certain separated part of the vessel of volume V. Examine, in particular, the case $V = V_0/2$.

2.158. An ideal gas is under standard conditions. Find the diameter of the sphere within whose volume the relative fluctuation of the number of molecules is equal to $\eta = 1.0 \cdot 10^{-3}$. What is the average number of molecules inside such a sphere?

2.159. One mole of an ideal gas consisting of monatomic molecules is enclosed in a vessel at a temperature $T_0 = 300$ K. How many times and in what way will the statistical weight of this system (gas) very if it is heated isochorically by $\Delta T = 1.0$ K?

2.5. LIQUIDS. CAPILLARY EFFECTS

• Additional (capillary) pressure in a liquid under an arbitrary surface (Laplace's formula):

$$\Delta p = \alpha \left(\frac{1}{R_1} + \frac{1}{R_2} \right), \qquad (2.5a)$$

where α is the surface tension of a given liquid.

• Free energy increment of the surface layer of a liquid:

$$dF = \alpha\, dS, \qquad (2.5b)$$

where dS is the area increment of the surface layer.

• Amount of heat required to form a unit area of the liquid surface layer during the isothermal increase of its surface:

$$q = -T \frac{d\alpha}{dT} \qquad (2.5c)$$

2.160. Find the capillary pressure.

(a) in mercury droplets of diameter $d = 1.5$ μm;

(b) inside a soap bubble of diameter $d = 3.0$ mm if the surface tension of the soap water solution is $a = 45$ mN/m.

2.161. In the bottom of a vessel with mercury there is a round hole of diameter $d = 70$ μm. At what maximum thickness of the mercury layer will the liquid still not flow out through this hole?

2.162. A vessel filled with air under pressure p_0 contains a soap bubble of diameter d. The air pressure having been reduced isothermally n-fold, the bubble diameter increased η-fold. Find the surface tension of the soap water solution.

2.163. Find the pressure in an air bubble of diameter $d = 4.0$ μm, located in water at a depth $h = 5.0$ m. The atmospheric pressure has the standard value p_0.

2.164. The diameter of a gas bubble formed at the bottom of a pond is $d = 4.0$ μm. When the bubble rises to the surface its diameter increases $n = 1.1$ times. Find how deep is the pond at that spot. The atmospheric pressure is standard, the gas expansion is assumed to be isothermal.

2.165. Find the difference in height of mercury columns in two communicating vertical capillaries whose diameters are $d_1 = 0.50$ mm and $d_2 = 1.00$ mm, if the contact angle $\theta = 138°$.

2.166. A vertical capillary with inside diameter 0.50 mm is submerged into water so that the length of its part protruding over the water surface is equal to $h = 25$ mm. Find the curvature radius of the meniscus.

2.167. A glass capillary of length $l = 110$ mm and inside diameter $d = 20$ μm is submerged vertically into water. The upper end of the capillary is sealed. The outside pressure is standard. To what length x has the capillary to be submorged to make the water levels inside and outside the capillary coincide?

2.168. When a vertical capillary of length l with the sealed upper end was brought in contact with the surface of a liquid, the level of this liquid rose to the height h. The liquid density is ρ, the inside diameter of the capillary is d, the contact angle is θ, the atmospheric pressure is p_0. Find the surface tension of the liquid.

2.169. A glass rod of diameter $d_1 = 1.5$ mm is inserted symmetrically into a glass capillary with inside diameter $d_2 = 2.0$ mm. Then the whole arrangement is vertically oriented and brought in contact with the surface of water. To what height will the water rise in the capillary?

2.170. Two vertical plates submerged partially in a wetting liquid form a wedge with a very small angle $\delta\varphi$. The edge of this wedge is vertical. The density of the liquid is ρ, its surface tension is α, the contact angle is θ. Find the height h, to which the liquid rises, as a function of the distance x from the edge.

2.171. A vertical water jet flows out of a round hole. One of the horizontal sections of the jet has the diameter $d = 2.0$ mm while the other section located $l = 20$ mm lower has the diameter which is $n = 1.5$ times less. Find the volume of the water flowing from the hole each second.

2.172. A water drop falls in air with a uniform velocity. Find the difference between the curvature radii of the drop's surface at the upper and lower points of the drop separated by the distance $h = 2.3$ mm.

2.173. A mercury drop shaped as a round tablet of radius R and thickness h is located between two horizontal glass plates. Assuming that $h \ll R$, find the mass m of a weight which has to be placed on the upper plate to diminish the distance between the plates n-times. The contact angle equals θ. Calculate m if $R = 2.0$ cm, $h = 0.38$ mm, $n = 2.0$, and $\theta = 135°$.

2.174. Find the attraction force between two parallel glass plates, separated by a distance $h = 0.10$ mm, after a water drop of mass $m = 70$ mg was introduced between them. The wetting is assumed to be complete.

2.175. Two glass discs of radius $R = 5.0$ cm were wetted with water and put together so that the thickness of the water layer between them was $h = 1.9$ µm. Assuming the wetting to be complete, find the force that has to be applied at right angles to the plates in order to pull them apart.

2.176. Two vertical parallel glass plates are partially submerged in water. The distance between the plates is $d = 0.10$ mm, and their width is $l = 12$ cm. Assuming that the water between the plates does not reach the upper edges of the plates and that the wetting is complete, find the force of their mutual attraction.

2.177. Find the lifetime of a soap bubble of radius R connected with the atmosphere through a capillary of length l and inside radius r. The surface tension is α, the viscosity coefficient of the gas is η.

2.178. A vertical capillary is brought in contact with the water surface. What amount of heat is liberated while the water rises along the capillary? The wetting is assumed to be complete, the surface tension equals α.

2.179. Find the free energy of the surface layer of
(a) a mercury droplet of diameter $d = 1.4$ mm;
(b) a soap bubble of diameter $d = 6.0$ mm if the surface tension of the soap water solution is equal to $\alpha = 45$ mN/m.

2.180. Find the increment of the free energy of the surface layer when two identical mercury droplets, each of diameter $d = 1.5$ mm, merge isothermally.

2.181. Find the work to be performed in order to blow a soap bubble of radius R if the outside air pressure is equal to p_0 and the surface tension of the soap water solution is equal to α.

2.182. A soap bubble of radius r is inflated with an ideal gas. The atmospheric pressure is p_0, the surface tension of the soap water solution is α. Find the difference between the molar heat capacity of the gas during its heating inside the bubble and the molar heat capacity of the gas under constant pressure, $C - C_p$.

2.183. Considering the Carnot cycle as applied to a liquid film, show that in an isothermal process the amount of heat required for the formation of a unit area of the surface layer is equal to $q = -T \cdot d\alpha/dT$, where $d\alpha/dT$ is the temperature derivative of the surface tension.

2.184. The surface of a soap film was increased isothermally by $\Delta\sigma$ at a temperature T. knowing the surface tension of the soap water solution α and the temperature coefficient $d\alpha/dT$, find the increment

(a) of the entropy of the film's surface layer;

(b) of the internal energy of the surface layer.

2.6. PHASE TRANSFORMATIONS

• Relations between Van der Waals constants and the parameters of the critical state of a substance:

$$V_M\, cr = 3b,\ p_{cr} = \frac{a}{27b^2},\ T_{cr} = \frac{8a}{27R^b}. \tag{2.6a}$$

• Relation between the critical parameters for a mole of substance:

$$p_{cr} V_{M\ cr} = (3/8)\, RT_{cr}. \tag{2.6b}$$

• Calusius-Clapeyron equation:

$$\frac{dp}{dT} = \frac{q_{12}}{T\,(V_2' - V_1')}, \tag{2.6c}$$

where q_{12} is the specific heat absorbed in the transformation $1 \to 2$, V_1' and V_2' are the specific volumes of phases 1 and 2.

2.185. A saturated water vapour is contained in a cylindrical vessel under a weightless piston at a temperature t = 100°C. As a result of a slow introduction of the piston a small fraction of the vapour Δm = 0.70 g gets condensed. What amount of work was performed over the gas? The vapour is assumed to be ideal, the volume of the liquid is to be neglected.

2.186. A vessel of volume V = 6.0 1 contains water together with its saturated vapour under a pressure of 40 atm and at a temperature of 250 °C. The specific volume of the vapour is equal V_v' = 50 1/kg under these conditions. The total mass of the system water-vapour equals m = 5.0 kg. Find the mass and the volume of the vapour.

2.187. The saturated water vapour is enclosed in a cylinder under a piston and occupies a volume V_0 = 5.0 1 at the temperature t = 100 °C. Find the mass of the liquid phase formed after the volume under the piston decreased isothermally to V = 1.6 1. The saturated vapour is assumed to be ideal.

2.188. A volume occupied by a saturated vapour is reduced isothermally n-fold. Find what fraction η of the final volume is occupied by the liquid phase if the specific volumes of the saturated vapour and the liquid phase differ by N times ($N > n$). Solve the same problem under the condition that the final volume of the substance corresponds to the midpoint of a horizontal portion of the isothermal line in the diagram p, V.

2.189. An amount of water of mass m = 1.00 kg, boiling at standard atmospheric pressure, turns completely into saturated vapour.

Assuming the saturated vapour to be an ideal gas find the increment of entropy and internal energy of the system.

2.190. Water of mass $m = 20$ g is enclosed in a thermally insulated cylinder at the temperature of 0 °C under a weightless piston whose area is $S = 410$ cm^2. The outside pressure is equal to standard atmospheric pressure. To what height will the piston rise when the water absorbs $Q = 20.0$ kJ of heat?

2.191. One gram of saturated water vapour is enclosed in a thermally insulated cylinder under a weightless piston. The outside pressure being standard, $m = 1.0$ g of water is introduced into the cylinder at a temperature $t_0 = 22$ °C. Neglecting the heat capacity of the cylinder and the friction of the piston against the cylinder's walls, find the work performed by the force of the atmospheric pressure during the lowering of the piston.

2.192. If an additional pressure Δp of a saturated vapour over a convex spherical surface of a liquid is considerably less than the vapour pressure over a plane surface, then $\Delta p = (\rho_v/\rho_l)\ 2\alpha/r$ where ρ_v and ρ_l are the densities of the vapour and the liquid, α is the surface tension, and r is the radius of curvature of the surface. Using this formula, find the diameter of water droplets at which the saturated vapour pressure exceeds the vapour pressure over the plane surface by $\eta = 1.0\%$ at a temperature $t = 27$ °C. The vapour is assumed to be an ideal gas.

2.193. Find the mass of all molecules leaving one square centimetre of water surface per second into a saturated water vapour above it at a temperature $t = 100$ °C. It is assumed that $\eta = 3.6\%$ of all water vapour molecules falling on the water surface are retained in the liquid phase.

2.194. Find the pressure of saturated tungsten vapour at a temperature $T = 2000$ K if a tungsten filament is known to lose a mass $m = 1.2 \cdot 10^{-13}$ g/(s · cm^2) from a unit area per unit time when evaporating into high vacuum at this temperature.

2.195. By what magnitude would the pressure exerted by water on the walls of the vessel have increased if the intermolecular attraction forces had vanished?

2.196. Find the internal pressure pl of a liquid of its density ρ and specific latent heat of vaporization q are known. The heat q is assumed to be equal to the work performed against the forces of the internal pressure, and the liquid obeys the Van der Waals equation. Calculate pl in water.

2.197. Demonstrate that Eqs. (2.6a) and (2.6b) are valid for a substance, obeying the Van der Waals equation, in critical state.

Instruction. Make use of the fact that the critical state corresponds to the point of inflection in the isothermal curve p (V).

2.198. Calculate the Van der Waals constants for carbon dioxide if its critical temperature $T_{cr} = 304$ K and critical pressure $p_{cr} = 73$ atm.

2.199. Find the specific volume of benzene (C_6H_6) in critical state if its critical temperature $T_{cr} = 562$ K and critical pressure $p_{cr} = 47$ atm.

2.200. Write the Van der Waals equation via the reduced parameters π, υ, and τ, having taken the corresponding critical values for the units of pressure, volume, and temperature. Using the equation obtained, find how many times the gas temperature exceeds its critical temperature if the gas pressure is 12 times as high as critical pressure, and the volume of gas is equal to half the critical volume.

2.201. Knowing the Van der Waals constants, find:

(a) the maximum volume which water of mass $m = 1.00$ kg can occupy in liquid state;

(b) the maximum pressure of the saturated water vapour.

2.202. Calculate the temperature of density of carbon dioxide in critical state, assuming the gas to be a Van der Waals one.

2.203. What fraction of the volume of vessel must liquid ether occupy at room temperature in order to pass into critical state when critical temperature is reached? Ether has $T_{cr} = 467$ K, $p_{cr} = 35.5$ atm, $M = 74$ g/mol.

2.204. Demonstrate that the straight line *1-5* corresponding to the isothermal-isobaric phase transition cuts the Van der Waals isotherm so that areas *I* and *II* are equal (Fig. 2.5).

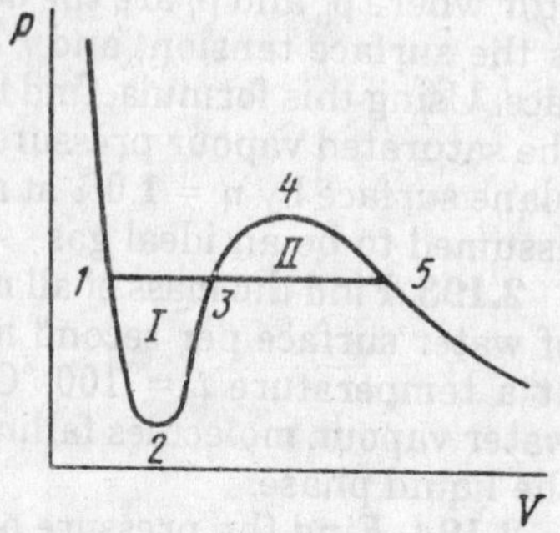

Fig. 2.5.

2.205. What fraction of water supercooled down to the temperature $t = -20$ °C under standard pressure turns into ice when the system passes into the equilibrium state? At what temperature of the supercooled water does it turn into ice completely?

2.206. Find the increment of the ice melting temperature in the vicinity of 0 °C when the pressure is increased by $\Delta p = 1.00$ atm. The specific volume of ice exceeds that of water by $\Delta V' = 0.091$ cm^3/g.

2.207. Find the specific volume of saturated water vapour under standard pressure if a decrease of pressure by $\Delta p = 3.2$ kPa is known to decrease the water boiling temperature by $\Delta t = 0.9$ K.

2.208. Assuming the saturated water vapour to be ideal, find its pressure at the temperature 101.1 °C.

2.209. A small amount of water and its saturated vapour are enclosed in a vessel at a temperature $t = 100$ °C. How much (in per cent) will the mass of the saturated vapour increase if the temperature of the system goes up by $\Delta T = 1.5$ K? Assume that the vapour is an ideal gas and the specific volume of water is negligible as compared to that of vapour.

2.210 Find the pressure of saturated vapour as a function of temperature $p\,(T)$ if at a temperature T_0 its pressure equals p_0.

Assume that: the specific latent heat of vaporization q is independent of T, the specific volume of liquid is negligible as compared to that of vapour, saturated vapour obeys the equation of state for an ideal gas. Investigate under what conditions these assumptions are permissible.

2.211. An ice which was initially under standard conditions was compressed up to the pressure $p = 640$ atm. Assuming the lowering of the ice melting temperature to be a linear function of pressure under the given conditions, find what fraction of the ice melted. The specific volume of water is less than that of ice by $\Delta V' = 0.09$ cm^3/g.

2.212. In the vicinity of the triple point the saturated vapour pressure p of carbon dioxide depends on temperature T as $\log p = a - b/T$, where a and b are constant. If p is expressed in atmospheres, then for the sublimation process $a = 9.05$ and $b = 1.80$ kK, and for the vaporization process $a = 6.78$ and $b = 1.31$ kK. Find:

(a) temperature and pressure at the triple point;

(b) the values of the specific latent heats of sublimation, vaporization, and melting in the vicinity of the triple point.

2.213. Water of mass m = 1.00 kg is heated from the temperature $t_1 = 10$ °C up to $t_2 = 100$ °C at which it evaporates completely. Find the entropy increment of the system.

2.214. The ice with the initial temperature $t_1 = 0$ °C was first melted, then heated to the temperature $t_2 = 100$ °C and evaporated. Find the increment of the system's specific entropy.

2.215. A piece of copper of mass $m = 90$ g at a temperature $t_1 = 90$ °C was placed in a calorimeter in which ice of mass 50 g was at a temperature – 3 °C. Find the entropy increment of the piece of copper by the moment the thermal equilibrium is reached.

2.216. A chunk of ice of mass $m_1 = 100$ g at a temperature $t_1 = 0$ °C was placed in a calorimeter in which water of mass $m_2 = 100$ g was at a temperature t_2. Assuming the heat capacity of the calorimeter to be negligible, find the entropy increment of the system by the moment the thermal equilibrium is reached. Consider two cases: (a) $t_2 = 60$ °C; (b) $t_2 = 94$ °C.

2.217. Molten lead of mass $m = 5.0$ g at a temperature $t_2 = 327$ °C (melting temperature of lead) was poured into a calorimeter packed with a large amount of ice at a temperature $t_1 = 0$ °C. Find the entropy increment of the system lead-ice by the moment the thermal equilibrium is reached. The specific latent heat of melting of lead is equal to $q = 22.5$ J/g and its specific heat capacity is equal to $c = 0.125$ J/(g . K).

2.218. A water vapour filling the space under the piston of a cylinder is compressed (or expanded) so that it remains saturated all the time, being just on the verge of condensation. Find the molar heat capacity C of the vapour in this process as a function of temperature T, assuming the vapour to be an ideal gas and neglecting the specific volume of water in comparison with that of vapour. Calculate C at a temperature $t = 100$ °C.

2.219. One mole of water being in equilibrium with a negligible amount of its saturated vapour at a temperature T_1 was completely converted into saturated vapour at a temperature T_2. Find the entropy increment of the system. The vapour is assumed to be an ideal gas, the specific volume of the liquid is negligible in comparison with that of the vapour.

2.7. TRANSPORT PHENOMENA

• Relative number of gas molecules traversing the distance s without collisions:

$$N/N_0 = e^{-s/\lambda} \tag{2.7a}$$

where λ is the mean free path.

• Mean free path of a gas molecule:

$$\lambda = \frac{1}{\sqrt{2}\,\pi d^2 n}, \tag{2.7b}$$

where d is the effective diameter of a molecule, and n is the number of molecules per unit volume.

• Coefficients of diffusion D, viscosity η, and heat conductivity $\varkappa$ of gases:

$$D = \frac{1}{3}\langle v\rangle\lambda,\quad \eta = \frac{1}{3}\langle v\rangle\lambda\rho,\quad \varkappa = \frac{1}{3}\langle v\rangle\lambda\rho c_V, \tag{2.7c}$$

where ρ is the gas density, and c_V is its specific heat capacity at constant volume.

• Friction force acting on a unit area of plates during their motion parallel to each other in a highly rarefied gas:

$$F = \frac{1}{6}\langle v\rangle\rho\,|u_1 - u_2|, \tag{2.7d}$$

where u_1 and u_2 are the velocities of the plates.

• Density of a thermal flux transferred between two walls by highly rarefied gas:

$$q = \frac{1}{6}\langle v\rangle\rho c_V\,|T_1 - T_2|, \tag{2.7e}$$

where T_1 and T_2 are the temperatures of the walls.

2.220. Calculate what fraction of gas molecules

(a) traverses without collisions the distances exceeding the mean free path λ;

(b) has the free path values lying within the interval from λ to 2λ.

2.221. A narrow molecular beam makes its way into a vessel filled with gas under low pressure. Find the mean free path of molecules if the beam intensity decreases η-fold over the distance Δl.

2.222. Let αdt be the probability of a gas molecule experiencing a collision during the time interval dt; α is a constant. Find:

(a) the probability of a molecule experiencing no collisions during the time interval t;

(b) the mean time interval between successive collisions.

2.223. Find the mean free path and the mean time interval between successive collisions of gaseous nitrogen molecules

(a) under standard conditions;

(b) at temperature $t = 0$ °C and pressure $p = 1.0$ nPa (such a pressure can be reached by means of contemporary vacuum pumps).

2.224. How many times does the mean free path of nitrogen molecules exceed the mean distance between the molecules under standard conditions?

2.225. Find the mean free path of gas molecules under standard conditions if the Van der Waals constant of this gas is equal to $b = 40$ ml/mol.

2.226. An acoustic wave propagates through nitrogen under standard conditions. At what frequency will the wavelength be equal to the mean free path of the gas molecules?

2.227. Oxygen is enclosed at the temperature 0 °C in a vessel with the characteristic dimension $l = 10$ mm (this is the linear dimension determining the character of a physical process in question). Find:

(a) the gas pressure below which the mean free path of the molecules $\lambda > l$;

(b) the corresponding molecular concentration and the mean distance between the molecules.

2.228. For the case of nitrogen under standard conditions find:

(a) the mean number of collisions experienced by each molecule per second;

(b) the total number of collisions occurring between the molecules within 1 cm^3 of nitrogen per second.

2.229. How does the mean free path λ and the number of collisions of each molecule per unit time ν depend on the absolute temperature of an ideal gas undergoing

(a) an isochoric process;

(b) an isobaric process?

2.230. As a result of some process the pressure of an ideal gas increases n-fold. How many times have the mean free path λ and the number of collisions of each molecule per unit time ν changed and how, if the process is

(a) isochoric; (b) isothermal?

2.231. An ideal gas consisting of rigid diatomic molecules goes through an adiabatic process. How do the mean free path λ and the number of collisions of each molecule per second ν depend in this process on

(a) the volume V; (b) the pressure p; (c) the temperature T?

2.232. An ideal gas goes through a polytropic process with exponent n. Find the mean free path λ and the number of collisions of each molecule per second ν as a function of

(a) the volume V; (b) the pressure p; (c) the temperature T.

2.233. Determine the molar heat capacity of a polytropic process through which an ideal gas consisting of rigid diatomic molecules goes and in which the number of collisions between the molecules remains constant

(a) in a unit volume; (b) in the total volume of the gas.

2.234. An ideal gas of molar mass M is enclosed in a vessel of volume V whose thin walls are kept at a constant temperature T. At a moment $t = 0$ a small hole of area S is opened, and the gas starts escaping into vacuum. Find the gas concentration n as a function of time t if at the initial moment $n\ (0) = n_0$.

2.235. A vessel filled with gas is divided into two equal parts *1* and *2* by a thin heat-insulating partition with two holes. One hole has a small diameter, and the other has a very large diameter (in comparison with the mean free path of molecules). In part 2 the gas is kept at a temperature η times higher than that of part 1. How will the concentration of molecules in part 2 change and how many times after the large hole is closed?

2.236. As a result of a certain process the viscosity coefficient of an ideal gas increases $\alpha = 2.0$ times and its diffusion coefficient $\beta = 4.0$ times. How does the gas pressure change and how many times?

2.237. How will a diffusion coefficient D and the viscosity coefficient of an ideal gas change if its volume increases n times:

(a) isothermally; (b) isobarically?

2.238. An ideal gas consists of rigid diatomic molecules. How will a diffusion coefficient D and viscosity coefficient η change and how many times if the gas volume is decreased adiabatically $n = 10$ times?

2.239. An ideal gas goes through a polytropic process. Find the polytropic exponent n if in this process the coefficient.

(a) of diffusion; (b) of viscosity; (c) of heat conductivity remains constant.

2.240. Knowing the viscosity coefficient of helium under standard conditions, calculate the effective diameter of the helium atom.

2.241. The heat conductivity of helium is 8.7 times that of argon (under standard conditions). Find the ratio of effective diameters of argon and helium atoms.

2.242. Under standard conditions helium fills up the space between two long coaxial cylinders. The mean radius of the cylinders is equal to R, the gap between them is equal to ΔR, with $\Delta R \ll R$. The outer cylinder rotates with a fairly low angular velocity ω about the stationary inner cylinder. Find the moment of friction forces acting on a unit length of the inner cylinder. Down to what magnitude should the helium pressure be lowered (keeping the temperature constant) to decrease the sought moment of friction forces $n = 10$ times if $\Delta R = 6$ mm?

2.243. A gas fills up the space between two long coaxial cylinders of radii R_1 and R_2, with $R_1 < R_2$. The outer cylinder rotates with a fairly low angular velocity ω about the stationary inner cylinder. The moment of friction forces acting on a unit length of the inner cylinder is equal to N_1. Find the viscosity coefficient η of the gas taking into account that the friction force acting on a unit area of the cylindrical surface of radius r is determined by the formula $\sigma = \eta r\ (\partial\omega/\partial r)$.

2.244. Two identical parallel discs have a common axis and are located at a distance h from each other. The radius of each disc is equal to a, with $a \gg h$. One disc is rotated with a low angular velocity ω relative to the other, stationary, disc. Find the moment of friction forces acting on the stationary disc if the viscosity coefficient of the gas between the discs is equal to η.

2.245. Solve the foregoing problem, assuming that the discs are located in an ultra-rarefied gas of molar mass M, at temperature T and under pressure p.

2.246. Making use of poiseuille equation (1.7d), find the mass μ of gas flowing per unit time through the pipe of length l and radius α if constant pressures p_1 and p_2 are maintained at its ends.

2.247. One end of a rod, enclosed in a thermally insulating sheath, is kept at a temperature T_1 while the other, at T_2. The rod is composed of two sections whose lengths are l_1 and l_2 and heat conductivity coefficients x_1 and x_2. Find the temperature of the interface.

2.248. Two rods whose lengths are l_1 and l_2 and heat conductivity coefficients x_1 and x_2 are placed end to end. Find the heat conductivity coefficient of a uniform rod of length $l_1 + l_2$ whose conductivity is the same as that of the system of these two rods. The lateral surfaces of the rods are assumed to be thermally insulated.

2.249. A rod of length l with thermally insulated lateral surface consists of material whose heat conductivity coefficient varies with temperature as $x = \alpha/T$, where α is a constant. The ends of the rod are kept at temperatures T_1 and T_2. Find the function $T(x)$, where x is the distance from the end whose temperature is T_1, and the heat flow density.

2.250. Two chunks of metal with heat capacities C_1 and C_2 are interconnected by a rod of length l and cross-sectional area S and fairly low heat conductivity x. The whole system is thermally insulated from the environment. At a moment $t = 0$ the temperature difference between the two chunks of metal equals $(\Delta T)_0$. Assuming the heat capacity of the rod to be negligible, find the temperature difference between the chunks as a function of time.

2.251. Find the temperature distribution in a substance placed between two parallel plates kept at temperatures T_1 and T_2. The plate separation is equal to l, the heat conductivity coefficient of the substance $x \propto \sqrt{T}$.

2.252. The space between two large horizontal plates is filled with helium. The plate separation equals $l = 50$ mm. The lower plate is kept at a temperature $T_1 = 290$ K, the upper, at $T_2 = 330$ K. Find the heat flow density if the gas pressure is close to standard.

2.253. The space between two large parallel plates separated by a distance $l = 5.0$ mm is filled with helium under a pressure $p = 1.0$ Pa. One plate is kept at a temperature $t_1 = 17$ °C and the other, at a temperature $t_2 = 37$ °C. Find the mean free path of helium atoms and the heat flow density.

2.254. Find the temperature distribution in the space between two coaxial cylinders of radii R_1 and R_2 filled with a uniform heat conducting substance if the temperatures of the cylinders are constant and are equal to T_1 and T_2 respectively.

2.255. Solve the foregoing problem for the case of two concentric spheres of radii H_1 and H_2 and temperatures T_1 and T_2.

2.256. A constant electric current flows along a uniform wire with cross-sectional radius R and heat conductivity coefficient x. A unit volume of the wire generates a thermal power w. Find the temperature distribution across the wire provided the steady-state temperature at the wire surface is equal to T_0.

2.257. The thermal power of density w is generated uniformly inside a uniform sphere of radius R and heat conductivity coefficient x. Find the temperature distribution in the sphere provided the steady-state temperature at the surface is equal to T_0.

3

ELECTRODYNAMICS

3.1. CONSTANT ELECTRIC FIELD IN VACUUM

• Strength and potential of the field of a point charge q:

$$E = \frac{1}{4\pi\varepsilon_0}\frac{q}{r^3}\, r, \; \varphi = \frac{1}{4\pi\varepsilon_0}\frac{q}{r}. \tag{3.1a}$$

• Relation between field strength and potential:

$$E = -\nabla\varphi, \tag{3.1b}$$

i.e. field strength is equal to the antigradient of the potential.

• Gauss's theorem and circulation of the vector E:

$$\oint \mathbf{E}\, dS = q/\varepsilon_0, \; \oint \mathbf{E}\, dr = 0. \tag{3.1c}$$

• Potential and strength of the field of a point dipole with electric moment p:

$$\varphi = \frac{1}{4\pi\varepsilon_0}\frac{pr}{r^2}, \; E = \frac{1}{4\pi\varepsilon_0}\frac{p}{r^3}\sqrt{1 + 3\cos^2\theta}, , \tag{3.1d}$$

where θ is the angle between the vectors r and p.

• Energy W of the dipole p in an external electric field, and the moment N of forces acting on the dipole:

$$W = -\mathbf{pE}, \; \mathbf{N} = [\mathbf{pE}]. \tag{3.1e}$$

• Force $\mathbf{F}$ acting on a dipole, and its projection F_x:

$$\mathbf{F} = p\,\frac{\partial \mathrm{E}}{\partial l}, \; F_x = p \cdot \nabla E_x, \tag{3.1f}$$

where $\partial E/\partial l$ is the derivative of the vector F. with respect to the dipole direction ∇E_x is the gradient of the function E_x.

3.1. Calculate the ratio of the electrostatic to gravitational interaction forces between two electrons, between two protons. At what value of the specific charge q/m of a particle would these forces become equal (in their absolute values) in the case of interaction of identical particles?

3.2. What would be the interaction force between two copper spheres, each of mass 1 g, separated by the distance 1 m, if the total electronic charge in them differed from the total charge of the nuclei by one per cent?

3.3. Two small equally charged spheres, each of mass m, are suspended from the same point by silk threads of length l. The distance between the spheres $x \ll l$. Find the rate dq/dt with which the charge leaks off each sphere if their approach velocity varies as $v = a/\sqrt{x}$, where a is a constant.

3.4. Two positive charges q_1 and q_2 are located at the points with radius vectors $\mathbf{r}_1$ and $\mathbf{r}_2$. Find a negative charge q_3 and a radius vector $\mathbf{r}_3$ of the point at which it has to be placed for the force acting on each of the three charges to be equal to zero.

3.5. A thin wire ring of radius r has an electric charge q. What will be the increment of the force stretching the wire if a point charge q_0 is placed at the ring's centre?

3.6. A positive point charge 50 μC is located in the plane xy at the point with radius vector $\mathbf{r}_0 = 2\mathbf{i} + 3\mathbf{j}$, where $\mathbf{i}$ and $\mathbf{j}$ are the unit vectors of the x and y axes. Find the vector of the electric field strength $\mathbf{E}$ and its magnitude at the point with radius vector $\mathbf{r} = 8\mathbf{i} - 5\mathbf{j}$. Here r_0 and r are expressed in metres.

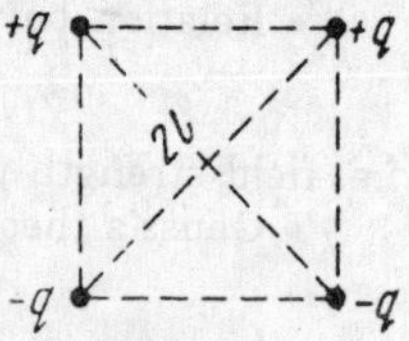

Fig. 3.1.

3.7. Point charges q and $-q$ are located at the vertices of a square with diagonals $2l$ as shown in Fig. 3.1. Find the magnitude of the electric field strength at a point located symmetrically with respect to the vertices of the square at a distance x from its centre.

3.8. A thin half-ring of radius $R = 20$ cm is uniformly charged with a total charge $q = 0.70$ nC. Find the magnitude of the electric field strength at the curvature centre of this half-ring.

3.9. A thin wire ring of radius r carries a charge q. Find the magnitude of the electric field strength on the axis of the ring as a function of distance l from its centre. Investigate the obtained function at $l \gg r$. Find the maximum strength magnitude and the corresponding distance l. Draw the approximate plot of the function $E(l)$.

3.10. A point charge q is located at the centre of a thin ring of radius R with uniformly distributed charge $-q$. Find the magnitude of the electric field strength vector at the point lying on the axis of the ring at a distance x from its centre, if $x \gg R$.

3.11. A system consists of a thin charged wire ring of radius R and a very long uniformly charged thread oriented along the axis of the ring, with one of its ends coinciding with the centre of the ring. The total charge of the ring is equal to q. The charge of the thread (per unit length) is equal to λ. Find the interaction force between the ring and the thread.

3.12. A thin nonconducting ring of radius R has a linear charge density $\lambda = \lambda_0 \cos \varphi$, where λ_0 is a constant, φ is the azimuthal angle. Find the magnitude of the electric field strength

(a) at the centre of the ring;

(b) on the axis of the ring as a function of the distance x from its centre. Investigate the obtained function at $x \gg R$.

3.13. A thin straight rod of length $2a$ carrying a uniformly distributed charge q is located in vacuum. Find the magnitude of the electric field strength as a function of the distance r from the rod's centre along the straight line

(a) perpendicular to the rod and passing through its centre;

(b) coinciding with the rod's direction (at the points lying outside the rod).

Investigate the obtained expressions at $r \gg a$.

3.14. A very long straight uniformly charged thread carried a charge λ per unit length. Find the magnitude and direction of the electric field strength at a point which is at a distance y from the thread and lies on the perpendicular passing through one of the thread's ends.

3.15 A thread carrying a uniform charge λ per unit length has the configurations shown in Fig. 3.2 *a* and *b*. Assuming a curvature

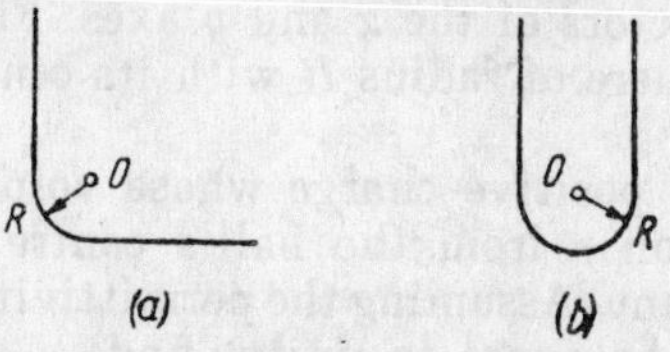

Fig. 3.2.

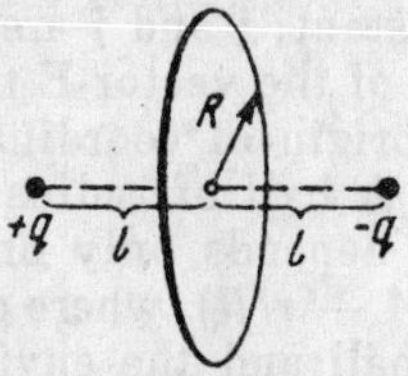

Fig. 3.3.

radius R to be considerably less than the length of the thread, find the magnitude of the electric field strength at the point O.

3.16. A sphere of radius r carries a surface charge of density σ = ar, where a is a constant vector, and r is the radius vector of a point of the sphere relative to its centre. Find the electric field strength vector at the centre of the sphere.

3.17. Suppose the surface charge density over a sphere of radius R depends on a polar angle θ as $\sigma = \sigma_0 \cos\theta$, where σ_0 is a positive constant. Show that such a charge distribution can be represented as a result of a small relative shift of two uniformly charged *balls* of radius R whose charges are equal in magnitude and opposite in sign. Resorting to this representation, find the electric field strength vector inside the given sphere.

3.18. Find the electric field strength vector at the centre of a ball of radius R with volume charge density ρ = ar, where a is a constant vector, and **r** is a radius vector drawn from the ball's centre.

3.19. A very long uniformly charged thread oriented along the axis of a circle of radius R rests on its centre with one of the ends. The charge of the thread per unit length is equal to λ. FInd the flux of the vector **E** across the circle areas.

3.20. Two point charges q and $-q$ are separated by the distance $2l$ (Fig. 3.3). Find the flux of the electric field strength vector across a circle of radius R.

3.21. A ball of radius R is uniformly charged with the volume density ρ. Find the flux of the electric field strength vector across the ball's section formed by the plane located at a distance $r_0 < R$ from the centre of the ball.

3.22. Each of the two long parallel threads carries a uniform charge λ per unit length. The threads are separated by a distance l. Find the maximum magnitude of the electric field strength in the symmetry plane of this system located between the threads.

3.23. An infinitely long cylindrical surface of circular cross-section is uniformly charged lengthwise with the surface density $\sigma = \sigma_0 \cos \varphi$, where φ is the polar angle of the cylindrical coordinate system whose z axis coincides with the axis of the given surface. Find the magnitude and direction of the electric field strength vector on the z axis.

3.24. The electric field strength depends only on the x and y coordinates according to the law $\mathbf{E} = a(x\mathbf{i} + y\mathbf{j})/(x^2 + y^2)$, where a is a constant, $\mathbf{i}$ and $\mathbf{j}$ are the unit vectors of the x and y axes. Find the flux of the vector $\mathbf{E}$ through a sphere of radius R with its centre at the origin of coordinates.

3.25. A ball of radius R carries a positive charge whose volume density depends only on a separation r from the ball's centre as $\rho = \rho_0 (1 - r/R)$, where ρ_0 is a constant. Assuming the permittivities of the ball and the environment to be equal to unity, find:

(a) the magnitude of the electric field strength as a function of the distance r both inside and outside the ball;

(b) the maximum intensity E_{max} and the corresponding distance r_m.

3.26. A system consists of a ball of radius R carrying a spherically symmetric charge and the surrounding space filled with a charge of volume density $\rho = \alpha/r$, where α is a constant, r is the distance from the centre of the ball. Find the ball's charge at which the magnitude of the electric field strength vector is independent of r outside the ball. How high is this strength? The permittivities of the ball and the surrounding space are assumed to be equal to unity.

3.27. A space is filled up with a charge with volume density $\rho = \rho_0 e^{-\alpha r^3}$, where ρ_0 and α are positive constants, r is the distance from the centre of this system. Find the magnitude of the electric field strength vector as a function of r. Investigate the obtained expression for the small and large values of r, i.e. at $\alpha r^3 \ll 1$ and $\alpha r^3 \gg 1$.

3.28. Inside a ball charged uniformly with volume density ρ there is a spherical cavity. The centre of the cavity is displaced with respect to the centre of the ball by a distance $\mathbf{a}$. Find the field strength $\mathbf{E}$ inside the cavity, assuming the permittivity equal to unity.

3.29. Inside an infinitely long circular cylinder charged uniformly with volume density ρ there is a circular cylindrical cavity. The distance between the axes of the cylinder and the cavity is equal to a. Find the electric field strength $\mathbf{E}$ inside the cavity. The permittivity is assumed to be equal to unity.

3.30. There are two thin wire rings, each of radius R, whose axes coincide. The charges of the rings are q and $-q$. Find the potential difference between the centres of the rings separated by a distance a.

3.31. There is an infinitely long straight thread carrying a charge with linear density $\lambda = 0.40\ \mu C/m$. Calculate the potential difference between points *1* and *2* if point *2* is removed $\eta = 2.0$ times farther from the thread than point *1*.

3.32. Find the electric field potential and strength at the centre of a hemisphere of radius R charged uniformly with the surface density σ.

3.33. A very thin round plate of radius R carrying a uniform surface charge density σ is located in vacuum. Find the electric field potential and strength along the plate's axis as a function of a distance l from its centre. Investigate the obtained expression at $l \to 0$ and $l \gg R$.

3.34. Find the potential φ at the edge of a thin disc of radius R carrying the uniformly distributed charge with surface density σ.

3.35. Find the electric field strength vector if the potential of this field has the form $\varphi = \mathbf{ar}$, where $\mathbf{a}$ is a constant vector, and $\mathbf{r}$ is the radius vector of a point of the field.

3.36. Determine the electric field strength vector if the potential of this field depends on x, y coordinates as

a) $\varphi = a(x^2 - y^2)$; (b) $\varphi = axy$,

where a is a constant. Draw the approximate shape of these fields using lines of force (in the x, y plane).

3.37. The potential of a certain electrostatic field has the form $\varphi = a(x^2 + y^2) + bz^2$, where a and b are constants. Find the magnitude and direction of the electric field strength vector. What shape have the equipotential surfaces in the following cases:

(a) $a > 0$, $b > 0$; (b) $a > 0$, $b < 0$?

3.38. A charge q is uniformly distributed over the volume of a sphere of radius R. Assuming the permittivity to be equal to unity throughout, find the potential

(a) at the centre of the sphere;

(b) inside the sphere as a function of the distance r from its centre.

3.39. Demonstrate that the potential of the field generated by a dipole with the electric moment $\mathbf{p}$ (Fig. 3.4) may be represented as $\varphi = \mathbf{pr}/4\pi\varepsilon_0 r^3$, where $\mathbf{r}$ is the radius vector. Using this expression, find the magnitude of the electric field strength vector as a function of r and θ.

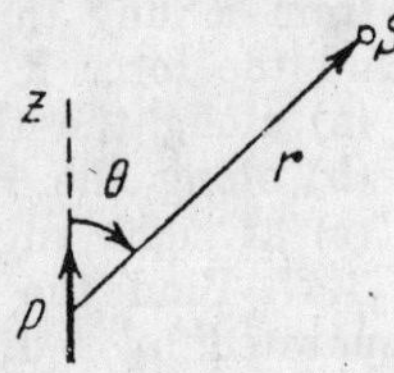

Fig. 3.4.

3.40. A point dipole with an electric moment p oriented in the positive direction of the z axis is located at the origin of coordinates. Find the projections E_z and $E_\perp$ of the electric field strength vector (on the plane perpendicular to the z axis at the point S (see Fig. 3.4)). At which points is $\mathbf{E}$ perpendicular to $\mathbf{p}$?

3.41. A point electric dipole with a moment $\mathbf{p}$ is placed in the external uniform electric field whose strength equals $\mathbf{E}_0$, with

$\mathbf{p} \uparrow\uparrow \mathbf{E}_0$. In this case one of the equipotential surfaces enclosing the dipole forms a sphere. Find the radius of this sphere.

3.42. Two thin parallel threads carry a uniform charge with linear densities λ and $-\lambda$. The distance between the threads is equal to l. Find the potential of the electric field and the magnitude of its strength vector at the distance $r \gg l$ at the angle θ to the vector $\mathbf{l}$ (Fig. 3.5).

3.43. Two coaxial rings, each of radius R, made of thin wire are separated by a small distance l ($l \ll R$) and carry the charges q and $-q$. Find the electric field potential and strength at the axis of the

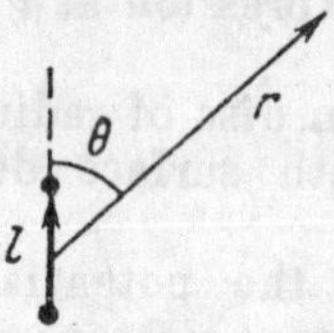

Fig. 3.5.

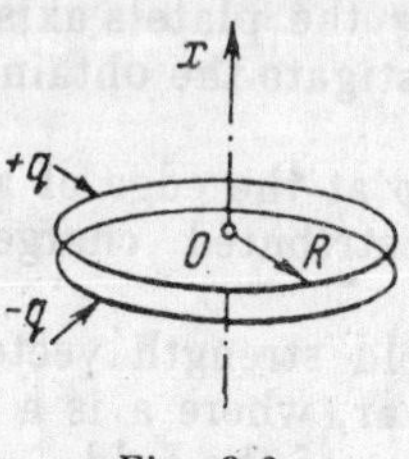

Fig. 3.6.

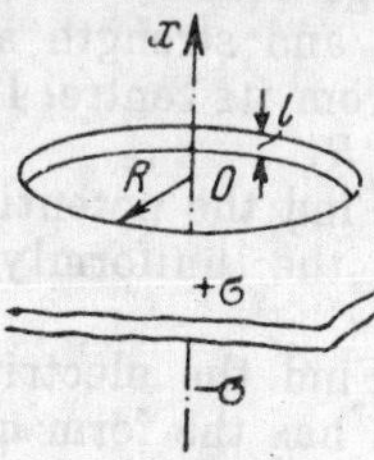

Fig. 3.7.

system as a function of the x coordinate (Fig. 3.6). Show in the same drawing the approximate plots of the functions obtained. Investigate these functions at $|x| \gg R$.

3.44. Two infinite planes separated by a distance l carry a uniform surface charge of densities σ and $-\sigma$ (Fig. 3.7). The planes have round coaxial holes of radius R, with $l \ll R$. Taking the origin O and the x coordinate axis as shown in the figure, find the potential of the electric field and the projection of its strength vector E_x on the axes of the system as functions of the x coordinate. Draw the approximate plot $\varphi(x)$.

3.45. An electric capacitor consists of thin round parallel plates, each of radius R, separated by a distance l ($l \ll R$) and uniformly charged with surface densities σ and $-\sigma$. Find the potential of the electric field and the magnitude of its strength vector at the axes of the capacitor as functions of a distance x from the plates if $x \gg l$. Investigate the obtained expressions at $x \gg R$.

3.46. A dipole with an electric moment $\mathbf{p}$ is located at a distance r from a long thread charged uniformly with a linear density λ. Find the force $\mathbf{F}$ acting on the dipole if the vector $\mathbf{p}$ is oriented

(a) along the thread;
(b) along the radius vector $\mathbf{r}$;
(c) at right angles to the thread and the radius vector $\mathbf{r}$.

3.47. Find the interaction force between two water molecules separated by a distance $l = 10$ nm if their electric moments are oriented along the same straight line. The moment of each molecule equals $p = 0.62 \cdot 10^{-29}$ C·m.

3.48. Find the potential $\varphi(x, y)$ of an electrostatic field $\mathbf{E} = a(y\mathbf{i} + x\mathbf{j})$, where a is a constant, $\mathbf{i}$ and $\mathbf{j}$ are the unit vectors of the x and y axes.

3.49. Find the potential $\varphi(x, y)$ of an electrostatic field $\mathbf{E} = 2axy\mathbf{i} + a(x^2 - y^2)\mathbf{j}$, where a is a constant, $\mathbf{i}$ and $\mathbf{j}$ are the unit vectors of the x and y axes.

3.50. Determine the potential $\varphi(x, y, z)$ of an electrostatic field $\mathbf{E} = ay\mathbf{i} + (ax + bz)\mathbf{j} + by\mathbf{k}$, where a and b are constants, $\mathbf{i}, \mathbf{j}, \mathbf{k}$ are the unit vectors of the axes x, y, z.

3.51. The field potential in a certain region of space depends only on the x coordinate as $\varphi = -ax^3 + b$, where a and b are constants. Find the distribution of the space charge $\rho(x)$.

3.52. A uniformly distributed space charge fills up the space between two large parallel plates separated by a distance d. The potential difference between the plates is equal to $\Delta\varphi$. At what value of charge density ρ is the field strength in the vicinity of one of the plates equal to zero? What will then be the field strength near the other plate?

3.53. The field potential inside a charged ball depends only on the distance from its centre as $\varphi = ar^2 + b$, where a and b are constants. Find the space charge distribution $\rho(r)$ inside the ball.

3.2. CONDUCTORS AND DIELECTRICS IN AN ELECTRIC FIELD

• Electric field strength near the surface of a conductor in vacuum:

$$E_n = \sigma/\varepsilon_0. \tag{3.2a}$$

• Flux of polarization **P** across a closed surface:

$$\oint \mathbf{P}\, d\mathbf{S} = -q', \tag{3.2b}$$

where q' is the algebraic sum of *bound* charges enclosed by this surface.

• Vector **D** and Gauss's theorem for it:

$$\mathbf{D} = \varepsilon_0\mathbf{E} + \mathbf{P}, \quad \oint \mathbf{D}\, d\mathbf{S} = q, \tag{3.2c}$$

where q is the algebraic sum of *extraneous* charges inside a closed surface.

• Relations at the boundary between two dielectrics:

$$P_{2n} - P_{1n} = -\sigma', \quad D_{2n} - D_{1n} = \sigma, \quad E_{2\tau} = E_{1\tau}, \tag{3.2d}$$

where σ' and σ are the surface densities of bound and extraneous charges, and the unit vector **n** of the normal is directed from medium 1 to medium 2.

• In isotropic dielectrics:

$$\mathbf{P} = \varkappa\varepsilon_0\mathbf{E}, \quad \mathbf{D} = \varepsilon\varepsilon_0\mathbf{E}, \quad \varepsilon = 1 + \varkappa. \tag{3.2e}$$

• In the case of an isotropic uniform dielectric filling up all the space between the equipotential surfaces:

$$\mathbf{E} = \mathbf{E}_0/\varepsilon. \tag{3.2f}$$

3.54. A small ball is suspended over an infinite horizontal conducting plane by means of an insulating elastic thread of stiffness k. As soon as the ball was charged, it descended by x cm and its separation from the plane became equal to l. Find the charge of the ball.

3.55. A point charge q is located at a distance l from the infinite conducting plane. What amount of work has to be performed in order to slowly remove this charge very far from the plane.

3.56. Two point charges, q and $-q$, are separated by a distance l, both being located at a distance $l/2$ from the infinite conducting plane. Find:

(a) the modulus of the vector of the electric force acting on each charge;

(b) the magnitude of the electric field strength vector at the midpoint between these charges.

3.57. A point charge q is located between two mutually perpendicular conducting half-planes. Its distance from each half-plane is equal to l. Find the modulus of the vector of the force acting on the charge.

3.58. A point dipole with an electric moment **p** is located at a distance l from an infinite conducting plane. Find the modulus of the vector of the force acting on the dipole if the vector **p** is perpendicular to the plane.

3.59. A point charge q is located at a distance l from an infinite conducting plane. Determine the surface density of charges induced on the plane as a function of separation r from the base of the perpendicular drawn to the plane from the charge.

3.60. A thin infinitely long thread carrying a charge λ per unit length is oriented parallel to the infinite conducting plane. The distance between the thread and the plane is equal to l. Find:

(a) the modulus of the vector of the force acting on a unit length of the thread;

(b) the distribution of surface charge density $\sigma(x)$ over the plane, where x is the distance from the plane perpendicular to the conducting surface and passing through the thread.

3.61. A very long straight thread is oriented at right angles to an infinite conducting plane; its end is separated from the plane by a distance l. The thread carries a uniform charge of linear density λ. Suppose the point O is the trace of the thread on the plane. Find the surface density of the induced charge on the plane

(a) at the point O;

(b) as a function of a distance r from the point O.

3.62. A thin wire ring of radius R carries a charge q. The ring is oriented parallel to an infinite conducting plane and is separated by a distance l from it. Find:

(a) the surface charge density at the point of the plane symmetrical with respect to the ring;

(b) the strength and the potential of the electric field at the centre of the ring.

3.63. Find the potential φ of an uncharged conducting sphere outside of which a point charge q is located at a distance l from the sphere's centre.

3.64. A point charge q is located at a distance r from the centre O of an uncharged conducting spherical layer whose inside and outside radii are equal to R_1 and R_2 respectively. Find the potential at the point O if $r < R_1$.

3.65. A system consists of two concentric conducting spheres, with the inside sphere of radius a carrying a positive charge q_1. What charge q_2 has to be deposited on the outside sphere of radius b to reduce the potential of the inside sphere to zero? How does the potential φ depend in this case on a distance r from the centre of the system? Draw the approximate plot of this dependence.

3.66. Four large metal plates are located at a small distance d from one another as shown in Fig. 3.8. The extreme plates are inter-

Fig. 3.8.

connected by means of a conductor while a potential difference $\Delta\varphi$ is applied to internal plates. Find:

(a) the values of the electric field strength between neighbouring plates;

(b) the total charge per unit area of each plate.

3.67. Two infinite conducting plates *1* and *2* are separated by a distance l. A point charge q is located between the plates at a distance x from plate *1*. Find the charges induced on each plate.

3.68. Find the electric force experienced by a charge reduced to a unit area of an arbitrary conductor if the surface density of the charge equals σ.

3.69. A metal ball of radius $R = 1.5$ cm has a charge $q = 10$ μC. Find the modulus of the vector of the resultant force acting on a charge located on one half of the ball.

3.70. When an uncharged conducting ball of radius R is placed in an external uniform electric field, a surface charge density $\sigma = \sigma_0 \cos\theta$ is induced on the ball's surface (here σ_0 is a constant, θ is a polar angle). Find the magnitude of the resultant electric force acting on an induced charge of the same sign.

3.71. An electric field of strength $E = 1.0$ kV/cm produces polarization in water equivalent to the correct orientation of only one out of N molecules. Find N. The electric moment of a water molecule equals $p = 0.62 \cdot 10^{-29}$ C·m.

3.72. A non-polar molecule with polarizability β is located at a great distance l from a polar molecule with electric moment **p**. Find the magnitude of the interaction force between the molecules if the vector **p** is oriented along a straight line passing through both molecules.

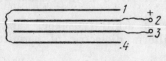

3.73. A non-polar molecule is located at the axis of a thin uniformly charged ring of radius R. At what distance x from the ring's centre is the magnitude of the force F acting on the given molecule
(a) equal to zero; (b) maximum?
Draw the approximate plot $F_x(x)$.

3.74. A point charge q is located at the centre of a ball made of uniform isotropic dielectric with permittivity ε. Find the polarization **P** as a function of the radius vector **r** relative to the centre of the system, as well as the charge q' inside a sphere whose radius is less than the radius of the ball.

3.75. Demonstrate that at a dielectric-conductor interface the surface density of the dielectric's bound charge $\sigma' = -\sigma(\varepsilon - 1)/\varepsilon$, where ε is the permittivity, σ is the surface density of the charge on the conductor.

3.76. A conductor of arbitrary shape, carrying a charge q, is surrounded with uniform dielectric of permittivity ε (Fig. 3.9).

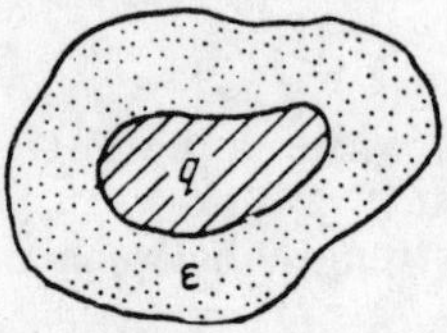

Fig. 3.9.

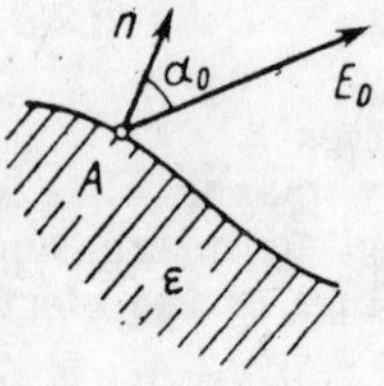

Fig. 3.10.

Find the total bound charges at the inner and outer surfaces of the dielectric.

3.77. A uniform isotropic dielectric is shaped as a spherical layer with radii a and b. Draw the approximate plots of the electric field strength E and the potential φ vs the distance r from the centre of the layer if the dielectric has a certain positive extraneous charge distributed uniformly:
(a) over the internal surface of the layer; (b) over the volume of the layer.

3.78. Near the point A (Fig. 3.10) lying on the boundary between glass and vacuum the electric field strength in vacuum is equal to $E_0 = 10.0$ V/m, the angle between the vector $\mathbf{E}_0$ and the normal **n** of the boundary line being equal to $\alpha_0 = 30°$. Find the field strength E in glass near the point A, the angle α between the vector **E** and **n**, as well as the surface density of the bound charges at the point A.

3.79. Near the plane surface of a uniform isotropic dielectric with permittivity ε the electric field strength in vacuum is equal to E_0, the vector $\mathbf{E}_0$ forming an angle θ with the normal of the dielectric's surface (Fig. 3.11). Assuming the field to be uniform both inside and outside the dielectric, find:
(a) the flux of the vector **E** through a sphere of radius R with centre located at the surface of the dielectric;

(b) the circulation of the vector $\mathbf{D}$ around the closed path Γ of length l (see Fig. 3.11) whose plane is perpendicular to the surface of the dielectric and parallel to the vector $\mathbf{E}_0$.

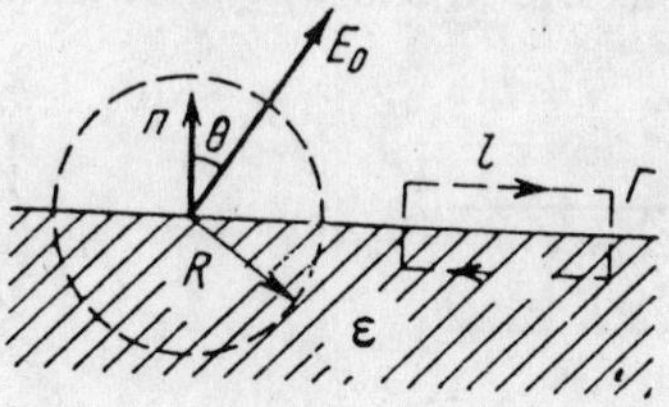

Fig. 3.11.

3.80. An infinite plane of uniform dielectric with permittivity ε is uniformly charged with extraneous charge of space density ρ. The thickness of the plate is equal to $2d$. Find:

(a) the magnitude of the electric field strength and the potential as functions of distance l from the middle point of the plane (where the potential is assumed to be equal to zero); having chosen the x coordinate axis perpendicular to the plate, draw the approximate plots of the projection $E_x(x)$ of the vector $\mathbf{E}$ and the potential $\varphi(x)$;

(b) the surface and space densities of the bound charge.

3.81. Extraneous charges are uniformly distributed with space density $\rho > 0$ over a ball of radius R made of uniform isotropic dielectric with permittivity ε. Find:

(a) the magnitude of the electric field strength as a function of distance r from the centre of the ball; draw the approximate plots $E(r)$ and $\varphi(r)$;

(b) the space and surface densities of the bound charges.

3.82. A round dielectric disc of radius R and thickness d is *statically* polarized so that it gains the uniform polarization $\mathbf{P}$, with the vector $\mathbf{P}$ lying in the plane of the disc. Find the strength $\mathbf{E}$ of the electric field at the centre of the disc if $d \ll R$.

3.83. Under certain conditions the polarization of an infinite uncharged dielectric plate takes the form $\mathbf{P} = \mathbf{P}_0(1 - x^2/d^2)$, where $\mathbf{P}_0$ is a vector perpendicular to the plate, x is the distance from the middle of the plate, d is its half-thickness. Find the strength $\mathbf{E}$ of the electric field inside the plate and the potential difference between its surfaces.

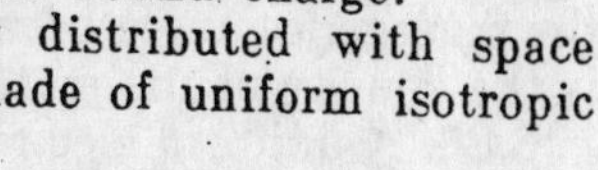

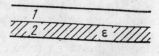

Fig. 3.12.

3.84. Initially the space between the plates of the capacitor is filled with air, and the field strength in the gap is equal to E_0. Then half the gap is filled with uniform isotropic dielectric with permittivity ε as shown in Fig. 3.12. Find the moduli of the vectors $\mathbf{E}$ and $\mathbf{D}$ in both parts of the gap (*1* and *2*) if the introduction of the dielectric

(a) does not change the voltage across the plates;
(b) leaves the charges at the plates constant.

3.85. Solve the foregoing problem for the case when half the gap is filled with the dielectric in the way shown in Fig. 3.13.

Fig. 3.13.

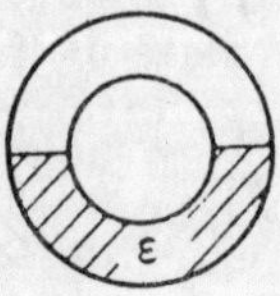

Fig. 3.14.

3.86. Half the space between two concentric electrodes of a spherical capacitor is filled, as shown in Fig. 3.14, with uniform isotropic dielectric with permittivity ε. The charge of the capacitor is q. Find the magnitude of the electric field strength between the electrodes as a function of distance r from the curvature centre of the electrodes.

3.87. Two small identical balls carrying the charges of the same sign are suspended from the same point by insulating threads of equal length. When the surrounding space was filled with kerosene the divergence angle between the threads remained constant. What is the density of the material of which the balls are made?

3.88. A uniform electric field of strength $E = 100$ V/m is generated inside a ball made of uniform isotropic dielectric with permittivity $\varepsilon = 5.00$. The radius of the ball is $R = 3.0$ cm. Find the maximum surface density o the bound charges and the total bound charge of one sign.

3.89. A point charge q is located in vacuum of a distance l from the plane surface of a uniform isotropic dielectric filling up all the half-space. The permittivity of the dielectric equal ε. Find:
(a) the surface density of the bound charges as a function of distance r from the point charge q; analyse the obtained result at $l \to 0$;
(b) the total bound charge on the surface of the dielectric.

3.90. Making use of the formulation and the solution of the foregoing problem, find the magnitude of the force exerted by the charges bound on the surface of the dielectric on the point charge q.

3.91. A point charge q is located on the plane dividing vacuum and infinite uniform isotropic dielectric with permittivity ε. Find the moduli of the vectors **D** and **E** as well as the potential φ as functions of distance r from the charge q.

3.92. A small conducting ball carrying a charge q is located in a uniform isotropic dielectric with permittivity ε at a distane l from an infinite boundary plane between the dielectric and vacuum. Find the surface density of the bound charges on the boundary plane as a function of distance r from the ball. Analyse the obtained result for $l \to 0$.

3.93. A half-space filled with uniform isotropic dielectric with permittivity ε has the conducting boundary plane. Inside the dielectric, at a distance l from this plane, there is a small metal ball possessing a charge q. Find the surface density of the bound charges at the boundary plane as a function of distance r from the ball.

3.94. A plate of thickness h made of uniform *statically* polarized dielectric is placed inside a capacitor whose parallel plates are interconnected by a conductor. The polarization of the dielectric is equal

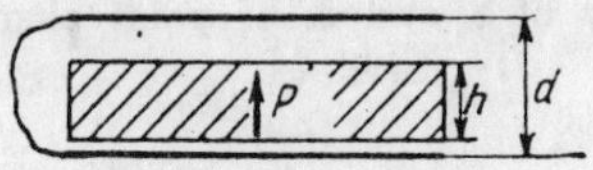

Fig. 3.15.

to $\mathbf{P}$ (Fig. 3.15). The separation between the capacitor plates is d. Find the strength and induction vectors for the electric field both inside and outside the plates.

3.95. A long round dielectric cylinder is polarized so that the vector $\mathbf{P} = \alpha\mathbf{r}$, where α is a positive constant and $\mathbf{r}$ is the distance from the axis. Find the space density ρ' of bound charges as a function of distance r from the axis.

3.96. A dielectric ball is polarized uniformly and *statically*. Its polarization equals $\mathbf{P}$. Taking into account that a ball polarized *in this way* may be represented as a result of a small shift of all positive charges of the dielectric relative to all negative charges,

(a) find the electric field strength $\mathbf{E}$ inside the ball;

(b) demonstrate that the field outside the ball is that of a dipole located at the centre of the ball, the potential of that field being equal to $\varphi = \mathbf{p}_0\mathbf{r}/4\pi\varepsilon_0$, where $\mathbf{p}_0$ is the electric moment of the ball, and $\mathbf{r}$ is the distance from its centre.

3.97. Utilizing the solution of the foregoing problem, find the electric field strength $\mathbf{E}_0$ in a spherical cavity in an infinite statically polarized uniform dielectric if the dielectric's polarization is $\mathbf{P}$, and far from the cavity the field strength is $\mathbf{E}$.

3.98. A uniform dielectric ball is placed in a uniform electric field of strength $\mathbf{E}_0$. Under these conditions the dielectric becomes polarized uniformly. Find the electric field strength $\mathbf{E}$ inside the ball and the polarization $\mathbf{P}$ of the dielectric whose permittivity equals ε. Make use of the result obtained in Problem 3.96.

3.99. An infinitely long round dielectric cylinder is polarized uniformly and statically, the polarization $\mathbf{P}$ being perpendicular to the axis of the cylinder. Find the electric field strength $\mathbf{E}$ inside the dielectric.

3.100. A long round cylinder made of uniform dielectric is placed in a uniform electric field of strength $\mathbf{E}_0$. The axis of the cylinder is perpendicular to vector $\mathbf{E}_0$. Under these conditions the dielectric becomes polarized uniformly. Making use of the result obtained in the foregoing problem, find the electric field strength E in the cylinder and the polarization P of the dielectric whose permittivity is equal to ε.

3.3. ELECTRIC CAPACITANCE. ENERGY OF AN ELECTRIC FIELD

• Capacitance of a parallel-plate capacitor:

$$C = \varepsilon\varepsilon_0 S/d. \tag{3.3a}$$

• Interaction energy of a system of point charges:

$$W = \frac{1}{2}\sum q_i\varphi_i. \tag{3.3b}$$

• Total electric energy of a system with continuous charge distribution:

$$W = \frac{1}{2}\int \varphi\rho\, dV. \tag{3.3c}$$

• Total electric energy of two charged bodies 1 and 2:

$$W = W_1 + W_2 + W_{12}, \tag{3.3d}$$

where W_1 and W_2 are the self-energies of the bodies, and W_{12} is the interaction energy.

• Energy of a charged capacitor:

$$W = \frac{qV}{2} = \frac{q^2}{2C} = \frac{CV^2}{2} \tag{3.3e}$$

• Volume density of electric field energy:

$$w = \frac{\mathbf{ED}}{2} = \frac{\varepsilon\varepsilon_0 E^2}{2} \tag{3.3f}$$

3.101. Find the capacitance of an isolated ball-shaped conductor of radius R_1 surrounded by an adjacent concentric layer of dielectric with permittivity ε and outside radius R_2.

3.102. Two parallel-plate air capacitors, each of capacitance C, were connected in series to a battery with emf $\mathscr{E}$. Then one of the capacitors was filled up with uniform dielectric with permittivity ε. How many times did the electric field strength in that capacitor decrease? What amount of charge flows through the battery?

3.103. The space between the plates of a parallel-plate capacitor is filled consecutively with two dielectric layers *1* and *2* having the thicknesses d_1 and d_2 and the permittivities ε_1 and ε_2 respectively. The area of each plate is equal to S. Find:

(a) the capacitance of the capacitor;

(b) the density σ' of the bound charges on the boundary plane if the voltage across the capacitor equals V and the electric field is directed from layer *1* to layer *2*.

3.104. The gap between the plates of a parallel-plate capacitor is filled with isotropic dielectric whose permittivity ε varies linearly from ε_1 to ε_2 ($\varepsilon_2 > \varepsilon_1$) in the direction perpendicular to the plates. The area of each plate equals S, the separation between the plates is equal to d. Find:

(a) the capacitance of the capacitor;

(b) the space density of the bound charges as a function of ε if the charge of the capacitor is q and the field $\mathbf{E}$ in it is directed toward the growing ε values.

3.105. Find the capacitance of a spherical capacitor whose electrodes have radii R_1 and $R_2 > R_1$ and which is filled with isotropic dielectric whose permittivity varies as $\varepsilon = a/r$, where a is a constant, and r is the distance from the centre of the capacitor.

3.106. A cylindrical capacitor is filled with two cylindrical layers of dielectric with permittivities ε_1 and ε_2. The inside radii of the layers are equal to R_1 and $R_2 > R_1$. The maximum permissible values of electric field strength are equal to E_{1m} and E_{2m} for these dielectrics. At what relationship between ε, R, and E_m will the voltage increase result in the field strength reaching the breakdown value for both dielectrics simultaneously?

3.107. There is a double-layer cylindrical capacitor whose parameters are shown in Fig. 3.16. The breakdown field strength values for these dielectrics are equal to E_1 and E_2 respectively. What is the breakdown voltage of this capacitor if $\varepsilon_1 R_1 E_1 < \varepsilon_2 R_2 E_2$?

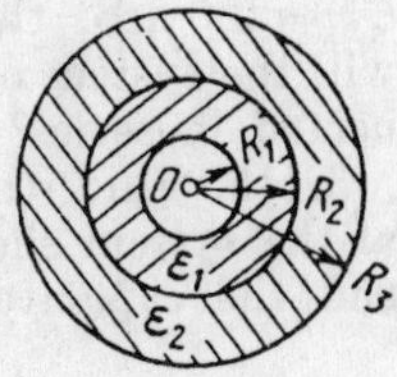

Fig. 3.16.

3.108. Two long straight wires with equal cross-sectional radii a are located parallel to each other in air. The distance between their axes equals b. Find the mutual capacitance of the wires per unit length under the condition $b \gg a$.

3.109. A long straight wire is located parallel to an infinite conducting plate. The wire cross-sectional radius is equal to a, the distance between the axis of the wire and the plane equals b. Find the mutual capacitance of this system per unit length of the wire under the condition $a \ll b$.

3.110. Find the capacitance of a system of two identical metal balls of radius a if the distance between their centres is equal to b, with $b \gg a$. The system is located in a uniform dielectric with permittivity ε.

3.111. Determine the capacitance of a system consisting of a metal ball of radius a and an infinite conducting plane separated from the centre of the ball by the distance l if $l \gg a$.

3.112. Find the capacitance of a system of identical capacitors between points A and B shown in

(a) Fig. 3.17a; (b) Fig. 3.17b.

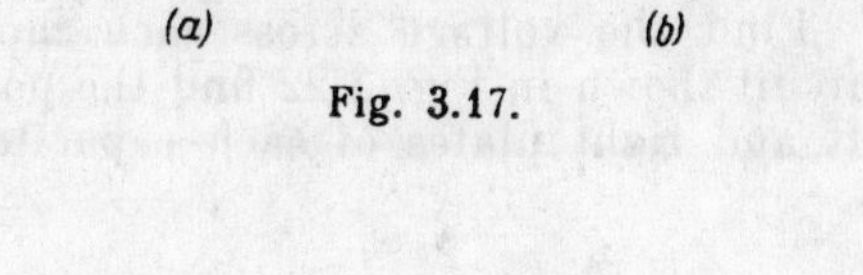

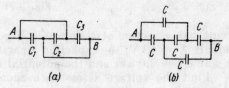

Fig. 3.17.

3.113. Four identical metal plates are located in air at equal distances d from one another. The area of each plate is equal to S. Find the capacitance of the system between points A and B if the plates are interconnected as shown
(a) in Fig. 3.18a; (b) in Fig. 3.18b.

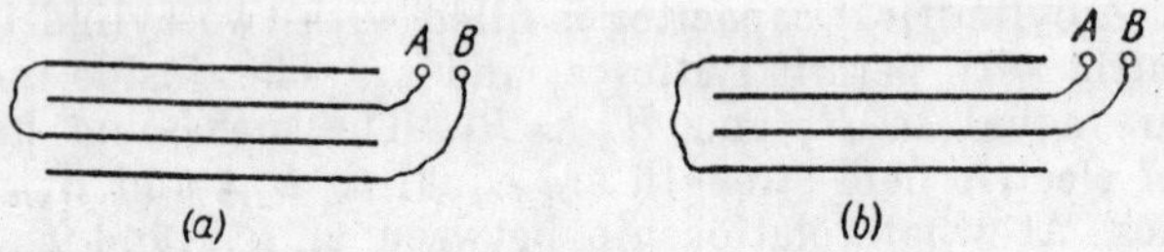

Fig. 3.18.

3.114. A capacitor of capacitance $C_1 = 1.0$ μF withstands the maximum voltage $V_1 = 6.0$ kV while a capacitor of capacitance $C_2 = 2.0$ μF, the maximum voltage $V_2 = 4.0$ kV. What voltage will the system of these two capacitors withstand if they are connected in series?

3.115. Find the potential difference between points A and B of the system shown in Fig. 3.19 if the emf is equal to $\mathscr{E} = 110$ V and the capacitance ratio $C_2/C_1 = \eta = 2.0$.

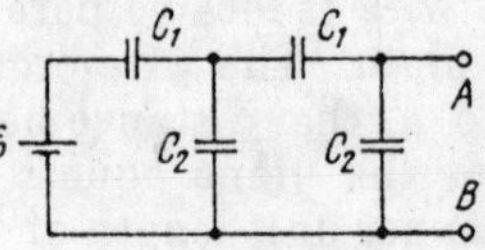

Fig. 3.19.

3.116. Find the capacitance of an infinite circuit formed by the repetition of the same link consisting of two identical capacitors, each with capacitance C (Fig. 3.20).

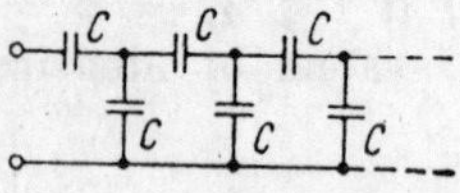

Fig. 3.20.

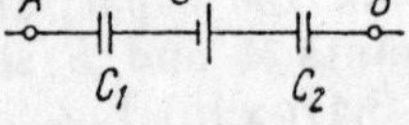

Fig. 3.21.

3.117. A circuit has a section AB shown in Fig. 3.21. The emf of the source equals $\mathscr{E} = 10$ V, the capacitor capacitances are equal to $C_1 = 1.0$ μF and $C_2 = 2.0$ μF, and the potential difference $\varphi_A - \varphi_B = 5.0$ V. Find the voltage across each capacitor.

3.118. In a circuit shown in Fig. 3.22 find the potential difference between the left and right plates of each capacitor.

3.119. Find the charge of each capacitor in the circuit shown in Fig. 3.22.

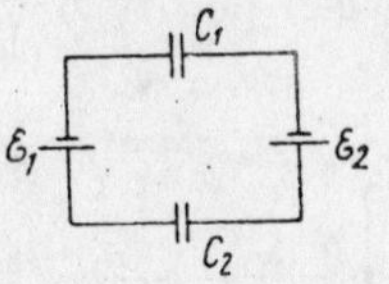

Fig. 3.22.

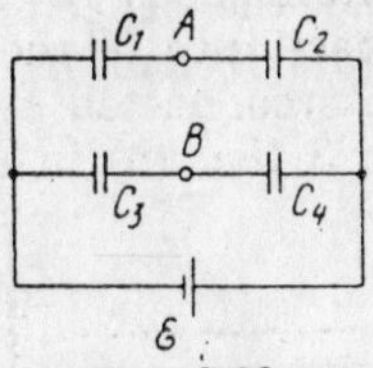

Fig. 3.23.

3.120. Determine the potential difference $\varphi_A - \varphi_B$ between points A and B of the circuit shown in Fig. 3.23. Under what condition is it equal to zero?

3.121. A capacitor of capacitance $C_1 = 1.0\ \mu F$ charged up to a voltage $V = 110$ V is connected in parallel to the terminals of a circuit consisting of two uncharged capacitors connected in series and possessing the capacitances $C_2 = 2.0\ \mu F$ and $C_3 = 3.0\ \mu F$. What charge will flow through the connecting wires?

3.122. What charges will flow after the shorting of the switch Sw in the circuit illustrated in Fig. 3.24 through sections 1 and 2 in the directions indicated by the arrows?

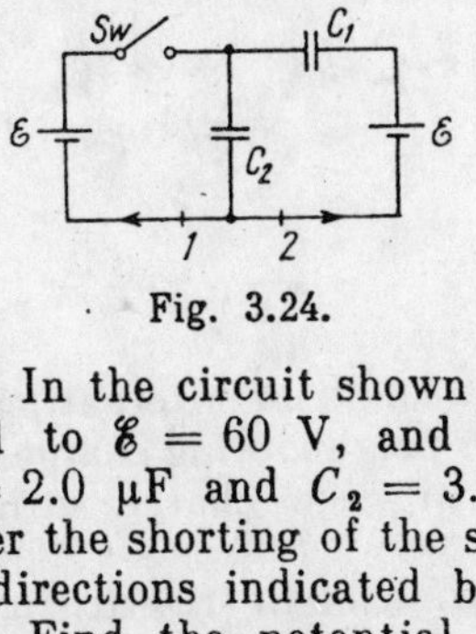

Fig. 3.24.

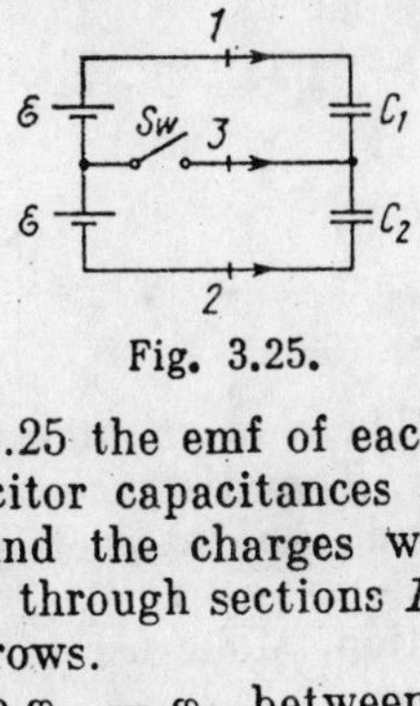

Fig. 3.25.

3.123. In the circuit shown in Fig. 3.25 the emf of each battery is equal to $\mathscr{E} = 60$ V, and the capacitor capacitances are equal to $C_1 = 2.0\ \mu F$ and $C_2 = 3.0\ \mu F$. Find the charges which will flow after the shorting of the switch Sw through sections 1, 2 and 3 in the directions indicated by the arrows.

3.124. Find the potential difference $\varphi_A - \varphi_B$ between points A and B of the circuit shown in Fig. 3.26.

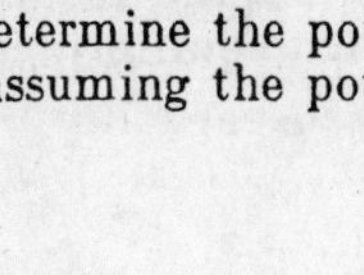

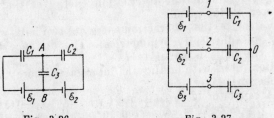

Fig. 3.26.

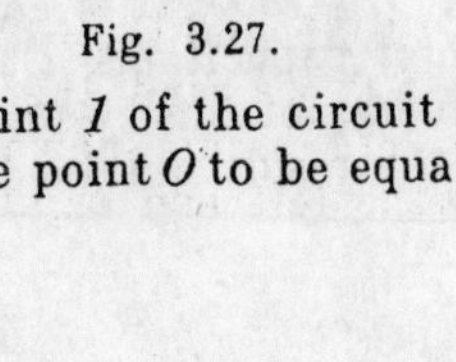

Fig. 3.27.

3.125. Determine the potential at point 1 of the circuit shown in Fig. 3.27, assuming the potential at the point O to be equal to zero.

Using the symmetry of the formula obtained, write the expressions for the potentials. at points *2* and *3*.

3.126. Find the capacitance of the circuit shown in Fig. 3.28 between points *A* and *B*.

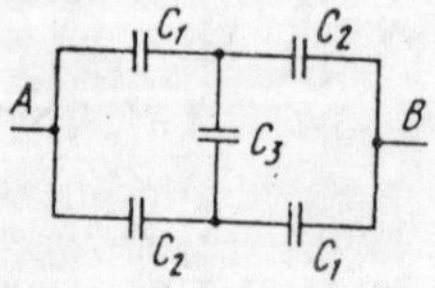

Fig. 3.28.

3.127. Determine the interaction energy of the point charges located at the corners of a square with the side *a* in the circuits shown in Fig. 3.29.

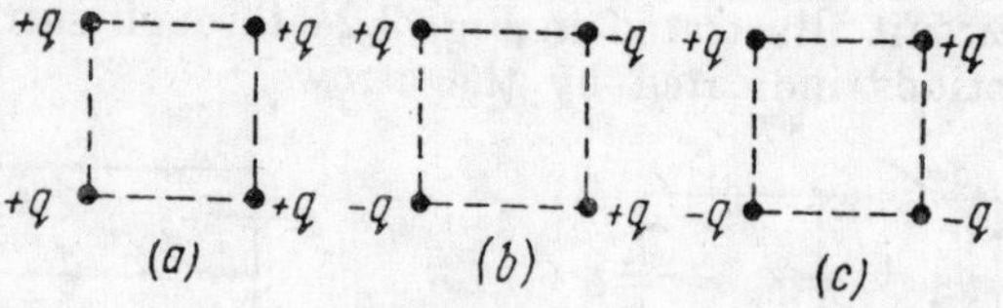

Fig. 3.29.

3.128. There is an infinite straight chain of alternating charges q and $-q$. The distance between the neighbouring charges is equal to a. Find the interaction energy of each charge with all the others.

Instruction. Make use of the expansion of $\ln(1+\alpha)$ in a power series in α.

3.129. A point charge q is located at a distance l from an infinite tonducting plane. Find the interaction energy of that charge with chose induced on the plane.

3.130. Calculate the interaction energy of two balls whose charges q_1 and q_2 are spherically symmetrical. The distance between the centres of the balls is equal to l.

Instruction. Start with finding the interaction energy of a ball and a thin spherical layer.

3.131. A capacitor of capacitance $C_1 = 1.0\ \mu F$ carrying initially a voltage $V = 300$ V is connected in parallel with an uncharged capacitor of capacitance $C_2 = 2.0\ \mu F$. Find the increment of the electric energy of this system by the moment equilibrium is reached. Explain the result obtained.

3.132. What amount of heat will be generated in the circuit shown in Fig. 3.30 after the switch *Sw* is shifted from position *1* to position *2*?

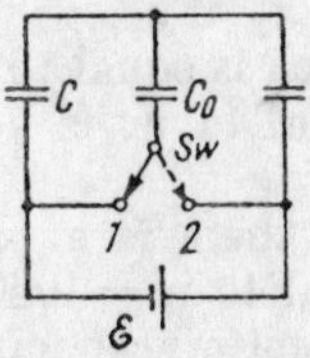

Fig. 3.30.

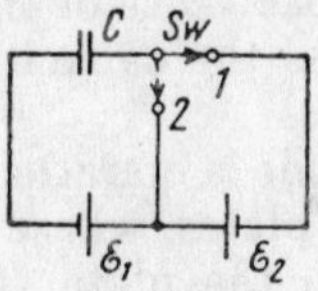

Fig. 3.31.

3.133. What amount of heat will be generated in the circuit shown in Fig. 3.31 after the switch *Sw* is shifted from position *1* to position *2*?

3.134. A system consists of two thin concentric metal shells of radii R_1 and R_2 with corresponding charges q_1 and q_2. Find the self-energy values W_1 and W_2 of each shell, the interaction energy of the shells W_{12}, and the total electric energy of the system.

3.135. A charge q is distributed uniformly over the volume of a ball of radius R. Assuming the permittivity to be equal to unity, find:

(a) the electrostatic self-energy of the ball;

(b) the ratio of the energy W_1 stored in the ball to the energy W_2 pervading the surrounding space.

3.136. A point charge $q = 3.0\ \mu C$ is located at the centre of a spherical layer of uniform isotropic dielectric with permittivity $\varepsilon = 3.0$. The inside radius of the layer is equal to $a = 250$ mm, the outside radius is $b = 500$ mm. Find the electrostatic energy inside the dielectric layer.

3.137. A spherical shell of radius R_1 with uniform charge q is expanded to a radius R_2. Find the work performed by the electric forces in this process.

3.138. A spherical shell of radius R_1 with a uniform charge q has a point charge q_0 at its centre. Find the work performed by the electric forces during the shell expansion from radius R_1 to radius R_2.

3.139. A spherical shell is uniformly charged with the surface density σ. Using the energy conservation law, find the magnitude of the electric force acting on a unit area of the shell.

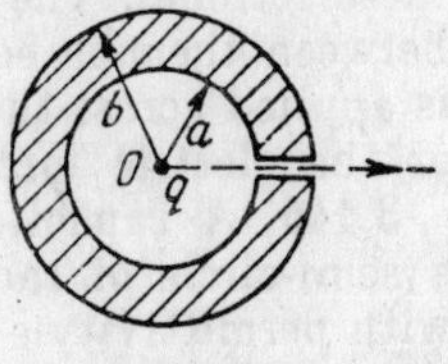

Fig. 3.32.

3.140. A point charge q is located at the centre O of a spherical uncharged conducting layer provided with a small orifice (Fig. 3.32). The inside and outside radii of the layer are equal to a and b respectively. What amount of work has to be performed to slowly transfer the charge q from the point O through the orifice and into infinity?

3.141. Each plate of a parallel-plate air capacitor has an area S. What amount of work has to be performed to slowly increase the distance between the plates from x_1 to x_2 if

(a) the capacitance of the capacitor, which is equal to q, or (b) the voltage across the capacitor, which is equal to V, is kept constant in the process?

3.142. Inside a parallel-plate capacitor there is a plate parallel to the outer plates, whose thickness is equal to $\eta = 0.60$ of the gap width. When the plate is absent the capacitor capacitance equals $c = 20$ nF. First, the capacitor was connected in parallel to a constant voltage source producing $V = 200$ V, then it was disconnected from it, after which the plate was slowly removed from the gap. Find the work performed during the removal, if the plate is

(a) made of metal; (b) made of glass.

3.143. A parallel-plate capacitor was lowered into water in a horizontal position, with water filling up the gap between the plates $d = 1.0$ mm wide. Then a constant voltage $V = 500$ V was applied to the capacitor. Find the water pressure increment in the gap.

3.144. A parallel-plate capacitor is located horizontally so that one of its plates is submerged into liquid while the other is over its surface (Fig. 3.33). The permittivity of the liquid is equal to ε, its density is equal to ρ. To what height will the level of the liquid in the capacitor rise after its plates get a charge of surface density σ?

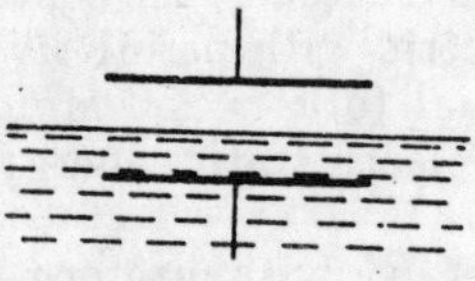

Fig. 3.33

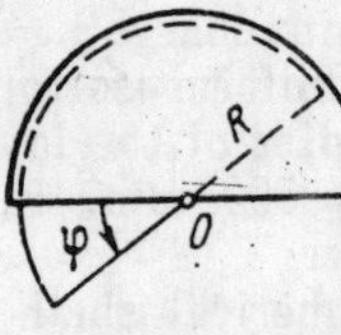

Fig. 3.34.

3.145. A cylindrical layer of dielectric with permittivity ε is inserted into a cylindrical capacitor to fill up all the space between the electrodes. The mean radius of the electrodes equals R, the gap between them is equal to d, with $d \ll R$. The constant voltage V is applied across the electrodes of the capacitor. Find the magnitude of the electric force pulling the dielectric into the capacitor.

3.146. A capacitor consists of two stationary plates shaped as a semi-circle of radius R and a movable plate made of dielectric with permittivity ε and capable of rotating about an axis O between the stationary plates (Fig. 3.34). The thickness of the movable plate is equal to d which is practically the separation between the stationary plates. A potential difference V is applied to the capacitor. Find the magnitude of the moment of forces relative to the axis O acting on the movable plate in the position shown in the figure.

3.4. ELECTRIC CURRENT

• Ohm's law for an inhomogeneous segment of a circuit:

$$I = \frac{V_{12}}{R} = \frac{\varphi_1 - \varphi_2 + \mathcal{E}_{12}}{R} \tag{3.4a}$$

where V_{12} is the voltage drop across the segment.

• Differential form of Ohm's law:

$$j = \sigma\,(\mathbf{E} + \mathbf{E}^*), \tag{3.4b}$$

where $\mathbf{E}^*$ is the strength of a field produced by extraneous forces.

• Kirchhoff's laws (for an electric circuit):

$$\sum I_k = 0,\ \sum I_k R_k = \sum \mathcal{E}_k \tag{3.4c}$$

• Power P of current and thermal power Q:

$$P = VI = (\varphi_1 - \varphi_2 + \mathcal{E}_{12})\,IQ = R\,I^2. \tag{3.4d}$$

• Specific power P_{sp} of current and specific thermal power Q_{sp}:

$$P_{sp} = j\,(\mathbf{E} + \mathbf{E}^*),\ Q_{sp} = \rho \mathbf{j}^2 \tag{3.4e}$$

• Current density in a metal:

$$\mathbf{j} = en\mathbf{u}, \tag{3.4f}$$

where u is the average velocity of carriers.

• Number of ions recombining per unit volume of gas per unit time:

$$n_r = rn^2. \tag{3.4g}$$

where r is recombination coefficient.

3.147. A long cylinder with uniformly charged surface and cross-sectional radius a = 1.0 cm moves with a constant velocity v = 10 m/s along its axis. An electric field strength at the surface of the cylinder is equal to E = 0.9 kV/cm. Find the resulting convection current, that is, the current caused by mechanical transfer of a charge.

3.148. An air cylindrical capacitor with a dc voltage V = 200 V applied across it is being submerged vertically into a vessel field with water at a velocity v = 5.0 mm/s. The electrodes of the capacitor are separated by a distance d = 2.0 mm, the mean curvature radius of the electrodes is equal to r = 50 mm. Find the current flowing in this case along lead wires, if $d \ll r$.

3.149. At the temperature 0 °C the electric resistance of conductor 2 is η times that of conductor *1*. Their temperature coefficients of resistance are equal to α_2 and α_1 respectively. Find the temperature coefficient of resistance of a circuit segment consisting of these two conductors when they are connected

(a) in series; (b) in parallel.

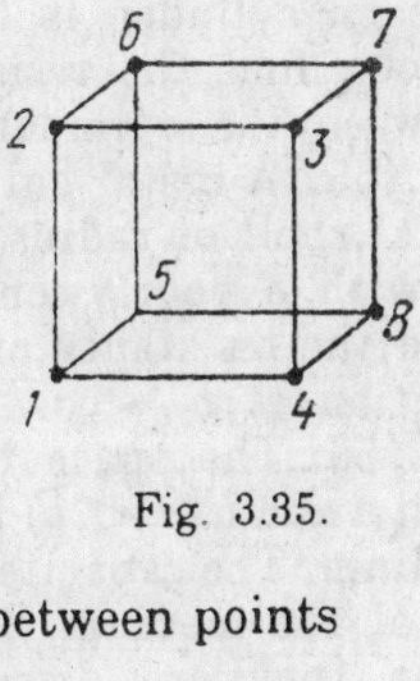

Fig. 3.35.

3.150. Find the resistance of a wire frame shaped as a cube (Fig. 3.35) when measured between points

(a) *1-7;* (b) *1-2*; (c) *1-3*.

The resistance of each edge of the frame is R

3.151. At what value of the resistance R_x in the circuit shown in Fig. 3.36 will the total resistance between points A and B be independent of the number of cells?

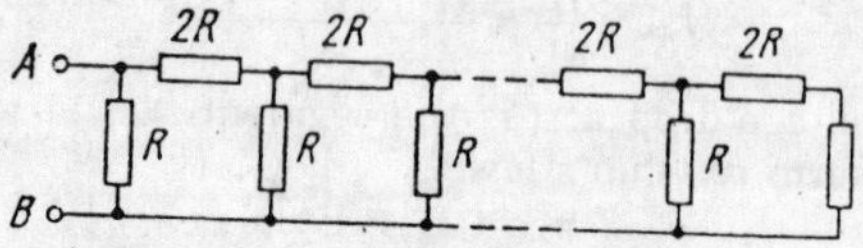

Fig. 3.36.

3.152. Fig. 3.37 shows an infinite circuit formed by the repetition of the same link, consisting of resistance $R_1 = 4.0\ \Omega$ and $R_2 = 3.0\ \Omega$. Find the resistance of this circuit between points A and B.

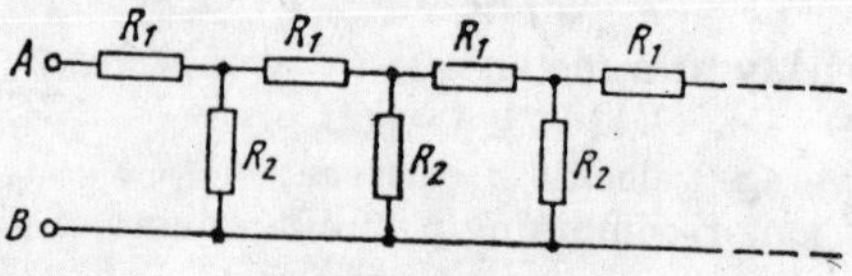

Fig. 3.37.

3.153. There is an infinite wire grid with square cells (Fig. 3.38). The resistance of each wire between neighbouring joint connections is equal to R_0. Find the resistance R of the whole grid between points A and B.

Instruction. Make use of principles of symmetry and superposition.

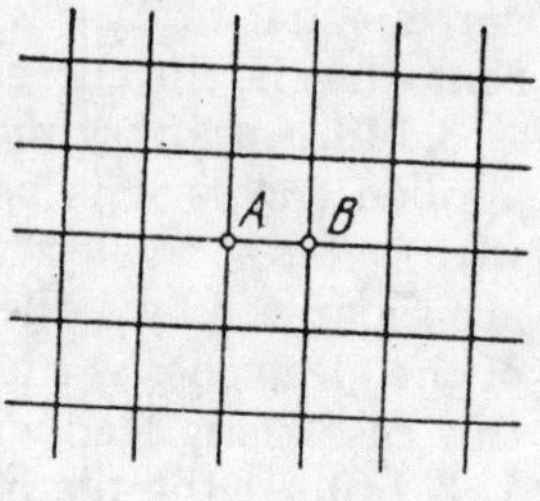

Fig. 3.38.

3.154. A homogeneous poorly conducting medium of resistivity ρ fills up the space between two thin coaxial ideally conducting cylinders. The radii of the cylinders are equal to a and b, with $a < b$, the length of each cylinder is l. Neglecting the edge effects, find the resistance of the medium between the cylinders.

3.155. A metal ball of radius a is surrounded by a thin concentric metal shell of radius b. The space between these electrodes is filled up with a poorly conducting homogeneous medium of resistivity ρ. Find the resistance of the interelectrode gap. Analyse the obtained solution at $b \to \infty$.

3.156. The space between two conducting concentric spheres of radii a and b ($a < b$) is filled up with homogeneous poorly conducting medium. The capacitance of such a system equals C. Find the resistivity of the medium if the potential difference between the spheres, when they are disconnected from an external voltage, decreases η-fold during the time interval Δt.

3.157. Two metal balls of the same radius a are located in a homogeneous poorly conducting medium with resistivity ρ. Find the resistance of the medium between the balls provided that the separation between them is much greater than the radius of the ball.

3.158. A metal ball of radius a is located at a distance l from an infinite ideally conducting plane. The space around the ball is filled with a homogeneous poorly conducting medium with resistivity ρ. In the case of $a \ll l$ find:

(a) the current density at the conducting plane as a function of distance r from the ball if the potential difference between the ball and the plane is equal to V;

(b) the electric resistance of the medium between the ball and the plane.

3.159. Two long parallel wires are located in a poorly conducting medium with resistivity ρ. The distance between the axes of the wires is equal to l, the cross-section radius of each wire equals a. In the case $a \ll l$ find:

(a) the current density at the point equally removed from the axes of the wires by a distance r if the potential difference between the wires is equal to V;

(b) the electric resistance of the medium per unit length of the wires.

3.160. The gap between the plates of a parallel-plate capacitor is filled with glass of resistivity $\rho = 100$ GΩ·m. The capacitance of the capacitor equals $C = 4.0$ nF. Find the leakage current of the capacitor when a voltage $V = 2.0$ kV is applied to it.

3.161. Two conductors of arbitrary shape are embedded into an infinite homogeneous poorly conducting medium with resistivity ρ and permittivity ε. Find the value of a product RC for this system, where R is the resistance of the medium between the conductors, and C is the mutual capacitance of the wires in the presence of the medium.

3.162. A conductor with resistivity ρ bounds on a dielectric with permittivity ε. At a certain point A at the conductor's surface the electric displacement equals D, the vector $\mathbf{D}$ being directed away from the conductor and forming an angle α with the normal of the surface. Find the surface density of charges on the conductor at the point A and the current density in the conductor in the vicinity of the same point.

3.163. The gap between the plates of a parallel-plate capacitor is filled up with an inhomogeneous poorly conducting medium whose conductivity varies linearly in the direction perpendicular to the plates from $\sigma_1 = 1.0$ pS/m to $\sigma_2 = 2.0$ pS/m. Each plate has an area $S = 230$ cm^2, and the separation between the plates is $d = 2.0$ mm. Find the current flowing through the capacitor due to a voltage $V = 300$ V.

3.164. Demonstrate that the law of refraction of direct current lines at the boundary between two conducting media has the form

$\tan \alpha_2/\tan \alpha_1 = \sigma_2 \sigma_1$, where σ_1 and σ_2 are the conductivities of the media, α_2 and α_1 are the angles between the current lines and the normal of the boundary surface.

3.165. Two cylindrical conductors with equal cross-sections and different resistivities ρ_1 and ρ_2 are put end to end. Find the charge at the boundary of the conductors if a current I flows from conductor *1* to conductor *2*.

3.166. The gap between the plates of a parallel-plate capacitor is filled up with two dielectric layers *1* and *2* with thicknesses d_1 and d_2, permittivities ε_1 and ε_2, and resistivities ρ_1 and ρ_2. A dc voltage V is applied to the capacitor, with electric field directed from layer 1 to layer *2*. Find σ, the surface density of extraneous charges at the boundary between the electric layers, and the condition under which $\sigma = 0$.

3.167. An inhomogeneous poorly conducting medium fills up the space between plates *1* and *2* of a parallel-plate capacitor. Its permittivity and resistivity very from values ε_1, ρ_1 at plate *1* to values ε_2, ρ_2 at plate 2. A dc voltage is applied to the capacitor through which a steady current I flows from plate *1* to plate *2*. Find the total extraneous charge in the given medium.

3.168. The space between the plates of a parallel-plate capacitor is filled up with inhomogeneous poorly conducting medium whose resistivity varies linearly in the direction perpendicular to the plates. The ratio of the maximum value of resistivity to the minimum one is equal to η. The gap width equals d. Find the volume density of the charge in the gap if a voltage V is applied to the capacitor. ε is assumed to be *1* everywhere.

3.169. A long round conductor of cross-sectional area S is made of material whose resistivity depends only on a distance r from the axis of the conductor as $r = \alpha/r^2$, where α is a constant. Find:

(a) the resistance per unit length of such a conductor;

(b) the electric field strength in the conductor due to which a current I flows through it.

3.170. A capacitor with capacitance $C = 400$ pF is connected via a resistnace $R = 650\ \Omega$ to a source of constant voltage V_0. How soon will the voltage developed across the capacitor reach a value $V = 0.90$ Vo?

3.171. A capacitor filled with dielectric of permittivity $\varepsilon = 2.1$ loses half the charge acquired during a time interval $= 3.0$ min. Assuming the charge to leak only through the dielectric filler, calculate its resistivity.

3.172. A circuit consists of a source of a constant emf ξ and a resistance R and a capacitor with capacitance C connected in series. The internal resistnace of the source is negligible. At a moment $t = 0$ the capacitance of the capacitor is abruptly decreased η-fold. Find the current flowing through the circuit as a function of time t.

3.173. An ammeter and a voltmeter are connected in series to a battery with an emf $\xi = 6.0$ V. When a certain resistnace is connected in parallel with the voltmeter, the readings of the latter decrease $\eta = 2.0$ times, whereas the readings of the ammeter increase the same number of times. Find the voltmeter readings after the connection of the resistance.

3.174. Find the potential difference $\varphi_1 - \varphi_2$ between points *1* and *2* of the circuit shown in Fig. 3.39 if $R_1 = 10\ \Omega$, $R_2 = 20\ \Omega$, $\mathcal{E}_1 = 5.0$ V, and $\mathcal{E}_2 = 2.0$ V. The internal resistances of the current sources are negligible.

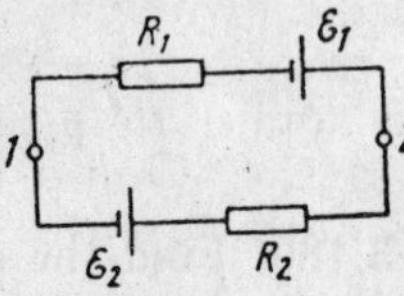

Fig. 3.39.

3.175. Two sources of current of equal emf are connected in series and have different internal resistances R_1 and R_2 $(R_2 > R_1)$. Find the external resistance R at which the potential difference across the terminals of one of the sources (which one in particular?) becomes equal to zero.

3.176. N sources of current with different emf's are connected as shown in Fig. 3.40. The emf's of the sources are proportional to

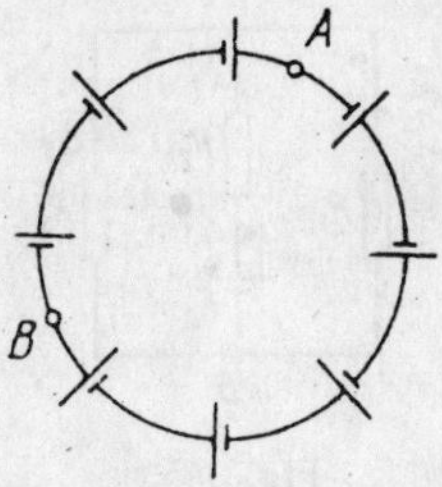

Fig. 3.40.

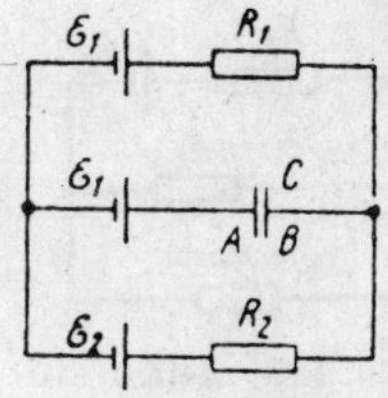

Fig. 3.41.

their internal resistances, i.e. $\mathcal{E} = \alpha R$, where α is an assigned constant. The lead wire resistance is negligible. Find:

(a) the current in the circuit;

(b) the potential difference between points A and B dividing the circuit in n and $N - n$ links.

3.177. In the circuit shown in Fig. 3.41 the sources have emf's $\mathcal{E}_1 = 1.0$ V and $\mathcal{E}_2 = 2.5$ V and the resistances have the values $R_1 = 10\ \Omega$ and $R_2 = 20\ \Omega$. The internal resistances of the sources are negligible. Find a potential difference $\varphi_A - \varphi_B$ between the plates A and B of the capacitor C.

3.178. In the circuit shown in Fig. 3.42 the emf of the source is equal to $\mathcal{E} = 5.0$ V and the resistances are equal to $R_1 = 4.0\ \Omega$ and $R_2 = 6.0\ \Omega$. The internal resistance of the source equals $R = 0.10\ \Omega$. Find the currents flowing through the resistances R_1 and R_2.

3.179. Fig. 3.43 illustrates a potentiometric circuit by means of which we can vary a voltage V applied to a certain device possessing a resistance R. The potentiometer has a length l and a resistance

R_0, and voltage V_0 is applied to its terminals. Find the voltage V fed to the device as a function of distance x. Analyse separately the case $R \gg R_0$.

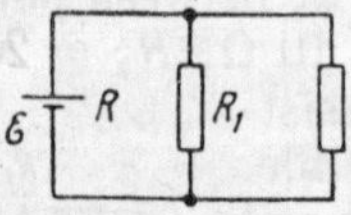

Fig. 3.42.

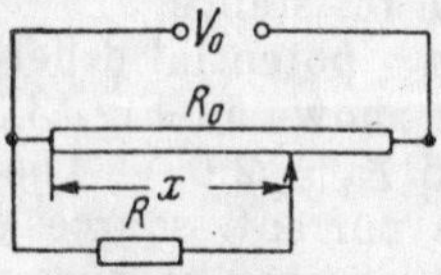

Fig. 3.43.

3.180. Find the emf and the internal resistance of a source which is equivalent to two batteries connected in parallel whose emf's are equal to $\mathscr{E}_1$ and $\mathscr{E}_2$ and internal resistances to R_1 and R_2.

3.181. Find the magnitude and direction of the current flowing through the resistance R in the circuit shown in Fig. 3.44 if the emf's of the sources are equal to $\mathscr{E}_1 = 1.5$ V and $\mathscr{E}_2 = 3.7$ V and the resistances are equal to $R_1 = 10\ \Omega$, $R_2 = 20\ \Omega$, $R = 5.0\ \Omega$. The internal resistances of the sources are negligible.

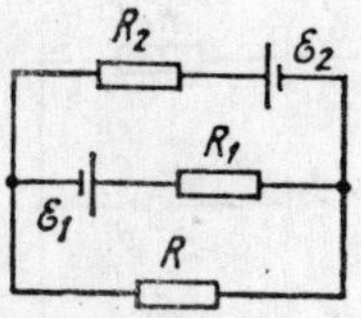

Fig. 3.44.

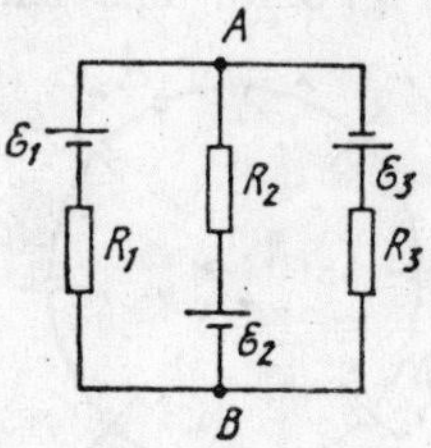

Fig. 3.45.

3.182. In the circuit shown in Fig. 3.45 the sources have emf's $\mathscr{E}_1 = 1.5$ V, $\mathscr{E}_2 = 2.0$ V, $\mathscr{E}_3 = 2.5$ V, and the resistances are equal to $R_1 = 10\ \Omega$, $R_2 = 20\ \Omega$, $R_3 = 30\ \Omega$. The internal resistances of the sources are negligible. Find:

(a) the current flowing through the resistance R_1;

(b) a potential difference $\varphi_A - \varphi_B$ between the points A and B.

3.183. Find the current flowing through the resistance R in the circuit shown in Fig. 3.46. The internal resistances of the batteries are negligible.

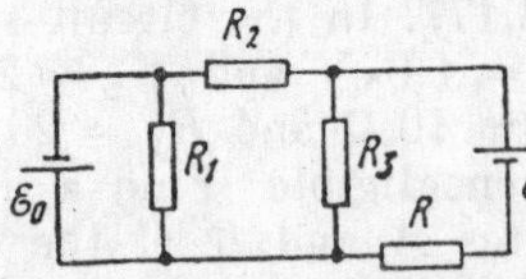

Fig. 3.46.

3.184. Find a potential difference $\varphi_A - \varphi_B$ between the plates of a capacitor C in the circuit shown in Fig. 3.47 if the sources have emf's $\mathscr{E}_1 = 4.0$ V and $\mathscr{E}_2 = 1.0$ V and the resistances are equal to $R_1 = 10\ \Omega$, $R_2 = 20\ \Omega$, and $R_3 = 30\ \Omega$. The internal resistances of the sources are negligible.

3.185. Find the current flowing through the resistance R_1 of the circuit shown in Fig. 3.48 if the resistances are equal to $R_1 = 10\ \Omega$, $R_2 = 20\ \Omega$, and $R_3 = 30\ \Omega$, and the potentials of points 1, 2, and 3 are equal to $\varphi_1 = 10\ V$, $\varphi_2 = 6$ V, and $\varphi_3 = 5$ V.,

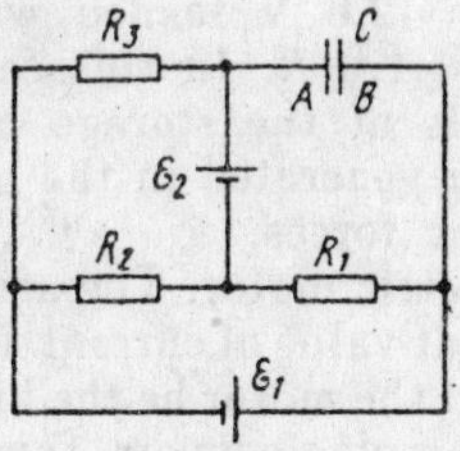

Fig. 3.47.

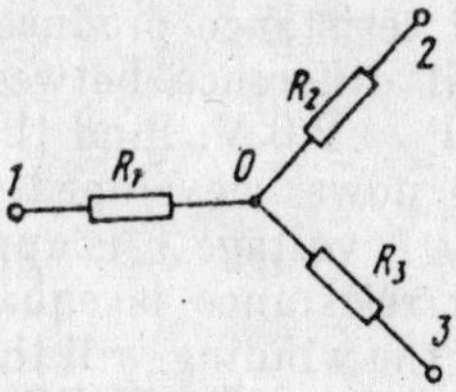

Fig. 3.48.

3.186. A constant voltage $V = 25\ V$ is maintained between points A and B of the circuit (Fig. 3.49). Find the magnitude and direction

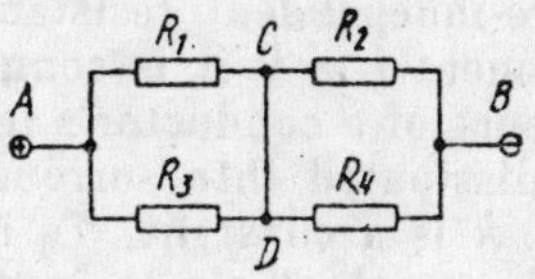

Fig. 3.49.

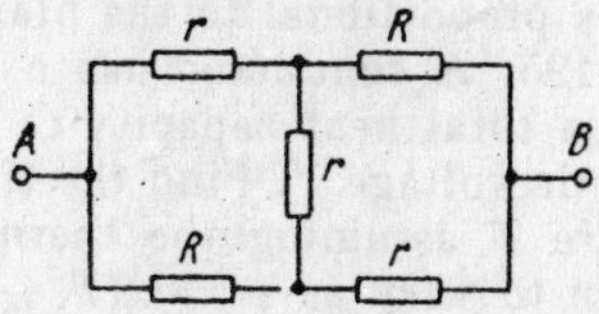

Fig. 3.50.

of the current flowing through the segment CD if the resistances are qual to $R_1 = 1.0\ \Omega$, $R_2 = 2.0\ \Omega$, $R_3 = 3.0\ \Omega$, and $R_4 = 4.0\ \Omega$.

3.187. Find the resistnace between points A and B of the ciruit shown in Fig. 3.50.

3.188. Find how the voltage across the capacitor C varies with time t (Fig. 3.51) after the shorting for the switch Sw at the moment $t = 0$.

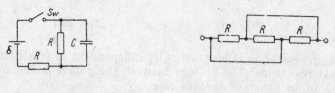

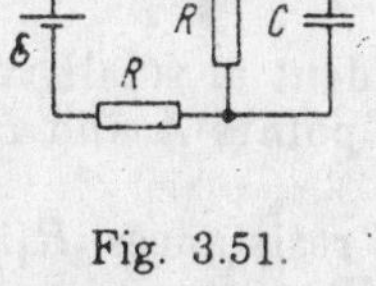

Fig. 3.51.

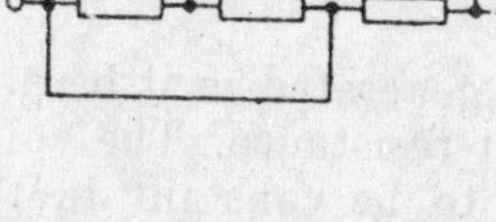

Fig. 3.52.

3.189. What amount of heat will be generated in a coil of resistance R due to a charge q passing through it if the current in the coil.

(a) decreases down to zero uniformly during a time interval Δt;

(b) decreases down to zero halving its value every Δt seconds?

3.190. A dc source with internal resistnace R_0 is loaded with three identical resistnace R interconnected as shwon in Fig. 3.52.

At what value of R will the thermal power generated in this circuit be the highest?

3.191. Make sure that the current distribution over two resistances R_1 and R_2 connected in parallel corresponds to the minimum thermal power generated in this circuit.

3.192. A storage battery with emf $\mathscr{E} = 2.6$ V loaded with an external resistance produces a current $I = 1.0$ A. In this case the potential difference between the terminals of the storage battery equals $V = 2.0$ V. Find the thermal power generated in the battery and the power developed in it by electric forces.

3.193. A voltage V is applied to a dc electric motor. The armature winding resistance is equal to R. At what value of current flowing through the winding will the useful power of the motor be the highest? What is it equal to? What is the motor efficiency in this case?

3.194. How much (in per cent) has a filament diameter decreased due to evaporation if the maintenance of the previous temperature required an increase of the voltage by $\eta = 1.0\%$? The amount of heat transferred from the filament into surrounding space is assumed to be proportional to the filament surface area.

3.195. A conductor has a temperature-independent resistance R and a total heat capacity C. At the moment $t = 0$ it is connected to a dc voltage V. Find the time dependence of a conductor's temperature T assuming the thermal power dissipated into surrounding space to vary as $q = k(T - T_0)$, where k is a constant, T_0 is the environmental temperature (equal to the conductor's temperature at the initial moment).

3.196. A circuit shown in Fig. 3.53 has resistances $R_1 = 20\ \Omega$ and $R_2 = 30\ \Omega$. At what value of the resistance R_x will the thermal

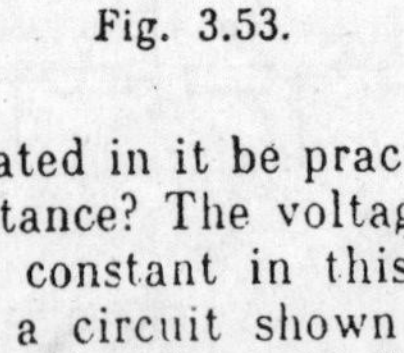

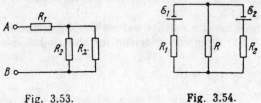

Fig. 3.53.

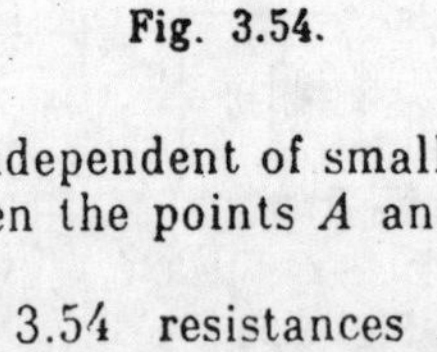

Fig. 3.54.

power generated in it be practically independent of small variations of that resistance? The voltage between the points A and B is supposed to be constant in this case.

3.197. In a circuit shown in Fig. 3.54 resistances R_1 and R_2 are known, as well as emf's $\mathscr{E}_1$ and $\mathscr{E}_2$. The internal resistances of the sources are negligible. At what value of the resistance R will the thermal power generated in it be the highest? What is it equal to?

3.198. A series-parallel combination battery consisting of a large number $N = 300$ of identical cells, each with an internal resistance

$r = 0.3\ \Omega$, is loaded with an external resistance $R = 10\ \Omega$. Find the number n of parallel groups consisting of an equal number of cells connected in series, at which the external resistance generates the highest thermal power.

3.199. A capacitor of capacitance $C = 5.00\ \mu F$ is connected to a source of constant emf $\mathscr{E} = 200$ V (Fig. 3.55). Then the switch *Sw* was thrown over from contact *1* to contact *2*. Find the amount of heat generated in a resistance $R_1 = 500\ \Omega$ if $R_2 = 330\ \Omega$.

3.200. Between the plates of a parallel-plate capacitor there is a metallic plate whose thickness takes up $\eta = 0.60$ of the capacitor

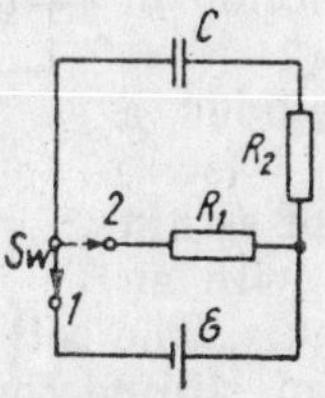

Fig. 3.55.

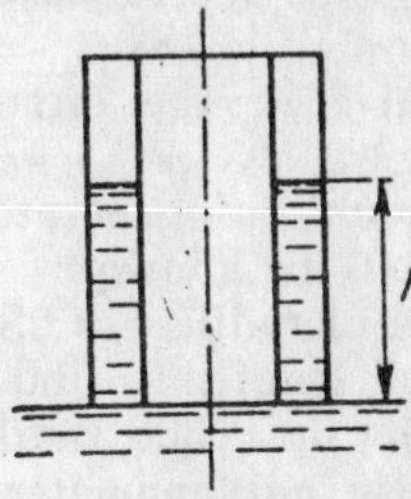

Fig. 3.56.

gap. When that plate is absent the capacitor has a capacity $C = 20$ nF. The capacitor is connected to a dc voltage source $V = 100$ V. The metallic plate is slowly extracted from the gap. Find:

(a) the energy increment of the capacitor;

(b) the mechanical work performed in the process of plate extraction.

3.201. A glass plate totally fills up the gap between the electrodes of a parallel-plate capacitor whose capacitance in the absence of that glass plate is equal to $C = 20$ nF. The capacitor is connected to a dc voltage source $V = 100$ V. The plate is slowly, and without friction, extracted from the gap. Find the capacitor energy increment and the mechanical work performed in the process of plate extraction.

3.202. A cylindrical capacitor connected to a dc voltage source V touches the surface of water with its end (Fig. 3.56). The separation d between the capacitor electrodes is substantially less than their mean radius. Find a height h to which the water level in the gap will rise. The capillary effects are to be neglected.

3.203. The radii of spherical capacitor electrodes are equal to a and b, with $a < b$. The interelectrode space is filled with homogeneous substance of permittivity ε and resistivity ρ. Initially the capacitor is not charged. At the moment $t = 0$ the internal electrode gets a charge q_0. Find:

(a) the time variation of the charge on the internal electrode;

(b) the amount of heat generated during the spreading of the charge.

3.204. The electrodes of a capacitor of capacitance $C = 2.00\ \mu F$ carry opposite charges $q_0 = 1.00$ mC. Then the electrodes are interconnected through a resistance $R = 5.0\ M\Omega$. Find:

(a) the charge flowing through that resistance during a time interval $\tau = 2.00$ s;

(b) the amount of heat generated in the resistance during the same interval.

3.205. In a circuit shown in Fig. 3.57 the capacitance of each capacitor is equal to C and the resistance, to R. One of the capacitors was connected to a voltage V_0 and then at the moment $t = 0$ was shorted by means of the switch Sw. Find:

(a) a current I in the circuit as a function of time t;

(b) the amount of generated heat provided a dependence $I(t)$ is known.

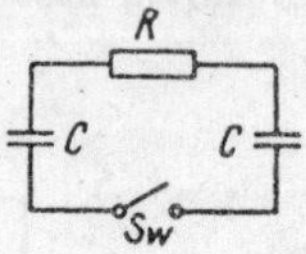

Fig. 3.57.

3.206. A coil of radius $r = 25$ cm wound of a thin copper wire of length $l = 500$ m rotates with an angular velocity $\omega = 300$ rad/s about its axis. The coil is connected to a ballistic galvanometer by means of sliding contacts. The total resistance of the circuit is equal to $R = 21\ \Omega$. Find the specific charge of current carriers in copper if a sudden stoppage of the coil makes a charge $q = 10$ nC flow through the galvanometer.

3.207. Find the total momentum of electrons in a straight wire of length $l = 1000$ m carrying a current $I = 70$ A.

3.208. A copper wire carries a current of density $j = 1.0$ A/mm^2. Assuming that one free electron corresponds to each copper atom, evaluate the distance which will be covered by an electron during its displacement $l = 10$ mm along the wire.

3.209. A straight copper wire of length $l = 1000$ m and cross-sectional area $S = 1.0$ mm^2 carries a current $I = 4.5$ A. Assuming that one free electron corresponds to each copper atom, find:

(a) the time it takes an electron to displace from one end of the wire to the other;

(b) the sum of electric forces acting on all free electrons in the given wire.

3.210. A homogeneous proton beam accelerated by a potential difference $V = 600$ kV has a round cross-section of radius $r = 5.0$ mm. Find the electric field strength on the surface of the beam and the potential difference between the surface and the axis of the beam if the beam current is equal to $I = 50$ mA.

3.211. Two large parallel plates are located in vacuum. One of them serves as a cathode, a source of electrons whose initial velocity is negligible. An electron flow directed toward the opposite plate produces a space charge causing the potential in the gap between the plates to vary as $\varphi = ax^{4/3}$, where a is a positive constant, and x is the distance from the cathode. Find:

(a) the volume density of the space charge as a function of x;

(b) the current density.

3.212. The air between two parallel plates separated by a distance $d = 20$ mm is ionized by X-ray radiation. Each plate has an area $S = 500$ cm^2. Find the concentration of positive ions if at a voltage $V = 100$ V a current $I = 3.0$ μA flows between the plates, which is well below the saturation current. The air ion mobilities are $u_0^+ = 1.37$ cm^2/(V·s) and $u_0^- = 1.91$ cm^2/(V·s).

3.213. A gas is ionized in the immediate vicinity of the surface of plane electrode *1* (Fig. 3.58) separated from electrode *2* by a distance l. An alternating voltage varying with time t as $V = V_0 \sin \omega t$ is applied to the electrodes. On decreasing the frequency ω it was observed that the galvanometer G indicates a current only at $\omega < \omega_0$, where ω_0 is a certain cut-off frequency. Find the mobility of ions reaching electrode *2* under these conditions.

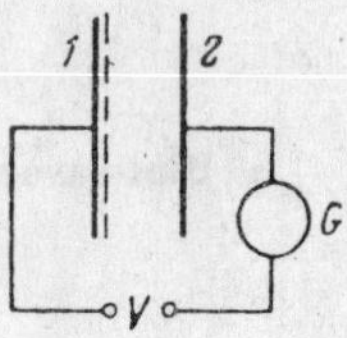

Fig. 3.58.

3.214. The air between two closely located plates is uniformly ionized by ultraviolet radiation. The air volume between the plates is equal to $V = 500$ cm^3, the observed saturation current is equal to $I_{sat} = 0.48$ μA. Find:

(a) the number of ion pairs produced in a unit volume per unit time;

(b) the equilibrium concentration of ion pairs if the recombination coefficient for air ions is equal to $r = 1.67 \cdot 10^{-6}$ cm^3/s.

3.215. Having been operated long enough, the ionizer producing $\dot{n}_i = 3.5 \cdot 10^9$ cm^{-3}·s^{-1} of ion pairs per unit volume of air per unit time was switched off. Assuming that the only process tending to reduce the number of ions in air is their recombination with coefficient $r = 1.67 \cdot 10^{-6}$ cm^3/s, find how soon after the ionizer's switching off the ion concentration decreases $\eta = 2.0$ times.

3.216. A parallel-plate air capacitor whose plates are separated by a distance $d = 5.0$ mm is first charged to a potential difference $V = 90$ V and then disconnected from a dc voltage source. Find the time interval during which the voltage across the capacitor decreases by $\eta = 1.0\%$, taking into account that the average number of ion pairs formed in air under standard conditions per unit volume per unit time is equal to $\dot{n}_i = 5.0$ cm^{-3}·s^{-1} and that the given voltage corresponds to the saturation current.

3.217. The gap between two plane plates of a capacitor equal to d is filled with a gas. One of the plates emits ν_0 electrons per second which, moving in an electric field, ionize gas molecules; this way each electron produces α new electrons (and ions) along a unit length of its path. Find the electronic current at the opposite plate, neglecting the ionization of gas molecules by formed ions.

3.218. The gas between the capacitor plates separated by a distance d is uniformly ionized by ultraviolet radiation so that n_i electrons per unit volume per second are formed. These electrons moving in the electric field of the capacitor ionize gas molecules, each electron producing α new electrons (and ions) per unit length of its path. Neglecting the ionization by ions, find the electronic current density at the plate possessing a higher potential.

3.5. CONSTANT MAGNETIC FIELD. MAGNETICS

• Magnetic field of a point charge q moving with non-relativistic velocity **v**:

$$\mathbf{B} = \frac{\mu_0}{4\pi} \frac{q\,[\mathbf{vr}]}{r^3}. \tag{3.5a}$$

• Biot-Savart law:

$$d\mathbf{B} = \frac{\mu_0}{4\pi} \frac{[\mathbf{jr}]}{r^3}\, dV, \quad d\mathbf{B} = \frac{\mu_0}{4\pi} \frac{I\,[d\mathbf{l}, \mathbf{r}]}{r^3}. \tag{3.5b}$$

• Circulation of a vector **B** and Gauss's theorem for it:

$$\oint \mathbf{B}\, d\mathbf{r} = \mu_0 I, \quad \oint \mathbf{B}\, d\mathbf{S} = 0. \tag{3.5c}$$

• Lorentz force:

$$\mathbf{F} = q\mathbf{E} + q\,[\mathbf{vB}]. \tag{3.5d}$$

• Ampere force:

$$d\mathbf{F} = [\mathbf{jB}]\, dV, \quad d\mathbf{F} = I\,[d\mathbf{l}, \mathbf{B}]. \tag{3.5e}$$

• Force and moment of forces acting on a magnetic dipole $\mathbf{p}_m = IS\mathbf{n}$:

$$\mathbf{F} = p_m \frac{\partial \mathbf{B}}{\partial n}, \quad \mathbf{N} = [\mathbf{p}_m \mathbf{B}], \tag{3.5f}$$

where $\partial\mathbf{B}/\partial n$ is the derivative of a vector **B** with respect to the dipole direction.

• Circulation of magnetization **J**:

$$\oint \mathbf{J}\, d\mathbf{r} = I', \tag{3.5g}$$

where I' is the total molecular current.

• Vector **H** and its circulation:

$$\mathbf{H} = \frac{\mathbf{B}}{\mu_0} - \mathbf{J}, \quad \oint \mathbf{H}\, d\mathbf{r} = I, \tag{3.5h}$$

where I is the algebraic sum of macroscopic currents.

• Relations at the boundary between two magnetics:

$$B_{1n} = B_{2n}, \quad H_{1\tau} = H_{2\tau}. \tag{3.5i}$$

• For the case of magnetics in which $\mathbf{J} = \chi\mathbf{H}$:

$$\mathbf{B} = \mu\mu_0\mathbf{H}, \quad \mu = 1 + \chi. \tag{3.5j}$$

3.219. A current $I = 1.00$ A circulates in a round thin-wire loop of radius $R = 100$ mm. Find the magnetic induction

(a) at the centre of the loop;

(b) at the point lying on the axis of the loop at a distance $x = 100$ mm from its centre.

3.220. A current I flows along a thin wire shaped as a regular polygon with n sides which can be inscribed into a circle of radius R. Find the magnetic induction at the centre of the polygon. Analyse the obtained expression at $n \to \infty$.

3.221. Find the magnetic induction at the centre of a rectangular wire frame whose diagonal is equal to $d = 16$ cm and the angle between the diagonals is equal to $\varphi = 30°$; the current flowing in the frame equals $I = 5.0$ A.

3.222. A current $I = 5.0$ A flows along a thin wire shaped as shown in Fig. 3.59. The radius of a curved part of the wire is equal to $R = 120$ mm, the angle $2\varphi = 90°$. Find the magnetic induction of the field at the point O.

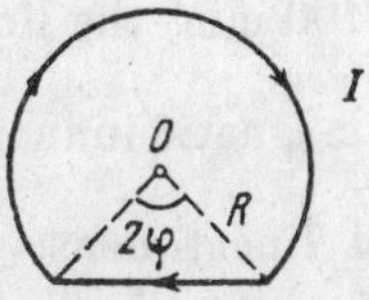

Fig. 3.59.

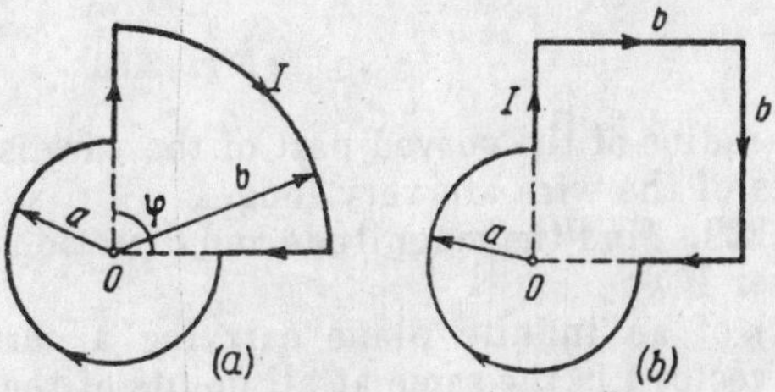

Fig. 3.60.

3.223. Find the magnetic induction of the field at the point O of a loop with current I, whose shape is illustrated

(a) in Fig. 3.60*a*, the radii a and b, as well as the angle φ are known;

(b) in Fig. 3.60*b*, the radius a and the side b are known.

3.224. A current I flows along a lengthy thin-walled tube of radius R with longitudinal slit of width h. Find the induction of the magnetic field inside the tube under the condition $h \ll R$.

3.225. A current I flows in a long straight wire with cross-section having the form of a thin half-ring of radius R (Fig. 3.61). Find the induction of the magnetic field at the point O.

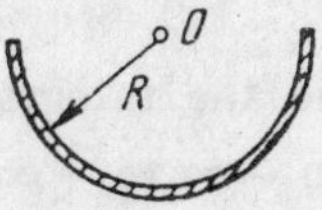

Fig. 3.61.

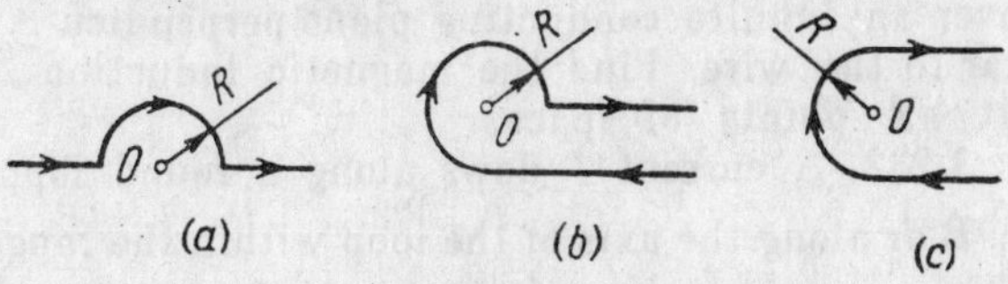

Fig. 3.62.

3.226. Find the magnetic induction of the field at the point O if a current-carrying wire has the shape shown in Fig. 3.62 *a*, *b*, *c*. The radius of the curved part of the wire is R, the linear parts are assumed to be very long.

3.227. A very long wire carrying a current $I = 5.0$ A is bent at right angles. Find the magnetic induction at a point lying on a perpendicular to the wire, drawn through the point of bending, at a distance $l = 35$ cm from it.

3.228. Find the magnetic induction at the point O if the wire carrying a current $I = 8.0$ A has the shape shown in Fig. 3.63 a, b, c.

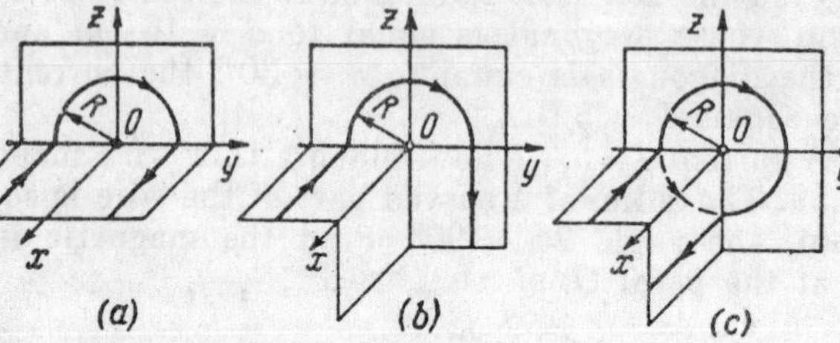

Fig. 3.63.

The radius of the curved part of the wire is $R = 100$ mm, the linear parts of the wire are very long.

3.229. Find the magnitude and direction of the magnetic induction vector **B**

(a) of an infinite plane carrying a current of linear density **i**; the vector **i** is the same at all points of the plane;

(b) of two parallel infinite planes carrying currents of linear densities **i** and —**i**; the vectors **i** and —**i** are constant at all points of the corresponding planes.

3.230. A uniform current of density j flows inside an infinite plate of thickness $2d$ parallel to its surface. Find the magnetic induction induced by this current as a function of the distance x from the median plane of the plate. The magnetic permeability is assumed to be equal to unity both inside and outside the plate.

3.231. A direct current I flows along a lengthy straight wire. From the point O (Fig. 3.64) the current spreads radially all over an infinite conducting plane perpendicular to the wire. Find the magnetic induction at all points of space.

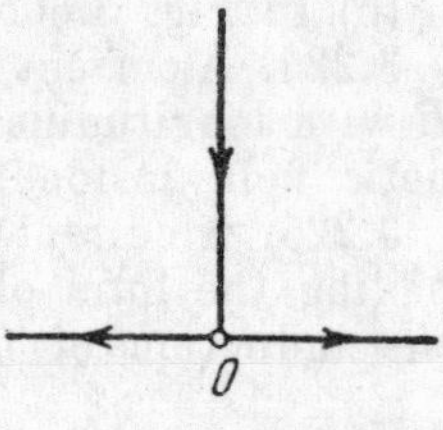

Fig. 3.64.

3.232. A current I flows along a round loop. Find the integral $\int \mathbf{B}\, d\mathbf{r}$ along the axis of the loop within the range from $-\infty$ to $+\infty$. Explain the result obtained.

3.233. A direct current of density **j** flows along a round uniform straight wire with cross-section radius R. Find the magnetic induction vector of this current at the point whose position relative to the axis of the wire is defined by a radius vector **r**. The magnetic permeability is assumed to be equal to unity throughout all the space.

3.234. Inside a long straight uniform wire of round cross-section there is a long round cylindrical cavity whose axis is parallel to the axis of the wire and displaced from the latter by a distance 1. A direct current of density **j** flows along the wire. Find the magnetic induction inside the cavity. Consider, in particular, the case **1** = 0.

3.235. Find the current density as a function of distance r from the axis of a radially symmetrical parallel stream of electrons if the magnetic induction inside the stream varies as $B = br^{\alpha}$, where b and α are positive constants.

3.236. A single-layer coil (solenoid) has length l and cross-section radius R. A number of turns per unit length is equal to n. Find the magnetic induction at the centre of the coil when a current I flows through it.

3.237. A very long straight solenoid has a cross-section radius R and n turns per unit length. A direct current I flows through the solenoid. Suppose that x is the distance from the end of the solenoid, measured along its axis. Find:

(a) the magnetic induction B on the axis as a function of x; draw an approximate plot of B vs the ratio x/R;

(b) the distance x_0 to the point on the axis at which the value of B differs by $\eta = 1\%$ from that in the middle section of the solenoid.

3.238. A thin conducting strip of width $h = 2.0$ cm is tightly wound in the shape of a very long coil with cross-section radius $R = 2.5$ cm to make a single-layer straight solenoid. A direct current $I = 5.0$ A flows through the strip. Find the magnetic induction inside and outside the solenoid as a function of the distance r from its axis.

3.239. $N = 2.5 \cdot 10^3$ wire turns are uniformly wound on a wooden toroidal core of very small cross-section. a current I flows through the wire. Find the ratio h of the magnetic induction inside the core to that at the centre of the toroid.

3.240. A direct current $I = 10$ A flows in a long straight round conductor. Find the magnetic flux through a half of wire's cross-section per one metre of its length.

3.241. A very long straight solenoid carries a current I. The cross-sectional area of the solenoid is equal to S, the number of turns per unit length is equal to n. Find the flux of the vector **B** through the end plane of the solenoid.

3.242. Fig. 3.65 shows a toroidal solenoid whose cross-section is rectangular. Find the magnetic flux through this cross-section if the current through the winding equals $I = 1.7$ A, the total number of turns is $N = 1000$, the ratio of the outside diameter to the inside one is $\eta = 1.6$, and the height is equal to $h = 5.0$ cm.

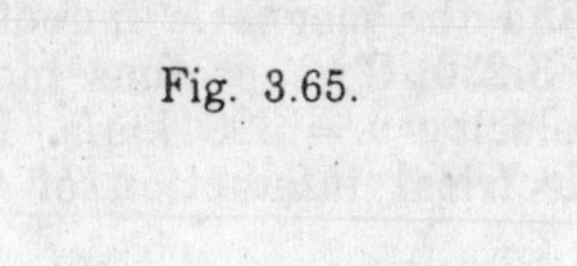

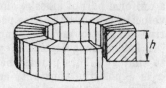

Fig. 3.65.

3.243. Find the magnetic moment of a thin round loop with current if the radius of the loop is equal to $R = 100$ mm and the magnetic induction at its centre is equal to $B = 6.0\ \mu$T.

3.244. Calculate the magnetic moment of a thin wire with a current $I = 0.8$ A, wound tightly on half a tore (Fig. 3.66). The diameter of the cross-section of the tore is equal to $d = 5.0$ cm, the number of turns is $N = 500$.

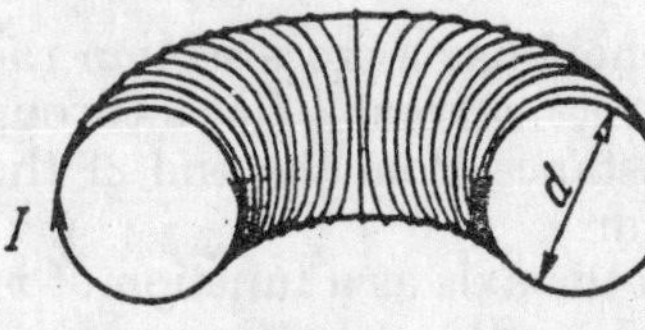

Fig. 3.66.

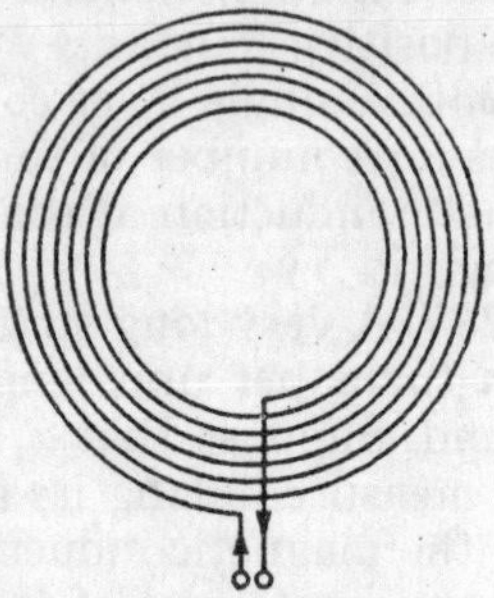

Fig. 3.67.

3.245. A thin insulated wire forms a plane spiral of $N = 100$ tight turns carrying a current $I = 8$ mA. The radii of inside and outside turns (Fig. 3.67) are equal to $a = 50$ mm and $b = 100$ mm. Find:

(a) the magnetic induction at the centre of the spiral;

(b) the magnetic moment of the spiral with a given current.

3.246. A non-conducting thin disc of radius R charged uniformly over one side with surface density σ rotates about its axis with an angular velocity ω. Find:

(a) the magnetic induction at the centre of the disc;

(b) the magnetic moment of the disc.

3.247. A non-conducting sphere of radius $R = 50$ mm charged uniformly with surface density $\sigma = 10.0\ \mu\text{C/m}^2$ rotates with an angular velocity $\omega = 70$ rad/s about the axis passing through its centre. Find the magnetic induction at the centre of the sphere.

3.248. A charge q is uniformly distributed over the volume of a uniform ball of mass m and radius R which rotates with an angular velocity ω about the axis passing through its centre. Find the respective magnetic moment and its ratio to the mechanical moment.

3.249. A long dielectric cylinder of radius R is statically polarized so that at all its points the polarization is equal to $\mathbf{P} = \alpha\mathbf{r}$, where α is a positive constant, and $\mathbf{r}$ is the distance from the axis. The cylinder is set into rotation about its axis with an angular velocity ω. Find the magnetic induction $\mathbf{B}$ at the centre of the cylinder.

3.250. Two protons move parallel to each other with an equal velocity $v = 300$ km/s. Find the ratio of forces of magnetic and electrical interaction of the protons.

3.251. Find the magnitude and direction of a force vector acting on a unit length of a thin wire, carrying a current $I = 8.0$ A, at a point O, if the wire is bent as shown in

(a) Fig. 3.68*a*, with curvature radius $R = 10$ cm;

(b) Fig. 3.68*b*, the distance between the long parallel segments of the wire being equal to $l = 20$ cm.

3.252. A coil carrying a current $I = 10$ mA is placed in a uniform magnetic field so that its axis coincides with the field direction. The single-layer winding of the coil is made of copper wire with

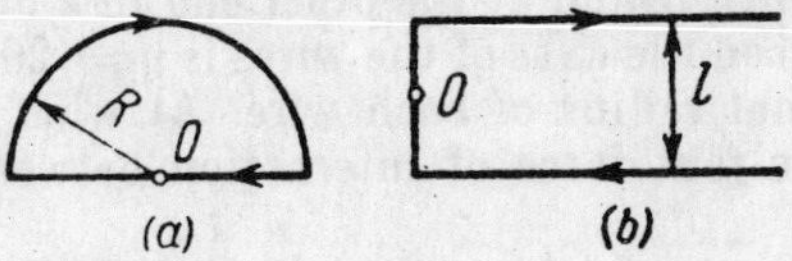

Fig. 3.68.

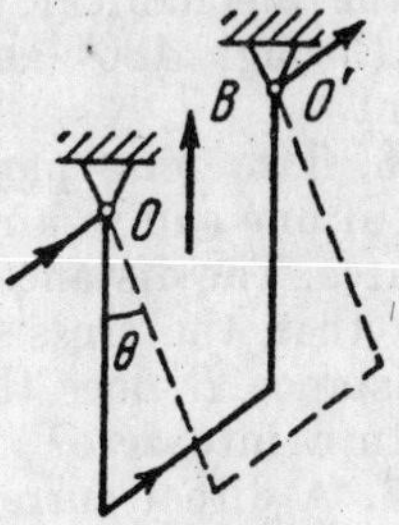

Fig. 3.69.

diameter $d = 0.10$ mm, radius of turns is equal to $R = 30$ mm. At what value of the induction of the external magnetic field can the coil winding be ruptured?

3.253. A copper wire with cross-sectional area $S = 2.5$ mm^2 bent to make three sides of a square can turn about a horizontal axis OO' (Fig. 3.69). The wire is located in uniform vertical magnetic field. Find the magnetic induction if on passing a current $I = 16$ A through the wire the latter deflects by an angle $\theta = 20°$.

3.254. A small coil C with $N = 200$ turns is mounted on one end of a balance beam and introduced between the poles of an electromagnet as shown in Fig. 3.70. The cross-sectional area of the coil

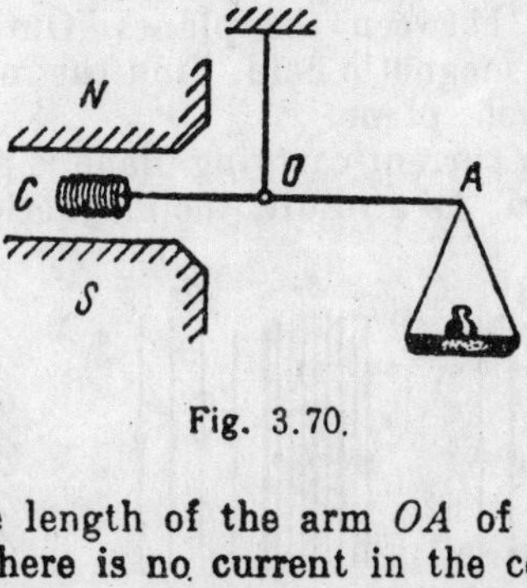

Fig. 3.70.

is $S = 1.0$ cm^2, the length of the arm OA of the balance beam is $l = 30$ cm. When there is no current in the coil the balance is in equilibrium. On passing a current $I = 22$ mA through the coil the equilibrium is restored by putting the additional counterweight of mass $\Delta m = 60$ mg on the balance pan. Find the magnetic induction at the spot where the coil is located.

3.255. A square frame carrying a current $I = 0.90$ A is located in the same plane as a long straight wire carrying a current $I_0 = 5.0$ A. The frame side has a length $a = 8.0$ cm. The axis of the frame passing through the midpoints of opposite sides is parallel to the wire and is separated from it by the distance which is $\eta = 1.5$ times greater than the side of the frame. Find:

(a) Ampere force acting on the frame;

(b) the mechanical work to be performed in order to turn the frame through 180° about its axis, with the currents maintained constant.

3.256. Two long parallel wires of negligible resistance are connected at one end to a resistance R and at the other end to a dc voltage source. The distance between the axes of the wires is $\eta = 20$ times greater than the cross-sectional radius of each wire. At what value of resistance R does the resultant force of interaction between the wires turn into zero?

3.257. A direct current I flows in a long straight conductor whose cross-section has the form of a thin half-ring of radius R. The same current flows in the opposite direction along a thin conductor located on the "axis" of the first conductor (point O in Fig. 3.61). Find the magnetic interaction force between the given conductors reduced to a unit of their length.

3.258. Two long thin parallel conductors of the shape shown in Fig. 3.71 carry direct currents I_1 and I_2. The separation between the conductors is a, the width of the right-hand conductor is equal to b. With both conductors lying in one plane, find the magnetic interaction force between them reduced to a unit of their length.

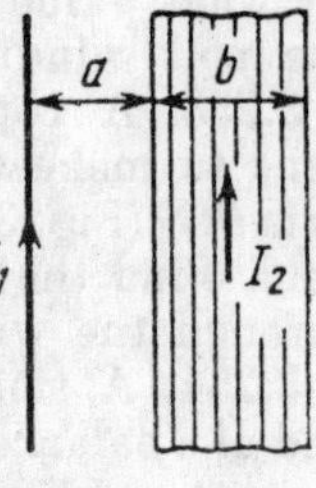

Fig. 3.71.

3.259. A system consists of two parallel planes carrying currents producing a uniform magnetic field of induction B between the planes. Outside this space there is no magnetic field. Find the magnetic force acting per unit area of each plane.

3.260. A conducting current-carrying plane is placed in an external uniform magnetic field. As a result, the magnetic induction becomes

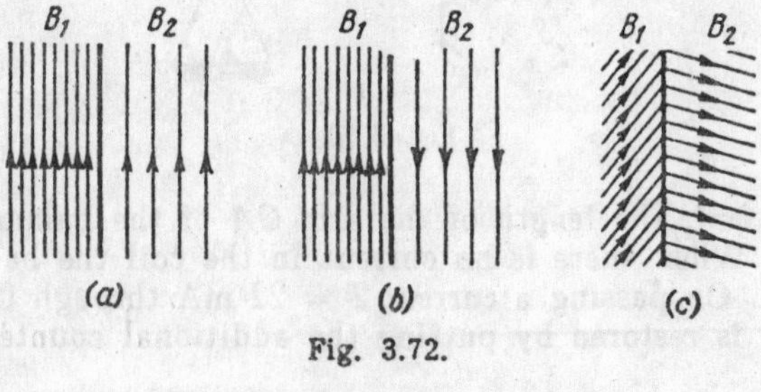

Fig. 3.72.

equal to B_1 on one side of the plane and to B_2, on the other. Find the magnetic force acting per unit area of the plane in the cases illustrated in Fig. 3.72. Determine the direction of the current in the plane in each case.

3.261. In an electromagnetic pump designed for transferring molten metals a pipe section with metal is located in a uniform magnetic field of induction B (Fig. 3.73). A current I is made to flow across this pipe section in the direction perpendicular both to the vector **B** and to the axis of the pipe. Find the gauge pressure produced by the pump if $B = 0.10$ T, $I = 100$ A, and $a = 2.0$ cm.

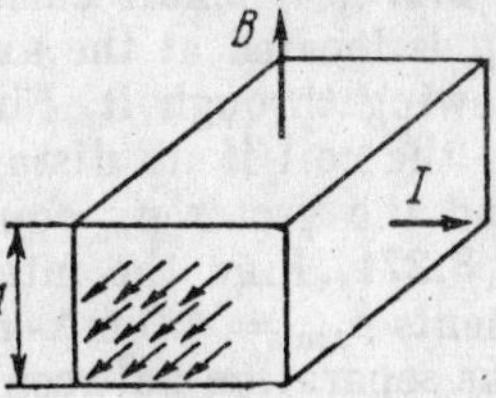

Fig. 3.73.

3.262. A current I flows in a long thin-walled cylinder of radius R. What pressure do the walls of the cylinder experience?

3.263. What pressure does the lateral surface of a long straight solenoid with n turns per unit length experience when a current I flows through it?

3.264. A current I flows in a long single-layer solenoid with cross-sectional radius R. The number of turns per unit length of the solenoid equals n. Find the limiting current at which the winding may rupture if the tensile strength of the wire is equal to F_{lim}.

3.265. A parallel-plate capacitor with area of each plate equal to S and the separation between them to d is put into a stream of conducting liquid with resistivity ρ. The liquid moves parallel to the plates with a constant velocity v. The whole system is located in a uniform magnetic field of induction B, vector **B** being parallel to the plates and perpendicular to the stream direction. The capacitor plates are interconnected by means of an external resistance R. What amount of power is generated in that resistance? At what value of R is the generated power the highest? What is this highest power equal to?

3.266. A straight round copper conductor of radius $R = 5.0$ mm carries a current $I = 50$ A. Find the potential difference between the axis of the conductor and its surface. The concentration of the conduction electrons in copper is equal to $n = 0.9 \cdot 10^{23}$ cm^{-3}.

3.267. In Hall effect measurements in a sodium conductor the strength of a transverse field was found to be equal to $E = 5.0$ μV/cm with a current density $j = 200$ A/cm^2 and magnetic induction $B = 1.00$ T. Find the concentration of the conduction electrons and its ratio to the total number of atoms in the given conductor.

3.268. Find the mobility of the conduction electrons in a copper conductor if in Hall effect measurements performed in the magnetic field of induction $B = 100$ mT the transverse electric field strength of the given conductor turned out to be $\eta = 3.1 \cdot 10^3$ times less than that of the longitudinal electric field.

3.269. A small current-carrying loop is located at a distance r from a long straight conductor with current I. The magnetic moment of the loop is equal to $\mathbf{p}_m$. Find the magnitude and direction of the force vector applied to the loop if the vector $\mathbf{p}_m$

(a) is parallel to the straight conductor;

(b) is oriented along the radius vector $\mathbf{r}$;

(c) coincides in direction with the magnetic field produced by the current I at the point where the loop is located.

3.270. A small current-carrying coil having a magnetic moment $\mathbf{p}_m$ is located at the axis of a round loop of radius R with current I flowing through it. Find the magnitude of the vector force applied to the coil if its distance from the centre of the loop is equal to x and the vector $\mathbf{p}_m$ coincides in direction with the axis of the loop.

3.271. Find the interaction force of two coils with magnetic moments $p_{1m} = 4.0\ \text{mA}\cdot\text{m}^2$ and $p_{2m} = 6.0\ \text{mA}\cdot\text{m}^2$ and collinear axes if the separation between the coils is equal to $l = 20$ cm which exceeds considerably their linear dimensions.

3.272. A permanent magnet has the shape of a sufficiently thin disc magnetized along its axis. The radius of the disc is $R = 1.0$ cm. Evaluate the magnitude of a molecular current I' flowing along the rim of the disc if the magnetic induction at the point on the axis of the disc, lying at a distance $x = 10$ cm from its centre, is equal to $B = 30\ \mu\text{T}$.

3.273. The magnetic induction in vacuum at a plane surface of a uniform isotropic magnetic is equal to B, the vector $\mathbf{B}$ forming an angle α with the normal of the surface. The permeability of the magnetic is equal to μ. Find the magnitude of the magnetic induction B' in the magnetic in the vicinity of its surface.

3.274. The magnetic induction in vacuum at a plane surface of a magnetic is equal to B and the vector $\mathbf{B}$ forms an angle θ with the

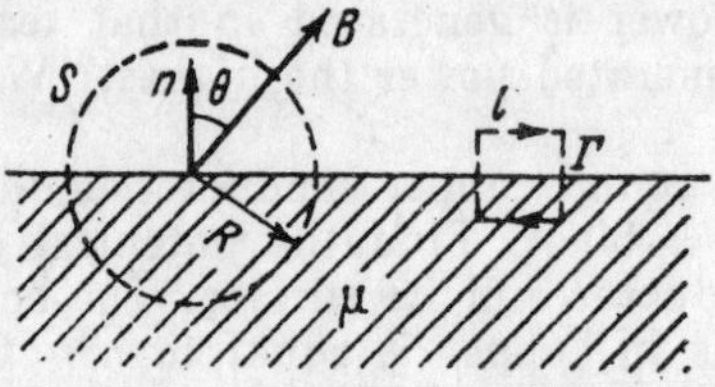

Fig. 3.74.

normal $\mathbf{n}$ of the surface (Fig. 3.74). The permeability of the magnetic is equal to μ. Find:

(a) the flux of the vector $\mathbf{H}$ through the spherical surface S of radius R, whose centre lies on the surface of the magnetic;

(b) the circulation of the vector $\mathbf{B}$ around the square path Γ with side l located as shown in the figure.

3.275. A direct current I flows in a long round uniform cylindrical wire made of paramagnetic with susceptibility χ. Find:

(a) the surface molecular current I'_s;

(b) the volume molecular current I'_v.
How are these currents directed towards each other?

3.276. Half of an infinitely long straight current-carrying solenoid is filled with magnetic substance as shown in Fig. 3.75. Draw the

Fig. 3.75.

approximate plots of magnetic induction B, strength H, and magnetization J on the axis as functions of x.

3.277. An infinitely long wire with a current I flowing in it is located in the bounary plane between two non-conducting media with permeabilities μ_1 and μ_2. Find the modulus of the magnetic induction vector throughout the space as a function of the distance r from the wire. It should be borne in mind that the lines of the vector B are circles whose centre lie on the axis of the wire.

3.278. Around current-carrying loop lies in the plane boundary between magnetic and vacuum. The permeability of the magnetic is equal to μ. Find the magnetic induction $\mathbf{B}$ at an arbitrary point on the axis of the loop if in the absence of the magnetic the magnetic induction at the same point become equal to $\mathbf{B}_0$. Generalize the obtained result to all points of the field.

3.279. When a ball made of uniform magnetic is introduced into an external uniform magnetic field with induction $\mathbf{B}_0$, it gets uniformly magnetized. Find the magnetic induction $\mathbf{B}$ inside the ball with permeability μ; recall that the magnetic field inside a uniformly magnetized ball is uniform and its strength is equal to $H = -\mathbf{J}/3$. where $\mathbf{J}$ is the magnetization.

3.280. N = 300 turns of thin wire are uniformly wound on a permanent magnet shaped as a cylinder whose length is equal to l = 15 cm. When a current I = 3.0 A was passed through the wiring the field outside the magnet disappeared. Find the coercive force H_c of the material from which the magent was manufactured.

3.281. A permanent magnet is shaped as a ring with a narrow gap between the poles. The mean diameter of the ring equals d = 20 cm. The width of the gap is equal to b = 2.0 mm and the magnetic induction in the gap is equal to B = 40 mT. Assuming that the scattering of the magnetic flux at the gap edges is negligible, find the modulus of the magnetic field strength vector inside the magnet.

3.282. An iron core shaped as a tore with mean radius R = 250 mm supports a winding with the total number of turns N = 1000. The core has a cross-cut of width b = 1.00 mm. With a current I = 0.85 A flowing through the winding, the magnetic induction in the gap is equal to B = 0.75 T. Assuming the scattering of the magnetic flux at the gap edges to be negligible, find the permeability of iron under these conditions.

3.283. Fig. 3.76 illustrates a basic magnetization curve of iron (commercial purity grade). Using this plot, draw the permeability

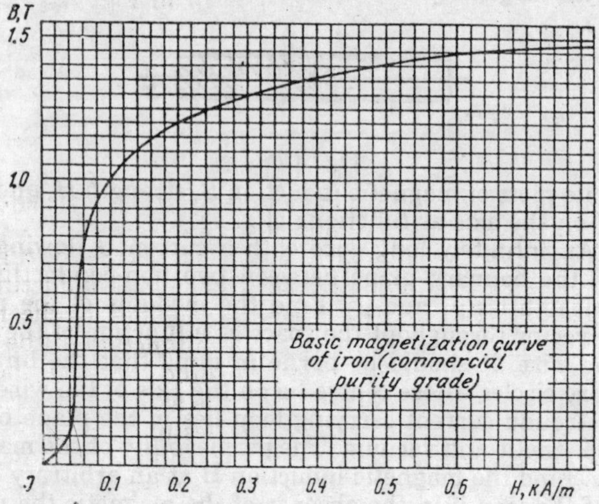

Fig. 3.76.

μ as a function of the magnetic field strength H. At what value of H is the permeability the greatest? What is μ_{max} equal to?

3.284. A thin iron ring with mean diameter $d = 50$ cm supports a winding consisting of $N = 800$ turns carrying current $I = 3.0$ A. The ring has a cross-cut of width $b = 2.0$ mm. Neglecting the scattering of the magnetic flux at the gap edges, and using the plot shown in Fig. 3.76, find the permeability of iron under these conditions.

3.285. A long thin cylindrical rod made of paramagnetic with magnetic susceptibility χ and having a cross-sectional area S is located along the axis of a current-carrying coil. One end of the rod is located at the coil centre where the magnetic induction is equal to B whereas the other end is located in the region where the magnetic field is practically absent. What is the force that the coil exerts on the rod?

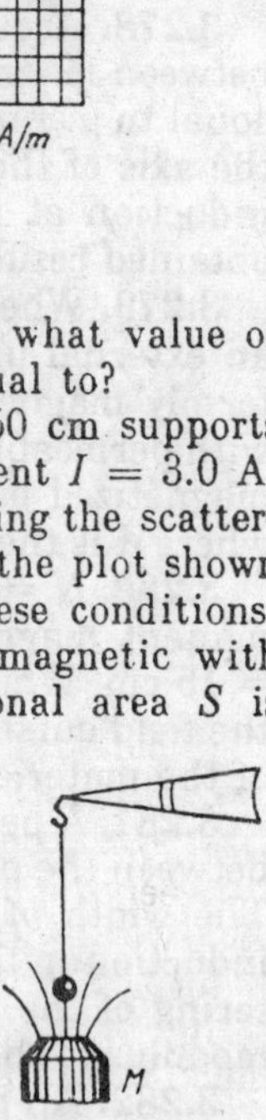

Fig. 3.77.

3.286. In the arrangement shown in Fig. 3.77 it is possible to measure (by means of a balance) the force with which a paramagnetic ball of volume $V = 41$ mm³ is attrabted to a pole of the electromagnet M. The magnetic induction at the axis of the poleshoe depends on the height x as $B = B_0 \exp(-ax^2)$, where $B_0 = 1.50$ T, $a = 100$ m^{-2}. Find:

(a) at what height x_m the ball experiences the maximum attraction;

(b) the magnetic susceptibility of the paramagnetic if the maximum attraction force equals $F_{max} = 160$ μN.

3.287. A small ball of volume V made of paramagnetic with susceptibility χ was slowly displaced along the axis of a current-carrying coil from the point where the magnetic induction equals B out to the region where the magnetic field is practically absent. What amount of work was performed during this process?

3.6. ELECTROMAGNETIC INDUCTION. MAXWELL'S EQUATIONS

- Faraday's law of electromagnetic induction:

$$\mathscr{E}_i = -\frac{d\Phi}{dt}. \tag{3.6a}$$

- In the case of a solenoid and doughnut coil:

$$\Phi = N\Phi_1, \tag{3.6b}$$

where N is the number of turns, Φ_1 is the magnetic flux through each turn.

- Inductance of a solenoid:

$$L = \mu\mu_0 n^2 V. \tag{3.6c}$$

- Intrinsic energy of a current and interaction energy of two currents:

$$W = \frac{LI^2}{2}, \qquad W_{12} = L_{12} I_1 I_2. \tag{3.6d}$$

- Volume density of magnetic field energy:

$$w = \frac{B^2}{2\mu\mu_0} = \frac{\mathbf{BH}}{2}. \tag{3.6e}$$

- Displacement current density:

$$\mathbf{j}_{dis} = \frac{\partial \mathbf{B}}{\partial t}. \tag{3.6f}$$

- Maxwell's equations in differential form:

$$\nabla \times \mathbf{E} = -\frac{\partial \mathbf{B}}{\partial t}, \qquad \nabla \cdot \mathbf{B} = 0,$$
$$\nabla \times \mathbf{H} = \mathbf{j} + \frac{\partial \mathbf{D}}{\partial t}, \qquad \nabla \cdot \mathbf{D} = \rho, \tag{3.6g}$$

where $\nabla \times \equiv$ rot (the rotor) and $\nabla \cdot \equiv$ div (the divergence).

- Field transformation formulas for transition from a reference frame K to a reference frame K' moving with the velocity $\mathbf{v}_0$ relative to it.

In the case $v_0 \ll c$

$$\mathbf{E}' = \mathbf{E} + [\mathbf{v}_0\mathbf{B}], \quad \mathbf{B}' = \mathbf{B} - [\mathbf{v}_0\mathbf{E}]/c^2 \tag{3.6h}$$

In the general case

$$\mathbf{E}'_{\parallel} = \mathbf{E}_{\parallel}, \qquad \mathbf{B}'_{\parallel} = \mathbf{B}_{\parallel},$$
$$\mathbf{E}'_{\perp} = \frac{\mathbf{E}_{\perp} + [\mathbf{v}_0\mathbf{B}]}{\sqrt{1-(v_0/c)^2}}, \qquad \mathbf{B}'_{\perp} = \frac{\mathbf{B}_{\perp} - [\mathbf{v}_0\mathbf{E}]/c^2}{\sqrt{1-(v_0/c)^2}}, \tag{3.6i}$$

where the symbols $\parallel$ and $\perp$ denote the field components, respectively parallel and perpendicular to the vector $\mathbf{v}_0$.

3.288. A wire bent as a parabola $y = ax^2$ is located in a uniform magnetic field of induction B, the vector **B** being perpendicular to the plane x, y. At the moment $t = 0$ a connector starts sliding translationwise from the parabola apex with a constant acceleration ω (Fig. 3.78). Find the emf of electromagnetic induction in the loop thus formed as a function of y.

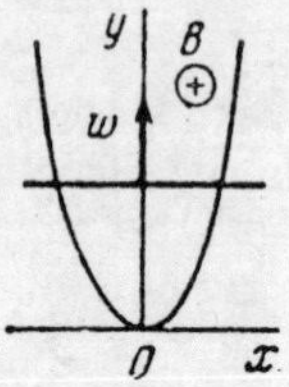

Fig. 3.78.

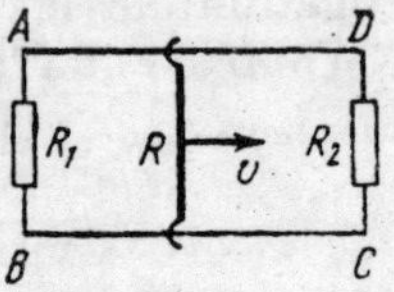

Fig. 3.79.

3.289. A rectangular loop with a sliding connector of length l is located in a uniform magnetic field perpendicular to the loop plane (Fig. 3.79). The magnetic induction is equal to B. The connector has an electric resistance R, the sides AB and CD have resistance R_1 and R_2 respectively. Neglecting the self-inductance of the loop, find the current flowing in the connector during its motion with a constant velocity v.

3.290. A metal disc of radius $a = 25$ cm rotates with a constant angular velocity $\omega = 130$ rad/s about its axis. Find the potential difference between the centre and the rim of the disc if.

(a) the external magnetic field is absent;

(b) the external uniform magnetic field of induction B = 5.0 mT is directed perpendicular to the disc.

3.291. A thin wire AC shaped as a semi-circle of diameter $d = 20$ cm rotates with a constant angular velocity $\omega = 100$ rad/s in a uniform magnetic field of induction $B = 5.0$ mT, with $\omega \uparrow\uparrow B$. the rotation axis passes through the end A of the wire and is perpendicular to the diameter AC. Find the value of a line integral $\int \mathbf{E}\, d\mathbf{r}$ along the wire from point A to point C. Generalize the obtained result.

3.292. A wire loop enclosing a semi-circle of radius   is located on the boundary of a uniform magnetic field of induction **B** (Fig. 3.80). At the moment $t = 0$ the loop is set into rotation with a constant angular acceleration b about an axis O coinciding with a line of vector B on the boundary. Find the emf induced in the loop as a function of time t. Draw the approximate plot of this function. The arrow in the figure shows the emf direction taken to the positive.

3.293. A long straight wire carrying a current I and II-shaped conductor with sliding connector are located in the same plane as shown in Fig. 3.81. The connector of length l and resistance R slides to the right with a constant velocity v. Find the current induced in

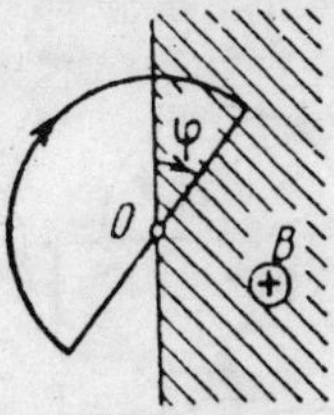

Fig. 3.80.

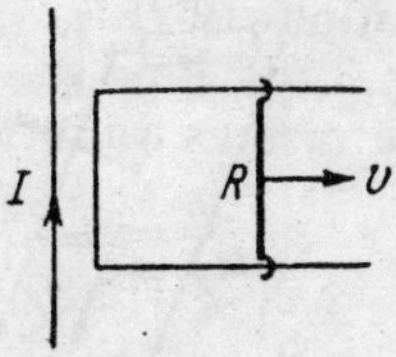

Fig. 3.81.

the loop as a function of separation r between the connector and the straight wire. The resistance of the II-shaped conductor and the self-inductance of the loop are assumed to be negligible.

3.294. A square frame with side a and a long straight wire carrying a current I are located in the same plane as shown in Fig. 3.82 The frame translates to the right with a constant velocity v. FInd the emf induced in the frame as a function of distance x.

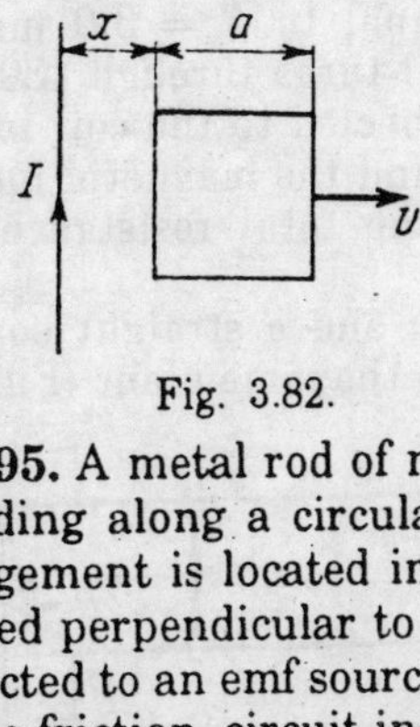

Fig. 3.82.

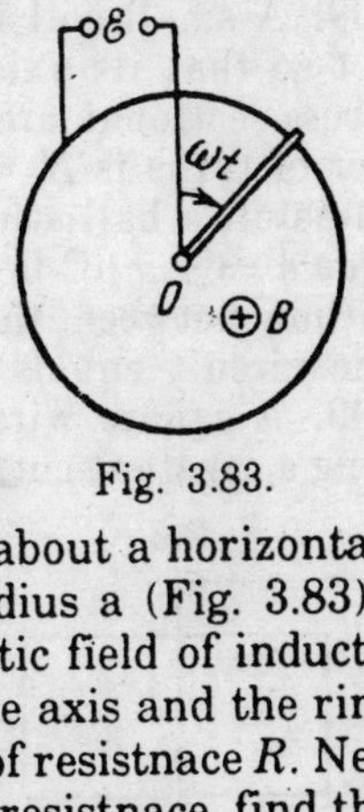

Fig. 3.83.

3.295. A metal rod of mass m can rotate about a horizontal axis O. sliding along a circular conductor of radius a (Fig. 3.83). The arrangement is located in a uniform magnetic field of induction B directed perpendicular to the ring plane. The axis and the ring are connected to an emf source to form a circuit of resistnace R. Neglecting the friction, circuit inductance, and ring resistnace, find the law according to which the source emf must vary to make the rod rotate with a constant angular velocity ω.

3.296. A copper connector of mass m slides down two smooth copper bars, set at an angle a to the horizontal, due to gravity (Fig. 3.84). At the top the bars are interconnected through a resistance R. The separation between the bars is equal to l. The system is located in a uniform magnetic field of induction B. perpendicular to the plane in which the connector slides. The resistnace of the bars, the connector and the sliding contacts, as well as the self-inductance of the loop, are assumed to be negligible. Find the steady-state velocity of the connector.

3.297. The system differs from the one examined in the foregoing problem (Fig. 3.84) by a capacitor of capacitance C replacing the resistance R. Find the acceleration of the connector.

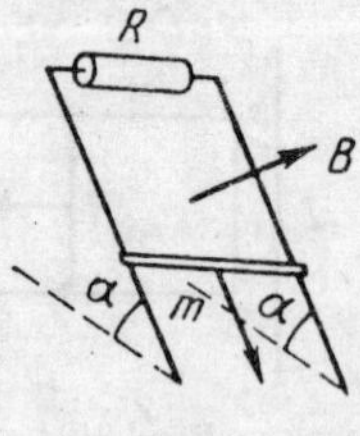

Fig. 3.84.

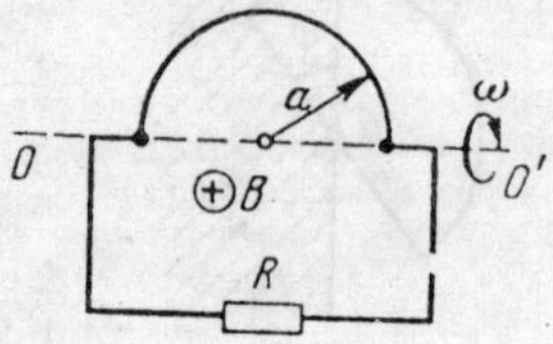

Fig. 3.85.

3.298. A wire shaped as a semi-circle of radius a rotates about an axis OO' with an angular velocity ω in a uniform magnetic field of induction B (Fig. 3.85). The rotation axis is perpendicular to the field direction. The total resistance of the circuit is equal to R. Neglecting the magnetic field of the induced current, find the mean amount of thermal power being generated in the loop during a rotation period.

3.299. A small coil is introduced between the poles of an electromagnet so that its axis coincides with the magnetic field direction. The cross-sectional area of the coil is equal to $S = 3.0\ \text{mm}^2$, the number of turns is $N = 60$. When the coil turns through 180° about its diameter, a ballistic galvanometer connected to the coil indicates a charge $q = 4.5\ \mu\text{C}$ flowing through it. Find the magnetic induction magnitude between the poles provided the total resistance of the electric circuit equals $R = 40\ \Omega$.

3.300. A square wire frame with side a and a straight conductor carrying a constant current I are located in the same plane (Fig. 3.86).

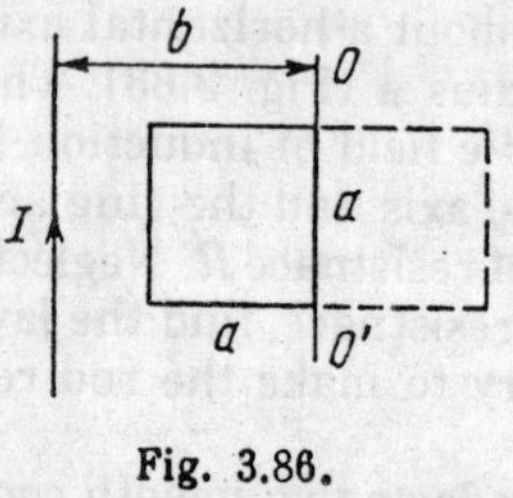

Fig. 3.86.

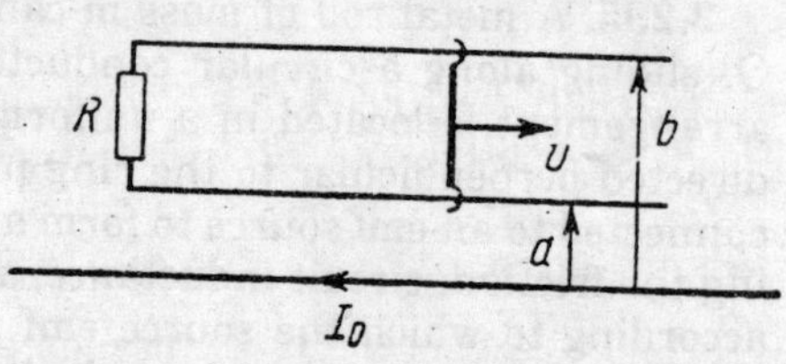

Fig. 3.87.

The inductance and the resistance of the frame are equal to L and R respectively. The frame was turned through 180° about the axis OO' separated from the current-carrying conductor by a distance b. Find the electric charge having flown through the frame.

3.301. A long straight wire carries a current I_0. At distances a and b from it there are two other wires, parallel to the former one, which are interconnected by a resistance R (Fig. 3.87). A connector slides without friction along the wires with a constant velocity v. Assuming the resistances of the wires, the connector, the sliding contacts, and the self-inductance of the freme to be negligible, find:

(a) the magnitude and the direction of the current induced in the connector;

(b) the force required to maintain the connector's velocity constant.

3.302. A conducting rod AB of mass m slides without friction over two long conducting rails separated by a distance l (Fig. 3.88). At the left end the rails are interconnected by a resistance R. The system is located in a uniform magnetic field perpendicular to the plane of the loop. At the moment $t = 0$ the rod AB starts moving to the right with an initial velocity v_0. Neglecting the resistances of the rails and the rod AB, as well as the self-inductance, find:

(a) the distance covered by the rod until it comes to a standstill;

(b) the amount of heat generated in the resistance R during this process.

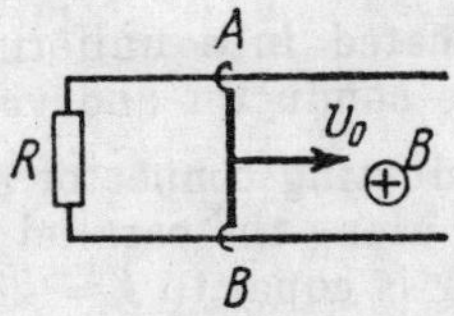

Fig. 3.88.

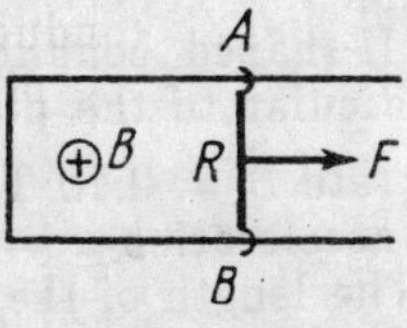

Fig. 3.89.

3.303. A connector AB can slide without friction along a П-shaped conductor located in a horizontal plane (Fig. 3.89). The connector has a length l, mass m, and resistance R. The whole system is located in a uniform magnetic field of induction B directed vertically. At the moment $t = 0$ a constant horizontal force F starts acting on the connector shifting it translationwise to the right. Find how the velocity of the connector varies with time t. The inductance of the loop and the resistance of the П-shaped conductor are assumed to be negligible.

3.304. Fig. 3.90 illustrates plane figures made of thin conductors which are located in a uniform magnetic field directed away from a

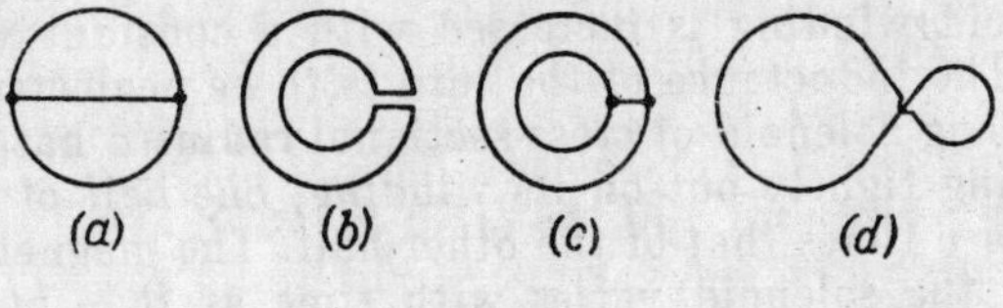

Fig. 3.90.

reader beyond the plane of the drawing. The magnetic induction starts diminishing. Find how the currents induced in these loops are directed.

3.305. A plane loop shown in Fig. 3.91 is shaped as two squares with sides $a = 20$ cm and $b = 10$ cm and is introduced into a uniform magnetic field at right angles to the loop's plane. The magnetic induction varies with time as $B = B_0 \sin \omega t$, where $B_0 = 10$ mT and $\omega = 100\ \text{s}^{-1}$. Find the amplitude of the current induced in the loop if its resistance per unit length is equal to $\rho = 50$ mΩ/m. The inductance of the loop is to be neglected.

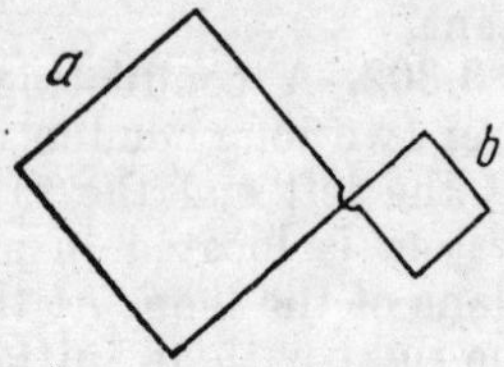

Fig. 3.91.

3.306. A plane spiral with a great number N of turns wound tightly to one another is located in a uniform magnetic field perpendicular to the spiral's plane. The outside radius of the spiral's turns is equal to a. The magnetic induction varies with time as $B = B_0 \sin \omega t$, where B_0 and ω are constants. Find the amplitude of emf induced in the spiral.

3.307. A Π-shaped conductor is located in a uniform magnetic field perpendicular to the plane of the conductor and varying with time at the rate $\dot{B} = 0.10$ T/s. A conducting connector starts moving with an acceleration $w = 10$ cm/s² along the parallel bars of the conductor. The length of the connector is equal to $l = 20$ cm. Find the emf induced in the loop $t = 2.0$ s after the beginning of the motion, if at the moment $t = 0$ the loop area and the magnetic induction are equal to zero. The inductance of the loop is to be neglected.

3.308. In a long straight solenoid with cross-sectional radius a and number of turns per unit length n a current varies with a constant velocity $\dot{I}$ A/s. Find the magnitude of the eddy current field strength as a function of the distance r from the solenoid axis. Draw the approximate plot of this function.

3.309. A long straight solenoid of cross-sectional diameter $d = 5$ cm and with $n = 20$ turns per one cm of its length has a round turn of copper wire of cross-sectional area $S = 1.0$ mm² tightly put on its winding. Find the current flowing in the turn if the current in the solenoid winding is increased with a constant velocity $\dot{I} = 100$ A/s. The inductance of the turn is to be neglected.

3.310. A long solenoid of cross-sectional radius a has a thin insulated wire ring tightly put on its winding; one half of the ring has the resistance η times that of the other half. The magnetic induction produced by the solenoid varies with time as $B = bt$, where b is a constant. Find the magnitude of the electric field strength in the ring.

3.311. A thin non-conducting ring of mass m carrying a charge q can freely rotate about its axis. At the initial moment the ring was at rest and no magnetic field was present. Then a practically uniform magnetic field was switched on, which was perpendicular to the plane of the ring and increased with time according to a certain law **B** (t). Find the angular velocity ω of the ring a function of the induction **B** (t).

3.312. A thin wire ring of radius a and resistnace r is located inside a long solenoid so that their axes coincide. The length of the solenoid is equal to l, its cross-sectional radius, to b. At a certain moment the solenoid was connected to a source of a constant voltage V. The total resistance of the circuit is equal to R. Assuming the inductance of the ring to be negligible, find the maximum value of the radial force acting per unit length of the ring.

3.313. A magnetic flux through a stationary loop with a resistance R varies during the time interval γ as $\Phi = at\ (\tau - t)$. Find the amount of heat generated in the loop during that time. The inductance of the loop is to be neglected.

3.314. In the middle of a long solenoid there is a coaxial ring of square cross-section, made of conducting material with resistivity ρ. The thickness of the ring is equal to h, its inside and outside radii are equal to a and b repsectively. Find the current induced in the ring if the magnetic induction produced by the solenoid varies with time as $B = \beta t$, where β is a constant. The inductance of the ring is to be neglected.

3.315. How many metres of a thin wire are required to manufacture a solenoid of length l_0 = 100 cm and inductance L = 1.0 mH if the solenoid's cross-sectional diameter is considerably less than its length?

3.316. Find the inductance of a solenoid of length l whose winding is made of copper wire of mass m. The winding resistance is equal to R. The solenoid diameter is considerably less than its length.

3.317. A coil of inductance L. = 300 mH and resistance R = 140 mΩ is connected to a constant voltage source. How soon will the coil current reach η = 50% of the steady-state value?

3.318. Calculate the time constant τ of a straight solenoid of length l = 1.0 m having a single-layer winding of copper wire whose total mass is equal to m = 1.0 kg. The cross-sectional diameter of the solenoid is assumed to be considerably less than its length.

Note. The time constant τ is the ratio L/R, where L is inductance and R is active resistance.

3.319. Find the inductance of a unit length of a cable consisting of two thin-walled coaxial metallic cylinders if the radius of the outside cylinder is η = 3.6 times that of the inside one. The permeability of a medium between the cylinders is assumed to be equal to unity.

3.320. Calculate the inductance of a doughtnut solenoid whose inside radius is equal to b and cross-section has the form of a square with side a. The solenoid winding consists of N turns. The space inside the solenoid is filled up with uniform paramagnetic having permeabuility μ.

3.321. Calculate the inductance of a unit length of a double tape line (Fig. 3.92) if the tapes are separated by a distance h which is considerably less than their width b, namely, $b/h = 50$.

3.322. Find the inductance of a unit length of a double line if the radius of each wire is η times less than the distance between the axes of the wires. The field inside the wires is to be neglected, the permeability is assumed to be equal to unity throughout, and $\eta \gg 1$.

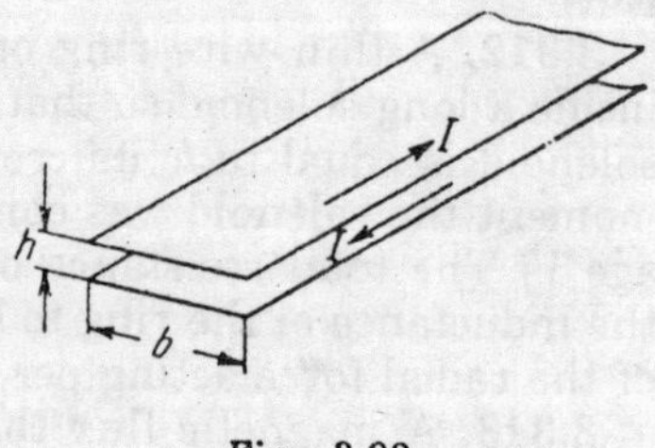

Fig. 3.92.

3.323. A superconducting round ring of radius a and inductance L was located in a uniform magnetic field of induction B. The ring plane was parallel to the vector **B**, and the current in the ring was equal to zero. Then the ring was turned through 90° so that its plane became perpendicular to the field. Find:

(a) the current induced in the ring after the turn;

(b) the work performed during the turn.

3.324. A current $I_0 = 1.9$ A flows in a long closed solenoid. The wire it is wound of is in a superconducting state. Find the current flowing in the solenoid when the length of the solenoid is increased by $\eta = 5\%$.

3.325. A ring of radius $a = 50$ mm made of thin wire of radius $b = 1.0$ mm was located in a uniform magnetic field with induction $B = 0.50$ mT so that the ring plane was perpendicular to the vector **B**. Then the ring was cooled down to a superconducting state, and the magnetic field was switched off. Find the ring current after that. Note that the inductance of a thin ring along which the surface current flows is equal to $L = \mu_0 a \left(\ln \frac{8a}{b} - 2\right)$.

3.326. A closed circuit consists of a source of constant emf $\mathscr{E}$ and a choke coil of inductance L connected in series. The active resistance of the whole circuit is equal to R. At the moment $t = 0$ the choke coil inductance was decreased abruptly η times. Find the current in the circuit as a function of time t.

Instruction. During a stepwise change of inductance the total magnetic flux (flux linkage) remains constant.

3.327. Find the time dependence of the current flowing through the inductance L of the circuit shown in Fig. 3.93 after the switch Sw is shorted at the moment $t = 0$.

3.328. In the circuit shown in Fig. 3.94 an emf $\mathscr{E}$, a resistance R, and coil inductances L_1 and L_2 are known. The internal resistance of the source and the coil resistances are negligible. Find the steady-state currents in the coils after the switch Sw was shorted.

3.329. Calculate the mutual inductance of a long straight wire and a rectangular frame with sides a and b. The frame and the wire lie in the same plane, with the side b being closest to the wire, separated by a distance l from it and oriented parallel to it.

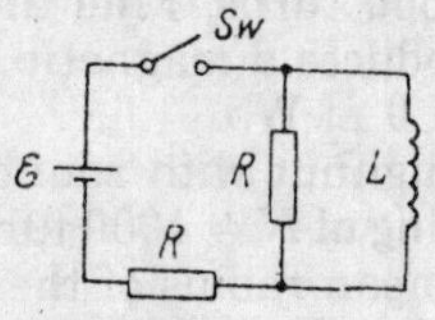

Fig. 3.93.

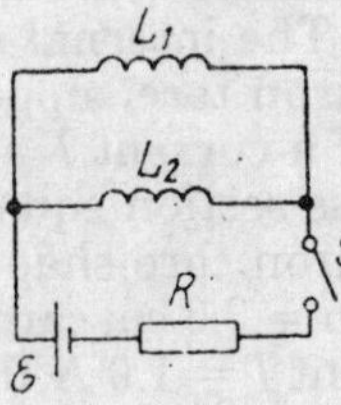

Fig. 3.94.

3.330. Determine the mutual inductance of a doughnut coil and an infinite straight wire passing along its axis. The coil has a rectangular cross-section, its inside radius is equal to a and the outside one, to b. The length of the doughnut's cross-sectional side parallel to the wire is equal to h. The coil has N turns. The system is located in a uniform magnetic with permeability μ.

3.331. Two thin concentric wires shaped as circles with radii a and b lie in the same plane. Allowing for $a \ll b$, find:
(a) their mutual inductance;
(b) the magnetic flux through the surface enclosed by the outside wire, when the inside wire carries a current I.

3.332. A small cylindrical magnet M (Fig. 3.95) is placed in the centre of a thin coil of radius a consisting of N turns. The coil is connected to a ballistic galvanometer. The active resistance of the whole circuit is equal to R. Find the magnetic moment of the magnet if its removal from the coil results in a charge q flowing through the galvanometer.

3.333. Find the approximate formula expressing the mutual inductance of two thin coaxial loops of the same radius a if their centres are separated by a distance l, with $l \gg a$.

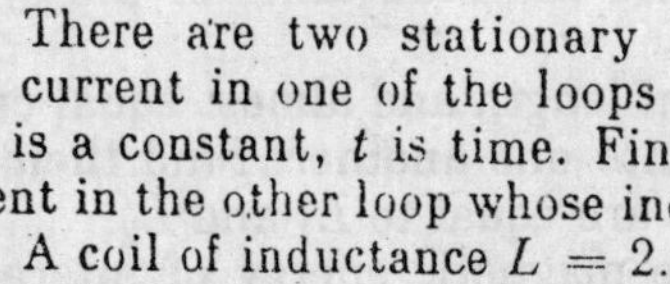

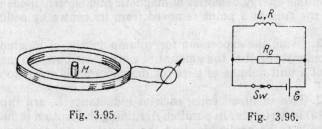

Fig. 3.95.

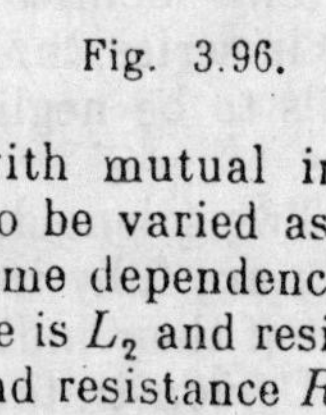

Fig. 3.96.

3.334. There are two stationary loops with mutual inductance L_{12}. The current in one of the loops starts to be varied as $I_1 = \alpha t$, where α is a constant, t is time. Find the time dependence $I_2(t)$ of the current in the other loop whose inductance is L_2 and resistance R.

3.335. A coil of inductance $L = 2.0$ μH and resistance $R = 1.0\ \Omega$ is connected to a source of constant emf $\mathscr{E} = 3.0$ V (Fig. 3.96). A resistance R_0 = 2.0 W is connected in parallel with the coil. Find the amount of heat generated in the coil after the switch *Sw* is disconnected. The internal resistnace of the source is negligible.

3.336. An iron tore supports N = 500 turns. Find the magnetic field energy if a current I = 2.0 A produces a magnetic flux across the tore's cross-section equal to Φ = 1.0 m Wb.

3.337. An iron core shaped as a doughnut with round cross-section of radius a = 3.0 cm carries a winding of N = 1000 turns through which a current I = 1.0 A flows. The mean radius of the doughtnut is b = 32 cm. Using the plot in Fig. 3.76, find the magnetic energy stored up in the core. A field strength H is supposed to be the same throughout the cross-section and equal to its magnitude in the centre of the cross-section.

3.338. A thin ring made of a magnetic has a mean diameter d = 30 cm and supports a winding of N = 800 turns. The cross-sectional area of the ring is equal to S = 5.0 cm2. The ring has a cross-cut of width b = 2.0 mm. When the winding carries a certain current, the permeability of the magnetic equals μ = 1400. Neglecting the dissipation of magnetic flux at the gap edges. find:

(a) the ratioof magnetic energies in the gap and in the magnetic;

(b) the inductance of the system; do it in two ways; using the flux and using the energy of the field.

3.339. A long cylinder of radius a carrying a uniform surface charge rotates about its axis with an angular velocity ω. Find the magnetic field energy per unit length of the cylinder if the linear change density equal λ and μ = 1.

3.340. At what magnitude of the electric field strength in vacuum the volume energy density of this field is the same as that of the magnetic field with induction B = 1.0 T (also in vacuum).

3.341. A thin uniformly charged ring of radius a = 10 cm rotates about its axis with an angular velocity ω = 100 rad/s. Find the ratio of volume energy densities of magnetic and electric fields on the axis of the ring at a point removed from its centre by a distance $l = a$.

3.342. Using the expression for volume density of magnetic energy, demonstrate that the amount of work contributed to magnetization of a unit volume of para- or diamagnetic, is equal to A = – **JB**/2.

3.343. Two identical coils, each of inductance L, are interconnected (a) in series, (b) in parallel. Assuming the mutual inductance of the coils to be negligible, find the inductance of the system in both cases.

3.344. Two solenoids of equal length and almost equal cross-sectional area are fully inserted into one another. Find their mutual inductance if their inductances are equal to L_1 and L_2.

3.345. Demonstrate that the magnetic energy of interaction of two current-carrying loops located in vacuum can be represented as $W_{ia} = (1/\mu^0) \int B_1 B_2 \, dV$, where B_1 and B_2 are the magnetic inductions within a volume element dV, produced individually by the currents of the first and the second loop respectively.

3.346. Find the interaction energy of two loops carrying currents I_1 and I_2 if both loops are shaped as circles of radii a and b, with $a \ll b$. The loops centres are located at the same point and their planes form an angle θ between them.

3.347. The space between two concentric metallic spheres is filled up with a uniform poorly conducting medium of resistivity ρ and permittivity ε. At the moment $t = 0$ the inside sphere obtains a certain charge. Find:

(a) the relation between the vectors of displacement current density and conduction current density at an arbitrary point of the medium at the same moment of time;

(b) the displacement current across an arbitrary closed surface wholly located in the medium and enclosing the internal sphere, if at the given moment of time the charge of that sphere is equal to q.

3.348. A parallel-plate capacitor is formed by two discs with a uniform poorly conducting medium between them. The capacitor was initially charged and then disconnected from a voltage source. Neglecting the edge effects, show that there is no magnetic field between capacitor plates.

3.349. A parallel-plate air condenser whose each plate has an area $S = 100\ \text{cm}^2$ is connected in series to an *ac* circuit. Find the electric field strength amplitude in the capacitor if the sinusoidal current amplitude in lead wires is equal to $I_m = 1.0$ mA and the current frequency equals $\omega = 1.6 \cdot 10^7\ \text{s}^{-1}$.

3.350. The space between the electrodes of a parallel-plate capacitor is filled with a uniform poorly conducting medium of conductivity σ and permittivity ε. The capacitor plates shaped as round discs are separated by a distance d. Neglecting the edge effects, find the magnetic field strength between the plates at a distance r from their axis if an ac voltage $V = V_m \cos \omega t$ is applied to the capacitor.

3.351. A long straight solenoid has n turns per unit length. An alternating current $I = I_m \sin \omega t$ flows through it. Find the displacement current density as a function of the distance r from the solenoid axis. The cross-sectional radius of the solenoid equals R.

3.352. A point charge q moves with a non-relativistic velocity v = const. Find the displacement current density $\mathbf{j}_d$ at a point located at a distance r from the charge on a straight line.

(a) coinciding with the charge path;

(b) perpendicular to the path and passing through the charge.

3.353. A thin wire ring of radius a carrying a charge q approaches the observation point P so that its centre moves rectilinearly with a constant velocity v. The plane of the ring remains perpendicular to the motion direction. At what distance x_m from the point P will the ring the located at the moment when the displacement current density at the point P becomes maximum? What is the magnitude of this maximum density?

3.354. A point charge q moves with a non-relativistic velocity $\mathbf{v}$ = const. Applying the theorem for the circulation of the vector $\mathbf{H}$ around the dotted circle shown in Fig. 3.97, find $\mathbf{H}$ at the point A as a function of a radius vector $\mathbf{r}$ and velocity $\mathbf{v}$ of the charge.

3.355. Using Maxwell's equations, show that

(a) a time-dependent magnetic field cannot exist without an electric field;

(b) a uniform electric field cannot exist in the presence of a time-dependent magnetic field;

(c) inside an empty cavity a uniform electric (or magnetic) field can be time-dependent.

3.356. Demonstrate that the law of electric charge conservation, i.e. $\nabla \cdot \mathbf{j} = -\partial\rho/\partial t$, follows from Maxwell's equations.

3.357. Demonstrate that Maxwell's equations $\nabla \times \mathbf{E} = -\partial\mathbf{B}/\partial t$ and $\nabla \cdot \mathbf{B} = 0$ are compatible, i.e. the first one does not contradict the second one.

3.358. In a certain region of the inertial reference frame there is magnetic field with induction B rotating with angular velocity $\boldsymbol{\omega}$. Find $\nabla \times \mathbf{E}$ in this region as a function of vectors $\boldsymbol{\omega}$ and $\mathbf{B}$.

3.359. In the inertial reference frame K there is a uniform magnetic field with induction $\mathbf{B}$. Find the electric field strength in the frame K' which moves relative to the frame K with a non-relativistic velocity $\mathbf{v}$, with $\mathbf{v} \perp \mathbf{B}$. To solve this problem, consider the forces acting on an imaginary charge in both reference frames at the moment when the velocity of the charge in the frame K' is equal to zero.

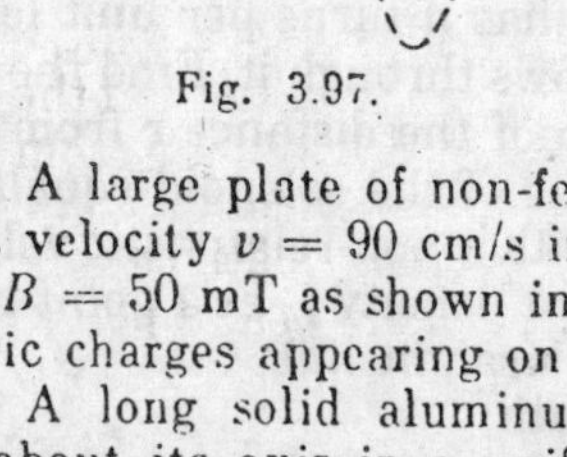

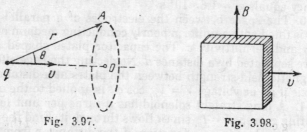

Fig. 3.97.

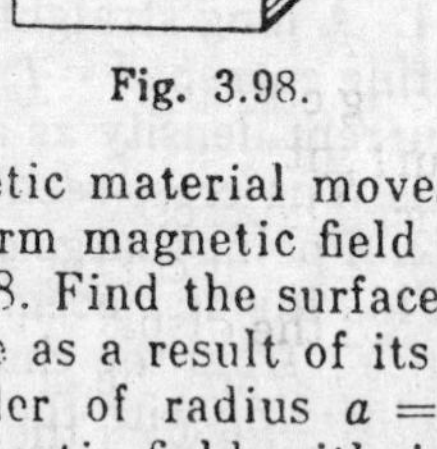

Fig. 3.98.

3.360. A large plate of non-ferromagnetic material moves with a constant velocity $v = 90$ cm/s in a uniform magnetic field with induction $B = 50$ mT as shown in Fig. 3.98. Find the surface density of electric charges appearing on the plate as a result of its motion.

3.361. A long solid aluminum cylinder of radius $a = 5.0$ cm rotates about its axis in a uniform magnetic field with induction $B = 10$ mT. The angular velocity of rotation equals $\omega = 45$ rad/s, with $\boldsymbol{\omega} \uparrow\uparrow \mathbf{B}$. Neglecting the magnetic field of appearing charges, find their space and surface densities.

3.362. A non-relativistic point charge q moves with a constant velocity $\mathbf{v}$. Using the field transformation formulas, find the magnetic induction $\mathbf{B}$ produced by this charge at the point whose position relative to the charge is determined by the radius vector $\mathbf{r}$.

3.363. Using Eqs. (3.6h), demonstrate that if in the inertial reverence frame K there is only electric or only magnetic field, in any other inertial frame K' both electric and magnetic fields will coexist simultaneously, with $\mathbf{E}' \perp \mathbf{B}'$.

3.364. In an inertial reverence frame K where is only magnetic field with induction $\mathbf{B} = b\,(y\mathbf{i} - x\mathbf{j})/(x^2 + y^2)$, where b is a constant, **i** and **j** are the unit vectors of the x and y axes. Find the electric field strength $\mathbf{E}'$ in the frame K' moving relative to the frame K with a constant non-relativistic velocity $v = v\mathbf{k}$; **k** is the unit vector of the z axis. The z' axis is assumed to coincide with the z axis. What is the shape of the field $\mathbf{E}'$?

3.365. In an inertial reference frame K there is only electric field of strength $\mathbf{E} = a\,(x\mathbf{i} + y\mathbf{j})/(x^2 + y^2)$, where a is a constant, **i** and **j** are the unit vectors of the x and y axes. Find the magnetic iduction $\mathbf{B}'$ in the frame K' moving relative to the frame K with a constant non-relativistic velocity $\mathbf{v} = v\mathbf{k}$; **k** is the unit vector of the z axis. The z' axis is assumed to coincide with the z axis. What is the shape of the magnetic induction $\mathbf{B}'$?

3.366. Demonstrate that the transformation formulas (3.6h) follow from the formulas (3.6i) at $v_0 \ll c$.

3.367. In an inertial reference frame K there is only a uniform electric field $E = 8$ kV/m in strength. Find the modulus and direction.

(a) of the vector $\mathbf{E}'$, (b) of the vector $\mathbf{B}'$ in the inertial reference frame K' moving with a constant velocity **v** relative to the frame K at an angle $\alpha = 45°$ to the vector **E**. The velocity of the frame K' is equal to a $\beta = 0.60$ fraction of the velocity of light.

3.368. Solve a problem differing from the foregoing one by a magnetic field with induction $B = 0.8$ T replacing the electric field.

3.369. Electromagnetic field has two invariant quantities. Using the transformation formulas (3.6i), demonstrate that these quantities are.

(a) **EB**; (b) $E^2 - c^2B^2$.

3.370. In an inertial reverence frame K there are two uniform mutually perpendicular fields: an electric field of strength $E = 40$ kV/m and a magnetic field induction $B = 0.20$ mT. Find the electric strength E' (or the magnetic induction B') in the reverence frame K' where only one field, electric or magnetic, is observed.

Instruction. Make use of the field invariants cited in the foregoing problem.

3.371. A point charge q moves uniformly and rectilinearly with a relativistic velocity equal to a β fraction of the velocity of light ($\beta = v/c$). Find the electric field strength **E** produced by the charge at the point whose radius vector relative to the charge is equal to r and forms an angle q with its velocity vector.

3.7. MOTION OF CHARGED PARTICLES IN ELECTRIC AND MAGNETIC FIELDS

• Lorentz force:

$$\mathbf{F} = q\mathbf{E} + q[\mathbf{vB}]. \qquad (3.7a)$$

• Motion equation of a relativistic particle:

$$\frac{d}{dt}\frac{m_0\mathbf{v}}{\sqrt{1-(v/c)^2}} = \mathbf{F}. \qquad (3.7b)$$

• Period of revolution of a charged particle in a uniform magnetic field:

$$T = \frac{2\pi m}{qB}, \qquad (3.7c)$$

where m is the relativistic mass of the particle, $m = m_0/\sqrt{1-(v/c)^2}$.

• Betatron condition, that is the condition for an electron to move along a circular orbit in a betatron:

$$B_0 = \frac{1}{2}\langle B\rangle, \qquad (3.7d)$$

where B_0 is the magnetic induction at an orbit's point, $\langle B\rangle$ is the mean value of the induction inside the orbit.

3.372. At the moment $t = 0$ an electron leaves one plate of a parallel-plate capacitor with a negligible velocity. An accelerating voltage, varying as $V = at$, where $a = 100$ V/s, is applied between the plates. The separation between the plates is $l = 5.0$ cm. What is the velocity of the electron at the moment it reaches the opposite plate?

3.373. A proton accelerated by a potential difference V gets into the uniform electric field of a parallel-plate capacitor whose plates extend over a length l in the motion direction. The field strength varies with time as $E = at$, where a is a constant. Assuming the proton to be non-relativistic, find the angle between the motion directions of the proton before and after its flight through the capacitor; the proton gets in the field at the moment $t = 0$. The edge effects are to be neglected.

3.374. A particle with specific charge q/m moves rectilinearly due to an electric field $E = E_0 - ax$, where a is a positive constant, x is the distance from the point where the particle was initially at rest. Find:

(a) the distance covered by the particle till the moment it came to a standstill;

(b) the acceleration of the particle at that moment.

3.375. An electron starts moving in a uniform electric field of strength $E = 10$ kV/cm. How soon after the start will the kinetic energy of the electron become equal to its rest energy?

3.376. Determine the acceleration of a relativistic electron moving along a uniform electric field of strength E at the moment when its kinetic energy becomes equal to T.

3.377. At the moment $t = 0$ a relativistic proton flies with a velocity $\mathbf{v}_0$ into the region where there is a uniform transverse electric field of strength $\mathbf{E}$, with $\mathbf{v}_0 \perp \mathbf{E}$. Find the time dependence of

(a) the angle θ between the proton's velocity vector **v** and the initial direction of its motion;

(b) the projection v_x of the vector **v** on the initial direction of motion.

3.378. A proton accelerated by a potential difference $V = 500$ kV flies through a uniform transverse magnetic field with induction $B = 0.51$ T. The field occupies a region of space $d = 10$ cm in thickness (Fig. 3.99). Find the angle α through which the proton deviates from the initial direction of its motion.

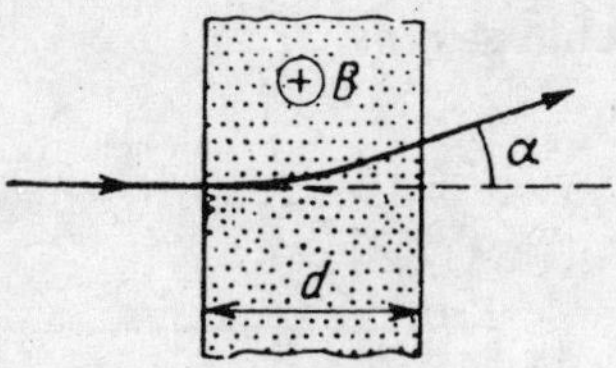

Fig. 3.99.

3.379. A charged particle moves along a circle of radius $r = 100$ mm in a uniform magnetic field with induction $B = 10.0$ mT. Find its velocity and period of revolution if that particle is

(a) a non-relativistic proton;

(b) a relativistic electron.

3.380. A relativistic particle with charge q and rest mass m_0 moves along a circle of radius r in a uniform magnetic field of induction B. Find:

(a) the modulus of the particle's momentum vector;

(b) the kinetic energy of the particle;

(c) the acceleration of the particle.

3.381. Up to what values of kinetic energy does the period of revolution of an electron and a proton in a uniform magnetic field exceed that at non-relativistic velocities by $\eta = 1.0\%$?

3.382. An electron accelerated by a potential difference $V = 1.0$ kV moves in a uniform magnetic field at an angle $\alpha = 30°$ to the vector **B** whose modulus is $B = 29$ mT. Find the pitch of the helical trajectory of the electron.

3.383. A slightly divergent beam of non-relativistic charged particles accelerated by a potential difference V propagates from a point A along the axis of a straight solenoid. The beam is brought into focus at a distance l from the point A at two successive values of magnetic induction B_1 and B_2. Find the specific charge q/m of the particles.

3.384. A non-relativistic electron originates at a point A lying on the axis of a straight solenoid and moves with velocity v at an angle α to the axis. The magnetic induction of the field is equal to B. Find the distance r from the axis to the point on the screen into which the electron strikes. The screen is oriented at right angles to the axis and is located at a distance l from the point A.

3.385. From the surface of a round wire of radius a carrying a direct current I an electron escapes with a velocity v_0 perpendicular to the surface. Find what will be the maximum distance of the electron from the axis of the wire before it turns back due to the action of the magnetic field generated by the current.

3.386. A non-relativistic charged particle flies through the electric field of a cylindrical capacitor and gets into a uniform transverse magnetic field with induction B (Fig. 3.100). In the capacitor the particle moves along the arc of a circle, in the magnetic field, along a semi-circle of radius r. The potential differnece applied to the capaciter is equal to V, the radii of the electrodes are eual to a and b, with $a < b$. Fidn the velocity of the particle and its specific charge q/m.

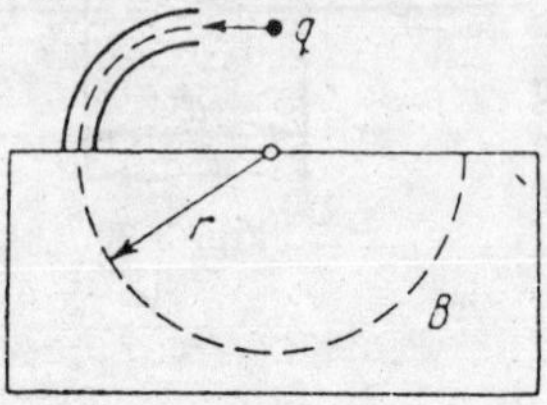

Fig. 3.100.

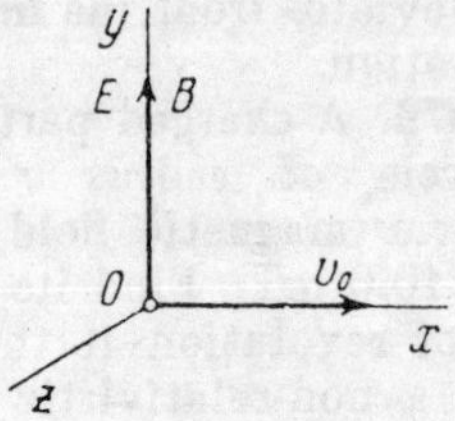

Fig. 3.101.

3.387. Uniform electric and magnetic fields with strength E and induction B respectively are directed along the y axis (Fig. 3.101). A particle with specific charge q/m leaves the origin O in the direction of the x axis with an initial non-relativistic velocity v_0. Find:

(a) the coordinate y_n of the particle when it crosses the y axis for the nth time;

(b) the angle α between the particle's velocity vector and the y axis at that moment.

3.388. A narrow beam of identical ions with specific charge q/m, possessing different velocities, enters the region of space, where there are uniform parallel electric and magnetic fields with strength E and induction B, at the point O (see Fig. 3.101) The beam direction coincides with the x axis at the point O. A plane screen oriented at right angles to the x axis is located at a distance l from the point O. Find the equation of the trace that the ions leave on the screen. Demonstrate that at $z \ll l$ it is the eouation of a parabola.

3.389. A non-relativistic proton beam passes without deviation through the region of space where there are uniform trnasverse mutually perpendicualr electric and magnetic fields with E = 120 kV/m and B = 50 mT. Then the beam strikes a grounded target Find the force with which the beam acts on the target if the beam current is equal to I = 0.80 mA.

3.390. Non-realtivistic protons move rectilinearly in the region of space where there are uniform mutually perpendicular electric and magnetic fields with E = 4.0 kV/m and B = 50 mT. The trajectory of the protons lies in the plane xz (Fig. 3.102) and forms an angle φ = 30° with the x axis. Find the pitch of the helical trajectory along which the protons will move after the electric field is switched off.

3.391. A beam of non-relativistic charged particles moves without deviation through the region of space A (Fig. 3.103) where the are transverse mutually perpendicular electric and magnetic fields with

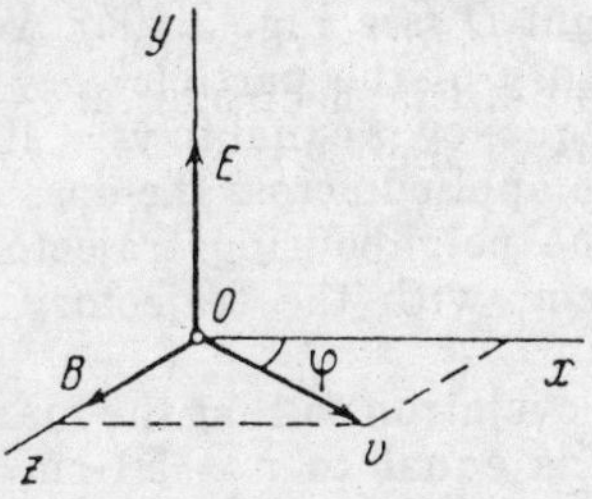

Fig. 3.102.

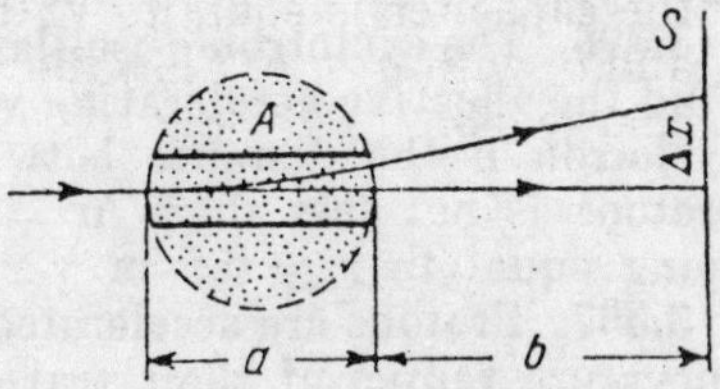

Fig. 3.103.

strength E and induction B. When the magnetic field is switched off, the trace of the beam on the screen S shifts by Δx. Knowing the distances a and b, find the specific charge q/m of the particles.

3.392. A particle with specific charge q/m moves in the region of space where there are uniform mutually perpendicular electric and magnetic fields with strength **E** and induction **B** (Fig. 3.104). At the moment $t = 0$ the particle was located at the point O and had zero velocity. For the non-relativistic case find:

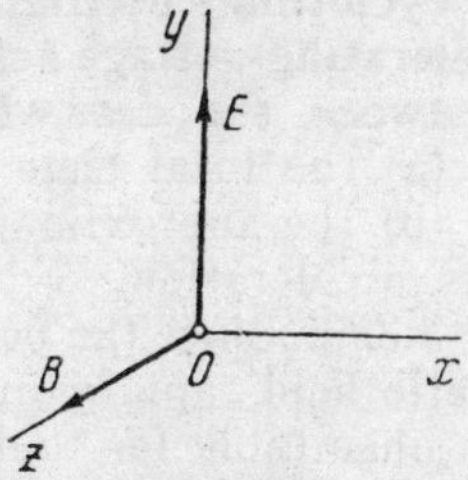

Fig. 3.104.

(a) the law of motion $x(t)$ and $y(t)$ of the particle; the shape of the trajectory;

(b) the length of the segment of the trajectory between two nearest points at which the velocity of the particle turns into zero;

(c) the mean value of the particle's velocity vector projection on the x axis (the drift velocity).

3.393. A system consists of a long cylindrical anode of radius a and a coaxial cylindrical cathode of radius b ($b < a$), a filament located along the axis of the system carries a heating current I producing a magnetic field in the surrounding space. Find the least potential differnee between the cathode and anode at which the thermal electrons leaving the cathode without initial velocity start reaching the anode.

3.394. Magnetron is a device consisting of a filament of radius a and a coaxial cylindrical anode of radius b which are located in a uniform magnetic field parallel to the filament. An acelerating potential differnece V is applied between the filament and the anode. Find the value of magnetic induction at which th electrons leaving the filament with zero, velocity reach the anode.

3.395. A charged particle with specific charge q/m starts moving in the region of space where there are uniform mutually perpendicualr electric and magnetic fields. The magnetic field is constant and has an induction B while the strength of the electric field varies with time as $E = E_m \cos \omega t$, where $\omega = qB/m$. For the non-relativistic case find the law of motion $x(t)$ and $y(t)$ of the particle if at the moment $t = 0$ it was located at the point O (see Fig. 3.104). What is the approximate shape of the trajectory of the particle?

3.396. The cyclotron's oscillator frequency is equal to $\nu = 10$ MHz. Find the effective accelerating voltage applied across the dees of that cyclotron if the distance between the neighbouring trajectories of protons is not less than $\Delta r = 1.0$ cm, with the trajectory radius being equal to $r = 0.5$ m.

3.397. Protons are accelerated in a cyclotron so that the maximum curvature radius of their trajectory is equal to $r = 50$ cm. Find:

(a) the kinetic energy of the protons when the acceleration is completed if the magnetic induction in the cyclotron is $B = 1.0$ T;

(b) the minimum frequency of the cyclotron's oscillator at which the kinetic energy of the protons amounts to $T = 20$ MeV by the end of acceleration.

3.398. Singly charged ions He^+ are accelerated in a cyclotron so that their maximum orbital radius is $r = 60$ cm. The frequency of a cyclotron's oscillator is equal to $\nu = 10.0$ MHz, the effective accelerating voltage across the dees is $V = 50$ kV. Neglecting the gap between the dees, find:

(a) the total time of acceleration of the ion;

(b) the approximate distance covered by the ion in the process of its acceleration.

3.399. Since the period of revolution of electrons in a uniform magnetic field rapidly increases with the growth of energy, a cyclotron is unsuitable for their acceleration. This drawback is rectified in a *microtron* (Fig. 3.105) in which a change ΔT in the period of revolution of an electron is made multiple with the period of accelerating field T_0. How many times has an electron to cross the accelerating gap of a microtron to acquire an energy $W = 4.6$ MeV if $\Delta T = T_0$, the magnetic induction is equal to $B = 107$ mT, and the frequency of accelerating field to $\nu = 3000$ MHz?

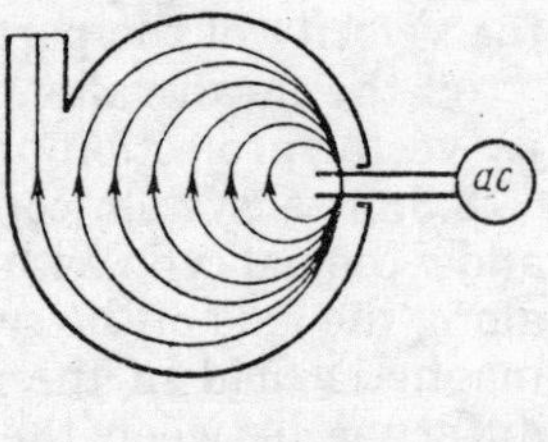

Fig. 3.105.

3.400. The ill effects associated with the variation of the period of revolution of the particle in a cyclotron due to the increase of its energy are eliminated by slow monitoring (modulating) the frequency of accelerating field. According to what law $\omega(t)$ should this frequency be monitored if the magnetic induction is equal to B and the particle acquires an energy ΔW per revolution? The charge of the particle is q and its mass is m.

3.401. A particle with specific charge q/m is located inside a round solenoid at a distance r from its axis. With the current switched into the winding, the magnetic induction of the field generated by the solenoid amounts to B. Find the velocity of the particle and the curvature radius of its trajectory, assuming that during the increase of current flowing in the solenoid the particle shifts by a negligible distance.

3.402. In a betatron the magnetic flux across an equilibrium orbit of radius $r = 25$ cm grows during the acceleration time at practically constant rate $\dot{\Phi} = 5.0$ Wb/s. In the process, the electrons acquire an energy $W = 25$ MeV. Find the number of revolutions made by the electron during the acceleration time and the corresponding distance covered by it.

3.403. Demonstrate that electrons move in a betatron along a round orbit of constant radius provided the magnetic induction on the orbit is equal to half the mean value of that inside the orbit (the betatron condition).

3.404. Using the betatron condition, find the radius of a round orbit of an electron if the magnetic induction is known as a function of distance r from the axis of the field. Examine this problem for the specific case $B = B_0 - ar^2$, where B_0 and a are positive constants.

3.405. Using the betatron condition, demonstrate that the strength of the eddy-current field has the extremum magnitude on an equilibrium orbit.

3.406. In a betatron the magnetic induction on an equilibrium orbit with radius $r = 20$ cm varies during a time interval $\Delta t = 1.0$ ms at practically constant rate from zero to $B = 0.40$ T. Find the energy acquired by the electron per revolution.

3.407. The magnetic induction in a betatron on an equilibrium orbit of radius r varies during the acceleration time at practically constant rate from zero to B. Assuming the initial velocity of the electron to be equal to zero, find:

(a) the energy acquired by the electron during the acceleration time;

(b) the corresponding distance covered by the electron if the acceleration time is equal to Δt.

4

OSCILLATIONS AND WAVES

4.1. MECHANICAL OSCILLATIONS

• Harmonic motion equation and its solution:

$$x + \omega_0^2 x = 0,\ x = \alpha \cos(\omega_0 t + \alpha) \quad (4.1a)$$

where ω_0 is the natural oscillation frequency.

• Damped oscillation equation and its solution:

$$z + 2\beta x + w_0^2 x = 0,\ x = a_0 e^{-\beta t} \cos(\omega t + \alpha), \quad (4.1b)$$

where β is the damping coefficient, ω is the frequency of damped oscillations:

$$\omega = \sqrt{\omega_0^2 - \beta^2} \quad (4.1c)$$

• Logarithmic damping decrement λ and quality factor Q:

$$\lambda = \beta T, \quad Q = \pi/\lambda, \quad (4.1d)$$

where $T = 2\pi/\omega$.

• Forced oscillation equation and its steady-state solution:

$$x + 2\beta x + \omega_0^2 x = f_0 \cos \omega t,\ x = a \cos(\omega t - \varphi), \quad (4.1e)$$

where

$$a = \frac{f_0}{\sqrt{(\omega_0^2 - \omega^2)^2 + 4\beta^2\omega^2}} \quad \tan\varphi = \frac{2\beta\omega}{\omega_0^2 - \omega^2} \quad (4.1f)$$

• Maximum shift amplitude occurs at

$$\omega_{res} = \sqrt{\omega_0^2 - 2\beta^2} \quad (4.1g)$$

4.1. A point oscillates along the x axis according to the law $x = a \cos(\omega t - \pi/4)$. Draw the approximate plots.

(a) of displacement x, velocity projection v_x, and acceleration projection w_x as functions of time t;

(b) velocity projection v_x and acceleration projection w_x a s functions of the coordinate x.

4.2. A point moves along the x axis according to the law $z = a \sin^2(\omega t - \pi/4)$. Find:

(a) the amplitude and period of oscillations; draw the plot $x(t)$;

(b) the velocity projection v_x as a function of the coordinate x; draw the plot $v_x(x)$.

4.3. A particle performs harmonic oscillations along the x axis about the equilibrium position $x = 0$. The oscillation frequency is $\omega = 4.00\ s^{-1}$. At a certain moment of time the particle has a coordinate $x_0 = 25.0$ cm and its velocity is equal to $v_{x0} = 100$ cm/s.

Find the coordinate x and the velocity v_x of the particle $t = 2.40$ s after that moment

4.4. Find the angular frequency and the amplitude of harmonic oscillations of a particle if at distances x_1 and x_2 from the equilibrium position its velocity equals v_1 and v_2 respectively.

4.5. A point performs harmonic oscillations along a straight line with a period $T = 0.60$s and an amplitude $a = 10.0$ cm. Find the mean velocity of the point averaged over the time interval during which it travels a distance $a/2$, starting from

(a) the extreme position;

(b) the equilibrium position.

4.6. At the moment $t = 0$ a point starts oscillating along the x axis according to the law $x = a \sin \omega t$. Find.

(a) the mean value of its velocity vector projection $\langle v_x \rangle$;

(b) the modulus of the mean velocity vector $[\langle v \rangle]$.

(c) the mean value of the velocity modulus ⟨v⟩ averaged over 3/8 of the period after the start.

4.7. A particle moves along the x axis according to the law $x = a \cos \omega t$. Find the distnace that the partcle covers during the time interval from $t = 0$ to t.

4.8. At the moment $t = 0$ a particle starts moving along the x axis so that its velocity projection varies as $v_x = 35 \cos \pi t$ cm/s, where t is expressed in seconds. Find the distance that this particle covers during $t = 2.80$ s after the start.

4.9. A particle performs harmonic oscillations along the x axis according to the law $x = a \cos \omega t$. Assuming the probability P of the particle of fall within an interval from $-a$ to $+a$ to be equal to unity, find how the probability density dP/dx depends on x. Here dP denotes the probability of the particle falling within an interval from x to $x + dx$. Plot dP/dx as a function of x.

4.10. Using graphical means, find an amplitude a of oscillations resulting from the superposition of the following oscillations of the same direction:

(a) $x_1 = 3.0 \cos (\omega t + \pi/3)$, $x_2 = 8.0 \sin (\omega t + \pi/6)$;

(b) $x_1 = 3.0 \cos \omega t$, $x_2 = 5.0 \cos (\omega t + \pi/4)$, $x_3 = 6.0 \sin \omega t$.

4.11. A point participates simultaneously in two harmonic oscillation of the same direction: $x_1 = \alpha \cos \omega t$ and $x_2 = a \cos 2\omega t$. Find the maximum velocity of the point.

4.12. The superposition of two harmonic oscillations of the same direction results in the oscillation of a point according to the law $x = a \cos 2.1t \cos 50.0t$, where t is expressed in seconds. Find the angular frequencies of the constituent oscillations and the period with which they beat.

4.13. A point A oscillates according to a certain harmonic law in the refernece frame K' which in its turn perform harmonic oscillations relative to the reference frame K. Both oscillations occur along the same direction. When the K' frame oscillates at the frequency 20 or 24 Hz, the beat frequency of the point A in the K frame turns out to be equal to ν. At what frequency of oscillation of the frame K' will the beat frequency of the point A become equal to 2ν?

4.14. A point moves in the plane xy according to the law $x = a \sin \omega t$, $y = b \cos \omega t$, where a, b, and ω are positive constants. Find:

(a) the trajectory equation $y(x)$ of the point and the direction of its motion along this trajectory;

(b) the acceleration $\mathbf{w}$ of the point as a function of its radius vector $\mathbf{r}$ relative to the origin of coordinates.

4.15. Find the trajectory equation $y(x)$ of a point if it moves according to the following laws:

(a) $x = a \sin \omega t$, $y = a \sin 2\omega t$;

(b) $x = a \sin \omega t$, $y = a \cos 2\omega t$.

Plot these trajectories.

4.16. A particle of mass m is located in a unidimensional potential field where the potential energy of the particle depends on the coordinate x as $U(x) = U_0 (1 - \cos ax)$; U_0 and a are constants. Find the period of small oscillations that the particle performs about the equilibrium position.

4.17. Solve the foregoing problem if the potential energy has the form $U(x) = a/x^2 - b/x$, where a and b are positive constants.

4.18. Find the period of small oscillations in a vertical plane performed by a ball of mass $m = 40$ g fixed at the middle of a horizontally stretched string $l = 1.0$ m in length. The tension of the string is assumed to be constant and equal to $F = 10$ N.

4.19. Determine the period of small oscillations of a mathematical pendulum, that is a ball suspended by a thread $l = 20$ cm in length, if it is located in a liquid whose density is $\eta = 3.0$ times less than that of the ball. The resistance of the liquid is to be neglected.

4.20. A ball is suspended by a thread of length l at the point O on the wall, forming a small angle α with the vertical (Fig. 4.1). Then

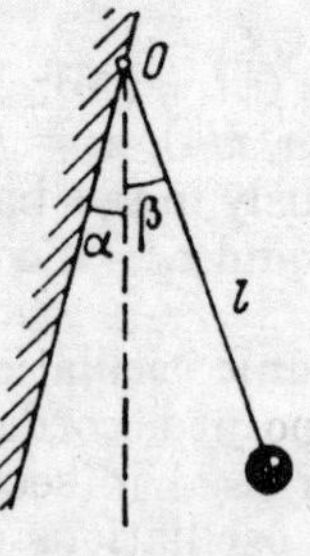

Fig. 4.1.

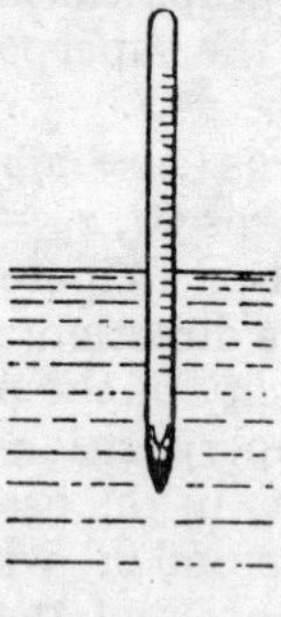

Fig. 4.2.

the thread with the ball was deviated through a small angle β ($\beta > \alpha$) and set free. Assuming the collision of the ball against the wall to be perfectly elastic, find the oscillation period of such a pendulum.

4.21. A pendulum clock is mounted in an elevator car which starts going up with a constant acceleration w, with $w < g$. At a height h the acceleration of the car reverses, its magnitude remaining constant. How soon after the start of the motion will the clock show the right time again?

4.22. Calculate the period of small oscillations of a hydrometer (Fig. 4.2) which was slightly pushed down in the vertical direction. The mass of the hydrometer is $m = 50$ g, the radius of its tube is $r = 3.2$ mm, the density of the liquid is $\rho = 1.00$ g/cm^3. The resistance of the liquid is assumed to be negligible.

4.23. A non-deformed spring whose ends are fixed has a stiffness $\varkappa = 13$ N/m. A small body of mass $m = 25$ g is attached at the point removed from one of the ends by $\eta = 1/3$ of the spring's length. Neglecting the mass of the spring, find the period of small longitudinal oscillations of the body. The force of gravity is assumed to be absent.

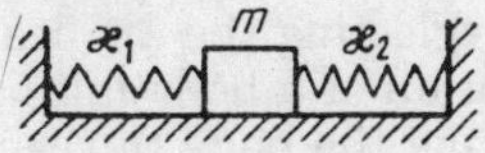

Fig. 4.3.

4.24. Determine the period of small longitudinal oscillations of a body with mass m in the system shown in Fig. 4.3. The stiffness values of the springs are $\varkappa_1$ and $\varkappa_2$. The friction and the masses of the springs are negligible.

4.25. Find the period of small vertical oscillations of a body with mass m in the system illustrated in Fig. 4.4. The stiffness values of the springs are $\varkappa_1$ and $\varkappa_2$, their masses are negligible.

4.26. A small body of mass m is fixed to the middle of a stretched string of length $2l$. In the equilibrium position the string tension is equal to T_0. Find the angular frequency of small oscillations of the body in the transverse direction. The mass of the string is negligible, the gravitational field is absent.

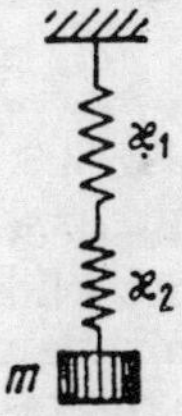

Fig. 4.4.

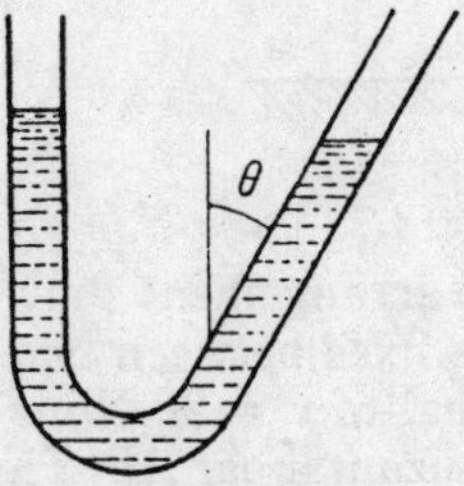

Fig. 4.5.

4.27. Determine the period of oscillations of mercury of mass $m = 200$ g poured into a bent tube (Fig. 4.5) whose right arm forms an angle $\theta = 30°$ with the vertical. The cross-sectional area of the tube is $S = 0.50$ cm^2. The viscosity of mercury is to be neglected.

4.28. A uniform rod is placed on two spinning wheels as shown in Fig. 4.6. The axes of the wheels are separated by a distance $l = 20$ cm, the coefficient of friction between the rod and the wheels is $k = 0.18$. Demonstrate that in this case the rod performs harmonic oscillations. Find the period of these oscillations.

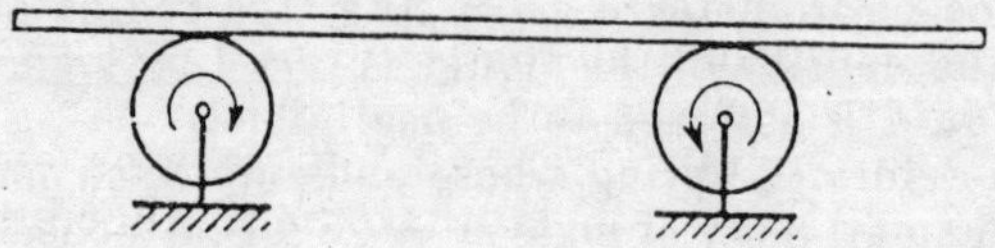

Fig. 4.6.

4.29. Imagine a shaft going all the way through the Earth from pole to pole along its rotation axis. Assuming the Earth to be a homogeneous ball and neglecting the air drag, find:

(a) the equation of motion of a body falling down into the shaft;

(b) how long does it take the body to reach the other end of the shaft;

(c) the velocity of the body at the Earth's centre.

4.30. Find the period of small oscillations of a mathematical pendulum of length l if its point of suspension O moves relative to the Earth's surface in an arbitrary direction with a constant acceleration w (Fig. 4.7). Calculate that period if $l = 21$ cm, $w = g/2$, and the angle between the vectors $\mathbf{w}$ and $\mathbf{g}$ equals $\beta = 120°$.

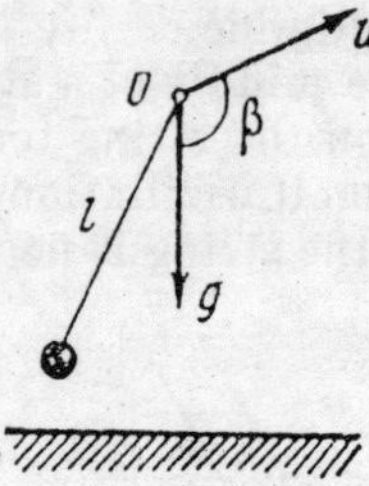

Fig. 4.7.

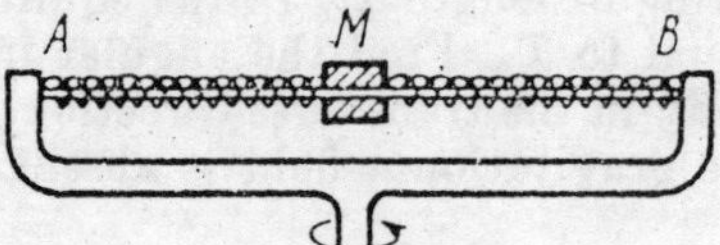

Fig. 4.8.

4.31. In the arrangement shown in Fig. 4.8. the sleeve M of mass $m = 0.20$ kg is fixed between two identical springs whose combined stiffness is equal to $x = 20$ N/m. The sleeve can slide without friction over a horizontal bar AB. The arrangement rotates with a constant angular velocity $\omega = 4.4$ rad/s about a vertical axis passing through the middle of the bar. Find the period of small oscillations of the sleeve. At what values of ω will there be no oscillations of the sleeve?

4.32. A plank with a bar placed on it performs horizontal harmonic oscillations with amplitude $a = 10$ cm. Find the coefficient of friction between the bar and the plank if the former starts sliding along the plank when the amplitude of oscillation of the plank becomes less than $T = 1.0$ s.

4.33. Find the time dependence of the angle of deviation of a mathematical pendulum 80 cm in length if at the initial moment the pendulum

(a) was deviated through the angle 3.0° and then set free without push;

(b) was in the equilibrium position and its lower end was imparted the horizontal velocity 0.22 m/s;

(c) was deviated through the angle 3.0° and its lower end was imparted the velocity 0.22 m/s directed toward the equilibrium position.

4.34. A body A of mass $m_1 = 1.00$ kg and a body B of mass $m_2 =$ 4.10 kg are inteconnected by a spring as shown in Fig. 4.9. The body A performs free vertical harmonic oscillations with amplitude $\alpha = 1.6$ cm and frequency $\omega = 25\ s^{-1}$. Neglecting the mass of the spring, find the maximum and minimum vlues of force that this system exerts on the bearing surface.

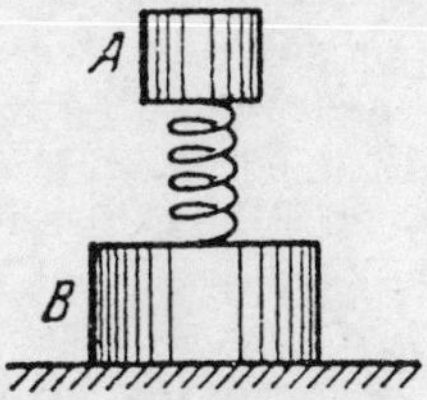

Fig. 4.9.

4.35. A plank with a body of mass m placed on it starts moving straight up according to the law $y = a\ (1 - \cos \omega t)$, where y is the displacement from the initial position. $\omega = 11\ s^{-1}$. Find:

(a) the time dependence of the force that the body exerts on the plank if $a = 4.0$ cm; plot this dependence;

(b) the minimum amplitude of oscillation of the plank at which the body starts falling behind the plank;

(c) the amplitude of oscillation of the plank at which the body springs up to a height $h = 50$ cm relative to the initial position (at the moment $t = 0$).

4.36. A body of mass m was suspended by a non-stretched spring, and than set free without push. The stiffness of the spring is x. Neglecting the mass of the spring, find:

(a) the law of motion $y\ (t)$, where y is the displacement of the body from the equilibrium position;

(b) the maximum and minimum tensions of the spring in the process of motion.

4.37. A particle of mass m moves due to the force $F = -\alpha mr$, where α is a positive constnat, r is the radius vector of the particle relative to the origin of coordinates. Find the trajectory of its mortion if at the initial moment $r = r_0\mathbf{i}$ and the velocity $v = v_0\mathbf{j}$, where **i** and **j** are the unit vectors of the x and y axes.

4.38. A body of mass m is suspended from a spring fixed to the celling of an elevator car. the stiffness of the spring is x. At the moment $t = 0$ the car starts going up with an acceleration w. Neglecting the mass of the spring, find the law of motion $y\ (t)$ of the body relative to the elevator car if $y\ (0) = 0$ and $y\ (0) = 0$. Consider the following two cases:

(a) $w = \text{const}$;
(b) $w = \alpha t$, where α is a constant.

4.39. A body of mass $m = 0.50$ kg is suspended from a rubber cord with elasticity coefficient $k = 50$ N/m. Find the maximum distance over which the body can be pulled down for the body's oscillations to remain harmonic. What is the energy of oscillation in this case?

4.40. A body of mass m fell from a height h onto the pan of a spring balance (Fig. 4.10). The masses of the pan and the spring are negligible, the stiffness of the latter is $\varkappa$. Having stuck to the pan, the body starts performing harmonic oscillations in the vertical direction. Find the amplitude and the energy of these oscillations.

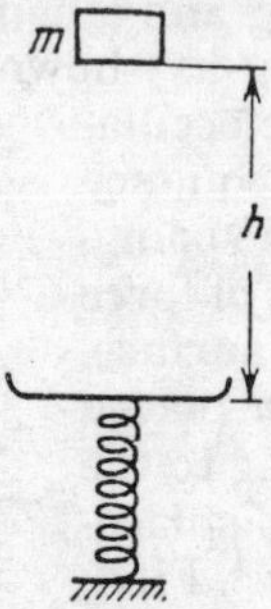

Fig. 4.10.

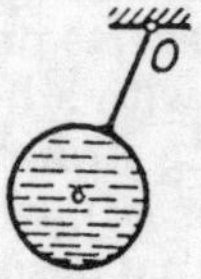

Fig. 4.11.

4.41. Solve the foregoing problem for the case of the pan having a mass M. Find the oscillation amplitude in this case.

4.42. A particle of mass m moves in the plane xy due to the force varying with velocity as $\mathbf{F} = a(\dot{y}\mathbf{i} - \dot{x}\mathbf{j})$, where a is a positive constant, $\mathbf{i}$ and $\mathbf{j}$ are the unit vectors of the x and y axes. At the initial moment $t = 0$ the particle was located at the point $x = y = 0$ and possessed a velocity $\mathbf{v}_0$ directed along the unit vector $\mathbf{j}$. Find the law of motion $x(t)$, $y(t)$ of the particle, and also the equation of its trajectory.

4.43. A pendulum is constructed as a light thin-walled sphere of radius R filled up with water and suspended at the point O from a light rigid rod (Fig. 4.11). The distance between the point O and the centre of the sphere is equal to l. How many times will the small oscillations of such a pendulum change after the water freezes? The viscosity of water and the change of its volume on freezing are to be neglected.

4.44. Find the frequency of small oscillations of a thin uniform vertical rod of mass m and length l hinged at the point O (Fig. 4.12). The combined stiffness of the springs is equal to $\varkappa$. The mass of the springs is negligible.

4.45. A uniform rod of mass $m = 1.5$ kg suspended by two identical threads $l = 90$ cm in length (Fig. 4.13) was turned through a small angle about the vertical axis passing through its middle point C. The threads deviated in the process through an angle $\alpha = 5.0°$. Then the rod was released to start performing small oscillations. Find:

(a) the oscillation period;
(b) the rod's oscillation energy.

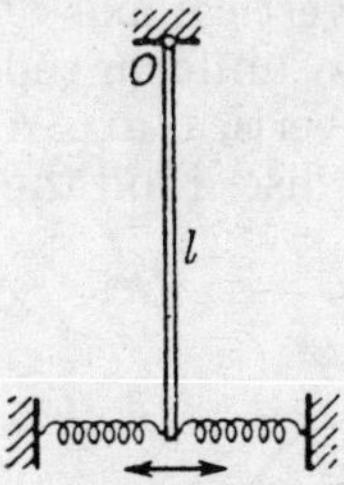

Fig. 4.12.

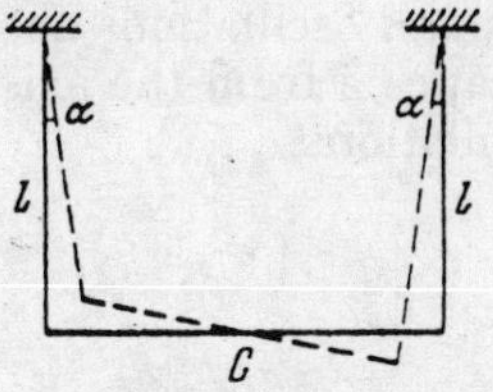

Fig. 4.13.

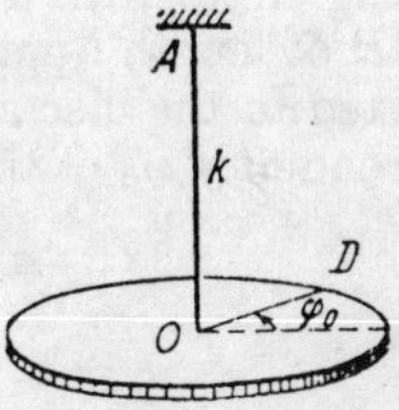

Fig. 4.14.

4.46. An arrangement illustrated in Fig. 4.14 consists of a horizontal uniform disc D of mass m and radius R and a thin rod AO whose torsional coefficient is equal to k. Find the amplitude and the energy of small torsional oscillations if at the initial moment the disc was deviated through an angle φ_0 from the equilibrium position and then imparted an angular velocity $\dot{\varphi}_0$.

4.47. A uniform rod of mass m and length l performs small oscillations about the horizontal axis passing through its upper end. Find the mean kinetic energy of the rod averaged over one oscillation period if at the initial moment it was deflected from the vertical by an angle θ_0 and then imparted an angular velocity $\dot{\theta}_0$.

4.48. A physical pendulum is positioned so that its centre of gravity is above the suspension point. From that position the pendulum started moving toward the stable equilibrium and passed it with an angular velocity ω. Neglecting the friction find the period of small oscillations of the pendulum.

4.49. A physical pendulum performs small oscillations about the horizontal axis with frequency $\omega_1 = 15.0\ s^{-1}$. When a small body of mass $m = 50$ g is fixed to the pendulum at a distance $l = 20$ cm below the axis, the oscillation frequency becomes equal to $\omega_2 = 10.0\ s^{-1}$. Find the moment of inertia of the pendulum relative to the oscillation axis.

4.50. Two physical pendulums perform small oscillations about the same horizontal axis with frequencies ω_1 and ω_2. Their moments of inertia relative to the given axis are equal to I_1 and I_2 respectively. In a state of stable equilibrium the pendulums were fastened rigidly together. What will be the frequency of small oscillations of the compound pendulum?

4.51. A uniform rod of length l performs small oscillations about the horizontal axis OO' perpendicular to the rod and passing through one of its points. Find the distance between the centre of inertia of the rod and the axis OO' at whcih the oscillation period of the shortest. What is the equal to?

4.52. A thin uniform plate shaped as an equilateral triangle with a height h performs small oscillations about the horizontal axis coinciding with one of its sides. Find the oscillation period and the reduced length of the given pendulum.

4.53. A smooth horizontal disc rotates about the vertical axis O (Fig. 4.15) with a constant angular velocity ω. A thin uniform rod AB of length l performs small oscillations about the vertical axis A fixed to the disc at a distance a from the axis of the disc. Find the frequency ω_0 of these oscillations.

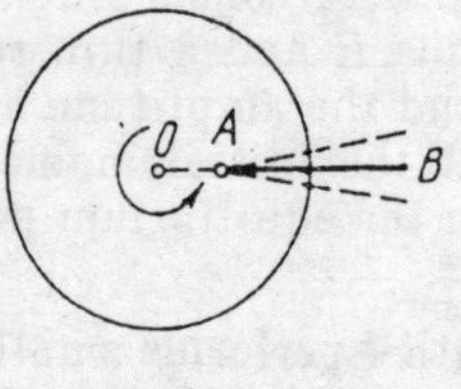

Fig. 4.15.

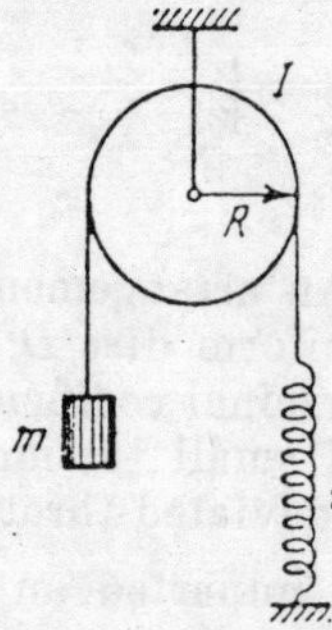

Fig. 4.16.

4.54. Find the frequency of small oscillations of the arrangement illustrated in Fig. 4.16. The radius of the pulley is R, its moment of inertia relative to the rotation axis is I, the mass of the body is m, and the spring stiffness is x. The mass of the thread and the spring is negligible the thread does not slide over the pulley, there is no friction in the axis of the pulley.

4.55. A uniform cylindrical pulley of mass M and radius R can freely rotate about the horizontal axis O (Fig. 4.17). The free end of

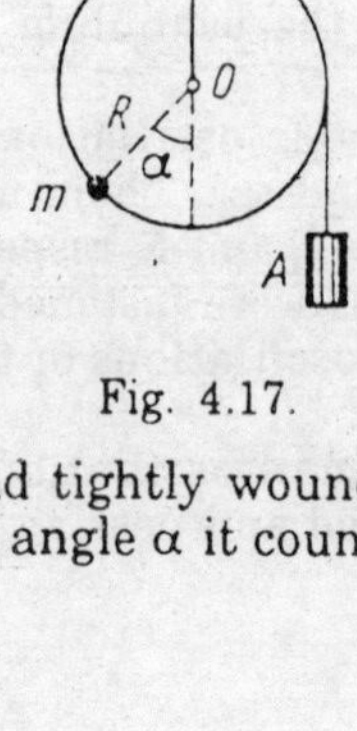

Fig. 4.17.

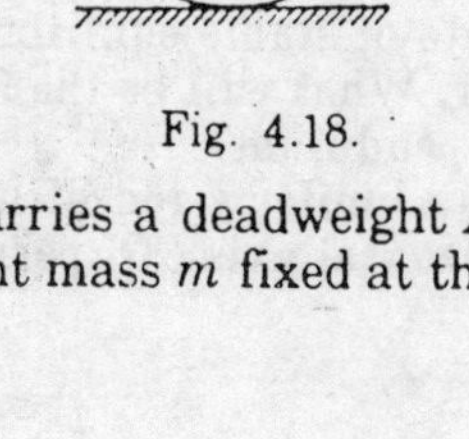

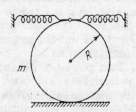

Fig. 4.18.

a thread tightly wound on the pulley carries a deadweight A. At a certain angle α it counterbalances a point mass m fixed at the rim of the pulley. Find the frequency of small oscilations is of the arrangement.

4.56. A solid uniform cylinder of radius r rolls without sliding along the inside surface of a cylinder of radius R, performing small oscillations. Find their period.

4.57. A soid uniform cylinder of mass m performs small oscillations due to the actionof two springs whose combined stiffness is equal to x (Fig. 4.18). Find the period of these oscillations in the absence of sliding.

4.58. The cubes with masses m_1 and m_2 were interconnected by a weightless spring of stiffness x and placed on a smooth horizontal surface. Then the cubes were drawn closer to each other and released simultaneously. Find the natural oscillation frequency of the system.

4.59. Two balls with masses m_1 = 1.0 kg and m_2 = 2.0 kg are slipped on a thin smooth horizontal rod (Fig. 4.19). The balls are

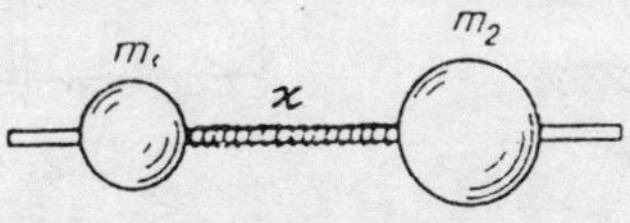

Fig. 4.19.

interconnected by a light spring of stiffness x = 24 N/m. The left hand ball is imparted the initial velocity v_1 = 12 cm/s. Find:

(a) The oscillation frequency of the system in the process of motion;

(b) the energy and the amplitude of oscillations.

4.60. Find the period of small torsional oscillations of system consisting of two discs slipped on a thin rod with torsional coefficient k. The moments of inertia of the discs relative to the rod's axis are equal to I_1 and I_2.

4.61. A mock-up of a CO_2 molecule consists of three balls interconnected by identical light springs and placed along a straight line in the state of equilibrium. Such a system can freely perform oscillations of two types, as shown by the arrows in Fig. 4.20. Knowing the masses of the atoms, find the ratio of frequencies of these oscillations.

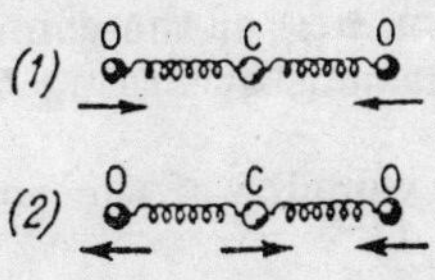

Fig. 4.20.

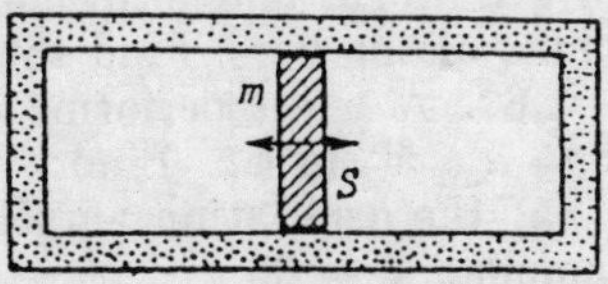

Fig. 4.21.

4.62. In a cylinder filled up with ideal gas and closed from both ends there is a piston of mass m and cross-sectional area S (Fig. 4.21).

In equilibrium the piston divides the cylinder into two equal parts, each with volume V_0. The gas pressure is p_0. The piston was slighlty displaced from the equilibrium position and released. Find its oscillation frequency, assuming the processes in the gas to be adiabatic and the friction negligible.

4.63. A small ball of mass $m = 21$ g suspended by an insulating thread at a height $h = 12$ cm from a large horizontal conducting plane performs small oscillations (Fig. 4.22). After a charge q had been imparted to the ball, the oscillation period changed $\eta = 2.0$ times. Find q.

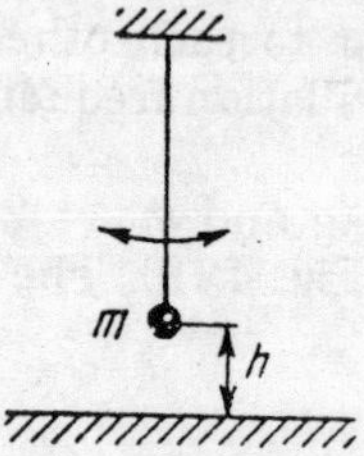

Fig. 4.22.

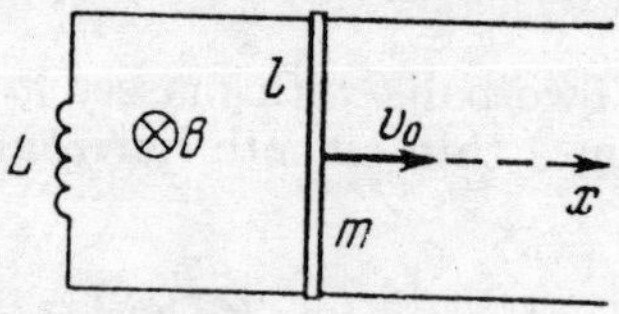

Fig. 4.23.

4.64. A small magnetic needle performs small oscillations about an axis perpendicular to the magnetic induction vector. On changing the magnetic induction the needle's oscillation period decreased $\eta = 5.0$ times. How much and in what way was the magnetic induction changed? The oscillation damping is assumed to be negligible.

4.65. A loop (Fig. 4.23) is formed by two parallel conductors connected by a solenoid with inductance L and a conducting rod of mass m which can freely (without friction) slide over the conductors. The conductors are located in a horizontal plane in a uniform vertical magnetic field with induction B. The distance between the conductors is equal to l. At the moment $t = 0$ the rod is imparted an initial velocity v_0 directed to the right. Find the law of its motion $x(t)$ if the electric resistance of the loop is negligible.

4.66. A coil of inductance L connects the upper ends of two vertical copper bars separated by a distance l. A horizontal conducting connector of mass m starts falling with zero initial velocity along the bars without losing contact with them. The whole system is located in a uniform magnetic field with induction B perpendicular to the plane of the bars. Find the law of motion $x(t)$ of the connector.

4.67. A point performs damped oscillations according to the law $x = a_0 e^{-\beta t} \sin \omega t$. Find:

(a) the oscillation amplitude and the velocity of the point at the moment $t = 0$;

(b) the moments of time at which the point reaches the extreme positions.

4.68. A body performs torsional oscillations according to the law $\varphi = \varphi_0 e^{-\beta t} \cos \omega t$. Find:

(a) the angular velocity $\dot{\varphi}$ and the angular acceleration $\ddot{\varphi}$ of the body at the moment $t = 0$;

(b) the moments of time at which the angular velocity becomes maximum.

4.69. A poin performs damped oscillations with frequency ω and damping coefficient β according to the law (4.1b). Find the initial amplitude a_0 and the initial phase α if at the moment $t = 0$ the displacement of the point and its velocity projection are equal to

(a) $x(0) = 0$ and $v_x(0) = \dot{x}_0$;

(b) $x(0) = x_0$ and $v_x(0) = 0$.

4.70. A point performs damped oscillations with frequency $\omega = 25\ s^{-1}$. Find the damping coefficient β if at the initial moment the velocity of the point is equal to zero and its displacement from the equilibrium position is $\eta = 1.020$ times less than the amplitude at that moment.

4.71. A point performs damped oscillations with frequency ω and damping coefficient β. Find the velocity amplitude of the point as a function of time t if at the moment $t = 0$

(a) its displacement amplitude is equal to a_0;

(b) the displacement of the point $x(0) = 0$ and its velocity projection $v_x(0) = \dot{x}_0$.

4.72. There are two damped oscillations with the following periods T and damping coefficients β: $T_1 = 0.10$ ms, $\beta_1 = 100\ s^{-1}$ and $T_2 = 10$ ms, $\beta_2 = 10\ s^{-1}$. Which of them decays faster?

4.73. A mathematical pendulum oscillates in a medium for which the logarithmic damping decrement is equal to $\lambda_0 = 1.50$. What will be the logarithmic damping decrement if the resistance of the medium increases $n = 2.00$ times? How many times has the resistance of the medium to be increased for the oscillations to become impossible?

4.74. A deadweight suspended from a weightless spring extends it by $\Delta x = 9.8$ cm. What will be the oscillation period of the deadweight when it is pushed slightly in the vertical direction? The logarithmic damping decrement is equal to $\lambda = 3.1$.

4.75. Find the quality factor of the oscillator whose displacement amplitude decreases $\eta = 2.0$ times every $n = 110$ oscillations.

4.76. A particle was displaced from the equilibrium position by a distance $l = 1.0$ cm and then left alone. What is the distance that the particle covers in the process of oscillations till the complete stop, if the logarithmic damping decrement is equal to $\lambda = 0.020$?

4.77. Find the quality factor of a mathematical pendulum $l = 50$ cm long if during the time interval $\tau = 5.2$ min its total mechanical energy decreases $\eta = 4.0 \cdot 10^4$ times.

4.78. A uniform disc of radius $R = 13$ cm can rotate about a horizontal axis perpendicular to its plane and passing through the edge of the disc. Find the period of small oscillations of that disc if the logarithmic damping decrement is equal to $\lambda = 1.00$.

4.79. A thin uniform disc of mass m and radius R suspended by an elastic thread in the horizontal plane performs torsional oscillations in a liquid. The moment of elastic forces emerging in the thread is equal to $N = \alpha\varphi$, where α is a constant and φ is the angle of rotation from the equilibrium position. The resistance force acting on a unit area of the disc is equal to $F_1 = \eta v$, where η is a constant and v is the velocity of the given element of the disc relative to the liquid. Find the frequency of small oscillation.

4.80. A disc A of radius R suspended by an elastic thread between two stationary planes (Fig. 4.24) performs torsional oscillations about its axis OO'. The moment of inertia of the disc relative to that axis is equal to I, the clearance between the disc and each of the planes is equal to h, with $h \ll R$. Find the viscosity of the gas surrounding the disc A if the oscillation period of the disc equals T and the logarithmic damping decrement, λ.

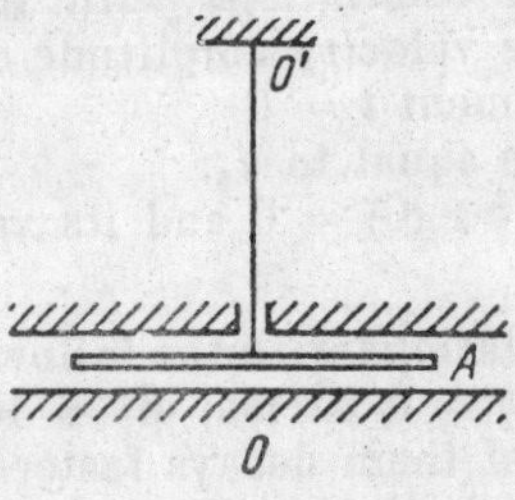

Fig. 4.24.

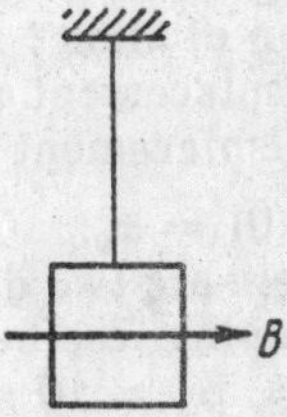

Fig. 4.25.

4.81. A conductor in the shape of a square frame with side a suspended by an elastic thread is located in a uniform horizontal magnetic field with induction B. In equilibrium the plane of the frame is parallel to the vector $\mathbf{B}$ (Fig. 4.25). Having been displaced from the equilibrium position, the frame performs small oscillations about a vertical axis passing through its centre. The moment of inertia of the frame relative to that axis is equal to I, its electric resistance is R. Neglecting the inductance of the frame, find the time interval after which the amplitude of the frame's deviation angle decreases e-fold.

4.82. A bar of mass $m = 0.50$ kg lying on a horizontal plane with a friction coefficient $k = 0.10$ is attached to the wall by means of a horizontal non-deformed spring. The stiffness of the spring is equal to $\varkappa = 2.45$ N/cm, its mass is negligible. The bar was displaced so that the spring was stretched by $x_0 = 3.0$ cm, and then released. Find:

(a) the period of oscillation of the bar;

(b) the total number of oscillations that the bar performs until it stops completely.

4.83. A ball of mass m can perform undamped harmonic oscillations about the point $x = 0$ with natural frequency ω_0. At the moment $t = 0$, when the ball was in equilibrium, a force $F_x = F_0 \cos \omega t$ coinciding with the x axis was applied to it. Find the law of forced oscillation $x(t)$ for that ball.

4.84. A particle of mass m can perform undamped harmonic oscillations due to an electric force with coefficient k. When the particle was in equilibrium, a permanent force F was applied to it for τ seconds. Find the oscillation amplitude that the particle acquired after the action of the force ceased. Draw the approximate plot $x(t)$ of oscillations. Investigate possible cases.

4.85. A ball of mass m when suspended by a spring stretches the latter by Δl. Due to external vertical force varying according to a harmonic law with amplitude F_0 the ball performs forced oscillations. The logarithmic damping decrement is equal to λ. Neglecting the mass of the spring, find the angular frequency of the external force at which the displacement amplitude of the ball is maximum. What is the magnitude of that amplitude?

4.86. The forced harmonic oscillations have equal displacement amplitudes at frequencies $\omega_1 = 400\ \text{s}^{-1}$ and $\omega_2 = 600\ \text{s}^{-1}$ Find the resonance frequency at which the displacement amplitude is maximum.

4.87. The velocity amplitude of a particle is equal to half the maximum value at the frequencies ω_1 and ω_2 of external harmonic force. Find:

(a) the frequency corresponding to the velocity resonance;

(b) the damping coefficient β and the damped oscillation frequency ω of the particle.

4.88. A certain resonance curve describes a mechanical oscillating system with logarithmic damping decrement $\lambda = 1.60$. For this curve find the ratio of the maximum displacement amplitude to the displacement amplitude at a very low frequency.

4.89. Due to the external vertical force $F_x = F_0 \cos \omega t$ a body suspended by a spring performs forced steady-state oscillations according to the law $x = a \cos(\omega t - \varphi)$. Find the work performed by the force F during one oscillation period.

4.90. A ball of mass $m = 50$ g is suspended by a weightless spring with stiffness $\varkappa = 20.0$ N/m. Due to external vertical harmonic force with frequency $\omega = 25.0\ \text{s}^{-1}$ the ball performs steady-state oscillations with amplitude $a = 1.3$ cm. In this case the displacement of the ball lags in phase behind the external force by $\varphi = \frac{3}{4}\pi$. Find:

(a) the quality factor of the given oscillator;

(b) the work performed by the external force during one oscillation period.

4.91. A ball of mass m suspended by a weightless spring can perform vertical oscillations with damping coefficient β. The natural oscillation frequency is equal to ω_0. Due to the external vertical force varying as $F = F_0 \cos \omega t$ the ball performs steady-state harmonic oscillations. Find:

(a) the mean power $\langle P \rangle$, developed by the force F, averaged over one oscillation period;

(b) the frequency ω of the force F at whcih $\langle P \rangle$ is maximum; what is $\langle P \rangle_{max}$ equal to?

4.92. An external harmonic force F whose frequency can be varied, with amplitude maintained constant, acts in a vertical direction on a ball suspended by a weightless spring. The damping coefficeint is η times less than the natural oscillation frequency ω_0 of the ball. How much, in per cent, does the mean power $\langle P \rangle$ developed by the force F at the frequency of displacement resonance differ from the maximum mean power $\langle P \rangle_{max}$? Averaging is performed over one oscillation period.

4.93. A uniform horizontal disc fixed at its centre to an elastic vertical rod performs forced torsional oscillations due to the moment of forces $N_z = N_m \cos \omega t$. The oscillations obey the law $\varphi = \varphi_m \cos(\omega t - \alpha)$. Find:

(a) the work performed by friction forces acting on the disc during one oscillation period;

(b) the quality factor of the given oscillator if the moment of inertia of the disc relative to the axis is equal to I.

4.2. ELECTRIC OSCILLATIONS

• Damped oscillation in a circuit

$$q = q_m e^{-\beta t} \cos(\omega t + \alpha),$$

where

$$\omega = \sqrt{\omega_0^2 - \beta^2}, \quad \omega_0 = \frac{1}{\sqrt{LC}}, \quad \beta = \frac{R}{2L} \qquad (4.2a)$$

• Logarithmic damping decrement λ and quality factor Q of a circuit are defined by Eqs. (4.1d). When damping is low:

$$\lambda = \pi R \sqrt{\frac{C}{L}}, \quad Q = \frac{1}{R}\sqrt{\frac{L}{C}} \qquad (4.2b)$$

• Steady-state forced oscillation in a circuit with a voltage $V = V_m \cos \omega t$ connected in series:

$$I = I_m \cos(\omega t - \varphi), \qquad (4.2c)$$

where

$$I_m = \frac{V_m}{\sqrt{R^2 + \left(\omega L - \frac{1}{\omega C}\right)^2}} \qquad (4.2d)$$

$$\tan \varphi = \frac{\omega L - \frac{1}{\omega C}}{R}$$

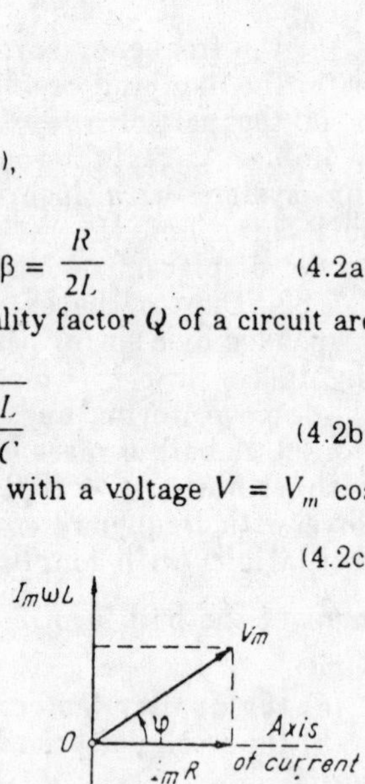

Fig. 4.26.

The corresponding vector diagram for voltages is shwon in Fig. 4.26.

• Power generated in an ac circuit.

$$P = VI \cos \varphi, \qquad (4.2e)$$

where V and I are the effective values of voltage and current:

$$V = V_m/\sqrt{2}, \quad I = I_m/\sqrt{2} \qquad (4.2f)$$

4.94. Due to a certain cause the free electrons in a plane copper plate shifted over a small distance x at right angles to its surface. As a result, a surface charge and a corresponding restoring force emerged, giving rise to so-called plasma oscillations. Find the angular frequency of these oscillations if the free electron concentration in copper is $n = 0.85 \cdot 10^{29}$ m^{-1}.

4.95. An oscillating circuit consisting of a capacitor with capacitance C and a coil of inductance L maintains free undamped oscillations with voltage amplitude across the capacitor equal to V_m. For an arbitrary moment of time find the relation between the current I in the circuit and the voltage V across the capacitor. Solve this roblem using Ohm's law and then the energy conservation law.

4.96. An oscillating circuit consists of a capacitor with capacitance C, a coil of inductance L with negligible resistnace, and a switch. With the switch disconnected, the capacitor was charged to a voltage V_m and then at the moment $t = 0$ the switch was closed. Find:

(a) the current $I(t)$ in the circuit as a function of time;

(b) the emf of self-inductance in the coil at the moments when the electric energy of the capacitor is equal to that of the current in the coil.

4.97. In an oscillating circuit consisting of a parallel-plate capacitor and an inductance coil with negligible active resistance the oscillations with energy W are sustained. The capacitor plates were slowly drawn apart to increase the oscillation frequency η-fold. What work was done in the process?

4.98. In an oscillating circuit shown in Fig. 4.27 the coil inductance is equal to $L = 2.5$ mH and the capacitor have capacitances $C_1 = 2.0$ μF and $C_2 = 3.0$ μF. The capacitors were charged to a voltage $V = 180$ V, and then the switch Sw was closed. Find:

(a) the natural oscillation frequency:

(b) the peak value of the current flowing through the coil.

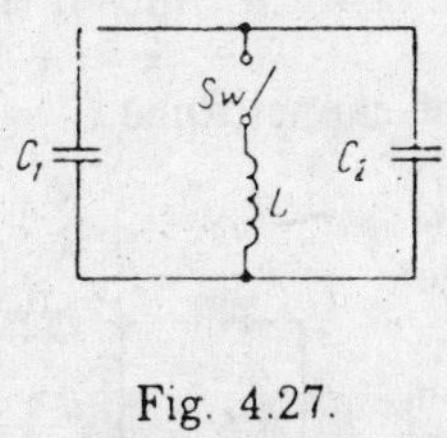

Fig. 4.27.

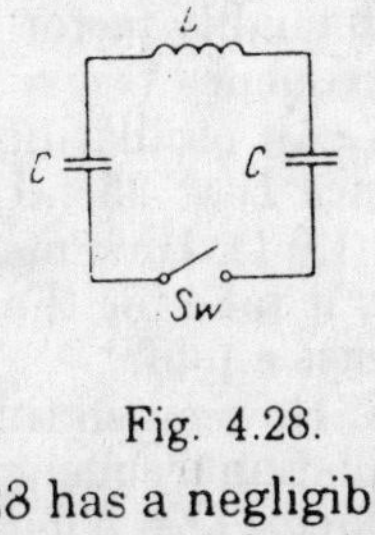

Fig. 4.28.

4.99. An electric circuit shown in Fig. 4.28 has a negligibly small active resistance. The left-hand capacitor was charged to a voltage V_0 and then at the moment $t = 0$ the switch Sw was closed. Find the time dependence of the voltage in left and right capacitors.

4.100. An oscillating circuit consists of an inductance coil L and a capacitor with capacitance C. The resistance of the coil and the lead wires is negligible. The coil is placed in a permanent magnetic field so that the total flux passing through all the turns of the coil is equal to Φ. At the moment $t = 0$ the magnetic field was switched off. Assuming the switching off time to be negligible compared to the natural oscillation period of the circuit, find the circuit current as a function of time t.

4.101. The free damped oscillations are maintained in a circuit, such that the voltage cross the capacitor varies as $V = V_m e^{-\beta t} \cos \omega t$. Find the moments of time when the modulus of the voltage across the capacitor reaches

(a) peak values;

(b) maximum (extremum) values.

4.102. A certain oscillating circuit consists of a capacitor with capacitance C, a coil with inductance L and active resistance R, and a switch. When the switch was disconnected, the capacitor was charged; then the switch was closed and oscillatins set in. Find the ratio of the voltage across the capacitor to its peak value at the moment immediately after closing the switch.

4.103. A circuit with capacitance C and inductance L generates free damped oscillations with current varying with time as $I = I_m e^{\beta t} \sin \omega t$. find the voltage across the capacitor as a function of time, and in particular, at the moment $t = 0$.

4.104. An oscillating circuit consists of a capacitor with capacitance $C = 40\ \mu F$ and a coil with inductance $L = 2.0$ mH and active resitance $R = 10\ \Omega$. Find the ratio of the energy of the coil's magnetic field to that of the capacitor's electric field at the moment when the current has the maximum value.

4.105. An oscillating circuit consists of two coils connected in series whose inductances are L_1 and L_2, active resistances are R_1 and R_2, and mutual inductance is negligible. These coils are to be replaced by one, keeping the frequency and the quality factor of the circuit constant. Find the inductance and the active resistance of such a coil.

4.106. How soon does the current amplitude in an oscillating circuit with quality factor $Q = 5000$ decrease $\eta = 2.0$ times if the oscillation frequency is $\upsilon = 2.2$ MHz?

4.107. An oscillating circuit consists of capacitance $C = 10\ \mu F$, inductance $L = 25$ mH, and active resistance R 1.0 Ω. How many oscillation periods does it take for the current amplitude to decrease e-fold?

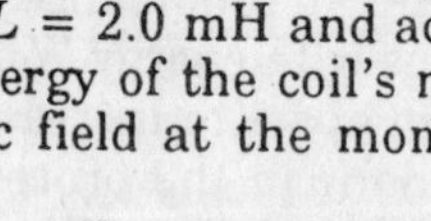

Fig. 4.29.

4.108. How much (in per cent) does the free oscillation frequency ω of a circuit with quality factor $Q = 5.0$ differ from the natural oscillation frequency ω_0 of that circuit?

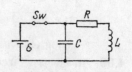

4.109. In a circuit shown in Fig. 4.29 the battery emf of equal to $\xi = 2.0$ V, its internal resistance is $r = 9.0\ \Omega$, the capacitance of the capacitor is $C = 10\ \mu F$, the coil inductance is $L = 100$ mH, and the resistance is $R = 1.0\ \Omega$. At a certain moment the switch Sw was disconnected. Find the energy of oscillations in the circuit

(a) immediately after the switch was disconnected;

(b) $t = 0.30$ s after the switch was disconnected.

4.110. Damped oscillations are induced in a circuit whose quality factor is $Q = 50$ and natural oscillation frequency is $\nu_0 = 5.5$ kHz. How soon will the energy stored in the circuit decrease $\eta = 2.0$ times?

4.111. An oscillating circuit incorporates a leaking capacitor. Its capacitance is equal to C and active resistance to R. The coil inductance is L. The resistance of the coil and the wires is negligible. Find:

(a) the damped oscillation frequency of such a circuit;

(b) its quality factor.

4.112. Find the quality factor of a circuit with capacitance $C = 2.0\ \mu$F and inductance $L = 5.0$ mH if the maintenance of undamped oscillations in the circuit with the voltage amplitude across the capacitor being equal to $V_m = 1.0$ V requires a power $\langle P \rangle = 0.10$ mW. The damping of oscillations is sufficiently low.

4.113. What mean power should be fed to an oscillating circuit with active resistance $R = 0.45\ \Omega$ to maintain undamped harmonic oscillations with current amplitude $I_m = 30$ mA?

4.114. An oscillating circuit consists of a capacitor with capacitance $C = 1.2$ nF and a coil with inductance $L = 6.0\ \mu$H and active resistance $R = 0.50\ \Omega$. What mean power should be fed to the circuit to maintain undamped harmonic oscillations with voltage amplitude across the capacitor being equal to $V_m = 10$ V?

4.115. Find the damped oscillation frequency of the circuit shown in Fig. 4.30. The capacitance C, inductance L, and active resistance R are supposed to be known. Find how must C, L, and R be interrelated to make oscillations possible.

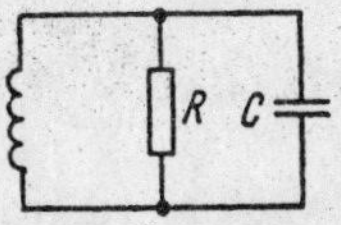

Fig. 4.30.

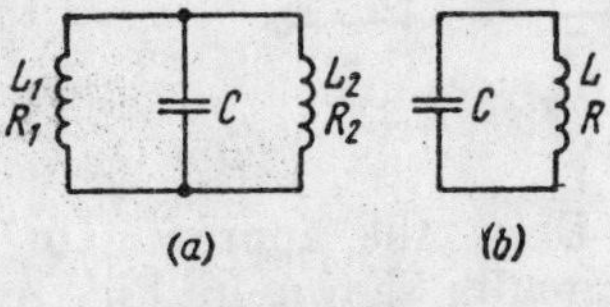

Fig. 4.31.

4.116. There are two oscillating circuits (Fig. 4.31) with capacitors of equal capacitances. How must inductances and active resistances of the coils be interrelated for the frequencies and damping of free oscillations in both circuits to be equal? The mutual inductance of coils in the left circuit is negligible.

4.117. A circuit consists of a capacitor with capacitance C and a coil of inductance L connected in series, as well as a switch and a resistance equal to the critical value for this circuit. With the switch disconnected, the capacitor was charged to a voltage V_0, and at the moment $t = 0$ the switch was closed. Find the current I in the circuit as a function of time t. What is I_{max} equal to?

4.118. A coil with active resistance R and inductance L was connected at the moment $t = 0$ to a source of voltage $V = V_m \cos \omega t$. Find the current in the coil as a function of time t.

4.119. A circuit consisting of a capacitor with capacitance C and a resistance R connected in series was connected at the moment $t = 0$ to a source of ac voltage $V = V_m \cos \omega t$. Find the current in the circuit as a function of time t.

4.120. A long one-layer solenoid tightly wound of wire with resistivity ρ has n turns per unit length. The thickness of the wire insulation is negligible. The cross-sectional radius of the solenoid is equal to a. Find the phase difference between current and alternating voltage fed to the solenoid with frequency ν.

4.121. A circuit consisting of a capacitor and an active resistance $R = 110\ \Omega$ connected in series is fed an alternating voltage with amplitude $V_m = 110$ V. In this case the amplitude of steady-state current is equal to $I_m = 0.50$ A. Find the phase difference between the current and the voltage fed.

4.122. Fig. 4.32 illustrates the simplest ripple filter. A voltage $V = V_0 (1 + \cos \omega t)$ is fed to the left input. Find:

(a) the output voltage $V'(t)$;

(b) the magnitude of the product RC at which the output amplitude of alternating voltage component is $\eta = 7.0$ times less than the direct voltage component, if $\omega = 314\ s^{-1}$.

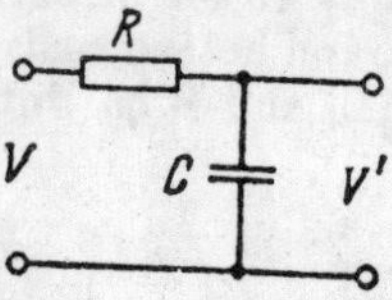

Fig. 4.32.

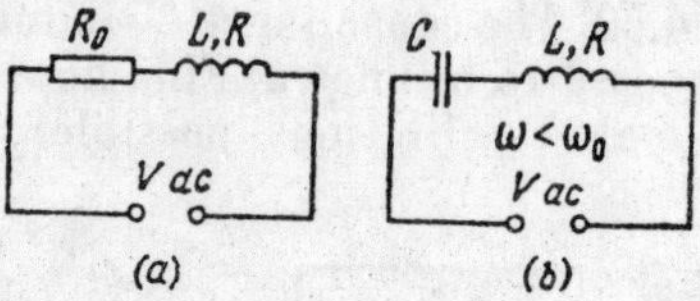

Fig. 4.33.

4.123. Draw the approximate voltage vector diagrams in the electric circuits shown in Fig. 4.33 *a*, *b*. The external voltage V is assumed to be alternating harmonically with frequency ω.

4.124. A series circuit consisting of a capacitor with capacitance $C = 22\ \mu F$ and a coil with active resistance $R = 20\ \Omega$ and inductance $L = 0.35$ H is connected to a source of alternating voltage with amplitude $V_m = 180$ V and frequency $\omega = 314\ s^{-1}$. Find:

(a) the current amplitude in the circuit;

(b) the phase difference between the current and the external voltage;

(c) the amplitudes of voltage across the capacitor and the coil.

4.125. A series circuit consisting of a capacitor with capacitance C, a resistance R, and a coil with inductance L and negligible active resistance is connected to an oscillator whose frequency can be varied without changing the voltage amplitude. Find the frequency at which the voltage amplitude is maximum

(a) across the capacitor;

(b) across the coil.

4.126. An alternating voltage with frequency $\omega = 314$ s^{-1} and amplitude $V_m = 180$ V is fed to a series circuit consisting of a capacitor and a coil with active resistance $R = 40\ \Omega$ and inductance $L = 0.36$ H. At what value of the capacitor's capacitance will the voltage amplitude across the coil be maximum? What is this amplitude equal to? What is the corresponding voltage amplitude across the condenser?

4.127. A capacitor with capacitance C whose interelectrode space is filled up with poorly conducting medium with active resistance R is connected to a source of alternating voltage $V = V_m \cos \omega t$. Find the time dependence of the steady-state current flowing in lead wires. The resistance of the wires is to be neglected.

4.128. An oscillating circuit consists of a capacitor of capacitance C and a solenoid with inductance L_1. The solenoid is inductively connected with a short-circuited coil having an inductance L_2 and a negligible active resistance. Their mutual inductance coefficient is equal to L_{12}. Find the natural frequency of the given oscillating circuit.

4.129. Find the quality factor of an oscillating circuit connected in series to a source of alternating emf if at resonance the voltage across the capacitor is n times that of the source.

4.130. An oscillating circuit consisting of a coil and a capacitor connected in series is fed an alternating emf, with coil inductance being chosen to provide the maximum current in the circuit. Find the quality factor of the system, provided an n-fold increase of inductance results in an η-fold decrease of the current in the circuit.

4.131. A series circuit consisting of a capacitor and a coil with active resistance is connected to a source of harmonic voltage whose frequency can be varied, keeping the voltage amplitude constant. At frequencies ω_1 and ω_2 the current amplitudes are n times less than the resonance amplitude. Find:

(a) the resonance frequency;

(b) the quality factor of the circuit.

4.132. Demonstrate that at low damping the quality factor Q of a circuit maintaining forced oscillations is approximately equal to $\omega_0/\Delta\omega$, where ω_0 is the natural oscillation frequency, $\Delta\omega$ is the width of the resonance curve $I(\omega)$ at the "height" which is $\sqrt{2}$ times less than the resonance current amplitude.

4.133. A circuit consisting of a capacitor and a coil connected in series is fed two alternating voltages of equal amplitudes but different frequencies. The frequency of one voltage is equal to the natural oscillation frequency (ω_0) of the circuit, the frequency of the other voltage is η times higher. Find the ratio of the current amplitudes

(I_0/I) generated by the two voltages if the quality factor of the system is equal to Q. Calculate this ratio for $Q = 10$ and 100, if $\eta = 1.10$.

4.134. It takes t_0 hours for a direct current I_0 to charge a storage battery. How long will it take to charge such a battery from the mains using a half-wave rectifier, if the effective current value is also equal to I_0?

4.135. Find the effective value of current if its mean value is I_0 and its time dependence is

(a) shown in Fig. 4.34;

(b) $I \sim |\sin \omega t|$.

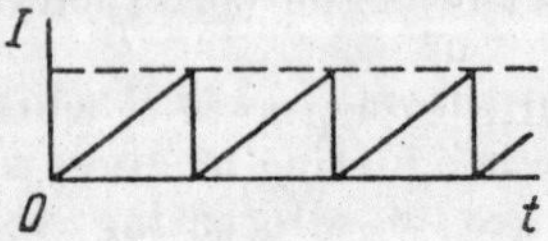

Fig. 4.34.

4.136. A solenoid with inductance $L = 7$ mH and active resistance $R = 44\ \Omega$ is first connected to a source of direct voltage V_0 and then to a source of sinusoidal voltage with effective value $V = V_0$. At what frequency of the oscillator will the power consumed by the solenoid be $\eta = 5.0$ times less than in the former case?

4.137. A coil with inductive resistance $X_L = 30\ \Omega$ and impedance $Z = 50\ \Omega$ is connected to the mains with effective voltage value $V = 100$ V. Find the phase difference between the current and the voltage, as well as the heat power generated in the coil.

4.138. A coil with inductance $L = 0.70$ H and active resistance $r = 20\ \Omega$ is connected in series with an inductance-free resistance R. An alternating voltage with effective value $V = 220$ V and frequency $\omega = 314\ \text{s}^{-1}$ is applied across the terminals of this circuit. At what value of the resistance R will the maximum heat power be generated in the circuit? What is it equal to?

4.139. A circuit consisting of a capacitor and a coil in series is connected to the mains. Varying the capacitance of the capacitor, the heat power generated in the coil was increased $n = 1.7$ times. How much (in per cent) was the value of $\cos \varphi$ changed in the process?

4.140. A source of sinusoidal emf with constant voltage is connected in series with an oscillating circuit with quality factor $Q = 100$. At a certain frequency of the external voltage the heat power generated in the circuit reaches the maximum value. How much (in per cent) should this frequency be shifted to decrease the power generated $n = 2.0$ times?

4.141. A series circuit consisting of an inductance-free resistance $R = 0.16$ kΩ and a coil with active resistance is connected to the mains with effective voltage $V = 220$ V. Find the heat power generated in the coil if the effective voltage values across the resistance R and the coil are equal to $V_1 = 80$ V and $V_2 = 180$ V respectively.

4.142. A coil and an inductance-free resistance $R = 25\ \Omega$ are connected in parallel to the ac mains. Find the heat power generated in the coil provided a current $I = 0.90$ A is drawn from the mains. The coil and the resistance R carry currents $I_1 = 0.50$ A and $I_2 = 0.60$ A respectively.

4.143. An alternating current of frequency $\omega = 314\ \text{s}^{-1}$ is fed to a circuit consisting of a capacitor of capacitance $C = 73\ \mu\text{F}$ and an active resistance $R = 100\ \Omega$ connected in parallel. Find the impedance of the circuit.

4.144. Draw the approximate vector diagrams of currents in the circuits shown in Fig. 4.35. The voltage applied across the points A and B is assumed to be sinusoidal; the parameters of each circuit are so chosen that the total current I_0 lags in phase behind the external voltage by an angle φ.

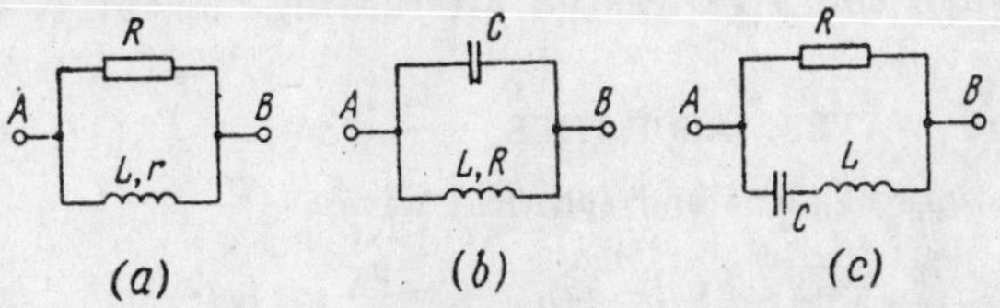

Fig. 4.35.

4.145. A capacitor with capacitance $C = 1.0\ \mu\text{F}$ and a coil with active resistance $R = 0.10\ \Omega$ and inductance $L = 1.0$ mH are connected in parallel to a source of sinusoidal voltage $V = 31$ V. Find:

(a) the frequency ω at which the resonance sets in;

(b) the effective value of the fed current in resonance, as well as the corresponding currents flowing through the coil and through the capacitor.

4.146. A capacitor with capacitance C and a coil with active resistance R and inductance L are connected in parallel to a source of sinusoidal voltage of frequency ω. Find the phase difference between the current fed to the circuit and the source voltage.

4.147. A circuit consists of a capacitor with capacitance C and a coil with active resistance R and inductance L connected in parallel. Find the impedance of the circuit at frequency ω of alternating voltage.

4.148. A ring of thin wire with active resistance R and inductance L rotates with constant angular velocity ω in the external uniform magnetic field perpendicular to the rotation axis. In the process, the flux of magnetic induction of external field across the ring varies with time as $\Phi = \Phi_0 \cos \omega t$. Demonstrate that

(a) the inductive current in the ring varies with time as $I = I_m \sin (\omega t - \varphi)$, where $I_m = \omega\Phi_0/\sqrt{R^2 + \omega^2 L^2}$ with $\tan \varphi = \omega L/R$;

(b) the mean mechanical power developed by external forces to maintain rotation is defined by the formula $P = \frac{1}{2}\omega^2\Phi_0^2 R/(R^2 + \omega^2 L^2)$.

4.149. A wooden core (Fig. 4.36) supports two coils: coil *1* with inductance L_1 and short-circuited coil *2* with active resistance R and inductance L_2. The mutual inductance of the coils depends on

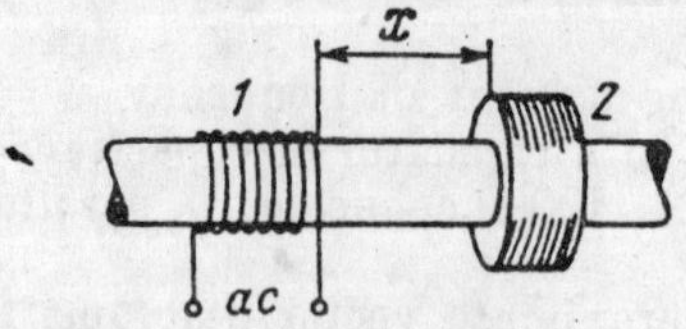

Fig. 4.36.

the distance x between them according to the law $L_{12}(x)$. Find the mean (averaged over time) value of the interaction force between the coils when coil *1* carries an alternating current $I_1 = I_0 \cos \omega t$.

4.3. ELASTIC WAVES. ACOUSTICS

- Equations of plane and spherical waves:

$$\xi = a \cos(\omega t - kx), \qquad \xi = \frac{a_0}{r} \cos(\omega t - kr). \tag{4.3a}$$

In the case of a homogeneous absorbing medium the factors $e^{-\gamma x}$ and $e^{-\gamma r}$ respectively appear in the formulas, where γ is the wave damping coefficient.

- Wave equation:

$$\frac{\partial^2 \xi}{\partial x^2} + \frac{\partial^2 \xi}{\partial y^2} + \frac{\partial^2 \xi}{\partial z^2} = \frac{1}{v^2} \frac{\partial^2 \xi}{\partial t^2}. \tag{4.3b}$$

- Phase velocity of longitudinal waves in an elastic medium ($v_{\parallel}$) and transverse waves in a string ($v_{\perp}$):

$$v_{\parallel} = \sqrt{E/\rho}, \quad v_{\perp} = \sqrt{T/\rho_1}, \tag{4.3c}$$

where E is Young's modulus, ρ is the density of the medium, T is the tension of the string, ρ_1 is its linear density.

- Volume density of energy of an elastic wave:

$$w = \rho a^2 \omega^2 \sin^2(\omega t - kx), \quad \langle w \rangle = {}^1/_2 \rho a^2 \omega^2. \tag{4.3d}$$

- Energy flow density, or the Umov vector for a travelling wave:

$$\mathbf{j} = w\mathbf{v}, \quad \langle \mathbf{j} \rangle = {}^1/_2 \rho a^2 \omega^2 \mathbf{v}. \tag{4.3e}$$

- Standing wave equation:

$$\xi = a \cos kx \cdot \cos \omega t. \tag{4.3f}$$

- Acoustical Doppler effect:

$$\nu = \nu_0 \frac{v + v_{ob}}{v - v_s}. \tag{4.3g}$$

- Loudness level (in bels):

$$L = \log(I/I_0). \tag{4.3h}$$

- Relation between the intensity I of a sound wave and the pressure oscillation amplitude $(\Delta p)_m$:

$$I = (\Delta p)_m^2 / 2\rho v. \tag{4.3i}$$

4.150. How long will it take sound waves to travel the distance l between the points A and B if the air temperature between them varies linearly from T_1 to T_2? The velocity of sound propagation in air is equal to $v = \alpha/\sqrt{T}$, where α is a constant.

4.151. A plane harmonic wave with frequency ω propagates at a velocity v in a direction forming angles α, β, γ with the x, y, z axes. Find the phase difference between the oscillations at the points of medium with coordinates x_1, y_1, z_1 and x_2, y_2, z_2.

4.152. A plane wave of freuqency ω propagates so that a certain phae of oscillation moves along the x, y, z axes with velocities v_1, v_2, v_3 respectively. Find the wave vector **k**, assuming the unit vectors e_x, e_y, e_z of the coordinate axes to be assigned.

4.153. A plane elastic wave $\xi = a \cos(\omega t - \mathrm{k}x)$ propagates in a medium K. Find the equation of this wave in a refernce frame K' moving in the positive direction of the x axis with a constant velocity V relative to the medium K. Investigate the expression obtained.

4.154. Demonstrate that any differentiable function $f(t + \alpha x)$, where α is a constant, provides a solution of wave equation. What is the physical meaning of the constant α?

4.155. The equation of a travelling plane sound wave has the form $\xi = 60 \cos(1800t - 5.3x)$, where ξ is expressed in micrometres, t in seconds, and x in metres. Find:

(a) the ratio of the displacement amplitude, with whch the particles of medium oscillate, to the wavelength;

(b) the velocity oscillation amplitude of particles of the medium and its ratio to the wave propagation velocity;

(c) the oscillation amplitude of relative deformation of the medium and its relation to the velocity oscillation amplitude of particles of the medium.

4.156. A plane wave $\xi = a \cos(\omega t - \mathrm{k}x)$ propagates in a homogeneous elastic medium. For the moment $t = 0$ draw.

(a) the plots of ξ, $\partial\xi/\partial t$, and $\partial\xi/\partial x$ vs x;

(a) the velocity direction of the particles of the medium at the points where $\xi = 0$, for the cases of longitudinal and transverse waves;

(b) the approximate plot of density distribution r (x) of the medium for the case of longitudinal waves.

4.157. A plane elastic wave $\xi = ae^{-\gamma x} \cos(\omega t - \mathrm{k}x)$, where a γ, ω, and k are constants, propagates in a homogeneous medium. Find the phase differece between the oscillations of the points where the perticles' displacement amplitudes differ by $\eta = 1.0\%$, if $\gamma = 0.42\ \mathrm{m}^{-1}$ and the wavelength is $\lambda = 50$ cm.

4.158. Find the radius vector defining the positin of a point source of spherical waves if that source is known to be located on the straight line between the points with radius vectors $\mathbf{r}_1$ and $\mathbf{r}_2$ at which the oscillation amplitudes of particles of the medium are equal to a_1 and a_2. The damping of the wave is negligible, the medium is homogeneous.

4.159. A point isotropic source generates sound oscillations with frequency $\nu = 1.45$ kHz. At a distance $r_0 = 5.0$ m from the source the displacement amplitude of particles of the medium is equal to $a_0 = 50$ μm, and at the point A located at a distance $r = 10.0$ m from the source the displacement amplitude is $\eta = 3.0$ times less than a_0. Find:

(a) the damping coefficient γ of the wave;

(b) the velocity oscillation amplitude of particles of the medium at the point A.

4.160. Two plane waves propagate in a homogeneous elastic medium, one along the x axis and the other along the y axis: $\xi_1 = a \cos(\omega t - kx)$, $\xi_2 = a \cos(\omega t - ky)$. Find the wave motion pattern of particles in the plane xy if both waves

(a) are transverse and their oscillation directions coincide;

(b) are longitudinal.

4.161. A plane undamped harmonic wave propagates in a medium. Find the mean space density of the total oscillation energy $\langle w \rangle$, if at any point of the medium the space density of energy becomes equal to w_0 one-sixth of an oscillation period after passing the displacement maximum.

4.162. A point isotropic sound source is located on the perpendicular to the plane of a ring drawn through the centre O of the ring. The distance between the point O and the source is $l = 1.00$ m, the radius of the ring is $R = 0.50$ m. Find the mean energy flow across the area enclosed by the ring if at the point O the intensity of sound is equal to $I_0 = 30$ μW/m². The damping of the waves is negligible.

4.163. A point isotropic source with sonic power $P = 0.10$ W is located at the centre of a round hollow cylinder with radius $R = 1.0$ m and height $h = 2.0$ m. Assuming the sound to be completely absorbed by the walls of the cylinder, find the mean energy flow reaching the lateral surface of the cylinder.

4.164. The equation of a plane standing wave in a homogeneous elastic medium has the form $\xi = a \cos kx \cdot \cos \omega t$. Plot:

(a) ξ and $\partial\xi/\partial x$ as functions of x at the moments $t = 0$ and $t = T/2$, where T is the oscillation period;

(b) the distribution of density $\rho(x)$ of the medium at the moments $t = 0$ and $t = T/2$ in the case of longitudinal oscillations;

(c) the velocity distribution of particles of the medium at the moment $t = T/4$; indicate the directions of velocities at the antinodes, both for longitudinal and transverse oscillations.

4.165. A longitudinal standing wave $\xi = a \cos kx \cdot \cos \omega t$ is maintained in a homogeneous medium of density ρ. Find the expressions for the space density of

(a) potential energy $w_p(x, t)$;

(b) kinetic energy $w_k(x, t)$.

Plot the space density distribution of the total energy w in the space between the displacement nodes at the moments $t = 0$ and $t = T/4$, where T is the oscillation period.

4.166. A string 120 cm in length sustains a standing wave, with the points of the string at which the displacement amplitude is equal to 3.5 mm being separated by 15.0 cm. Find the maximum displacement amplitude. To which overtone do these oscillations correspond?

4.167. Find the ratio of the fundamental tone frequencies of two identical strings after one of them was stretched by $\eta_1 = 2.0\%$ and the other, by $\eta_2 = 4.0\%$. The tension is assumed to be proportional to the elongation.

4.168. Determine in what way and how many times will the fundamental tone frequency of a stretched wire change if its length is shortened by 35% and the tension increased by 70%.

4.169. To determine the sound propagation velocity in air by acoustic resonance technique one can use a pipe with a piston and a sonic membrane closing one of its ends. Find the velocity of sound if the distance between the adjacent positions of the piston at which resonance is observed at a frequency $\nu = 2000$ Hz is equal to $l = 8.5$ cm.

4.170. Find the number of possible natural oscillations of air column in a pipe whose frequencies lie below $\nu_0 = 1250$ Hz. The length of the pipe is $l = 85$ cm. The velocity of sound is $v = 340$ m/s. Consider the two cases:

(a) the pipe is closed from one end;

(b) the pipe is opened from both ends.

The open ends of the pipe are assumed to be the antinodes of displacement.

4.171. A copper rod of length $l = 50$ cm is clamped at its midpoint. Find the number of natural longitudinal oscillations of the rod in the frequency range from 20 to 50 kHz. What are those frequencies equal to?

4.172. A string of mass m is fixed at both ends. The fundamental tone oscillations are excited with circular frequency ω and maximum displacement amplitude a_{max}. Find:

(a) the maximum kinetic energy of the string;

(b) the mean kinetic energy of the string averaged over one oscillation period.

4.173. A standing wave $\xi = a \sin kx \cdot \cos \omega t$ is maintained in a homogeneous rod with cross-sectional area S and density ρ. Find the total mechanical energy confined between the sections corresponding to the adjacent displacement nodes.

4.174. A source of sonic oscillations with frequency $\nu_0 = 1000$ Hz moves at right angles to the wall with a velocity $u = 0.17$ m/s. Two stationary receivers R_1 and R_2 are located on a straight line, coinciding with the trajectory of the source, in the following succession: R_1-source-R_2-wall. Which receiver registers the beatings and what is the beat frequency? The velocity of sound is equal to $v = 340$ m/s.

4.175. A stationary observer receives sonic oscillations from two tuning forks one of which approaches, and the other recedes with the same velocity. As this takes place, the observer hears the beatings with frequency $\nu = 2.0$ Hz. Find the velocity of each tuning fork if their oscillation frequency is $\nu_0 = 680$ Hz and the velocity of sound in air is $v = 340$ m/s.

4.176. A receiver and a source of sonic oscillations of frequency $\nu_0 = 2000$ Hz are located on the x axis. The source swings harmonically along that axis with a circular frequency ω and an amplitude $a = 50$ cm. At what value of ω will the frequency bandwidth registered by the stationary receiver be equal to $\Delta\nu = 200$ Hz? The velocity of sound is equal to $v = 340$ m/s.

4.177. A source of sonic oscillations with frequency $\nu_0 = 1700$ Hz and a receiver are located at the same point. At the moment $t = 0$ the source starts receding from the receiver with constant acceleration $w = 10.0$ m/s². Assuming the velocity of sound to be equal to $v = 340$ m/s, find the oscillation frequency registered by the stationary receiver $t = 10.0$ s after the start of motion.

4.178. A source of sound with natural frequency $\nu_0 = 1.8$ kHz moves uniformly along a straight line separated from a stationary observer by a distance $l = 250$ m. The velocity of the source is equal to $\eta = 0.80$ fraction of the velocity of sound. Find:

(a) the frequency of sound received by the observer at the moment when the source gets closest to him;

(b) the distance between the source and the observer at the moment when the observer receives a frequency $\nu = \nu_0$.

4.179. A stationary source sends forth monochromatic sound. A wall approaches it with velocity $u = 33$ cm/s. The propagation velocity of sound in the medium is $v = 330$ m/s. In what way and how much, in per cent, does the wavelength of sound change on reflection from the wall?

4.180. A source of sonic oscillations with frequency $\nu_0 = 1700$ Hz and a receiver are located on the same normal to a wall. Both the source and the receiver are stationary, and the wall recedes from the source with velocity $u = 6.0$ cm/s. Find the beat frequency registered by the receiver. The velocity of sound is equal to $v = 340$ m/s.

4.181. Find the damping coefficient γ of a sound wave if at distances $r_1 = 10$ m and $r_2 = 20$ m from a point isotropic source of sound the sound wave intensity values differ by a factor $\eta = 4.5$.

4.182. A plane sound wave propagates along the x axis. The damping coefficient of the wave is $\gamma = 0.0230$ m^{-1}. At the point $x = 0$ the loudness level is $L = 60$ dB. Find:

(a) the loudness level at a point with coordinate $x = 50$ m;

(b) the coordinate x of the point at which the sound is not heard any more.

4.183. At a distance $r_0 = 20.0$ m from a point isotropic source of sound the loudness level $L_0 = 30.0$ dB. Neglecting the damping of the sound wave, find:

(a) the loudness level at a distance $r = 10.0$ m from the source;

(b) the distance from the source at which the sound is not heard.

4.184. An observer A located at a distance $r_A = 5.0$ m from a ringing tuning fork notes the sound to fade away $\tau = 19$ s later than an observer B who is located at a distance $r_B = 50$ m from the tuning fork. Find the damping coefficient β of oscillations of the tuning fork. The sound velocity $v = 340$ m/s.

4.185. A plane longitudinal harmonic wave propagates in a medium with density ρ. The velocity of the wave propagation is v. Assuming that the density variations of the medium, induced by the propagating wave, $\Delta\rho \ll \rho$, demonstrate that

(a) the pressure increment in the medium $\Delta p = -\rho v^2 (\partial\xi/\partial x)$, where $\partial\xi/\partial x$ is the relative deformation;

(b) the wave intensity is defined by Eq. (4.3i).

4.186. A ball of radius $R = 50$ cm is located in the way of propagation of a plane sound wave. The sonic wavelength is $\lambda = 20$ cm, the frequency is $\nu = 1700$ Hz, the pressure oscillation amplitude in air is $(\Delta p)_m = 3.5$ Pa. Find the mean energy flow, averaged over an oscillation period, reaching the surface of the ball.

4.187. A point A is located at a distance $r = 1.5$ m from a point isotropic source of sound of frequency $\nu = 600$ Hz. The sonic power of the source is $P = 0.80$ W. Neglecting the damping of the waves and assuming the velocity of sound in air to be equal to $v = 340$ m/s, find at the point A:

(a) the pressure oscillation amplitude $(\Delta p)_m$ and its ratio to the air pressure;

(b) the oscillation amplitude of particles of the medium; compare it with the wavelength of sound.

4.188. At a distance $r = 100$ m from a point isotropic source of sound of frequency 200 Hz the loudness level is equal to $L = 50$ dB. The audibility threshold at this frequency corresponds to the sound intensity $I_0 = 0.10$ nW/m². The damping coefficient of the sound wave is $\gamma = 5.0 \cdot 10^{-4}$ m^{-1}. Find the sonic power of the source.

4.4. ELECTROMAGNETIC WAVES. RADIATION

- Phase velocity of an electromagnetic wave:

$$v = c/\sqrt{\varepsilon\mu}, \quad \text{where } c = 1/\sqrt{\varepsilon_0\mu_0}. \tag{4.4a}$$

- In a travelling electromagnetic wave:

$$E\sqrt{\varepsilon\varepsilon_0} = H\sqrt{\mu\mu_0}. \tag{4.4b}$$

- Space density of the energy of an electromagnetic field:

$$w = \frac{\mathbf{ED}}{2} + \frac{\mathbf{BH}}{2}. \tag{4.4c}$$

- Flow density of electromagnetic energy, the Poynting vector:

$$\mathbf{S} = [\mathbf{EH}]. \tag{4.4d}$$

- Energy flow density of electric dipole radiation in a far field zone:

$$S \sim \frac{1}{r^2}\sin^2\theta. \tag{4.4e}$$

where r is the distance from the dipole, θ is the angle between the radius vector $\mathbf{r}$ and the axis of the dipole.

• Radiation power of an electric dipole with moment $\mathbf{p}(t)$ and of a charge q, moving with acceleration $\mathbf{w}$:

$$P=\frac{1}{4\pi\varepsilon_0}\frac{2\ddot{\mathbf{p}}^2}{3c^3},\quad P=\frac{1}{4\pi\varepsilon_0}\frac{2q^2\mathbf{w}^2}{3c^3}. \tag{4.4f}$$

4.189. An electromagnetic wave of frequency $\nu = 3.0$ MHz passes from vacuum into a non-magnetic medium with permittivity $\varepsilon = 4.0$. Find the increment of its wavelength.

4.190. A plane electromagnetic wave falls at right angles to the surface of a plane-parallel plate of thickness l. The plate is made of non-magnetic substance whose permittivity decreases exponentially from a value ε_1 at the front surface down to a value ε_2 at the rear one. How long does it take a given wave phase to travel across this plate?

4.191. A plane electromagnetic wave of frequency $\nu = 10$ MHz propagates in a poorly conducting medium with conductivity $\sigma = 10$ mS/m and permittivity $\varepsilon = 9$. Find the ratio of amplitudes of conduction and displacement current densities.

4.192. A plane electromagnetic wave $\mathbf{E} = \mathbf{E}_m \cos(\omega t - \mathbf{kr})$ propagates in vacuum. Assuming the vectors $\mathbf{E}_m$ and $\mathbf{k}$ to be known, find the vector $\mathbf{H}$ as a function of time t at the point with radius vector $\mathbf{r} = 0$.

4.193. A plane electromagnetic wave $\mathbf{E} = \mathbf{E}_m \cos(\omega t - \mathbf{kr})$, where $\mathbf{E}_m = E_m\mathbf{e}_y$, $\mathbf{k} = k\mathbf{e}_x$, $\mathbf{e}_x$, $\mathbf{e}_y$ are the unit vectors of the x, y axes, propagates in vacuum. Find the vector $\mathbf{H}$ at the point with radius vector $\mathbf{r} = x\mathbf{e}_x$ at the moment (a) $t = 0$, (b) $t = t_0$. Consider the case when $E_m = 160$ V/m, $k = 0.51$ m^{-1}, $x = 7.7$ m, and $t_0 = 33$ ns.

4.194. A plane electromagnetic wave $\mathbf{E} = \mathbf{E}_m \cos(\omega t - kx)$ propagating in vacuum induces the emf $\mathscr{E}_{ind}$ in a square frame with side l. The orientation of the frame is shown in Fig. 4.37. Find the amplitude value $\mathscr{E}_{ind}$, if $E_m = 0.50$ mV/m, the frequency $\nu = 5.0$ MHz and $l = 50$ cm.

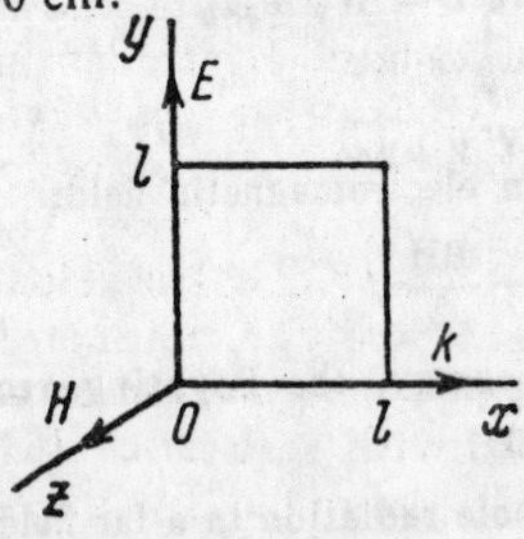

Fig. 4.37.

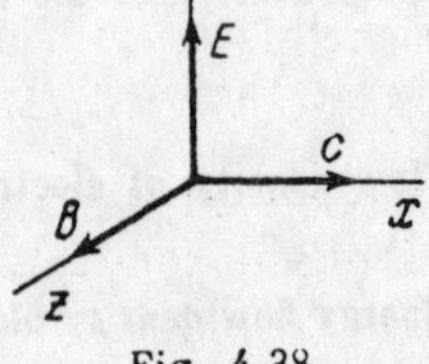

Fig. 4.38.

4.195. Proceeding from Maxwell's equations show that in the case of a plane electromagnetic wave (Fig. 4.38) propagating in vacuum the following relations hold:

$$\frac{\partial E}{\partial t} = -c^2 \frac{\partial B}{\partial x}, \quad \frac{\partial B}{\partial t} = -\frac{\partial E}{\partial x}.$$

4.196. Find the mean Poynting vector $\langle \mathbf{S} \rangle$ of a plane electromagnetic wave $\mathbf{E} = \mathbf{E}_m \cos(\omega t - \mathbf{kr})$ if the wave propagates in vacuum.

4.197. A plane harmonic electromagnetic wave with plane polarization propagates in vacuum. The electric component of the wave has a strength amplitude $E_m = 50$ mV/m, the frequency is $\nu = 100$ MHz. Find:

(a) the efficient value of the displacement current density;

(b) the mean energy flow density averaged over an oscillation period.

4.198. A ball of radius $R = 50$ cm is located in a non-magnetic medium with permittivity $\varepsilon = 4.0$. In that medium a plane electromagnetic wave propagates, the strength amplitude of whose electric component is equal to $E_m = 200$ V/m. What amount of energy reaches the ball during a time interval $t = 1.0$ min?

4.199. A standing electromagnetic wave with electric component $\mathbf{E} = \mathbf{E}_m \cos kx \cdot \cos \omega t$ is sustained along the x axis in vacuum. Find the magnetic component of the wave $\mathbf{B}(x, t)$. Draw the approximate distribution pattern of the wave's electric and magnetic components ($\mathbf{E}$ and $\mathbf{B}$) at the moments $t = 0$ and $t = T/4$, where T is the oscillation period.

4.200. A standing electromagnetic wave $\mathbf{E} = \mathbf{E}_m \cos kx \cdot \cos \omega t$ is sustained along the x axis in vacuum. Find the projection of the Poynting vector on the x axis $S_x(x, t)$ and the mean value of that projection averaged over an oscillation period.

4.201. A parallel-plate air capacitor whose electrodes are shaped as discs of radius $R = 6.0$ cm is connected to a source of an alternating sinusoidal voltage with frequency $\omega = 1000$ s^{-1}. Find the ratio of peak values of magnetic and electric energies within the capacitor.

4.202. An alternating sinusoidal current of frequency $\omega = 1000$ s^{-1} flows in the winding of a straight solenoid whose cross-sectional radius is equal to $R = 6.0$ cm. Find the ratio of peak values of electric and magnetic energies within the solenoid.

4.203. A parallel-plate capacity whose electrodes are shaped as round discs is charged slowly. Demonstrate that the flux of the Poynting vector across the capacitor's lateral surface is equal to the increment of the capacitor's energy per unit time. The dissipation of field at the edge is to be neglected in calculations.

4.204. A current I flows along a straight conductor with round cross-section. Find the flux of the Poynting vector across the lateral surface of the conductor's segment with resistance R.

4.205. Non-relativistic protons accelerated by a potential difference U form a round beam with current I. Find the magnitude and direction of the Poynting vector outside the beam at a distance r from its axis.

4.206. A current flowing in the winding of a long straight solenoid is increased at a sufficiently slow rate. Demonstrate that the rate at which the energy of the magnetic field in the solenoid increases is equal to the flux of the Poynting vector across the lateral surface of the solenoid.

4.207. Fig. 4.39 illustrates a segment of a double line carrying direct current whose direction is indicated by the arrows. Taking into account that the potential $\varphi_2 > \varphi_1$, and making use of the Poynting vector, establish on which side (left or right) the source of the current is located.

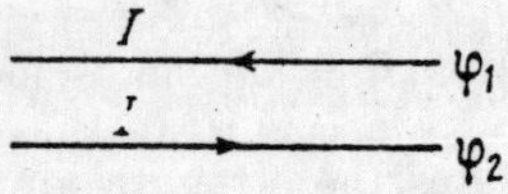

Fig. 4.39.

4.208. The energy is transferred from a source of constant voltage V to a consumer by means of a long straight coaxial cable with negligible active resistance. The consumed current is I. Find the energy flux across the cross-section of the cable. The conductive sheath is supposed to be thin.

4.209. A source of ac voltage $V = V_0 \cos \omega t$ delivers energy to a consumer by means of a long straight coaxial cable with negligible active resistance. The current in the circuit varies as $I = I_0 \cos (\omega t - \varphi)$. Find the time-averaged energy flux through the cross-section of the cable. The sheath is thin.

4.210. Demonstrate that at the boundary between two media the normal components of the Poynting vector are continuous, i.e. $S_{1n} = S_{2n}$.

4.211. Demonstrate that a closed system of charged non-relativistic particles with identical specific charges emits no dipole radiation.

4.212. Find the mean radiation power of an electron performing harmonic oscillations with amplitude $a = 0.10$ nm and frequency $\omega = 6.5 \cdot 10^{14}$ s^{-1}

4.213. Find the radiation power developed by a non-relativistic particle with charge e and mass m, moving along a circular orbit of radius R in the field of a stationary point charge q.

4.214. A particle with charge e and mass m flies with non-relativistic velocity v at a distance b past a stationary particle with charge q. Neglecting the bending of the trajectory of the moving particle, find the energy lost by this particle due to radiation during the total flight time.

4.215. A non-relativistic proton enters a half-space along the normal to the transverse uniform magnetic field whose induction equals $B = 1.0$ T. Find the ratio of the energy lost by the proton due to radiation during its motion in the field to its initial kinetic energy.

4.216. A non-relativistic charged particle moves in a transverse uniform magnetic field with induction B. Find the time dependence of the particle's kinetic energy diminishing due to radiation. How soon will its kinetic energy decrease e-fold? Calculate this time interval for the case (a) of an electron, (b) of a proton.

4.217. A charged particle moves along the y axis according to the law $y = a \cos \omega t$, and the point of observation P is located on the x axis at a distance l from the particle ($l \gg a$). Find the ratio of electromagnetic radiation flow densities S_1/S_2 at the point P at the moments when the coordinate of the particle $y_1 = 0$ and $y_2 = a$. Calculate that ratio if $\omega = 3.3 \cdot 10^6\ \text{s}^{-1}$ and $l = 190$ m.

4.218. A charged particle moves uniformly with velocity v along a circle of radius R in the plane xy (Fig. 4.40). An observer is located

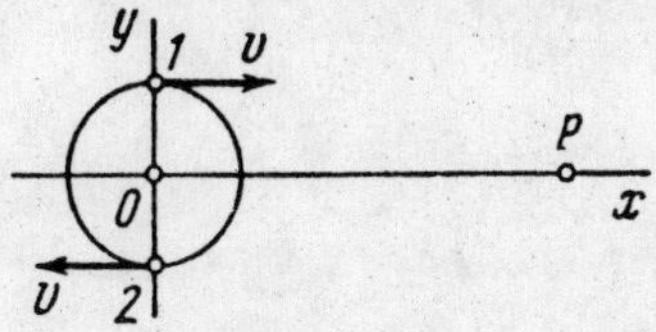

Fig. 4.40.

on the x axis at a point P which is removed from the centre of the circle by a distance much exceeding R. Find:

(a) the relationship between the observed values of the y projection of the particle's acceleration and the y coordinate of the particle;

(b) the ratio of electromagnetic radiation flow densities S_1/S_2 at the point P at the moments of time when the particle moves, from the standpoint of the observer P, toward him and away from him, as shown in the figure.

4.219. An electromagnetic wave emitted by an elementary dipole propagates in vacuum so that in the far field zone the mean value of the energy flow density is equal to S_0 at the point removed from the dipole by a distance r along the perpendicular drawn to the dipole's axis. Find the mean radiation power of the dipole.

4.220. The mean power radiated by an elementary dipole is equal to P_0. Find the mean space density of energy of the electromagnetic field in vacuum in the far field zone at the point removed from the dipole by a distance r along the perpendicular drawn to the dipole's axis.

4.221. An electric dipole whose modulus is constant and whose moment is equal to p rotates with constant angular velocity ω about the axis drawn at right angles to the axis of the dipole and passing through its midpoint. Find the power radiated by such a dipole.

4.222. A free electron is located in the field of a plane electromagnetic wave. Neglecting the magnetic component of the wave disturbing its motion, find the ratio of the mean energy radiated by the oscillating electron per unit time to the mean value of the energy flow density of the incident wave.

4.223. A plane electromagnetic wave with frequency ω falls upon an elastically bonded electron whose natural frequency equals ω_0. Neglecting the damping of oscillations, find the ratio of the mean energy dissipated by the electron per unit time to the mean value of the energy flow density of the incident wave.

4.224. Assuming a particle to have the form of a ball and to absorb all incident light, find the radius of a particle for which its gravitational attraction to the Sun is counterbalanced by the force that light exerts on it. The power of light radiated by the Sun equals $P = 4 \cdot 10^{26}$ W, and the density of the particle is $\rho = 1.0$ g/cm³.

5

OPTICS

5.1. PHOTOMETRY AND GEOMETRICAL OPTICS

• Spectral response of an eye $V(\lambda)$ is shown in Fig. 5.1.

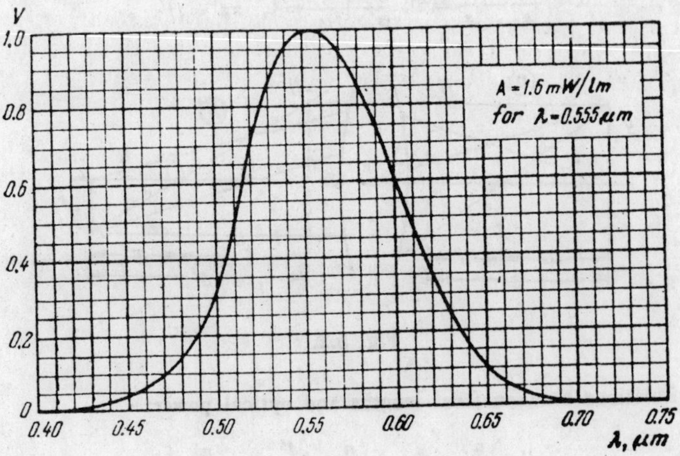

Fig. 5.1.

• Luminous intensity I and illuminance E:

$$I = \frac{d\Phi}{d\Omega}, E = \frac{d\Phi_{inc}}{dS} \tag{5.1a}$$

• Illuminance produced by a point isotropic source:

$$E = \frac{I \cos \alpha}{r^2} \tag{5.1b}$$

where α is the angle between the normal to the surface and the direction to the source.

• Luminosity M and luminance L:

$$M = \frac{d\Phi_{emit}}{dS}, L = \frac{d\Phi}{d\Omega\, \Delta S \cos \theta} \tag{5.1c}$$

• For a Lambert source L = const and luminosity

$$M = \pi L. \tag{5.1d}$$

• Relation between refractive angle θ of a prism and least deviation angle α:

$$\sin\frac{\alpha+\theta}{2}=n\sin\frac{\theta}{2}, \quad (5.1e)$$

where n is the refractive index of the prism.

• Equation of spherical mirror:

$$\frac{1}{s'}+\frac{1}{s}=\frac{2}{R}, \quad (5.1f)$$

where R is the curvature radius of the mirror.

• Equations for aligned optical system (Fig. 5.2):

$$\frac{n'}{s'}-\frac{n}{s}=\Phi,\quad \frac{f'}{s'}+\frac{f}{s}=1,\quad xx'=ff'. \quad (5.1g)$$

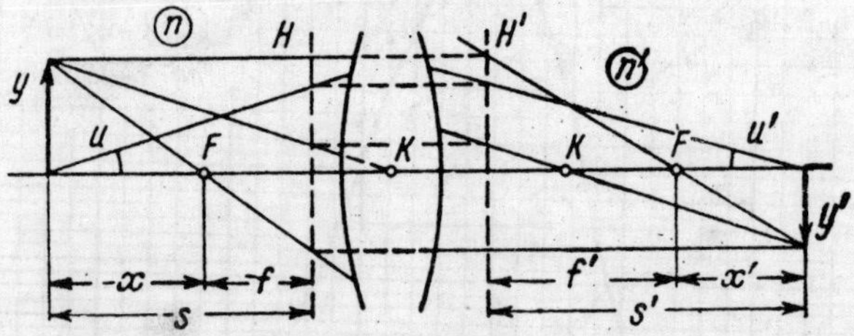

Fig. 5.2.

• Relations between focal lengths and optical power:

$$f'=\frac{n'}{\Phi},\quad f=-\frac{n}{\Phi},\quad \frac{f'}{f}=-\frac{n'}{n}. \quad (5.1h)$$

• Optical power of a spherical refractive surface:

$$\Phi=\frac{n'-n}{R}. \quad (5.1i)$$

• Optical power of a thin lens in a medium with refractive index n_0:

$$\Phi=(n-n_0)\left(\frac{1}{R_1}-\frac{1}{R_2}\right), \quad (5.1j)$$

where n is the refractive index of the lens.

• Optical power of a thick lens:

$$\Phi=\Phi_1+\Phi_2-\frac{d}{n}\Phi_1\Phi_2, \quad (5.1k)$$

where d is the thickness of the lens. This equation is also valid for a system of two thin lenses separated by a medium with refractive index n.

• Principal planes H and H' are removed from the crest points O and O' of surfaces of a thick lens (Fig. 5.3) by the following distances:

$$X = \frac{d}{n}\frac{\Phi_2}{\Phi}, \quad X' = -\frac{d}{n}\frac{\Phi_1}{\Phi}. \tag{5.1l}$$

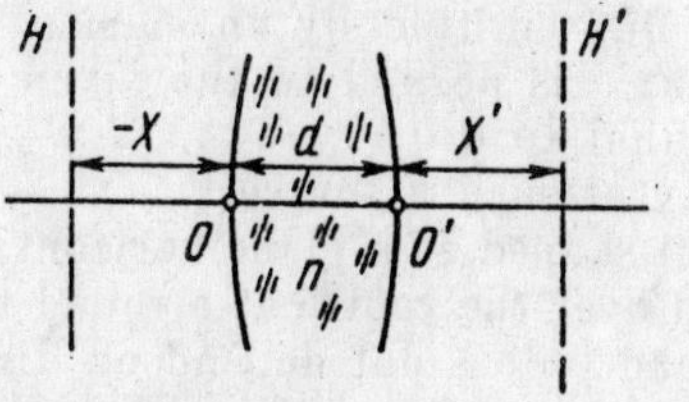

Fig. 5.3.

• Lagrange-Helmholtz invariant:

$$nyu = \text{const.} \tag{5.1m}$$

• Magnifying power of an optical device:

$$\Gamma = \frac{\tan\psi'}{\tan\psi}, \tag{5.1n}$$

where ψ' and ψ are the angles subtended at the eye by an image formed by the optical device and by the corresponding object at a distance for convenient viewing (in the case of a microscope or magnifying glass that distance is equal to $l_0 = 25$ cm).

5.1. Making use of the spectral response curve for an eye (see Fig. 5.1), find:

(a) the energy flux corresponding to the luminous flux of 1.0 lm at the wavelengths 0.51 and 0.64 μm;

(b) the luminous flux corresponding to the wavelength interval from 0.58 to 0.63 μm if the respective energy flux, equal to $\Phi_e = 4.5$ mW, is uniformly distributed over all wavelengths of the interval. The function $V(\lambda)$ is assumed to be linear in the given spectral interval.

5.2. A point isotropic source emits a luminous flux $\Phi = 10$ lm with wavelength $\lambda = 0.59$ μm. Find the peak strength values of electric and magnetic fields in the luminous flux at a distance $r = 1.0$ m from the source. Make use of the curve illustrated in Fig. 5.1.

5.3. Find the mean illuminance of the irradiated part of an opaque sphere receiving

(a) a parallel luminous flux resulting in illuminance E_0 at the point of normal incidence;

(b) light from a point isotropic source located at a distance $l = 100$ cm from the centre of the sphere; the radius of the sphere is $R = 60$ cm and the luminous intensity is $I = 36$ cd.

5.4. Determine the luminosity of a surface whose luminance depends on direction as $L = L_0 \cos\theta$, where θ is the angle between the radiation direction and the normal to the surface.

5.5. A certain luminous surface obeys Lambert's law. Its luminance is equal to L. Find:

(a) the luminous flux emitted by an element ΔS of this surface into a cone whose axis is normal to the given element and whose aperture angle is equal to θ;

(b) the luminosity of such a source.

5.6. An illuminant shaped as a plane horizontal disc $S = 100\ \text{cm}^2$ in area is suspended over the centre of a round table of radius $R = 1.0$ m. Its luminance does not depend on direction and is equal to $L = 1.6 \cdot 10^4\ \text{cd/m}^2$. At what height over the table should the illuminant be suspended to provide maximum illuminance at the circumference of the table? How great will that illuminance be? The illuminant is assumed to be a point source.

5.7. A point source is suspended at a height $h = 1.0$ m over the centre of a round table of radius $R = 1.0$ m. The luminous intensity I of the source depends on direction so that illuminance at all points of the table is the same. Find the function $I(\theta)$, where θ is the angle between the radiation direction and the vertical, as well as the luminous flux reaching the table if $I(0) = I_0 = 100$ cd.

5.8. A vertical shaft of light from a projector forms a light spot $S = 100\ \text{cm}^2$ in area on the ceiling of a round room of radius $R = 2.0$ m. The illuminance of the spot is equal to $E = 1000$ lx. The reflection coefficient of the ceiling is equal to $\rho = 0.80$. Find the maximum illuminance of the wall produced by the light reflected from the ceiling. The reflection is assumed to obey Lambert's law.

5.9. A luminous dome shaped as a hemisphere rests on a horizontal plane. Its luminosity is uniform. Determine the illuminance at the centre of that plane if its luminance equals L and is independent of direction.

5.10. A Lambert source has the form of an infinite plane. Its luminance is equal to L. Find the illuminance of an area element oriented parallel to the given source.

5.11. An illuminant shaped as a plane horizontal disc of radius $R = 25$ cm is suspended over a table at a height $h = 75$ cm. The illuminance of the table below the centre of the illuminant is equal to $E_0 = 70$ lx. Assuming the source to obey Lambert's law, find its luminosity.

5.12. A small lamp having the form of a uniformly luminous sphere of radius $R = 6.0$ cm is suspended at a height $h = 3.0$ m above the floor. The luminance of the lamp is equal to $L = 2.0 \cdot 10^4\ \text{cd/m}^2$ and is independent of direction. Find the illuminance of the floor directly below the lamp.

5.13. Write the law of reflection of a light beam from a mirror in vector form, using the directing unit vectors **e** and **e′** of the incident and reflected beams and the unit vector **n** of the outside normal to the mirror surface.

5.14. Demonstrate that a light beam reflected from three mutually perpendicular plane mirrors in succession reverses its direction.

5.15. At what value of the angle of incident θ_1 is a shaft of light reflected from the surface of water perpendicular to the refracted shaft?

5.16. Two optical media have a plane boundary between them. Suppose θ_{1cr} is the critical angle of incidence of a beam and θ_1 is the angle of incidence at which the refracted beam is perpendicular to the reflected one (the beam is assumed to come from an optically denser medium). Find the relative refractive index of these media if $\sin\theta_{1cr}/\sin\theta_1 = \eta = 1.28$.

5.17. A light beam falls upon a plane-parallel glass plate $d=6.0$ cm in thickness. The angle of incidence is $\theta = 60°$. Find the value of deflection of the beam which passed through that plate.

5.18. A man standing on the edge of a swimming pool looks at a stone lying on the bottom. The depth of the swimming pool is equal to h. At what distance from the surface of water is the image of the stone formed if the line of vision makes an angle θ with the normal to the surface?

5.19. Demonstrate that in a prism with small refracting angle θ the shaft of light deviates through the angle $\alpha \simeq (n-1)\,\theta$ regardless of the angle of incidence, provided that the latter is also small.

5.20. A shaft of light passes through a prism with refracting angle θ and refractive index n. Let α be the diffraction angle of the shaft. Demonstrate that if the shaft of light passes through the prism symmetrically,

(a) the angle α is the least;

(b) the relationship between the angles α and θ is defined by Eq. (5.1e).

5.21. The least deflection angle of a certain glass prism is equal to its refracting angle. Find the latter.

5.22. Find the minimum and maximum deflection angles for a light ray passing through a glass prism with refracting angle $\theta = 60°$.

5.23. A trihedral prism with refracting angle 60° provides the least deflection angle 37° in air. Find the least deflection angle of that prism in water.

5.24. A light ray composed of two monochromatic components passes through a trihedral prism with refracting angle $\theta = 60°$. Find the angle $\Delta\alpha$ between the components of the ray after its passage through the prism if their respective indices of refraction are equal to 1.515 and 1.520. The prism is oriented to provide the least deflection angle.

5.25. Using Fermat's principle derive the laws of deflection and refraction of light on the plane interface between two media.

5.26. By means of plotting find:

(a) the path of a light ray after reflection from a concave and convex spherical mirrors (see Fig. 5.4, where F is the focal point, OO' is the optical axis);

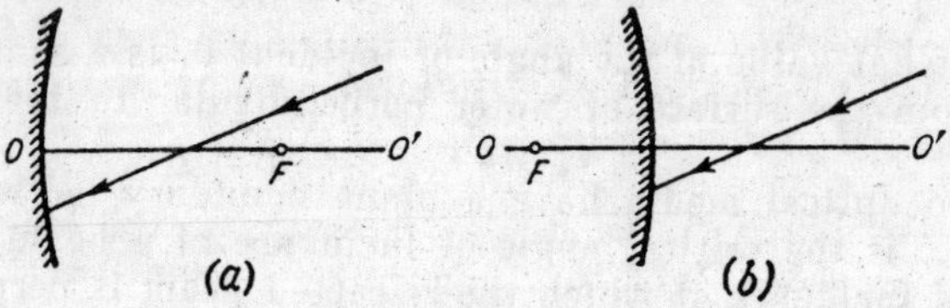

Fig. 5.4.

(b) the positions of the mirror and its focal point in the cases illustrated in Fig. 5.5, where P and P' are the conjugate points.

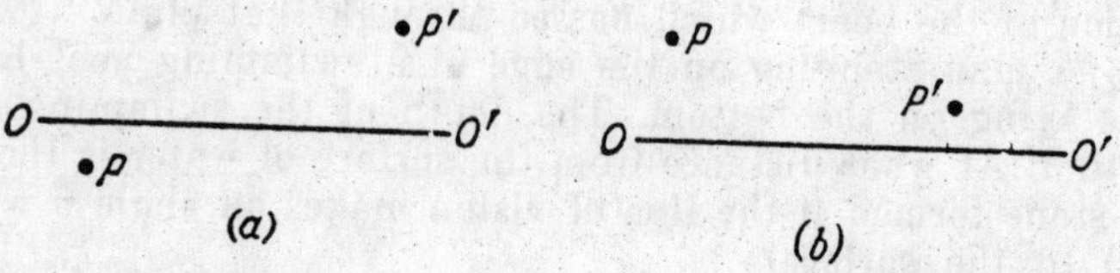

Fig. 5.5.

5.27. Determine the focal length of a concave mirror if:

(a) with the distance between an object and its image being equal to $l = 15$ cm, the transverse magnification $\beta = -2.0$;

(b) in a certain position of the object the transverse magnification is $\beta_1 = -0.50$ and in another position displaced with respect to the former by a distance $l = 5.0$ cm the transverse magnification $\beta_2 = -0.25$.

5.28. A point source with luminous intensity $I_0 = 100$ cd is positioned at a distance $s = 20.0$ cm from the crest of a concave mirror with focal length $f = 25.0$ cm. Find the luminous intensity of the reflected ray if the reflection coefficient of the mirror is $\rho = 0.80$.

5.29. Proceeding from Fermat's principle derive the refraction formula for paraxial rays on a spherical boundary surface of radius R between media with refractive indices n and n'.

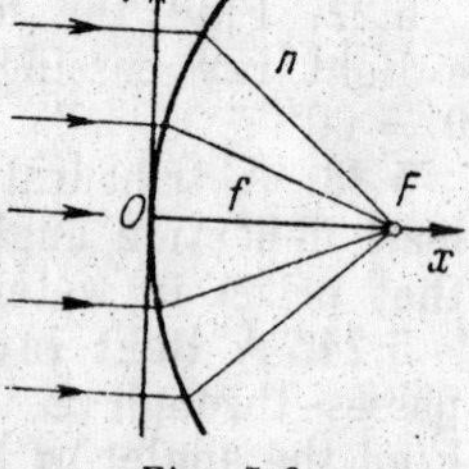

Fig. 5.6.

5.30. A parallel beam of light falls from vacuum on a surface enclosing a medium with refractive index n (Fig. 5.6). Find the shape of that surface, $x(r)$, if the beam is brought into focus at the point F at a distance f from the crest O. What is the maximum radius of a beam that can still be focussed?

5.31. A point source is located at a distance of 20 cm from the front surface of a symmetrical glass biconvex lens. The lens is 5.0 cm thick and the curvature radius of its surfaces is 5.0 cm. How far beyond the rear surface of this lens is the image of the source formed?

5.32. An object is placed in front of convex surface of a glass plano-convex lens of thickness $d = 9.0$ cm. The image of that object is formed on the plane surface of the lens serving as a screen. Find:

(a) the transverse magnification if the curvature radius of the lens's convex surface is $R = 2.5$ cm;

(b) the image illuminance if the luminance of the object is $L = 7700$ cd/m^2 and the entrance aperture diameter of the lens is $D = 5.0$ mm; losses of light are negligible.

5.33. Find the optical power and the focal lengths

(a) of a thin glass lens in liquid with refractive index $n_0 = 1.7$ if its optical power in air is $\Phi_0 = -5.0$ D;

(b) of a thin symmetrical biconvex glass lens, with air on one side and water on the other side, if the optical power of that lens in air is $\Phi_0 = +10$ D.

5.34. By means of plotting find:

(a) the path of a ray of light beyond thin converging and diverging lenses (Fig. 5.7, where OO' is the optical axis, F and F' are the front and rear focal points);

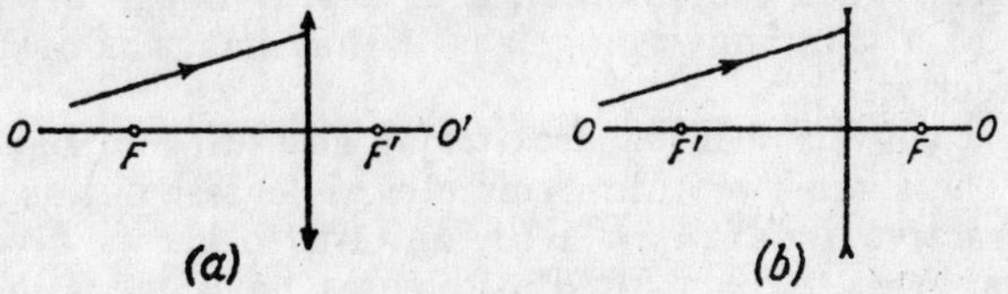

Fig. 5.7.

(b) the position of a thin lens and its focal points if the position of the optical axis OO' and the positions of the cojugate points P, P' (see Fig. 5.5) are known; the media on both sides of the lenses are identical;

(c) the path of ray *2* beyond the converging and diverging lenses (Fig. 5.8) if the path of ray *1* and the positions of the lens and of its

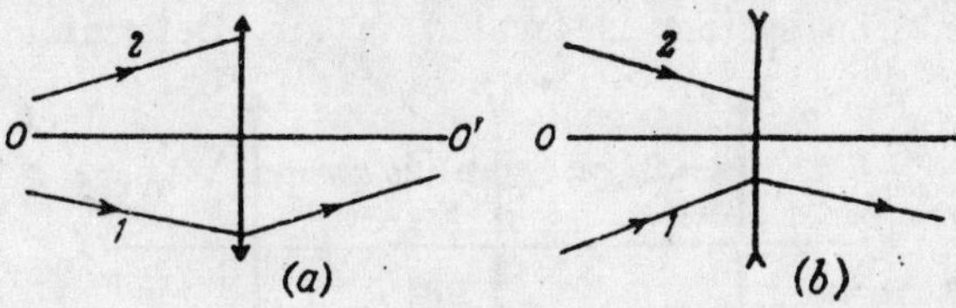

Fig. 5.8.

optical axis OO' are all known; the media on both sides of the lenses are identical.

5.35. A thin converging lens with focal length $f = 25$ cm projects the image of an object on a screen removed from the lens by a distance $l = 5.0$ m. Then the screen was drawn closer to the lens by a distance $\Delta l = 18$ cm. By what distance should the object be shifted for its image to become sharp again?

5.36. A source of light is located at a distance $l = 90$ cm from a screen. A thin converging lens provides the sharp image of the source when placed between the source of light and the screen at two positions. Determine the focal length of the lens if

(a) the distance between the two positions of the lens is $\Delta l = 30$ cm;

(b) the transverse dimensions of the image at one position of the lens are $\eta = 4.0$ greater than those at the other position.

5.37. A thin converging lens is placed between an object and a screen whose positions are fixed. There are two positions of the lens at which the sharp image of the object is formed on the screen. Find the transverse dimension of the object if at one position of the lens the image dimension equals $h' = 2.0$ mm and at the other, $h'' = 4.5$ mm.

5.38. A thin converging lens with aperture ratio $D : f = 1 : 3.5$ (D is the lens diameter, f is its focal length) provides the image of a sufficiently distant object on a photographic plate. The object luminance is $L = 260$ cd/m². The losses of light in the lens amount to $\alpha = 0.10$. Find the illuminance of the image.

5.39. How does the luminance of a real image depend on diameter D of a thin converging lens if that image is observed

(a) directly;

(b) on a white screen backscattering according to Lambert's law?

5.40. There are two thin symmetrical lenses: one is converging, with refractive index $n_1 = 1.70$, and the other is diverging with refractive index $n_2 = 1.51$. Both lenses have the same curvature radius of their surfaces equal to $R = 10$ cm. The lenses were put close together and submerged into water. What is the focal length of this system in water?

5.41. Determine the focal length of a concave spherical mirror which is manufactured in the form of a thin symmetric biconvex glass lens one of whose surfaces is silvered. The curvature radius of the lens surface is $R = 40$ cm.

5.42. Figure 5.9 illustrates an aligned system consisting of three thin lenses. The system is located in air. Determine:

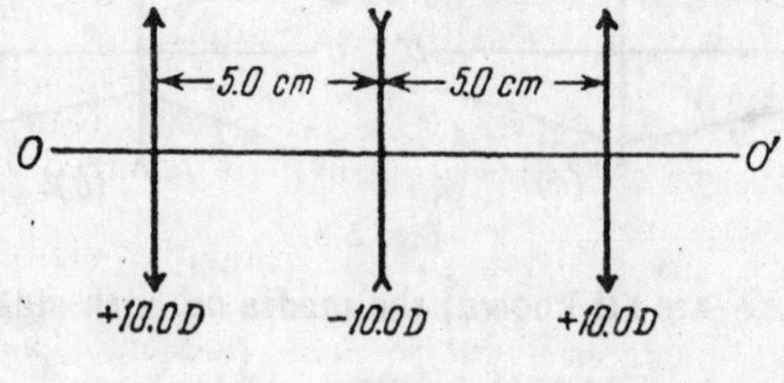

Fig. 5.9.

(a) the position of the point of convergence of a parallel ray incoming from the left after passing through the system;

(b) the distance between the first lens and a point lying on the axis to the left of the system, at which that point and its image are located symmetrically with respect to the lens system.

5.43. A Galilean telescope of 10-fold magnification has the length of 45 cm when adjusted to infinity. Determine:

(a) the focal lengths of the telescope's objective and ocular;

(b) by what distance the ocular should be displaced to adjust the telescope to the distance of 50 m.

5.44. Find the magnification of a Keplerian telescope adjusted to infinity if the mounting of the objective has a diameter D and the image of that mounting formed by the telescope's ocular has a diameter d.

5.45. On passing through a telescope a flux of light increases its intensity $\eta = 4.0 \cdot 10^4$ times. Find the angular dimension of a distant object if its image formed by that telescope has an angular dimension $\psi' = 2.0°$.

5.46. A Keplerian telescope with magnification $\Gamma = 15$ was submerged into water which filled up the inside of the telescope. To make the system work as a telescope again within the former dimensions, the objective was replaced. What has the magnification of the telescope become equal to? The refractive index of the glass of which the ocular is made is equal to $n = 1.50$.

5.47. At what magnification Γ of a telescope with a diameter of the objective $D = 6.0$ cm is the illuminance of the image of an object on the retina not less than without the telescope? The pupil diameter is assumed to be equal to $d_0 = 3.0$ mm. The losses of light in the telescope are negligible.

5.48. The optical powers of the objective and the ocular of a microscope are equal to 100 and 20 D respectively. The microscope magnification is equal to 50. What will the magnification of the microscope be when the distance between the objective and the ocular is increased by 2.0 cm?

5.49. A microscope has a numerical aperture $\sin \alpha = 0.12$, where α is the aperture angle subtended by the entrance pupil of the microscope. Assuming the diameter of an eye's pupil to be equal to $d_0 = 4.0$ mm, determine the microscope magnification at which

(a) the diameter of the beam of light coming from the microscope is equal to the diameter of the eye's pupil;

(b) the illuminance of the image on the retina is independent of magnification (consider the case when the beam of light passing through the system "microscope-eye" is bounded by the mounting of the objective).

5.50. Find the positions of the principal planes, the focal and nodal points of a thin biconvex symmetric glass lens with curvature radius of its surfaces equal to $R = 7.50$ cm. There is air on one side of the lens and water on the other.

5.51. By means of plotting find the positions of focal points and principal planes of aligned optical systems illustrated in Fig. 5.10:

(a) a telephoto lens, that is a combination of a converging and a diverging thin lenses ($f_1 = 1.5\ a$, $f_2 = -1.5\ a$);

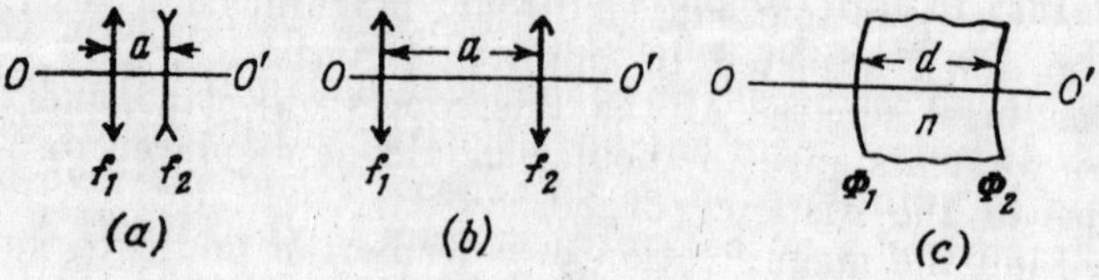

Fig. 5.10.

(b) a system of two thin converging lenses ($f_1 = 1.5\ a$, $f_2 = 0.5\ a$);

(c) a thick convex-concave lens ($d = 4$ cm, $n = 1.5$, $\Phi_1 = +50$ D, $\Phi_2 = -50$ D).

5.52. An optical system is located in air. Let OO' be its optical axis, F and F' are the front and rear focal points, H and H' are the front and rear principal planes, P and P' are the conjugate points. By means of plotting find:

(a) the positions F' and H' (Fig. 5.11a);

(b) the position of the point S' conjugate to the point S (Fig. 5.11b);

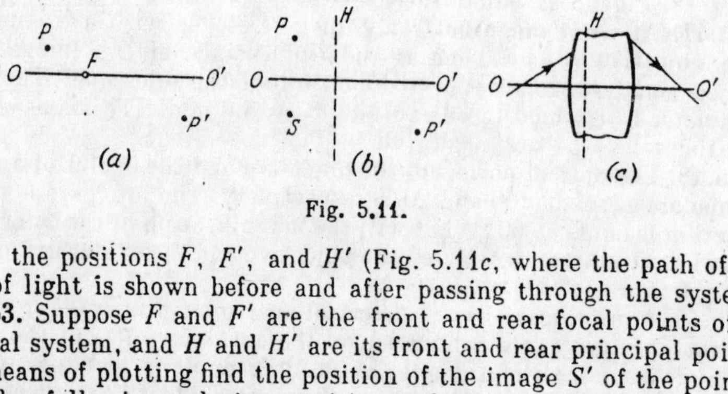

Fig. 5.11.

(c) the positions F, F', and H' (Fig. 5.11c, where the path of the ray of light is shown before and after passing through the system).

5.53. Suppose F and F' are the front and rear focal points of an optical system, and H and H' are its front and rear principal points. By means of plotting find the position of the image S' of the point S for the following relative positions of the points S, F, F', H, and H':

(a) $FSHH'F'$; (b) $HSF'FH'$; (c) $H'SF'FH$; (d) $F'H'SHF$.

5.54. A telephoto lens consists of two thin lenses, the front converging lens and the rear diverging lens with optical powers $\Phi_1 = +10$ D and $\Phi_2 = -10$ D. Find:

(a) the focal length and the positions of principal axes of that system if the lenses are separated by a distance $d = 4.0$ cm;

(b) the distance d between the lenses at which the ratio of a focal length f of the system to a distance l between the converging lens and the rear principal focal point is the highest. What is this ratio equal to?

5.55. Calculate the positions of the principal planes and focal points of a thick convex-concave glass lens if the curvature radius of the convex surface is equal to $R_1 = 10.0$ cm and of the concave surface to $R_2 = 5.0$ cm and the lens thickness is $d = 3.0$ cm.

5.56. An aligned optical system consists of two thin lenses with focal lengths f_1 and f_2, the distance between the lenses being equal to d. The given system has to be replaced by one thin lens which, at any position of an object, would provide the same transverse magnification as the system. What must the focal length of this lens be equal to and in what position must it be placed with respect to the two-lens system?

5.57. A system consists of a thin symmetrical converging glass lens with the curvature radius of its surfaces $R = 38$ cm and a plane mirror oriented at right angles to the optical axis of the lens. The distance between the lens and the mirror is $l = 12$ cm. What is the optical power of this system when the space between the lens and the mirror is filled up with water?

5.58. At what thickness will a thick convex-concave glass lens in air

(a) serve as a telescope provided the curvature radius of its convex surface is $\Delta R = 1.5$ cm greater than that of its concave surface?

(b) have the optical power equal to -1.0 D if the curvature radii of its convex and concave surfaces are equal to 10.0 and 7.5 cm respectively?

5.59. Find the positions of the principal planes, the focal length and the sign of the optical power of a thick convex-concave glass lens

(a) whose thickness is equal to d and curvature radii of the surfaces are the same and equal to R;

(b) whose refractive surfaces are concentric and have the curvature radii R_1 and R_2 $(R_2 > R_1)$.

5.60. A telescope system consists of two glass balls with radii $R_1 = 5.0$ cm and $R_2 = 1.0$ cm. What are the distance between the centres of the balls and the magnification of the system if the bigger ball serves as an objective?

5.61. Two identical thick symmetrical biconvex lenses are put close together. The thickness of each lens equals the curvature radius of its surfaces, i.e. $d = R = 3.0$ cm. Find the optical power of this system in air.

5.62. A ray of light propagating in an isotropic medium with refractive index n varying gradually from point to point has a curvature radius ρ determined by the formula

$$\frac{1}{\rho} = \frac{\partial}{\partial N}(\ln n),$$

where the derivative is taken with respect to the principal normal to the ray. Derive this formula, assuming that in such a medium the law of refraction $n \sin\theta = \text{const}$ holds. Here θ is the angle between the ray and the direction of the vector ∇n at a given point.

5.63. Find the curvature radius of a ray of light propagating in a horizontal direction close to the Earth's surface where the gradient of the refractive index in air is equal to approximately $3 \cdot 10^{-8}$ m^{-1}. At what value of that gradient would the ray of light propagate all the way round the Earth?

5.2. INTERFERENCE OF LIGHT

• Width of a fringe:

$$\Delta x = \frac{l}{d} \lambda, \tag{5.2a}$$

where l is the distance from the sources to the screen, d is the distance between the sources.

• Temporal and spatial coherences. Coherence length and coherence radius:

$$l_{coh} \simeq \frac{\lambda^2}{\Delta\lambda}, \quad \rho_{coh} \simeq \frac{\lambda}{\psi}, \tag{5.2b}$$

where ψ is the angular dimension of the source.

• Condition for interference maxima in the case of light reflected from a thin plate of thickness b:

$$2b\sqrt{n^2 - \sin^2\theta_1} = (k + 1/2)\,\lambda, \tag{5.2c}$$

where k is an integer.

• Newton's rings produced on reflection of light from the surfaces of an air interlayer formed between a lens of radius R and a glass plate with which the convex surface of the lens is in contact. The radii of the rings:

$$r = \sqrt{\lambda R k/2}, \tag{5.2d}$$

with the rings being bright if $k = 1, 3, 5, \ldots$, and dark if $k = 2, 4, 6, \ldots$ The value $k = 0$ corresponds to the middle of the central dark spot.

5.64. Demonstrate that when two harmonic oscillations are added, the time-averaged energy of the resultant oscillation is equal to the sum of the energies of the constituent oscillations, if both of them

(a) have the same direction and are incoherent, and all the values of the phase difference between the oscillations are equally probable;

(b) are mutually perpendicular, have the same frequency and an arbitrary phase difference.

5.65. By means of plotting find the amplitude of the oscillation resulting from the addition of the following three oscillations of the same direction:

$$\xi_1 = a\cos\omega t, \quad \xi_2 = 2a\sin\omega t, \quad \xi_3 = 1.5a\cos(\omega t + \pi/3).$$

5.66. A certain oscillation results from the addition of coherent oscillations of the same direction $\xi_k = a\cos[\omega t + (k - 1)\varphi]$, where k is the number of the oscillation ($k = 1, 2, \ldots, N$), φ is the phase difference between the kth and $(k - 1)$th oscillations. Find the amplitude of the resultant oscillation.

5.67. A system illustrated in Fig. 5.12 consists of two coherent point sources *1* and *2* located in a certain plane so that their dipole moments are oriented at right angles to that plane. The sources are separated by a distance d, the radiation wavelength is equal to λ. Taking into account that the oscillations of source *2* lag in phase behind the oscillations of source *1* by φ ($\varphi < \pi$), find:

(a) the angles θ at which the radiation intensity is maximum;

(b) the conditions under which the radiation intensity in the direction $\theta = \pi$ is maximum and in the opposite direction, minimum.

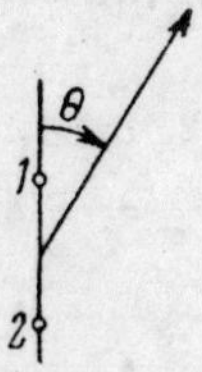

Fig. 5.12.

5.68. A stationary radiating system consists of a linear chain of parallel oscillators separated by a distance d, with the oscillation phase varying linearly along the chain. Find the time dependence of the phase difference $\Delta\varphi$ between the neighbouring oscillators at which the principal radiation maximum of the system will be "scanning" the surroundings with the constant angular velocity ω.

5.69. In Lloyd's mirror experiment (Fig. 5.13) a light wave emitted directly by the source S (narrow slit) interferes with the wave reflected from a mirror M. As a result, an interference fringe pattern is

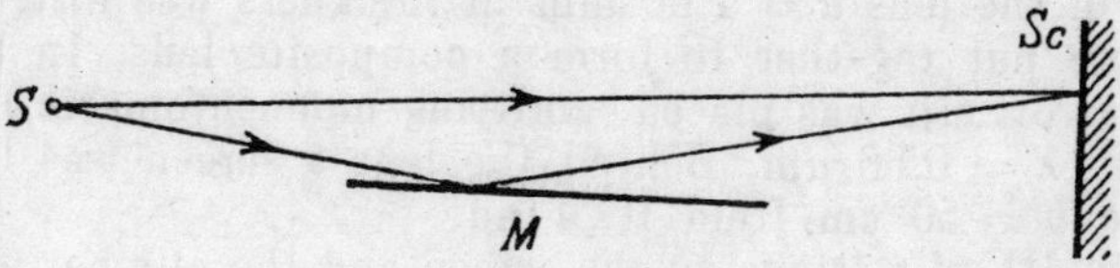

Fig. 5.13.

formed on the screen Sc. The source and the mirror are separated by a distance $l = 100$ cm. At a certain position of the source the fringe width on the screen was equal to $\Delta x = 0.25$ mm, and after the source was moved away from the mirror plane by $\Delta h = 0.60$ mm, the fringe width decreased $\eta = 1.5$ times. Find the wavelength of light.

5.70. Two coherent plane light waves propagating with a divergence angle $\psi \ll 1$ fall almost normally on a screen. The amplitudes of the waves are equal. Demonstrate that the distance between the neighbouring maxima on the screen is equal to $\Delta x = \lambda/\psi$, where λ is the wavelength.

5.71. Figure 5.14 illustrates the interference experiment with Fresnel mirrors. The angle between the mirrors is $\alpha = 12'$, the distances from the mirrors' intersection line to the narrow slit S and the screen Sc are equal to $r = 10.0$ cm and $b = 130$ cm respectively. The wavelength of light is $\lambda = 0.55$ μm. Find:

(a) the width of a fringe on the screen and the number of possible maxima;

(b) the shift of the interference pattern on the screen when the slit is displaced by $\delta l = 1.0$ mm along the arc of radius r with centre at the point O;

(c) at what maximum width δ_{max} of the slit the interference fringes on the screen are still observed sufficiently sharp.

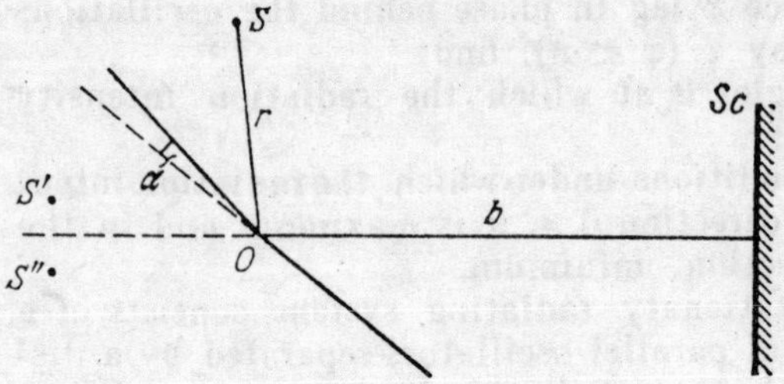

Fig. 5.14.

5.72. A plane light wave falls on Fresnel mirrors with an angle $\alpha = 2.0'$ between them. Determine the wavelength of light if the width of the fringe on the screen $\Delta x = 0.55$ mm.

5.73. A lens of diameter 5.0 cm and focal length $f = 25.0$ cm was cut along the diameter into two identical halves. In the process the layer of the lens $a = 1.00$ mm in thickness was lost. Then the halves were put together to form a composite lens. In this focal plane a narrow slit was placed, emitting monochromatic light with wavelength $\lambda = 0.60$ μm. Behind the lens a screen was located at a distance $b = 50$ cm from it. Find:

(a) the width of a fringe on the screen and the number of possible maxima;

(b) the maximum width of the slit δ_{max} at which the fringes on the screen will be still observed sufficiently sharp.

5.74. The distances from a Fresnel biprism to a narrow slit and a screen are equal to $a = 25$ cm and $b = 100$ cm respectively. The refracting angle of the glass biprism is equal to $\theta = 20'$. Find the wavelength of light if the width of the fringe on the screen is $\Delta x = 0.55$ mm.

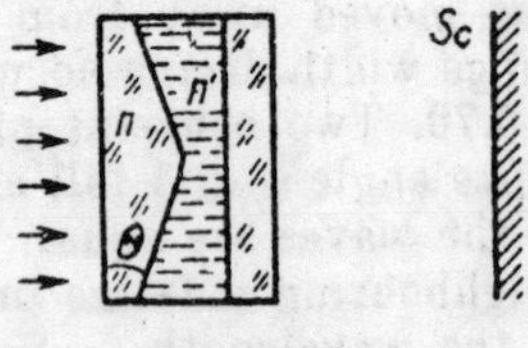

Fig. 5.15.

5.75. A plane light wave with wavelength $\lambda = 0.70$ μm falls normally on the base of a biprism made of glass ($n = 1.520$) with refracting angle $\theta = 5.0°$. Behind the biprism (Fig. 5.15) there is a plane-parallel plate, with the space between them filled up with benzene ($n' = 1.500$). Find the width of a fringe on the screen Sc placed behind this system.

5.76. A plane monochromatic light wave falls normally on a diaphragm with two narrow slits separated by a distance $d = 2.5$ mm

A fringe pattern is formed on a screen placed at a distance $l =$ $= 100$ cm behind the diaphragm. By what distance and in which direction will these fringes be displaced when one of the slits is covered by a glass plate of thickness $h = 10$ μm?

5.77. Figure 5.16 illustrates an interferometer used in measurements of refractive indices of transparent substances. Here S is

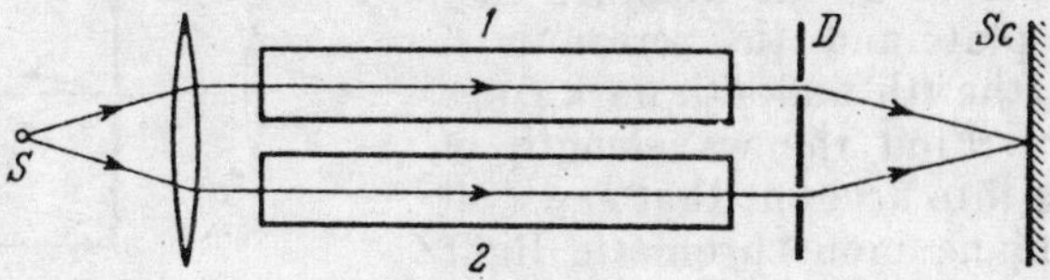

Fig. 5.16.

a narrow slit illuminated by monochromatic light with wavelength $\lambda = 589$ nm, *1* and *2* are identical tubes with air of length $l =$ $= 10.0$ cm each, D is a diaphragm with two slits. After the air in tube *1* was replaced with ammonia gas, the interference pattern on the screen Sc was displaced upward by $N = 17$ fringes. The refractive index of air is equal to $n = 1.000277$. Determine the refractive index of ammonia gas.

5.78. An electromagnetic wave falls normally on the boundary between two isotropic dielectrics with refractive indices n_1 and n_2. Making use of the continuity condition for the tangential components, **E** and **H** across the boundary, demonstrate that at the interface the electric field vector **E**

(a) of the transmitted wave experiences no phase jump;

(b) of the reflected wave is subjected to the phase jump equal to π if it is reflected from a medium of higher optical density.

5.79. A parallel beam of white light falls on a thin film whose refractive index is equal to $n = 1.33$. The angle of indices is $\theta_1 =$ $= 52°$. What must the film thickness be equal to for the reflected light to be coloured yellow ($\lambda = 0.60$ μm) most intensively?

5.80. Find the minimum thickness of a film with refractive index 1.33 at which light with wavelength 0.64 μm experiences maximum reflection while light with wavelength 0.40 μm is not reflected at all. The incidence angle of light is equal to 30°.

5.81. To decrease light losses due to reflection from the glass surface the latter is coated with a thin layer of substance whose refractive index $n' = \sqrt{n}$, where n is the refractive index of the glass. In this case the amplitudes of electromagnetic oscillations reflected from both coated surfaces are equal. At what thickness of that coating is the glass reflectivity in the direction of the normal equal to zero for light with wavelength λ?

5.82. Diffused monochromatic light with wavelength $\lambda = 0.60$ μm falls on a thin film with refractive index $n = 1.5$. Determine the film thickness if the angular separation of neighbouring maxima observed in reflected light at the angles close to $\theta = 45°$ to the normal is equal to $\delta\theta = 3.0°$.

5.83. Monochromatic light passes through an orifice in a screen Sc (Fig. 5.17) and being reflected from a thin transparent plate P produces fringes of equal inclination on the screen. The thickness of the plate is equal to d, the distance between the plate and the screen is l, the radii of the ith and kth dark rings are r_i and r_k. Find the wavelength of light taking into account that $r_{i,k} \ll l$.

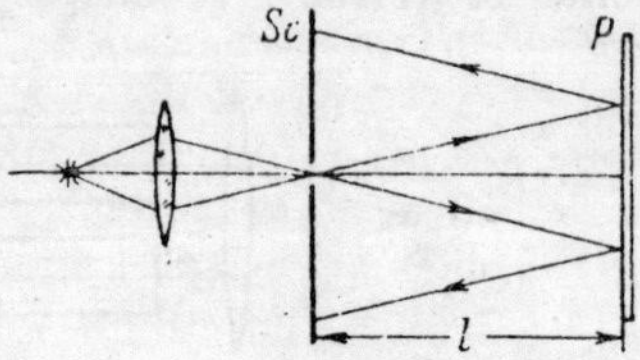

Fig. 5.17.

5.84. A plane monochromatic light wave with wavelength λ falls on the surface of a glass wedge whose faces form an angle $\alpha \ll 1$. The plane of incidence is perpendicular to the edge, the angle of incidence is θ_1. Find the distance between the neighbouring fringe maxima on the screen placed at right angles to reflected light.

5.85. Light with wavelength $\lambda = 0.55$ μm from a distant point source falls normally on the surface of a glass wedge. A fringe pattern whose neighbouring maxima on the surface of the wedge are separated by a distance $\Delta x = 0.21$ mm is observed in reflected light. Find:

(a) the angle between the wedge faces;

(b) the degree of light monochromatism ($\Delta\lambda/\lambda$) if the fringes disappear at a distance $l \simeq 1.5$ cm from the wedge's edge.

5.86. The convex surface of a plano-convex glass lens comes into contact with a glass plate. The curvature radius of the lens's convex surface is R, the wavelength of light is equal to λ. Find the width Δr of a Newton ring as a function of its radius r in the region where $\Delta r \ll r$.

5.87. The convex surface of a plano-convex glass lens with curvature radius $R = 40$ cm comes into contact with a glass plate. A certain ring observed in reflected light has a radius $r = 2.5$ mm. Watching the given ring, the lens was gradually removed from the plate by a distance $\Delta h = 5.0$ μm. What has the radius of that ring become equal to?

5.88. At the crest of a spherical surface of a plano-convex lens there is a ground-off plane spot of radius $r_0 = 3.0$ mm through which the lens comes into contact with a glass plate. The curvature radius of the lens's convex surface is equal to $R = 150$ cm. Find the radius of the sixth bright ring when observed in reflected light with wavelength $\lambda = 655$ nm.

5.89. A plano-convex glass lens with curvature radius of spherical surface $R = 12.5$ cm is *pressed* against a glass plate. The diameters of the tenth and fifteenth dark Newton's rings in reflected light are equal to $d_1 = 1.00$ mm and $d_2 = 1.50$ mm. Find the wavelength of light.

5.90. Two plano-convex thin glass lenses are brought into contact with their spherical surfaces. Find the optical power of such a system if in reflected light with wavelength $\lambda = 0.60$ μm the diameter of the fifth bright ring is $d = 1.50$ mm.

5.91. Two thin symmetric glass lenses, one biconvex and the other biconcave, are brought into contact to make a system with optical power $\Phi = 0.50$ D. Newton's rings are observed in reflected light with wavelength $\lambda = 0.61$ μm. Determine:

(a) the radius of the tenth dark ring;

(b) how the radius of that ring will change when the space between the lenses is filled up with water.

5.92. The spherical surface of a plano-convex lens comes into contact with a glass plate. The space between the lens and the plate is filled up with carbon dioxide. The refractive indices of the lens, carbon dioxide, and the plate are equal to $n_1 = 1.50$, $n_2 = 1.63$, and $n_3 = 1.70$ respectively. The curvature radius of the spherical surface of the lens is equal to $R = 100$ cm. Determine the radius of the fifth dark Newton's ring in reflected light with wavelength $\lambda = 0.50$ μm.

5.93. In a two-beam interferometer the orange mercury line composed of two wavelengths $\lambda_1 = 576.97$ nm and $\lambda_2 = 579.03$ nm is employed. What is the least order of interference at which the sharpness of the fringe pattern is the worst?

5.94. In Michelson's interferometer the yellow sodium line composed of two wavelengths $\lambda_1 = 589.0$ nm and $\lambda_2 = 589.6$ nm was used. In the process of translational displacement of one of the mirrors the interference pattern vanished periodically (why?). Find the displacement of the mirror between two successive appearances of the sharpest pattern.

5.95. When a Fabry-Perot étalon is illuminated by monochromatic light with wavelength λ an interference pattern, the system of con-

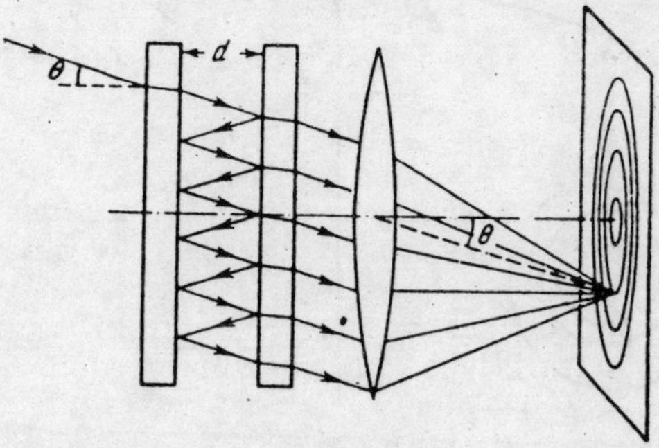

Fig. 5.18.

centric rings, appears in the focal plane of a lens (Fig. 5.18). The thickness of the étalon is equal to d. Determine how

(a) the position of rings;
(b) the angular width of fringes
depends on the order of interference.

5.96. For the Fabry-Perot étalon of thickness $d = 2.5$ cm find:
(a) the highest order of interference of light with wavelength $\lambda = 0.50$ μm;
(b) the dispersion region $\Delta\lambda$, i.e. the spectral interval of wavelengths, within which there is still no overlap with other orders of interference if the observation is carried out approximately at wavelength $\lambda = 0.50$ μm.

5.3. DIFFRACTION OF LIGHT

• Radius of the periphery of the kth Fresnel zone:

$$r_k = \sqrt{k\lambda \frac{ab}{a+b}}, \quad k = 1, 2, 3, \ldots, \tag{5.3a}$$

• Cornu's spiral (Fig. 5.19). The numbers along that spiral correspond to the values of parameter v. In the case of a plane wave $v = x\sqrt{2/b\lambda}$, where x

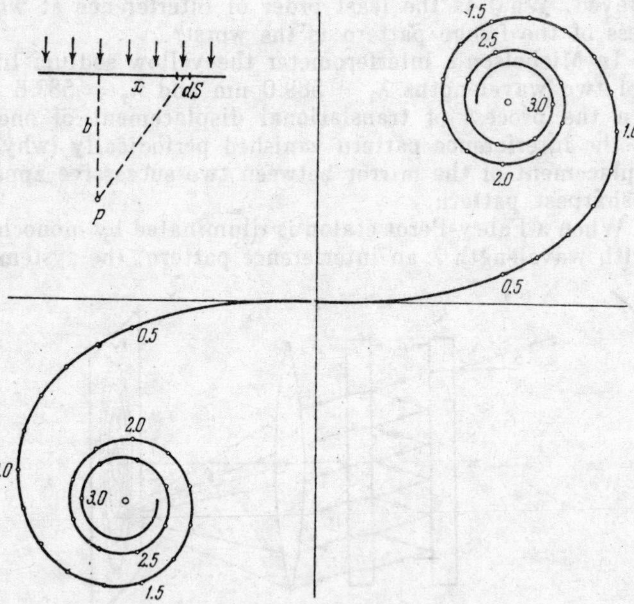

Fig. 5.19.

and b are the distances defining the position of the element dS of a wavefront relative to the observation point P as shown in the upper left corner of the figure.

• Fraunhofer diffraction produced by light falling normally from a slit. Condition of intensity minima:

$$b \sin \theta = \pm k\lambda, \quad k = 1, 2, 3, \ldots, \tag{5.3b}$$

where b is the width of the slit, θ is the diffraction angle.

• Diffraction grating, with light falling normally. The main Fraunhofer maxima appear under the condition

$$d \sin \theta = \pm k\lambda, \quad k = 0, 1, 2, \ldots, \tag{5.3c}$$

the condition of additional minima:

$$d \sin \theta = \pm \frac{k'}{N} \lambda, \tag{5.3d}$$

where $k' = 1, 2, \ldots$, except for $0, N, 2N, \ldots$.

• Angular dispersion of a diffraction grating:

$$D = \frac{\delta\theta}{\delta\lambda} = \frac{k}{d \cos \theta}. \tag{5.3e}$$

• Resolving power of a diffraction grating:

$$R = \frac{\lambda}{\delta\lambda} = kN, \tag{5.3f}$$

where N is the number of lines of the grating.

• Resolving power of an objective

$$R = \frac{1}{\delta\psi} = \frac{D}{1.22\,\lambda}, \tag{5.3g}$$

where $\delta\psi$ is the least angular separation resolved by the objective, D is the diameter of the objective.

• Bragg's equation. The condition of diffraction maxima:

$$2d \sin \alpha = \pm k\lambda, \tag{5.3h}$$

d is the interplanar distance, α is the glancing angle, $k = 1, 2, 3, \ldots$.

A plane light wave falls normally on a diaphragm with round aperture opening the first N Fresnel zones for a point P on a screen located at a distance b from the diaphragm. The wavelength of light is equal to λ. Find the intensity of light I_0 in front of the diaphragm if the distribution of intensity of light $I(r)$ on the screen is known. Here r is the distance from the point P.

5.98. A point source of light with wavelength $\lambda = 0.50\ \mu m$ is located at a distance $a = 100$ cm in front of a diaphragm with round aperture of radius $r = 1.0$ mm. Find the distance b between the diaphragm and the observation point for which the number of Fresnel zones in the aperture equals $k = 3$.

5.99. A diaphragm with round aperture, whose radius r can be varied during the experiment, is placed between a point source of light and a screen. The distances from the diaphragm to the source and the screen are equal to $a = 100$ cm and $b = 125$ cm. Determine the wavelength of light if the intensity maximum at the centre of the diffraction pattern of the screen is observed at $r_1 = 1.00$ mm and the next maximum at $r_2 = 1.29$ mm.

5.100. A plane monochromatic light wave with intensity I_0 falls normally on an opaque screen with a round aperture. What is the intensity of light I behind the screen at the point for which the aperture

(a) is equal to the first Fresnel zone; to the internal half of the first zone;

(b) was made equal to the first Fresnel zone and then half of it was closed (along the diameter)?

5.101. A plane monochromatic light wave with intensity I_0 falls normally on an opaque disc closing the first Fresnel zone for the observation point P. What did the intensity of light I at the point P become equal to after

(a) half of the disc (along the diameter) was removed;

(b) half of the external half of the first Fresnel zone was removed (along the diameter)?

5.102. A plane monochromatic light wave with intensity I_0 falls normally on the surfaces of the opaque screens shown in Fig. 5.20. Find the intensity of light I at a point P

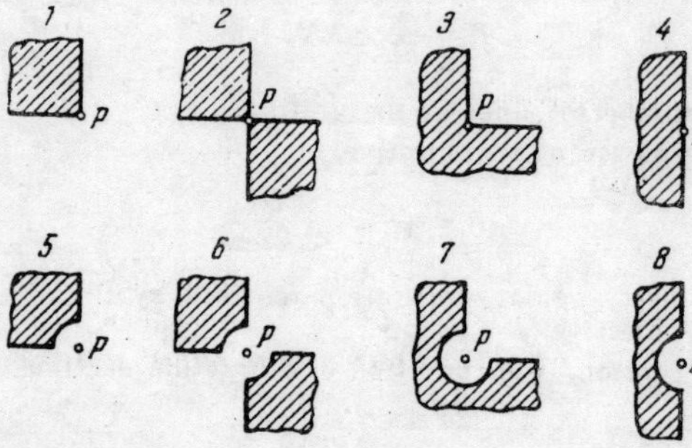

Fig. 5.20.

(a) located behind the corner points of screens *1-3* and behind the edge of half-plane *4*;

(b) for which the rounded-off edge of screens *5-8* coincides with the boundary of the first Fresnel zone.

Derive the general formula describing the results obtained for screens *1-4*; the same, for screens *5-8*.

5.103. A plane light wave with wavelength $\lambda = 0.60\ \mu m$ falls normally on a sufficiently large glass plate having a round recess on the opposite side (Fig. 5.21). For the observation point P that recess corresponds to the first one and a half Fresnel zones. Find the depth h of the recess at which the intensity of light at the point P is

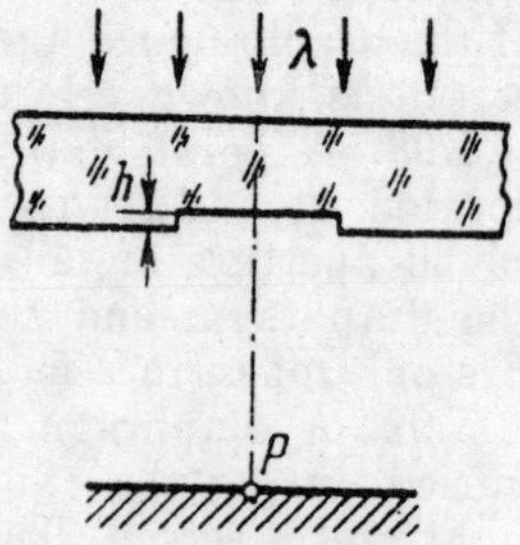

Fig. 5.21.

(a) maximum;

(b) minimum;

(c) equal to the intensity of incident light.

5.104. A plane light wave with wavelength λ and intensity I_0 falls normally on a large glass plate whose opposite side serves as an opaque screen with a round aperture equal to the first Fresnel zone for the observation point P. In the middle of the aperture there is a round recess equal to half the Fresnel zone. What must the depth h of that recess be for the intensity of light at the point P to be the highest? What is this intensity equal to?

5.105. A plane light wave with wavelength $\lambda = 0.57$ μm falls normally on a surface of a glass ($n = 1.60$) disc which shuts one and a half Fresnel zones for the observation point P. What must the minimum thickness of that disc be for the intensity of light at the point P to be the highest? Take into account the interference of light on its passing through the disc.

5.106. A plane light wave with wavelength $\lambda = 0.54$ μm goes through a thin converging lens with focal length $f = 50$ cm and an aperture stop fixed immediately after the lens, and reaches a screen placed at a distance $b = 75$ cm from the aperture stop. At what aperture radii has the centre of the diffraction pattern on the screen the maximum illuminance?

5.107. A plane monochromatic light wave falls normally on a round aperture. At a distance $b = 9.0$ m from it there is a screen showing a certain diffraction pattern. The aperture diameter was decreased $\eta = 3.0$ times. Find the new distance b' at which the screen should be positioned to obtain the diffraction pattern similar to the previous one but diminished η times.

5.108. An opaque ball of diameter $D = 40$ mm is placed between a source of light with wavelength $\lambda = 0.55$ μm and a photographic plate. The distance between the source and the ball is equal to $a = 12$ m and that between the ball and the photographic plate is equal to $b = 18$ m. Find:

(a) the image dimension y' on the plate if the transverse dimension of the source is $y = 6.0$ mm;

(b) the minimum height of irregularities, covering the surface of the ball at random, at which the ball obstructs light.

Note. As calculations and experience show, that happens when the height of irregularities is comparable with the width of the Fresnel zone along which the edge of an opaque screen passes.

5.109. A point source of monochromatic light is positioned in front of a zone plate at a distance $a = 1.5$ m from it. The image of the source is formed at a distance $b = 1.0$ m from the plate. Find the focal length of the zone plate.

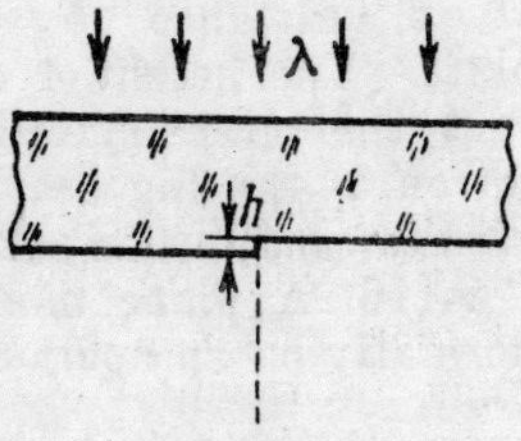

Fig. 5.22.

5.110. A plane light wave with wavelength $\lambda = 0.60$ μm and intensity I_0 falls normally on a large glass plate whose side view is shown in

Fig. 5.22. At what height h of the ledge will the intensity of light at points located directly below be

(a) minimum;

(b) twice as low as I_0 (the losses due to reflection are to be neglected).

5.111. A plane monochromatic light wave falls normally on an opaque half-plane. A screen is located at a distance $b = 100$ cm behind the half-plane. Making use of the Cornu spiral (Fig. 5.19), find:

(a) the ratio of intensities of the first maximum and the neighbouring minimum;

(b) the wavelength of light if the first two maxima are separated by a distance $\Delta x = 0.63$ mm.

5.112. A plane light wave with wavelength 0.60 μm falls normally on a long opaque strip 0.70 mm wide. Behind it a screen is placed at a distance 100 cm. Using Fig. 5.19, find the ratio of intensities of light in the middle of the diffraction pattern and at the edge of the geometrical shadow.

5.113. A plane monochromatic light wave falls normally on a long rectangular slit behind which a screen is positioned at a distance $b = 60$ cm. First the width of the slit was adjusted so that in the middle of the diffraction pattern the lowest minimum was observed. After widening the slit by $\Delta h = 0.70$ mm, the next minimum was obtained in the centre of the pattern. Find the wavelength of light.

5.114. A plane light wave with wavelength $\lambda = 0.65$ μm falls normally on a large glass plate whose opposite side has a long rectangular recess 0.60 mm wide. Using Fig. 5.19, find the depth h of the recess at which the diffraction pattern on the screen 77 cm away from the plate has the maximum illuminance at its centre.

5.115. A plane light wave with wavelength $\lambda = 0.65$ μm falls normally on a large glass plate whose opposite side has a ledge and an opaque strip of width $a = 0.30$ mm (Fig. 5.23). A screen is placed at a distance $b = 110$ cm from the plate. The height h of the ledge is such that the intensity of light at point 2 of the screen is the highest possible. Making use of Fig. 5.19, find the ratio of intensities at points 1 and 2.

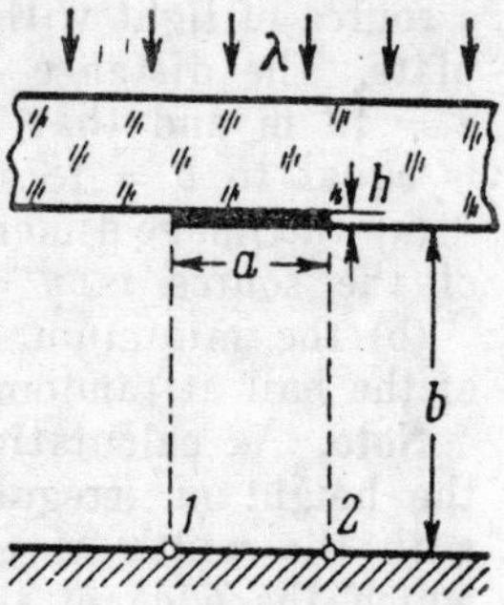

Fig. 5.23.

5.116. A plane monochromatic light wave of intensity I_0 falls normally on an opaque screen with a long slit having a semicircular

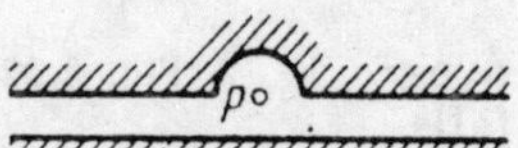

Fig. 5.24.

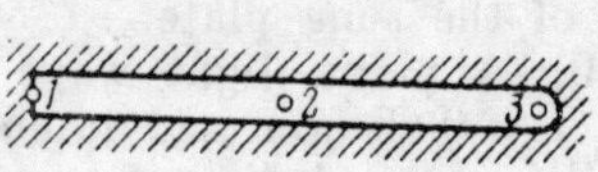

Fig. 5.25.

cut on one side (Fig. 5.24). The edge of the cut coincides with the boundary line of the first Fresnel zone for the observation point P. The width of the slit meausres 0.90 of the radius of the cut. Using Fig. 5.19. find the intensity of light at the point P.

5.117. A plane monochromatic light wave falls normally on an opaque screen with a long slit whose shape is shown in Fig. 5.25. Making use of Fig. 5.19, find the ratio of intensities of light at point *1*, *2*, and *3* located behind the screen at equal distances from it. For point *3* the rounded-off edge of the slit coincides with the boundary line of the first Fresnel zone.

5.118. A plane monochromatic light wave falls normally on an opaque screen shaped as a long strip with a round hole in the middle. For the observation point P the hole corresponds to half the Fresnel zone. with the hole diameter being $\eta = 1.07$ times less than the width of the strip. Using Fig. 5.19, find the intensity of light at the point P provided that the intensity of the incident light is equal to I_0.

5.119. Light with wavelength λ falls normally on a long rectangular slit of width b. Find the angular distribution of the intensity of light in the case of Fraunhofer diffraction, as well as the angular position of minima.

5.120. Making use of the result obtained in the foregoing problem, find the conditions defining the angular position of maxima of the first, the second, and the third order.

5.121. Light with wavelength $\lambda = 0.50$ μm falls on a slit of width $b = 10$ μm at an angle $\theta_0 = 30°$ to its normal. Find the angular position of the first minima located on both sides of the central Fraunhofer maximum.

5.122. A plane light wave with wavelength $\lambda = 0.60$ μm falls normally on the face of a glass wedge with refracting angle $\Theta = 15°$. The opposite face of the wedge is opaque and has a slit of width $b = 10$ μm parallel to the edge. Find:

(a) the angle $\Delta\theta$ between the direction to the Fraunhofer maximum of zeroth order and that of incident light:

(b) the angular width of the Fraunhofer maximum of the zeroth order.

5.123. A monochromatic beam falls on a reflection grating with period $d = 1.0$ mm at a glancing angle $\alpha_0 = 1.0°$. When it is diffracted at a glancing angle $\alpha = 3.0°$ a Fraunholfer maximum of second order occurs. Find the wavelength of light.

5.124. Draw the approximate diffraction pattern originating in the case of the Fraunhofer diffraction from a grating consisting of three identical slits if the ratio of the grating period to the slit width is equal to

(a) two;

(b) three.

5.125. With light falling normally on a diffraction grating, the angle of diffraction of second order is equal to 45° for a wavelength

$\lambda_1 = 0.65$ μm. Find the angle of diffraction of third order for a wave length $\lambda_2 = 0.50$ μm.

5.126. Light with wavelength 535 nm falls normally on a diffraction grating. Find its period if the diffraction angle 35° corresponds to one of the Fraunhofer maxima and the highest order of spectrum is equal to five.

5.127. Find the wavelength of monochromatic light falling normally on a diffraction grating with period $d = 2.2$ μm if the angle between the directions to the Fraunhofer maxima of the first and the second order is equal to $\Delta\theta = 15°$.

5.128. Light with wavelength 530 nm falls on a transparent diffraction grating with period 1.50 μm. Find the angle, relative to the grating normal, at which the Fraunhofer maximum of highest order is observed provided the light falls on the grating

(a) at right angles;

(b) at the angle 60° to the normal.

5.129. Light with wavelength $\lambda = 0.60$ μm falls normally on a diffraction grating inscribed on a plane surface of a plano-convex cylindrical glass lens with curvature radius $R = 20$ cm. The period of the grating is equal to $d = 6.0$ μm. Find the distance between the principal maxima of first order located symmetrically in the focal plane of that lens.

5.130. A plane light wave with wavelength $\lambda = 0.50$ μm falls normally on the face of a glass wedge with an angle $\Theta = 30°$. On the opposite face of the wedge a transparent diffraction grating with period $d = 2.00$ μm is inscribed, whose lines are parallel to the wedge's edge. Find the angles that the direction of incident light forms with the directions to the principal Fraunhofer maxima of the zero and the first order. What is the highest order of the spectrum? At what angle to the direction of incident light is it observed?

5.131. A plane light wave with wavelength λ falls normally on a phase diffraction grating whose side view is shown in Fig. 5.26. The grating is cut on a glass plate with refractive index n. Find the depth h of the lines at which the intensity of the central Fraunhofer maximum is equal to zero. What is in this case the diffraction angle corresponding to the first maximum?

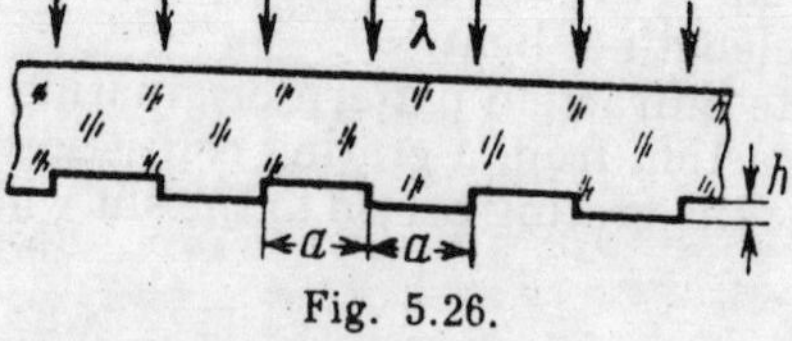

Fig. 5.26.

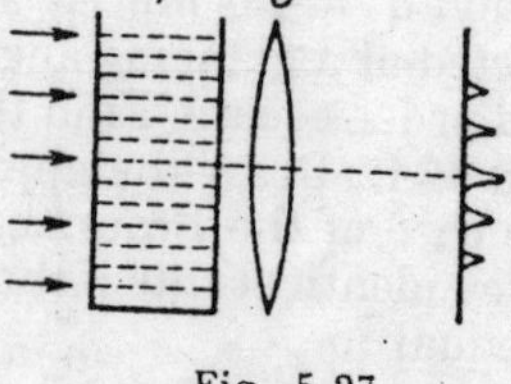

Fig. 5.27.

5.132. Figure 5.27 illustrates an arrangement employed in observations of diffraction of light by ultrasound. A plane light wave with wavelength $\lambda = 0.55$ μm passes through the water-filled tank T

in which a standing ultrasonic wave is sustained at a frequency $\nu = 4.7$ MHz. As a result of diffraction of light by the optically inhomogeneous periodic structure a diffraction spectrum can be observed in the focal plane of the objective O with focal length $f = 35$ cm. The separation between neighbouring maxima is $\Delta x = 0.60$ mm. Find the propagation velocity of ultrasonic oscillations in water.

5.133. To measure the angular distance ψ between the components of a double star by Michelson's method, in front of a telescope's lens a diaphragm was placed, which had two narrow parallel slits separated by an adjustable distance d. While diminishing d, the first smearing of the pattern was observed in the focal plane of the objective at $d = 95$ cm. Find ψ, assuming the wavelength of light to be equal to $\lambda = 0.55$ µm.

5.134. A transparent diffraction grating has a period $d = 1.50$ µm. Find the angular dispersion D (in angular minutes per nanometres) corresponding to the maximum of highest order for a spectral line of wavelength $\lambda = 530$ nm of light falling on the grating

(a) at right angles;

(b) at the angle $\theta_0 = 45°$ to the normal.

5.135. Light with wavelength λ falls on a diffraction grating at right angles. Find the angular dispersion of the grating as a function of diffraction angle θ.

5.136. Light with wavelength $\lambda = 589.0$ nm falls normally on a diffraction grating with period $d = 2.5$ µm, comprising $N = 10\,000$ lines. Find the angular width of the diffraction maximum of second order.

5.137. Demonstrate that when light falls on a diffraction grating at right angles, the maximum resolving power of the grating cannot exceed the value l/λ, where l is the width of the grating and λ is the wavelength of light.

5.138. Using a diffraction grating as an example, demonstrate that the frequency difference of two maxima resolved according to Rayleigh's criterion is equal to the reciprocal of the difference of propagation times of the extreme interfering oscillations, i.e. $\delta\nu = 1/\delta t$.

5.139. Light composed of two spectral lines with wavelengths 600.000 and 600.050 nm falls normally on a diffraction grating 10.0 mm wide. At a certain diffraction angle θ these lines are close to being resolved (according to Rayleigh's criterion). Find θ.

5.140. Light falls normally on a transparent diffraction grating of width $l = 6.5$ cm with 200 lines per millimetre. The spectrum under investigation includes a spectral line with $\lambda = 670.8$ nm consisting of two components differing by $\delta\lambda = 0.015$ nm. Find:

(a) in what order of the spectrum these components will be resolved;

(b) the least difference of wavelengths that can be resolved by this grating in a wavelength region $\lambda \approx 670$ nm.

5.141. With light falling normally on a transparent diffraction grating 10 mm wide, it was found that the components of the yellow line of sodium (589.0 and 589.6 nm) are resolved beginning with the fifth order of the spectrum. Evaluate:

(a) the period of this grating;

(b) what must be the width of the grating with the same period for a doublet $\lambda = 460.0$ nm whose components differ by 0.13 nm to be resolved in the third order of the spectrum.

5.142. A transparent diffraction grating of a quartz spectrograph is 25 mm wide and has 250 lines per millimetre. The focal length of an objective in whose focal plane a photographic plate is located is equal to 80 cm. Light falls on the grating at right angles. The spectrum under investigation includes a doublet with components of wavelengths 310.154 and 310.184 nm. Determine:

(a) the distances on the photographic plate between the components of this doublet in the spectra of the first and the second order;

(b) whether these components will be resolved in these orders of the spectrum.

5.143. The ultimate resolving power $\lambda/\delta\lambda$ of the spectrograph's trihedral prism is determined by diffraction of light at the prism edges (as in the case of a slit). When the prism is oriented to the least deviation angle in accordance with Rayleigh's criterion,

$$\lambda/\delta\lambda = b \mid dn/d\lambda \mid,$$

where b is the width of the prism's base (Fig. 5.28), and $dn/d\lambda$ is the dispersion of its material. Derive this formula.

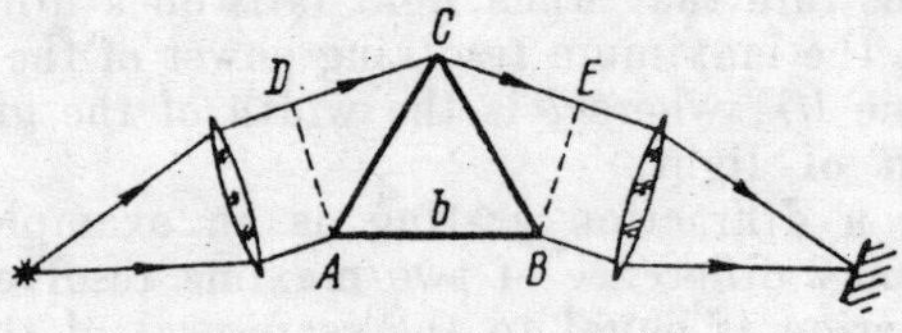

Fig. 5.28.

5.144. A spectrograph's trihedral prism is manufactured from glass whose refractive index varies with wavelength as $n = A + B/\lambda^2$, where A and B are constants, with B being equal to 0.010 μm^2. Making use of the formula from the foregoing problem, find:

(a) how the resolving power of the prism depends on λ; calculate the value of $\lambda/\delta\lambda$ in the vicinity of $\lambda_1 = 434$ nm and $\lambda_2 = 656$ nm if the width of the prism's base is $b = 5.0$ cm;

(b) the width of the prism's base capable of resolving the yellow doublet of sodium (589.0 and 589.6 nm).

5.145. How wide is the base of a trihedral prism which has the same resolving power as a diffraction grating with 10 000 lines in the second order of the spectrum if $|dn/d\lambda| = 0.10\ \mu m^{-1}$?

5.146. There is a telescope whose objective has a diameter $D = 5.0$ cm. Find the resolving power of the objective and the minimum separation between two points at a distance $l = 3.0$ km from the telescope, which it can resolve (assume $\lambda = 0.55$ μm).

5.147. Calculate the minimum separation between two points on the Moon which can be resolved by a reflecting telescope with mirror diameter 5 m. The wavelength of light is assumed to be equal to $\lambda = 0.55$ μm.

5.148. Determine the minimum multiplication of a telescope with diameter of objective $D = 5.0$ cm with which the resolving power of the objective is totally employed if the diameter of the eye's pupil is $d_0 = 4.0$ mm.

5.149. There is a microscope whose objective's numerical aperture is $\sin \alpha = 0.24$, where α is the half-angle subtended by the objective's rim. Find the minimum separation resolved by this microscope when an object is illuminated by light with wavelength $\lambda = 0.55$ μm.

5.150. Find the minimum magnification of a microscope, whose objective's numerical aperture is $\sin \alpha = 0.24$, at which the resolving power of the objective is totally employed if the diameter of the eye's pupil is $d_0 = 4.0$ mm.

5.151. A beam of X-rays with wavelength λ falls at a glancing angle 60.0° on a linear chain of scattering centres with period a. Find the angles of incidence corresponding to all diffraction maxima if $\lambda = 2a/5$.

5.152. A beam of X-rays with wavelength $\lambda = 40$ pm falls normally on a plane rectangular array of scattering centres and produces a system of diffraction maxima (Fig. 5.29) on a plane screen removed from the array by a distance $l = 10$ cm. Find the array periods a and b along the x and y axes if the distances between symmetrically located maxima of second order are equal to $\Delta x = 60$ mm (along the x axis) and $\Delta y = 40$ mm (along the y axis).

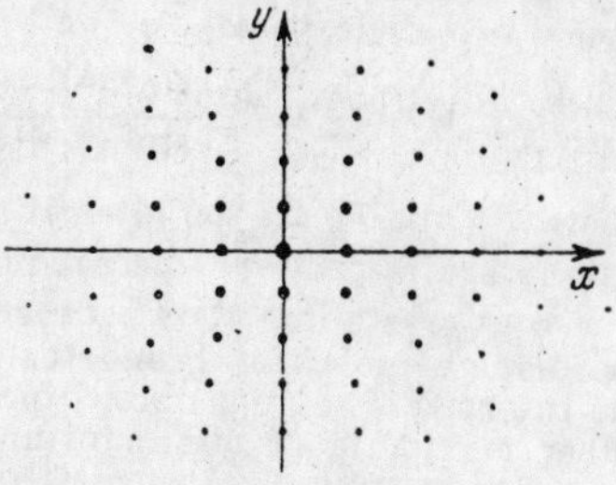

Fig. 5.29.

5.153. A beam of X-rays impinges on a three-dimensional rectangular array whose periods are a, b, and c. The direction of the incident beam coincides with the direction along which the array period is equal to a. Find the directions to the diffraction maxima and the wavelengths at which these maxima will be observed.

5.154. A narrow beam of X-rays impinges on the natural facet of a NaCl single crystal, whose density is $\rho = 2.16$ g/cm³ at a glancing angle $\alpha = 60.0°$. The mirror reflection from this facet produces a maximum of second order. Find the wavelength of radiation.

5.155. A beam of X-rays with wavelength $\lambda = 174$ pm falls on the surface of a single crystal rotating about its axis which is parallel to its surface and perpendicular to the direction of the incident beam. In this case the directions to the maxima of second and third order from the system of planes parallel to the surface of the single crystal form an angle $\alpha = 60°$ between them. Find the corresponding interplanar distance.

5.156. On transmitting a beam of X-rays with wavelength $\lambda = 17.8$ pm through a polycrystalline specimen a system of diffraction rings is produced on a screen located at a distance $l = 15$ cm from the specimen. Determine the radius of the bright ring corresponding to second order of reflection from the system of planes with interplanar distance $d = 155$ pm.

5.4. POLARIZATION OF LIGHT

• Degree of polarization of light:

$$P = \frac{I_{max} - I_{min}}{I_{max} + I_{min}}. \tag{5.4a}$$

• Malus's law:

$$I = I_0 \cos^2 \varphi. \tag{5.4b}$$

• Brewster's law:

$$\tan \theta_B = n_2/n_1. \tag{5.4c}$$

• Fresnel equations for intensity of light reflected at the boundary between two dielectrics:

$$I'_\perp = I_\perp \frac{\sin^2(\theta_1 - \theta_2)}{\sin^2(\theta_1 + \theta_2)}, \quad I'_\parallel = I_\parallel \frac{\tan^2(\theta_1 - \theta_2)}{\tan^2(\theta_1 + \theta_2)}, \tag{5.4d}$$

where $I_\perp$ and $I_\parallel$ are the intensities of incident light whose electric vector oscillations are respectively perpendicular and parallel to the plane of incidence.

• A crystalline plate between two polarizers P and P'. If the angle between the plane of polarizer P and the optical axis OO' of the plate is equal to 45°, the intensity I' of light which passes through the polarizer P' turns out to be either maximum or minimum under the following conditions:

Polarizers P and P'	$\delta = 2\pi k$	$\delta = (2k+1)\pi$
parallel	$I'_\parallel = \max$	$I'_\parallel = \min$
crossed	$I'_\perp = \min$	$I'_\perp = \max$

(5.4e)

Here $\delta = 2\pi(n_0 - n_e)d/\lambda$ is the phase difference between the ordinary and extraordinary rays, $k = 0, 1, 2, \ldots$

• Natural and magnetic rotation of the plane of polarization:

$$\varphi_{nat} = \alpha l, \quad \varphi_{magn} = VlH, \tag{5.4f}$$

where α is the rotation constant, V is Verdet's constant.

5.157. A plane monochromatic wave of natural light with intensity I_0 falls normally on a screen composed of two touching Polaroid half-planes. The principal direction of one Polaroid is parallel, and of the other perpendicular, to the boundary between them. What kind of diffraction pattern is formed behind the screen? What is the intensity of light behind the screen at the points of the plane perpendicular to the screen and passing through the boundary between the Polaroids?

5.158 A plane monochromatic wave of natural light with intensity I_0 falls normally on an opaque screen with round hole corresponding to the first Fresnel zone for the observation point P. Find the intensity of light at the point P after the hole was covered with two identical Polaroids whose principal directions are mutually perpendicular and the boundary between them passes

(a) along the diameter of the hole;

(b) along the circumference of the circle limiting the first half of the Fresnel zone.

5.159. A beam of plane-polarized light falls on a polarizer which rotates about the axis of the ray with angular velocity $\omega = 21$ rad/s. Find the energy of light passing through the polarizer per one revolution if the flux of energy of the incident ray is equal to $\Phi_0 = 4.0$ mW.

5.160. A beam of natural light falls on a system of $N = 6$ Nicol prisms whose transmission planes are turned each through an angle $\varphi = 30°$ with respect to that of the foregoing prism. What fraction of luminous flux passes through this system?

5.161. Natural light falls on a system of three identical in-line Polaroids, the principal direction of the middle Polaroid forming an angle $\varphi = 60°$ with those of two other Polaroids. The maximum transmission coefficient of each Polaroid is equal to $\tau = 0.81$ when plane-polarized light falls on them. How many times will the intensity of the light decrease after its passing through the system?

5.162. The degree of polarization of partially polarized light is $P = 0.25$. Find the ratio of intensities of the polarized component of this light and the natural component.

5.163. A Nicol prism is placed in the way of partially polarized beam of light. When the prism is turned from the position of maximum transmission through an angle $\varphi = 60°$, the intensity of transmitted light decreased by a factor of $\eta = 3.0$. Find the degree of polarization of incident light.

5.164. Two identical imperfect polarizers are placed in the way of a natural beam of light. When the polarizers' planes are parallel, the system transmits $\eta = 10.0$ times more light than in the case of crossed planes. Find the degree of polarization of light produced

(a) by each polarizer separately;

(b) by the whole system when the planes of the polarizers are parallel.

5.165. Two parallel plane-polarized beams of light of equal intensity whose oscillation planes N_1 and N_2 form a small angle φ between them (Fig. 5.30) fall on a Nicol prism. To equalize the intensities of the beams emerging behind the prism, its principal direction N must be aligned along the bisecting line A or B. Find the value of the angle φ at which the rotation of the Nicol prism through a small angle $\delta\varphi \ll \varphi$ from the position A results in the fractional change of intensities of the beams $\Delta I/I$ by the value $\eta = 100$ times exceeding that resulting due to rotation through the same angle from the position B.

5.166. Resorting to the Fresnel equations, demonstrate that light reflected from the surface of dielectric will be totally polarized if the angle of incidence θ_1 satisfies the condition $\tan\theta_1 = n$, where n is the refractive index of the dielectric. What is in this case the angle between the reflected and refracted rays?

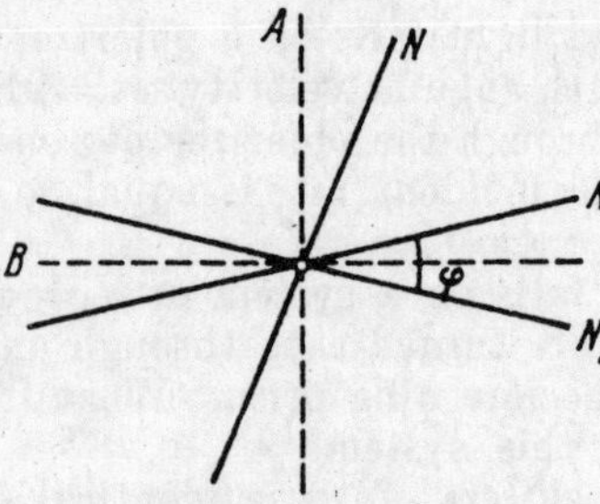

Fig. 5.30.

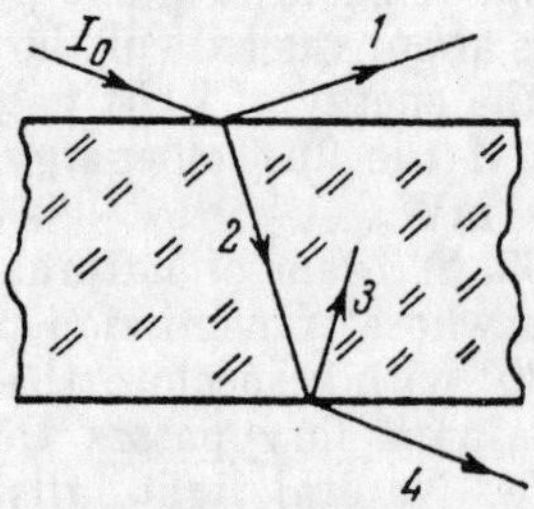

Fig. 5.31.

5.167. Natural light falls at the Brewster angle on the surface of glass. Using the Fresnel equations, find

(a) the reflection coefficient;

(b) the degree of polarization of refracted light.

5.168. A plane beam of natural light with intensity I_0 falls on the surface of water at the Brewster angle. A fraction $\rho = 0.039$ of luminous flux is reflected. Find the intensity of the refracted beam.

5.169. A beam of plane-polarized light falls on the surface of water at the Brewster angle. The polarization plane of the electric vector of the electromagnetic wave makes an angle $\varphi = 45°$ with the incidence plane. Find the reflection coefficient.

5.170. A narrow beam of natural light falls on the surface of a thick transparent plane-parallel plate at the Brewster angle. As a result, a fraction $\rho = 0.080$ of luminous flux is reflected from its top surface. Find the degree of polarization of beams *1-4* (Fig. 5.31)

5.171. A narrow beam of light of intensity I_0 falls on a plane-parallel glass plate (Fig. 5.31) at the Brewster angle. Using the Fresnel equations, find:

(a) the intensity of the transmitted beam I_4 if the oscillation plane of the incident plane-polarized light is perpendicular to the incidence plane;

(b) the degree of polarization of the transmitted light if the light falling on the plate is natural.

5.172. A narrow beam of natural light falls on a set of N thick plane-parallel glass plates at the Brewster angle. Find:

(a) the degree P of polarization of the transmitted beam;

(b) what P is equal to when $N = 1$, 2, 5, and 10.

5.173. Using the Fresnel equations, find:

(a) the reflection coefficient of natural light falling normally on the surface of glass;

(b) the relative loss of luminous flux due to reflections of a paraxial ray of natural light passing through an aligned optical system comprising five glass lenses (secondary reflections of light are to be neglected).

5.174. A light wave falls normally on the surface of glass coated with a layer of transparent substance. Neglecting secondary reflections, demonstrate that the amplitudes of light waves reflected from the two surfaces of such a layer will be equal under the condition $n' = \sqrt{n}$, where n' and n are the refractive indices of the layer and the glass respectively.

5.175. A beam of natural light falls on the surface of glass at an angle of 45°. Using the Fresnel equations, find the degree of polarization of

(a) reflected light;

(b) refracted light.

5.176. Using Huygens's principle, construct the wavefronts and the propagation directions of the ordinary and extraordinary rays in a positive uniaxial crystal whose optical axis

(a) is perpendicular to the incidence plane and parallel to the surface of the crystal;

(b) lies in the incidence plane and is parallel to the surface of the crystal;

(c) lies in the incidence plane at an angle of 45° to the surface of the crystal, and light falls at right angles to the optical axis.

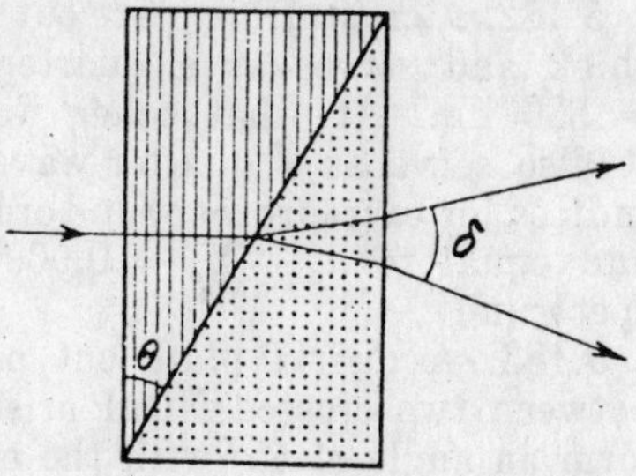

Fig. 5.32.

5.177. A narrow beam of natural light with wavelength $\lambda = 589$ nm falls normally on the surface of a Wollaston polarizing prism made of Iceland spar as shown in Fig. 5.32. The optical axes of the two parts of the prism are mutually perpendicular. Find the angle δ between the directions of the beams behind the prism if the angle θ is equal to 30°.

5.178. What kind of polarization has a plane electromagnetic wave if the projections of the vector **E** on the x and y axes are perpendicular to the propagation direction and are defined by the following equations:

(a) $E_x = E\cos(\omega t - kz)$, $E_y = E\sin(\omega t - kz)$;
(b) $E_x = E\cos(\omega t - kz)$, $E_y = E\cos(\omega t - kz + \pi/4)$;
(c) $E_x = E\cos(\omega t - kz)$, $E_y = E\cos(\omega t - kz + \pi)$?

5.179. One has to manufacture a quartz plate cut parallel to its optical axis and not exceeding 0.50 mm in thickness. Find the maximum thickness of the plate allowing plane-polarized light with wavelength $\lambda = 589$ nm
(a) to experience only rotation of polarization plane;
(b) to acquire circular polarization
after passing through that plate.

5.180. A quartz plate cut parallel to the optical axis is placed between two crossed Nicol prisms. The angle between the principal directions of the Nicol prisms and the plate is equal to 45°. The thickness of the plate is $d = 0.50$ mm. At what wavelengths in the interval from 0.50 to 0.60 μm is the intensity of light which passed through that system independent of rotation of the rear prism? The difference of refractive indices for ordinary and extraordinary rays in that wavelength interval is assumed to be $\Delta n = 0.0090$.

5.181. White natural light falls on a system of two crossed Nicol prisms having between them a quartz plate 1.50 mm thick, cut parallel to the optical axis. The axis of the plate forms an angle of 45° with the principal directions of the Nicol prisms. The light transmitted through that system was split into the spectrum. How many dark fringes will be observed in the wavelength interval from 0.55 to 0.66 μm? The difference of refractive indices for ordinary and extraordinary rays in that wavelength interval is assumed to be equal to 0.0090.

5.182. A crystalline plate cut parallel to its optical axis is 0.25 mm thick and serves as a quarter-wave plate for a wavelength $\lambda = 530$ nm. At what other wavelengths of visible spectrum will it also serve as a quarter-wave plate? The difference of refractive indices for extraordinary and ordinary rays is assumed to be constant and equal to $n_e - n_o = 0.0090$ at all wavelengths of the visible spectrum.

5.183. A quartz plate cut parallel to its optical axis is placed between two crossed Nicol prisms so that their principle directions form an angle of 45° with the optical axis of the plate. What is the minimum thickness of that plate transmitting light of wavelength $\lambda_1 = 643$ nm with maximum intensity while greatly reducing the intensity of transmitting light of wavelength $\lambda_2 = 564$ nm? The difference of refractive indices for extraordinary and ordinary rays is assumed to be equal to $n_e - n_o = 0.0090$ for both wavelengths.

5.184. A quartz wedge with refracting angle $\Theta = 3.5°$ is inserted between two crossed Polaroids. The optical axis of the wedge is parallel to its edge and forms an angle of 45° with the principal directions of the Polaroids. On transmission of light with wavelength $\lambda = 550$ nm through this system, an interference fringe pattern is formed. The width of each fringe is $\Delta x = 1.0$ mm. Find the difference of refractive indices of quartz for ordinary and extraordinary rays at the wavelength indicated above.

5.185. Natural monochromatic light of intensity I_0 falls on a system of two Polaroids between which a crystalline plate is inserted, cut parallel to its optical axis. The plate introduces a phase difference δ between the ordinary and extraordinary rays. Demonstrate that the intensity of light transmitted through that system is equal to

$$I = \frac{1}{2} I_0 [\cos^2(\varphi - \varphi') - \sin 2\varphi \cdot \sin 2\varphi' \ \sin^2(\delta/2)],$$

where φ and φ' are the angles between the optical axis of the crystal and the principal directions of the Polaroids. In particular, consider the cases of crossed and parallel Polaroids.

5.186. Monochromatic light with circular polarization falls normally on a crystalline plate cut parallel to the optical axis. Behind the plate there is a Nicol prism whose principal direction forms an angle φ with the optical axis of the plate. Demonstrate that the intensity of light transmitted through that system is equal to

$$I = I_0 (1 + \sin 2\varphi \cdot \sin \delta),$$

where δ is the phase difference between the ordinary and extraordinary rays which is introduced by the plate.

5.187. Explain how, using a Polaroid and a quarter-wave plate made of positive uniaxial crystal ($n_e > n_o$), to distinguish

(a) light with left-hand circular polarization from that with right-hand polarization;

(b) natural light from light with circular polarization and from the composition of natural light and that with circular polarization.

5.188. Light with wavelength λ falls on a system of crossed polarizer P and analyzer A between which a Babinet compensator C is inserted (Fig. 5.33). The compensator consists of two quartz wedges with the optical axis of one of them being parallel to the edge, and of the other, perpendicular to it. The principal directions of the polarizer and the analyser form an angle of 45° with the optical axes of the compensator. The refracting angle of the wedges is equal to Θ ($\Theta \ll 1$) and the difference of refractive indices of quartz is $n_e - n_o$. The insertion of investigated birefringent sample S, with the optical axis oriented as shown in the figure, results in displacement of the fringes upward by δx mm. Find:

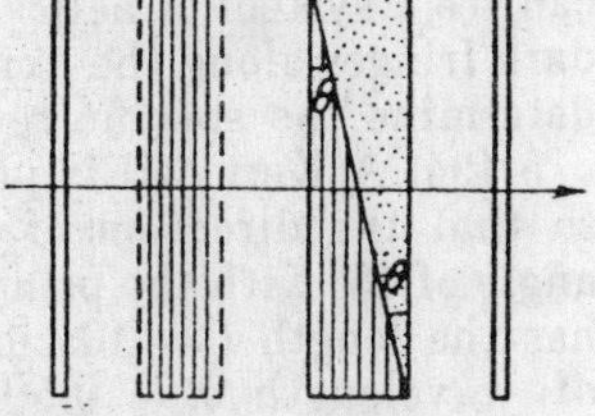

Fig. 5.33.

(a) the width of the fringe Δx;

(b) the magnitude and the sign of the optical path difference of ordinary and extraordinary rays, which appears due to the sample S.

5.189. Using the tables of the Appendix, calculate the difference of refractive indices of quartz for light of wavelength $\lambda = 589.5$ nm with right-hand and left-hand circular polarizations.

5.190. Plane-polarized light of wavelength 0.59 μm falls on a trihedral quartz prism P (Fig. 5.34) with refracting angle $\Theta = 30°$. Inside the prism light propagates along the optical axis whose direction is shown by hatching. Behind the Polaroid Pol an interference pattern of bright and dark fringes of width $\Delta x = 15.0$ mm is observed. Find the specific rotation constant of quartz and the distribution of intensity of light behind the Polaroid.

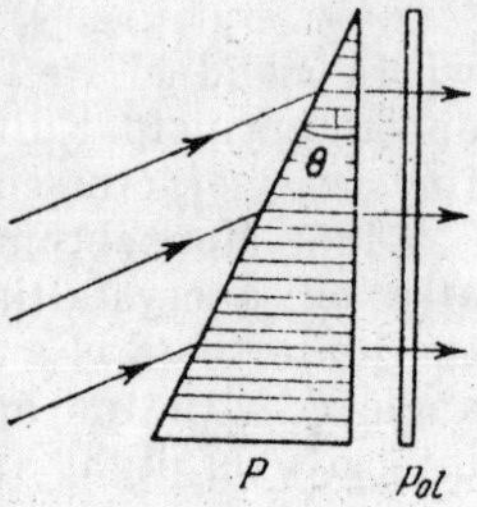

Fig. 5.34.

5.191. Natural monochromatic light falls on a system of two crossed Nicol prisms between which a quartz plate cut at right angles to its optical axis is inserted. Find the minimum thickness of the plate at which this system will transmit $\eta = 0.30$ of luminous flux if the specific rotation constant of quartz is equal to $\alpha = 17$ ang.deg/mm.

5.192. Light passes through a system of two crossed Nicol prisms between which a quartz plate cut at right angles to its optical axis is placed. Determine the minimum thickness of the plate which allows light of wavelength 436 nm to be completely cut off by the system and transmits half the light of wavelength 497 nm. The specific rotation constant of quartz for these wavelengths is equal to 41.5 and 31.1 angular degrees per mm respectively.

5.193. Plane-polarized light of wavelength 589 nm propagates along the axis of a cylindrical glass vessel filled with slightly turbid sugar solution of concentration 500 g/l. Viewing from the side, one can see a system of helical fringes, with 50 cm between neighbouring dark fringes along the axis. Explain the emergence of the fringes and determine the specific rotation constant of the solution.

5.194. A Kerr cell is positioned between two crossed Nicol prisms so that the direction of electric field **E** in the capacitor forms an angle of 45° with the principal directions of the prisms. The capacitor has the length $l = 10$ cm and is filled up with nitrobenzene. Light of wavelength $\lambda = 0.50$ μm passes through the system. Taking into account that in this case the Kerr constant is equal to $B = 2.2 \cdot 10^{-10}$ cm/V², find:

(a) the minimum strength of electric field E in the capacitor at which the intensity of light that passes through this system is independent of rotation of the rear prism;

(b) how many times per second light will be interrupted when a sinusoidal voltage of frequency $\nu = 10$ MHz and strength amplitude $E_m = 50$ kV/cm is applied to the capacitor.

Note. The Kerr constant is the coefficient B in the equation $n_e - n_o = B\lambda E^2$.

5.195. Monochromatic plane-polarized light with angular frequency ω passes through a certain substance along a uniform magnetic field H. Find the difference of refractive indices for right-hand and left-hand components of light beam with circular polarization if the Verdet constant is equal to V.

5.196. A certain substance is placed in a longitudinal magnetic field of a solenoid located between two Polaroids. The length of the tube with substance is equal to $l = 30$ cm. Find the Verdet constant if at a field strength $H = 56.5$ kA/m the angle of rotation of polarization plane is equal to $\varphi_1 = +5°10'$ for one direction of the field and to $\varphi_2 = -3°20'$, for the opposite direction.

5.197. A narrow beam of plane-polarized light passes through dextrorotatory positive compound placed into a longitudinal magnetic field as shown in Fig. 5.35. Find the angle through which the

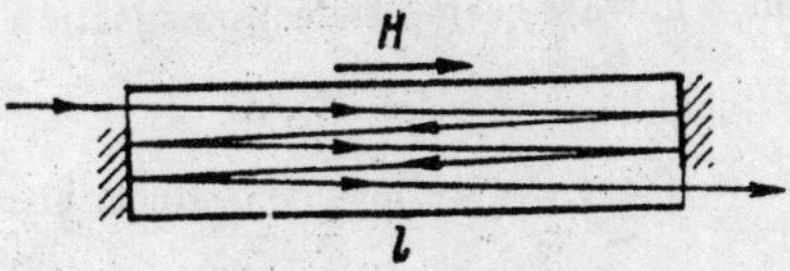

Fig. 5.35.

polarization plane of the transmitted beam will turn if the length of the tube with the compound is equal to l, the specific rotation constant of the compound is equal to α, the Verdet constant is V, and the magnetic field strength is H.

5.198. A tube of length $l = 26$ cm is filled with benzene and placed in a longitudinal magnetic field of a solenoid positioned between two Polaroids. The angle between the principle directions of the Polaroids is equal to 45°. Find the minimum strength of the magnetic field at which light of the wavelength 589 nm propagates through that system only in one direction (optical valve). What happens if the direction of the given magnetic field is changed to the opposite one?

5.199. Experience shows that a body irradiated with light with circular polarization acquires a torque. This happens because such a light possesses an angular momentum whose flow density in vacuum is equal to $M = I/\omega$, where I is the intensity of light, ω is the angular oscillation frequency. Suppose light with circular polarization and wavelength $\lambda = 0.70$ µm falls normally on a uniform black disc of mass $m = 10$ mg which can freely rotate about its axis. How soon will its angular velocity become equal to $\omega_0 = 1.0$ rad/s provided $I = 10$ W/cm²?

5.5. DISPERSION AND ABSORPTION OF LIGHT

• Permittivity of substance according to elementary theory of dispersion:

$$\varepsilon = 1 + \sum_k \frac{n_k e^2/m\varepsilon_0}{\omega_{0k}^2 - \omega^2}, \qquad (5.5a)$$

where n_k is the concentration of electrons of natural frequency ω_{0k}.

• Relation between refractive index and permittivity of substance:

$$n = \sqrt{\varepsilon}. \qquad (5.5b)$$

• Phase velocity v and group velocity u:

$$v = \omega/k, \quad u = d\omega/dk. \qquad (5.5c)$$

• Rayleigh's formula:

$$u = v - \lambda \frac{dv}{d\lambda}. \qquad (5.5d)$$

• Attenuation of a narrow beam of electromagnetic radiation:

$$I = I_0 e^{-\mu d}, \qquad (5.5e)$$

where $\mu = \varkappa + \varkappa'$, μ, $\varkappa$, $\varkappa'$ are the coefficients of linear attenuation, absorption, and scattering.

5.200. A free electron is located in the field of a monochromatic light wave. The intensity of light is $I = 150\ \text{W/m}^2$, its frequency is $\omega = 3.4 \cdot 10^{15}\ \text{s}^{-1}$. Find:

(a) the electron's oscillation amplitude and its velocity amplitude;

(b) the ratio F_m/F_e, where F_m and F_e are the amplitudes of forces with which the magnetic and electric components of the light wave field act on the electron; demonstrate that that ratio is equal to $\frac{1}{2} v/c$, where v is the electron's velocity amplitude and c is the velocity of light.

Instruction. The action of the magnetic field component can be disregarded in the equation of motion of the electron since the calculations show it to be negligible.

5.201. An electromagnetic wave of frequency ω propagates in dilute plasma. The free electron concentration in plasma is equal to n_0. Neglecting the interaction of the wave and plasma ions, find:

(a) the frequency dependence of plasma permittivity;

(b) how the phase velocity of the electromagnetic wave depends on its wavelength λ in plasma.

5.202. Find the free electron concentration in ionosphere if its refractive index is equal to $n = 0.90$ for radiowaves of frequency $\nu = 100$ MHz.

5.203. Assuming electrons of substance to be free when subjected to hard X-rays, determine by what magnitude the refractive index of graphite differs from unity in the case of X-rays whose wavelength in vacuum is equal to $\lambda = 50$ pm.

5.204. An electron experiences a quasi-elastic force kx and a "friction force" $\gamma\dot{x}$ in the field of electromagnetic radiation. The E-component of the field varies as $E = E_0 \cos \omega t$. Neglecting the action of the magnetic component of the field, find:

(a) the motion equation of the electron;

(b) the mean power absorbed by the electron; the frequency at which that power is maximum and the expression for the maximum mean power.

5.205. In some cases permittivity of substance turns out to be a complex or a negative quantity, and refractive index, respectively, a complex ($n' = n + i\varkappa$) or an imaginary ($n' = i\varkappa$) quantity. Write the equation of a plane wave for both of these cases and find out the physical meaning of such refractive indices.

5.206. A sounding of dilute plasma by radiowaves of various frequencies reveals that radiowaves with wavelengths exceeding $\lambda_0 = 0.75$ m experience total internal reflection. Find the free electron concentration in that plasma.

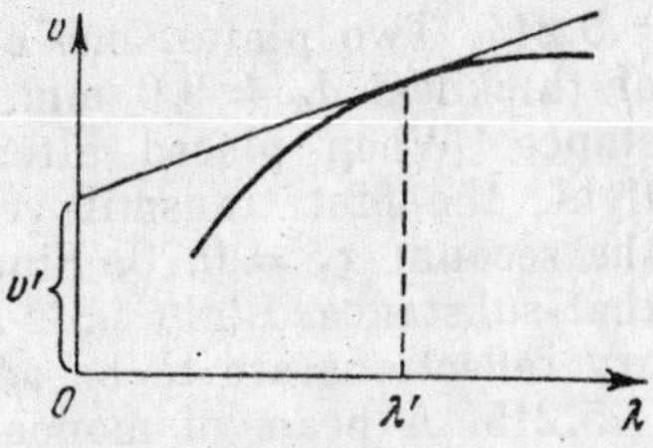

Fig. 5.36.

5.207. Using the definition of the group velocity u, derive Rayleigh's formula (5.5d). Demonstrate that in the vicinity of $\lambda = \lambda'$ the velocity u is equal to the segment v' cut by the tangent of the curve $v(\lambda)$ at the point λ' (Fig. 5.36).

5.208. Find the relation between the group velocity u and phase velocity v for the following dispersion laws:

(a) $v \propto 1/\sqrt{\lambda}$;

(b) $v \propto k$;

(c) $v \propto 1/\omega^2$.

Here λ, k, and ω are the wavelength, wave number, and angular frequency.

5.209. In a certain medium the relationship between the group and phase velocities of an electromagnetic wave has the form $uv = c^2$, where c is the velocity of light in vacuum. Find the dependence of permittivity of that medium on wave frequency, $\varepsilon(\omega)$.

5.210. The refractive index of carbon dioxide at the wavelengths 509, 534, and 589 nm is equal to 1.647, 1.640, and 1.630 respectively. Calculate the phase and group velocities of light in the vicinity of $\lambda = 534$ nm.

5.211. A train of plane light waves propagates in the medium where the phase velocity v is a linear function of wavelength: $v = a + b\lambda$, where a and b are some positive constants. Demonstrate that in such a medium the shape of an arbitrary train of light waves is restored after the time interval $\tau = 1/b$.

5.212. A beam of natural light of intensity I_0 falls on a system of two crossed Nicol prisms between which a tube filled with certain solution is placed in a longitudinal magnetic field of strength H. The length of the tube is l, the coefficient of linear absorption of solution is $\varkappa$, and the Verdet constant is V. Find the intensity of light transmitted through that system.

5.213. A plane monochromatic light wave of intensity I_0 falls normally on a plane-parallel plate both of whose surfaces have a reflection coefficient ρ. Taking into account multiple reflections, find the intensity of the transmitted light if

(a) the plate is perfectly transparent, i.e. the absorption is absent;

(b) the coefficient of linear absorption is equal to $\varkappa$, and the plate thickness is d.

5.214. Two plates, one of thickness $d_1 = 3.8$ mm and the other of thickness $d_2 = 9.0$ mm, are manufactured from a certain substance. When placed alternately in the way of monochromatic light, the first transmits $\tau_1 = 0.84$ fraction of luminous flux and the second, $\tau_2 = 0.70$. Find the coefficient of linear absorption of that substance. Light falls at right angles to the plates. The secondary reflections are to be neglected.

5.215. A beam of monochromatic light passes through a pile of $N = 5$ identical plane-parallel glass plates each of thickness $l = 0.50$ cm. The coefficient of reflection at each surface of the plates is $\rho = 0.050$. The ratio of the intensity of light transmitted through the pile of plates to the intensity of incident light is $\tau = 0.55$. Neglecting the secondary reflections of light, find the absorption coefficient of the given glass.

5.216. A beam of monochromatic light falls normally on the surface of a plane-parallel plate of thickness l. The absorption coefficient of the substance the plate is made of varies linearly along the normal to its surface from $\varkappa_1$ to $\varkappa_2$. The coefficient of reflection at each surface of the plate is equal to ρ. Neglecting the secondary reflections, find the transmission coefficient of such a plate.

5.217. A beam of light of intensity I_0 falls normally on a transparent plane-parallel plate of thickness l. The beam contains all the wavelengths in the interval from λ_1 to λ_2 of equal spectral intensity. Find the intensity of the transmitted beam if in this wavelength interval the absorption coefficient is a linear function of λ, with extreme values $\varkappa_1$ and $\varkappa_2$. The coefficient of reflection at each surface is equal to ρ. The secondary reflections are to be neglected.

5.218. A light filter is a plate of thickness d whose absorption coefficient depends on wavelength λ as

$$\varkappa(\lambda) = \alpha(1 - \lambda/\lambda_0)^2 \text{ cm}^{-1},$$

where α and λ_0 are constants. Find the passband $\Delta\lambda$ of this light filter, that is the band at whose edges the attenuation of light is η times that at the wavelength λ_0. The coefficient of reflection from the surfaces of the light filter is assumed to be the same at all wavelengths.

5.219. A point source of monochromatic light emitting a luminous flux Φ is positioned at the centre of a spherical layer of substance. The inside radius of the layer is a, the outside one is b. The coefficient of linear absorption of the substance is equal to $\varkappa$, the reflection coefficient of the surfaces is equal to ρ. Neglecting the secondary reflections, find the intensity of light that passes through that layer.

5.220. How many times will the intensity of a narrow X-ray beam of wavelength 20 pm decrease after passing through a lead plate of thickness $d = 1.0$ mm if the mass absorption coefficient for the given radiation wavelength is equal to $\mu/\rho = 3.6$ cm²/g?

5.221. A narrow beam of X-ray radiation of wavelength 62 pm penetrates an aluminium screen 2.6 cm thick. How thick must a lead screen be to attenuate the beam just as much? The mass absorption coefficients of aluminium and lead for this radiation are equal to 3.48 and 72.0 cm²/g respectively.

5.222. Find the thickness of aluminium layer which reduces by half the intensity of a narrow monochromatic X-ray beam if the corresponding mass absorption coefficient is $\mu/\rho = 0.32$ cm²/g.

5.223. How many 50%-absorption layers are there in the plate reducing the intensity of a narrow X-ray beam $\eta = 50$ times?

5.6. OPTICS OF MOVING SOURCES

- Doppler effect for $\ll c$:

$$\frac{\Delta\omega}{\omega} = \frac{v}{c}\cos\theta \tag{5.6a}$$

where v is the velocity of a source, θ is the angle between the source's motion direction and the observation line.

- Doppler effect in the general case:

$$\omega = \omega_0 \frac{\sqrt{1-\beta^2}}{1-\beta\cos\theta}, \tag{5.6b}$$

where $\beta = v/c$.

- If $\theta = 0$, the Doppler effect is called radial, and if $\theta = \pi/2$, transverse.
- Vavilov-Cherenkov effect:

$$\cos\theta = \frac{c}{nv} \tag{5.6c}$$

where θ is the angle between the radiation propagation direction and the velocity vector v of a particle.

5.224. In the Fizeau experiment on measurement of the velocity of light the distance between the gear wheel and the mirror is $l = 7.0$ km, the number of teeth is $z = 720$. Two successive disappearances of light are observed at the following rotation velocities of the wheel: $n_1 = 283$ rps and $n_2 = 313$ rps. Find the velocity of light.

5.225. A source of light moves with velocity v relative to a receiver. Demonstrate that for $v \ll c$ the fractional variation of frequency of light is defined by Eq. (5.6a).

5.226. One of the spectral lines emitted by excited He^+ ions has a wavelength $\lambda = 410$ nm. Find the Doppler shift $\Delta\lambda$ of that line when observed at an angle $\theta = 30°$ to the beam of moving ions possessing kinetic energy $T = 10$ MeV.

5.227. When a spectral line of wavelength $\lambda = 0.59$ μm is observed in the directions to the opposite edges of the solar disc along its equator, there is a difference in wavelengths equal to $\delta\lambda = 8.0$ pm. Find the period of the Sun's revolution about its own axis.

5.228. The Doppler effect has made it possible to discover the double stars which are so distant that their resolution by means of a telescope is impossible. The spectral lines of such stars periodically become doublets indicating that the radiation does come from two stars revolving about their centre of mass. Assuming the masses of the two stars to be equal, find the distance between them and their masses if the maximum splitting of the spectral lines is equal to $(\Delta\lambda/\lambda)_m = 1.2 \cdot 10^{-4}$ and occurs every $\tau = 30$ days.

5.229. A plane electromagnetic wave of frequency ω_0 falls normally on the surface of a mirror approaching with a relativistic velocity V. Making use of the Doppler formula, find the frequency of the reflected wave. Simplify the obtained expression for the case $V \ll c$.

5.230. A radar operates at a wavelength $\lambda = 50.0$ cm. Find the velocity of an approaching aircraft if the beat frequency between the transmitted signal and the signal reflected from the aircraft is equal to $\Delta\nu = 1.00$ kHz at the radar location.

5.231. Taking into account that the wave phase $\omega t - kx$ is an invariant, i.e. it retains its value on transition from one inertial frame to another, determine how the frequency ω and the wave number k entering the expression for the wave phase are transformed. Examine the unidimensional case.

5.232. How fast does a certain nebula recede if the hydrogen line $\lambda = 434$ nm in its spectrum is displaced by 130 nm toward longer wavelengths?

5.233. How fast should a car move for the driver to perceive a red traffic light ($\lambda \approx 0.70$ μm) as a green one ($\lambda' \approx 0.55$ μm)?

5.234. An observer moves with velocity $v_1 = \frac{1}{2}c$ along a straight line. In front of him a source of monochromatic light moves with velocity $v_2 = \frac{3}{4}c$ in the same direction and along the same straight line. The proper frequency of light is equal to ω_0. Find the frequency of light registered by the observer.

5.235. One of the spectral lines of atomic hydrogen has the wavelength $\lambda = 656.3$ nm. Find the Doppler shift $\Delta\lambda$ of that line when observed at right angles to the beam of hydrogen atoms with kinetic energy $T = 1.0$ MeV (the transverse Doppler effect).

5.236. A source emitting electromagnetic signals with proper frequency $\omega_0 = 3.0 \cdot 10^{10}$ s^{-1} moves at a constant velocity $v = 0.80\,c$ along a straight line separated from a stationary observer P by a distance l (Fig. 5.37). Find the frequency of the signals perceived by the observer at the moment when

(a) the source is at the point O;

(b) the observer sees it at the point O.

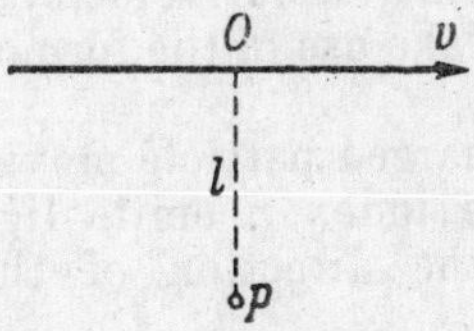

Fig. 5.37.

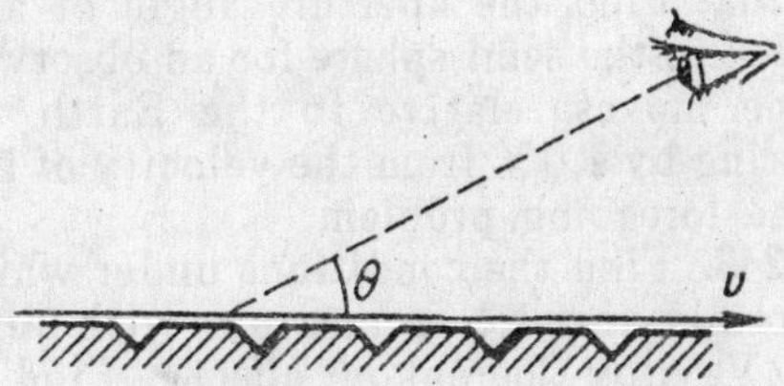

Fig. 5.38.

5.237. A narrow beam of electrons passes immediately over the surface of a metallic mirror with a diffraction grating with period $d = 2.0$ μm inscribed on it. The electrons move with velocity v, comparable to c, at right angles to the lines of the grating. The trajectory of the electrons can be seen in the form of a strip, whose colouring depends on the observation angle θ (Fig. 5.38). Interpret this phenomenon. Find the wavelength of the radiation observed at an angle $\theta = 45°$.

5.238. A gas consists of atoms of mass m being in thermodynamic equilibrium at temperature T. Suppose ω_0 is the natural frequency of light emitted by the atoms.

(a) Demonstrate that the spectral distribution of the emitted light is defined by the formula

$$I_\omega = I_0 e^{-a(1-\omega/\omega_0)^2},$$

(I_0 is the spectral intensity corresponding to the frequency ω_0, $a = mc^2/2kT$).

(b) Find the relative width $\Delta\omega/\omega_0$ of a given spectral line, i.e. the width of the line between the frequencies at which $I_\omega = I_0/2$.

5.239. A plane electromagnetic wave propagates in a medium moving with constant velocity $V \ll c$ relative to an inertial frame K. Find the velocity of that wave in the frame K if the refractive index of the medium is equal to n and the propagation direction of the wave coincides with that of the medium.

5.240. Aberration of light is the apparent displacement of stars attributable to the effect of the orbital motion of the Earth. The direction to a star in the ecliptic plane varies periodically, and the star performs apparent oscillations within an angle $\delta\theta = 41''$. Find the orbital velocity of the Earth.

5.241. Demonstrate that the angle θ between the propagation direction of light and the x axis transforms on transition from the reference frame K to K' according to the formula

$$\cos\theta' = \frac{\cos\theta - \beta}{1 - \beta\cos\theta},$$

where $\beta = V/c$ and V is the velocity of the frame K' with respect to the frame K. The x and x' axes of the reference frames coincide.

5.242. Find the aperture angle of a cone in which all the stars located in the semi-sphere for an observer on the Earth will be visible if one moves relative to the Earth with relativistic velocity V differing by 1.0% from the velocity of light. Make use of the formula of the foregoing problem.

5.243. Find the conditions under which a charged particle moving uniformly through a medium with refractive index n emits light (the Vavilov-Cherenkov effect). Find also the direction of that radiation.

Instruction. Consider the interference of oscillations induced by the particle at various moments of time.

5.244. Find the lowest values of the kinetic energy of an electron and a proton causing the emergence of Cherenkov's radiation in a medium with refractive index $n = 1.60$. For what particles is this minimum value of kinetic energy equal to $T_{min} = 29.6$ MeV?

5.245. Find the kinetic energy of electrons emitting light in a medium with refractive index $n = 1.50$ at an angle $\theta = 30°$ to their propagation direction.

5.7. THERMAL RADIATION. QUANTUM NATURE OF LIGHT

• Radiosity

$$M_e = \frac{c}{4} u, \tag{5.7a}$$

where u is the space density of thermal radiation energy.

• Wien's formula and Wien's displacement law:

$$u_\omega = \omega^3 F(\omega/T), \quad T\lambda_m = b, \tag{5.7b}$$

where λ_m is the wavelength corresponding to the maximum of the function u_λ.

• Stefan-Boltzmann law:

$$M_e = \sigma T^4, \tag{5.7c}$$

where σ is the Stefan-Boltzmann constant.

• Planck's formula:

$$u_\omega = \frac{\hbar\omega^3}{\pi^2 c^3} \frac{1}{e^{\hbar\omega/kT} - 1}. \tag{5.7d}$$

• Einstein's photoelectric equation:

$$\hbar\omega = A + \frac{mv^2_{max}}{2}. \tag{5.7e}$$

• **Compton effect:**

$$\Delta\lambda = 2\pi \lambda\!\!\!^{-}_C (1 - \cos\theta), \qquad (5.7f)$$

where $\lambda\!\!\!^{-}_C = \hbar/mc$ is Compton's wavelength.

5.246. Using Wien's formula, demonstrate that
(a) the most probable radiation frequency $\omega_{pr} \backsim T$;
(b) the maximum spectral density of thermal radiation $(u_\omega)_{max} \backsim T^3$;
(c) the radiosity $M_e \backsim T^4$.

5.247. The temperature of one of the two heated black bodies is $T_1 = 2500$ K. Find the temperature of the other body if the wavelength corresponding to its maximum emissive capacity exceeds by $\Delta\lambda = 0.50$ μm the wavelength corresponding to the maximum emissive capacity of the first black body.

5.248. The radiosity of a black body is $M_e = 3.0$ W/cm². Find the wavelength corresponding to the maximum emissive capacity of that body.

5.249. The spectral composition of solar radiation is much the same as that of a black body whose maximum emission corresponds to the wavelength 0.48 μm. Find the mass lost by the Sun every second due to radiation. Evaluate the time interval during which the mass of the Sun diminishes by 1 per cent.

5.250. Find the temperature of totally ionized hydrogen plasma of density $\rho = 0.10$ g/cm³ at which the thermal radiation pressure is equal to the gas kinetic pressure of the particles of plasma. Take into account that the thermal radiation pressure $p = u/3$, where u is the space density of radiation energy, and at high temperatures all substances obey the equation of state of an ideal gas.

5.251. A copper ball of diameter $d = 1.2$ cm was placed in an evacuated vessel whose walls are kept at the absolute zero temperature. The initial temperature of the ball is $T_0 = 300$ K. Assuming the surface of the ball to be absolutely black, find how soon its temperature decreases $\eta = 2.0$ times.

5.252. There are two cavities (Fig. 5.39) with small holes of equal diameters $d = 1.0$ cm and perfectly reflecting outer surfaces. The

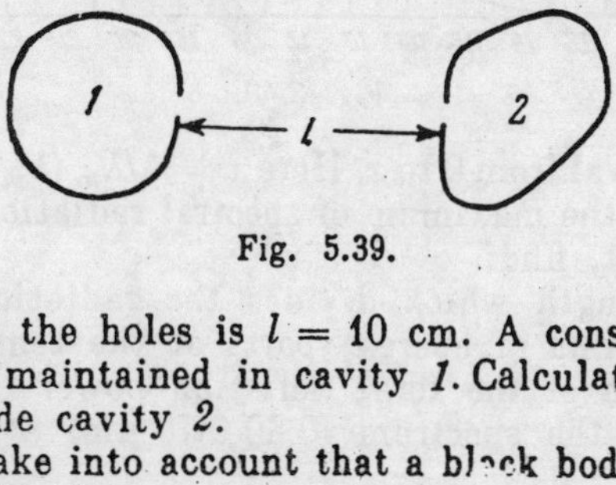

Fig. 5.39.

distance between the holes is $l = 10$ cm. A constant temperature $T_1 = 1700$ K is maintained in cavity *1*. Calculate the steady-state temperature inside cavity *2*.

Instruction. Take into account that a black body radiation obeys the cosine emission law.

5.253. A cavity of volume $V = 1.0$ l is filled with thermal radiation at a temperature $T = 1000$ K. Find:

(a) the heat capacity C_V; (b) the entropy S of that radiation.

5.254. Assuming the spectral distribution of thermal radiation energy to obey Wien's formula $u(\omega, T) = A\omega^3 \exp(-a\omega/T)$, where $a = 7.64$ ps·K, find for a temperature $T = 2000$ K the most probable

(a) radiation frequency; (b) radiation wavelength.

5.255. Using Planck's formula, derive the approximate expressions for the space spectral density u_ω of radiation

(a) in the range where $\hbar\omega \ll kT$ (Rayleigh-Jeans formula);

(b) in the range where $\hbar\omega \gg kT$ (Wien's formula).

5.256. Transform Planck's formula for space spectral density u_ω of radiation from the variable ω to the variables ν (linear frequency) and λ (wavelength).

5.257. Using Planck's formula, find the power radiated by a unit area of a black body within a narrow wavelength interval $\Delta\lambda = 1.0$ nm close to the maximum of spectral radiation density at a temperature $T = 3000$ K of the body.

5.258. Fig. 5.40 shows the plot of the function $y(x)$ representing a fraction of the total power of thermal radiation falling within

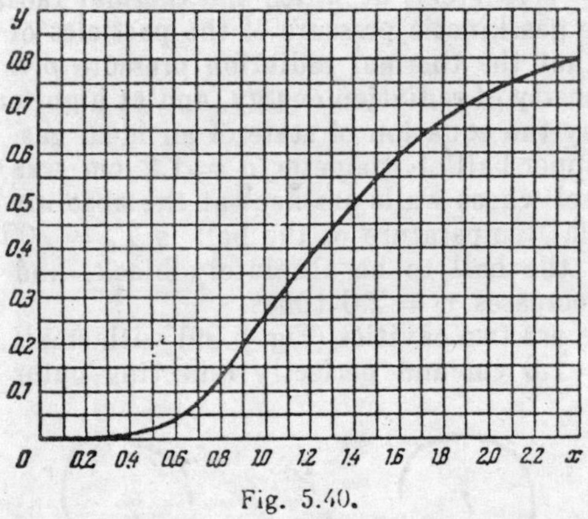

Fig. 5.40.

the spectral interval from 0 to x. Here $x = \lambda/\lambda_m$ (λ_m is the wavelength corresponding to the maximum of spectral radiation density).

Using this plot, find:

(a) the wavelength which divides the radiation spectrum into two equal (in terms of energy) parts at the temperature 3700 K;

(b) the fraction of the total radiation power falling within the visible range of the spectrum (0.40-0.76 μm) at the temperature 5000 K;

(c) how many times the power radiated at wavelengths exceeding 0.76 μm will increase if the temperature rises from 3000 to 5000 K.

5.259. Making use of Planck's formula, derive the expressions determining the number of photons per 1 cm^3 of a cavity at a temperature T in the spectral intervals (ω, $\omega + d\omega$) and (λ, $\lambda + d\lambda$).

5.260. An isotropic point source emits light with wavelength $\lambda = 589$ nm. The radiation power of the source is $P = 10$ W. Find:

(a) the mean density of the flow of photons at a distance $r = 2.0$ m from the source;

(b) the distance between the source and the point at which the mean concentration of photons is equal to $n = 100$ cm^{-3}.

5.261. From the standpoint of the corpuscular theory demonstrate that the momentum transferred by a beam of parallel light rays per unit time does not depend on its spectral composition but depends only on the energy flux Φ_e.

5.262. A laser emits a light pulse of duration $\tau = 0.13$ ms and energy $E = 10$ J. Find the mean pressure exerted by such a light pulse when it is focussed into a spot of diameter $d = 10$ µm on a surface perpendicular to the beam and possessing a reflection coefficient $\rho = 0.50$.

5.263. A short light pulse of energy $E = 7.5$ J falls in the form of a narrow and almost parallel beam on a mirror plate whose reflection coefficient is $\rho = 0.60$. The angle of incidence is 30°. In terms of the corpuscular theory find the momentum transferred to the plate.

5.264. A plane light wave of intensity $I = 0.20$ W/cm^2 falls on a plane mirror surface with reflection coefficient $\rho = 0.8$. The angle of incidence is 45°. In terms of the corpuscular theory find the magnitude of the normal pressure exerted by light on that surface.

5.265. A plane light wave of intensity $I = 0.70$ W/cm^2 illuminates a sphere with ideal mirror surface. The radius of the sphere is $R = 5.0$ cm. From the standpoint of the corpuscular theory find the force that light exerts on the sphere.

5.266. An isotropic point source of radiation power P is located on the axis of an ideal mirror plate. The distance between the source and the plate exceeds the radius of the plate η-fold. In terms of the corpuscular theory find the force that light exerts on the plate.

5.267. In a reference frame K a photon of frequency ω falls normally on a mirror approaching it with relativistic velocity V. Find the momentum imparted to the mirror during the reflection of the photon

(a) in the reference frame fixed to the mirror;

(b) in the frame K.

5.268. A small ideal mirror of mass $m = 10$ mg is suspended by a weightless thread of length $l = 10$ cm. Find the angle through which the thread will be deflected when a short laser pulse with energy $E = 13$ J is shot in the horizontal direction at right angles to the mirror. Where does the mirror get its kinetic energy?

5.269. A photon of frequency ω_0 is emitted from the surface of a star whose mass is M and radius R. Find the gravitational shift of frequency $\Delta\omega/\omega_0$ of the photon at a very great distance from the star.

5.270. A voltage applied to an X-ray tube being increased $\eta = 1.5$ times, the short-wave limit of an X-ray continuous spectrum shifts by $\Delta\lambda = 26$ pm. Find the initial voltage applied to the tube.

5.271. A narrow X-ray beam falls on a NaCl single crystal. The least angle of incidence at which the mirror reflection from the system of crystallographic planes is still observed is equal to $\alpha = 4.1°$. The interplanar distance is $d = 0.28$ nm. How high is the voltage applied to the X-ray tube?

5.272. Find the wavelength of the short-wave limit of an X-ray continuous spectrum if electrons approach the anticathode of the tube with velocity $v = 0.85\,c$, where c is the velocity of light.

5.273. Find the photoelectric threshold for zinc and the maximum velocity of photoelectrons liberated from its surface by electromagnetic radiation with wavelength 250 nm.

5.274. Illuminating the surface of a certain metal alternately with light of wavelengths $\lambda_1 = 0.35$ μm and $\lambda_2 = 0.54$ μm, it was found that the corresponding maximum velocities of photoelectrons differ by a factor $\eta = 2.0$. Find the work function of that metal.

5.275. Up to what maximum potential will a copper ball, remote from all other bodies, be charged when irradiated by electromagnetic radiation of wavelength $\lambda = 140$ nm?

5.276. Find the maximum kinetic energy of photoelectrons liberated from the surface of lithium by electromagnetic radiation whose electric component varies with time as $E = a\,(1 + \cos\omega t)\cos\omega_0 t$, where a is a constant, $\omega = 6.0\cdot10^{14}\ \text{s}^{-1}$ and $\omega_0 = 3.60\cdot10^{15}\ \text{s}^{-1}$.

5.277. Electromagnetic radiation of wavelength $\lambda = 0.30$ μm falls on a photocell operating in the saturation mode. The corresponding spectral sensitivity of the photocell is $J = 4.8$ mA/W. Find the yield of photoelectrons, i.e. the number of photoelectrons produced by each incident photon.

5.278. There is a vacuum photocell whose one electrode is made of cesium and the other of copper. Find the maximum velocity of photoelectrons approaching the copper electrode when the cesium electrode is subjected to electromagnetic radiation of wavelength 0.22 μm and the electrodes are shorted outside the cell.

5.279. A photoelectric current emerging in the circuit of a vacuum photocell when its zinc electrode is subjected to electromagnetic radiation of wavelength 262 nm is cancelled if an external decelerating voltage 1.5 V is applied. Find the magnitude and polarity of the outer contact potential difference of the given photocell.

5.280. Compose the expression for a quantity whose dimension is length, using velocity of light c, mass of a particle m, and Planck's constant $\hbar$. What is that quantity?

5.281. Using the conservation laws, demonstrate that a free electron cannot absorb a photon completely.

5.282. Explain the following features of Compton scattering of light by matter:

(a) the increase in wavelength $\Delta\lambda$ is independent of the nature of the scattering substance;

(b) the intensity of the displaced component of scattered light grows with the increasing angle of scattering and with the diminishing atomic number of the substance;

(c) the presence of a non-displaced component in the scattered radiation.

5.283. A narrow monochromatic X-ray beam falls on a scattering substance. The wavelengths of radiation scattered at angles $\theta_1 = 60°$ and $\theta_2 = 120°$ differ by a factor $\eta = 2.0$. Assuming the free electrons to be responsible for the scattering, find the incident radiation wavelength.

5.284. A photon with energy $\hbar\omega = 1.00$ MeV is scattered by a stationary free electron. Find the kinetic energy of a Compton electron if the photon's wavelength changed by $\eta = 25\%$ due to scattering.

5.285. A photon of wavelength $\lambda = 6.0$ pm is scattered at right angles by a stationary free electron. Find:

(a) the frequency of the scattered photon;

(b) the kinetic energy of the Compton electron.

5.286. A photon with energy $\hbar\omega = 250$ keV is scattered at an angle $\theta = 120°$ by a stationary free electron. Find the energy of the scattered photon.

5.287. A photon with momentum $p = 1.02$ MeV/c, where c is the velocity of light, is scattered by a stationary free electron, changing in the process its momentum to the value $p' = 0.255$ MeV/c. At what angle is the photon scattered?

5.288. A photon is scattered at an angle $\theta = 120°$ by a stationary free electron. As a result, the electron acquires a kinetic energy $T = 0.45$ MeV. Find the energy that the photon had prior to scattering.

5.289. Find the wavelength of X-ray radiation if the maximum kinetic energy of Compton electrons is $T_{max} = 0.19$ MeV.

5.290. A photon with energy $\hbar\omega = 0.15$ MeV is scattered by a stationary free electron changing its wavelength by $\Delta\lambda = 3.0$ pm. Find the angle at which the Compton electron moves.

5.291. A photon with energy exceeding $\eta = 2.0$ times the rest energy of an electron experienced a head-on collision with a stationary free electron. Find the curvature radius of the trajectory of the Compton electron in a magnetic field $B = 0.12$ T. The Compton electron is assumed to move at right angles to the direction of the field.

5.292. Having collided with a relativistic electron, a photon is deflected through an angle $\theta = 60°$ while the electron stops. Find the Compton displacement of the wavelength of the scattered photon.

6

ATOMIC AND NUCLEAR PHYSICS

6.1. SCATTERING OF PARTICLES. RUTHERFORD-BOHR ATOM

• Angle θ at which a charged particle is deflected by the Coulomb field of a stationary atomic nucleus is defined by the formula:

$$\tan\frac{\theta}{2}, \frac{q_1 q_2}{2bT} \qquad (6.1a)$$

where q_1 and q_2 are the charges of the particle and the nucleus, b is the aiming parameter. T is the kinetic energy of a striking particle.

• Rutherford formula. The relative number of particles scattered into an elementary solid angle $d\Omega$ at an angle θ to their initial propagation direction:

$$\frac{dN}{N} = n\left(\frac{q_1 q_2}{4T}\right)^2 \frac{d\Omega}{\sin^4(\theta/2)}, \qquad (6.1b)$$

where n is the number of nuclei of the foil per unit area of its surfae, $d\Omega = \sin\theta\, d\theta\, d\varphi$.

• Generalized Balmer formula (Fig. 6.1):

$$\omega = RZ^2\left(\frac{1}{n_1^2} - \frac{1}{n_2^2}\right), R \frac{me^4}{2h^3} \qquad (6.1c)$$

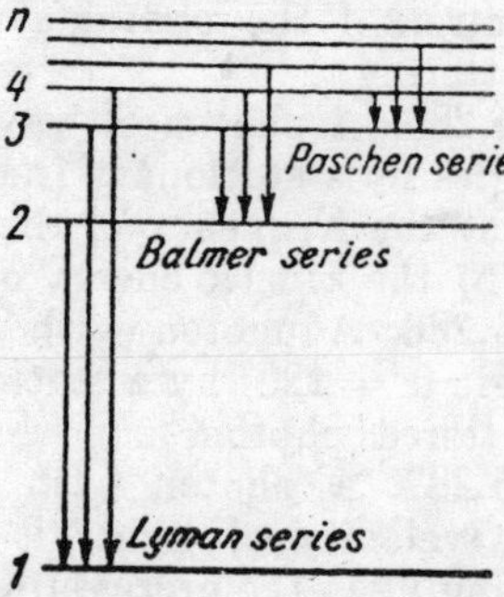

Fig. 6.1.

where ω is the transition frequency (in s^{-1}) between energy levels with quantum number n_1 and n_2, R is the Rydberg constant, Z is the serial number of a hydrogen-like ion.

6.1. Employing Thomson's model, calculate the radius of a hydrogen atom and the wavelength of emitted light if the ionization energy of the atom is known to be equal to E = 13.6 eV.

6.2. An alpha particle with kinetic energy 0.27 MeV is deflected through an angle of 60° by a golden foil. Find the corresponding value of aiming parameter.

6.3. To what minimum distance will an alpha particle with kinetic energy T = 0.40 MeV approach in the case of a head-on collision to.

(a) a stationary Pb nucleus;

(b) a stationary free Li^7 nucleus?

6.4. An alpha particle with kinetic energy T = 0.50 MeV is deflected through an angle of θ = 90° by the Coulomb field of a stationary Hg nucleus. Find:

* All the formulas in this Part are givne in the Gaussian system of units.

(a) the least curvature radius of its trajectory;

(b) the minimum approach distance between the particle and the nucleus.

6.5. A proton with kinetic energy T and aiming parameter b was deflected by the Coulomb field of a stationary Au nucleus. Find the momentum imparted to the given nucleus as a result of scattering.

6.6. A proton with kinetic energy $T = 10$ MeV flies past a stationary free electron at a distance $b = 10$ pm. Find the energy acquired by the electron, assuming the proton's trajectory to be rectilinear and the electron to be practically motionless as the proton flies by.

6.7. A particle with kinetic energy T is deflected by a spherical potential well of radius R and depth U_0, i.e. by the field in which the potential energy of the particle takes the form

$$U = \begin{cases} 0 \text{ for } r > R, \\ -U_0 \text{ for } r < R, \end{cases}$$

where r is the distance from the centre of the well. Find the relationship between the aiming parameter b of the particle and the angle θ through which it deflects from the initial motion direction.

6.8. A stationary ball of radius R is irradiated by a parallel stream of particles whose radius is r. Assuming the collision of a particle and the ball to be elastic, find:

(a) the deflection angle θ of a particle as a function of its aiming parameter b;

(b) the fraction of particles which after a collision with the ball are scattered into the angular interval between θ and $\theta + d\theta$;

(c) the probability of a particle to be deflected, after a collision with the ball, into the front hemisphere $\left(\theta < \frac{\pi}{2}\right)$.

6.9. A narrow beam of alpha particles with kinetic energy 1.0 MeV falls normally on a platinum foil 1.0 μm thick. The scattered particles are observed at an angle of 60° to the incident beam direction by means of a counter with a circular inlet area 1.0 cm^2 located at the distance 10 cm from the scattering section of the foil. What fraction of scattered alpha particles reaches the counter inlet?

6.10. A narrow beam of alpha particles with kinetic energy $T = 0.50$ MeV and intensity $I = 5.0 \cdot 10^5$ particles per second falls normally on a golden foil. Find the thickness of the foil if at a distance $r = 15$ cm from a scattering section of that foil the flux density of scattered particles at the angle $\theta = 60°$ to the incident beam is equal to $J = 40$ particles/($cm^2 \cdot s$).

6.11. A narrow beam of alpha particles falls normally on a silver foil behind which a counter is set to register the scattered particles. On substitution of platinum foil of the same mass thickness for the silver foil, the number of alpha particles registered per unit time increased $\eta = 1.52$ times. Find the atomic number of platinum, assuming the atomic number of silver and the atomic masses of both platinum and silver to be known.

6.12. A narrow beam of alpha particles with kinetic energy $T = 0.50$ MeV falls normally on a golden foil whose mass thickness is $\rho d = 1.5$ mg/cm^2. The beam intensity is $I_0 = 5.0 \cdot 10^5$ particles per second. Find the number of alpha particles scattered by the foil during a time interval $\tau = 30$ min into the angular interval:

(a) 59-61°; (b) over $\theta_0 = 60°$.

6.13. A narrow beam of protons with velocity $v = 6 \cdot 10^6$ m/s falls normally on a silver foil of thickness $d = 1.0$ μm. Find the probability of the protons to be scattered into the rear hemisphere ($\theta > 90°$).

6.14. A narrow beam of alpha particles with kinetic energy $T = 600$ keV falls normally on a golden foil incorporating $n = 1.1 \cdot 10^{19}$ nuclei/cm^2. Find the fraction of alpha particles scattered through the angles $\theta < \theta_0 = 20°$.

6.15. A narrow beam of protons with kinetic energy $T = 1.4$ MeV falls normally on a brass foil whose mass thickness $\rho d = 1.5$ mg/cm^2. The weight ratio of copper and zinc in the foil is equal to 7 : 3 respectively. Find the fraction of the protons scattered through the angles exceeding $\theta_0 = 30°$.

6.16. Find the effective cross section of a uranium nucleus corresponding to the scattering of alpha particles with kinetic energy $T = 1.5$ MeV through the angles exceeding $\theta_0 = 60°$.

6.17. The effective cross section of a gold nucleus corresponding to the scattering of monoenergetic alpha particles within the angular interval from 90° to 180° is equal to $\Delta\sigma = 0.50$ kb. Find:

(a) the energy of alpha particles;

(b) the differential cross section of scattering $d\sigma/d\Omega$ (kb/sr) corresponding to the angle $\theta = 60°$.

6.18. In accordance with classical electrodynamics an electron moving with acceleration **w** loses its energy due to radiation as

$$\frac{dE}{dt} = -\frac{2e^2}{3c^3} \mathbf{w}^2,$$

where e is the electron charge, c is the velocity of light. Estimate the time during which the energy of an electron performing almost harmonic oscillations with frequency $\omega = 5 \cdot 10^{15}$ s^{-1} will decrease $\eta = 10$ times.

6.19. Making use of the formula of the foregoing problem, estimate the time during which an electron moving in a hydrogen atom along a circular orbit of radius $r = 50$ pm would have fallen onto the nucleus. For the sake of simplicity assume the vector **w** to be permanently directed toward the centre of the atom.

6.20. Demonstrate that the frequency ω of a photon emerging when an electron jumps between neighbouring circular orbits of a hydrogen-like ion satisfies the inequality $\omega_n > \omega > \omega_{n+1}$, where ω_n and ω_{n+1} are the frequencies of revolution of that electron around the nucleus along the circular orbits. Make sure that as $n \to \infty$ the frequency of the photon $\omega \to \omega_n$.

6.21. A particle of mass m moves along a circular orbit in a centrosymmetrical potential field $U(r) = kr^2/2$. Using the Bohr quantization condition, find the permissible orbital radii and energy levels of that particle.

6.22. Calculate for a hydrogen atom and a He^+ ion:

(a) the radius of the first Bohr orbit and the velocity of an electron moving along it;

(b) the kinetic energy and the binding energy of an electron in the ground state;

(c) the ionization potential, the first excitation potential and the wavelength of the resonance line ($n' = 2 \to n = 1$).

6.23. Calculate the angular frequency of an electron occupying the second Bohr orbit of He^+ ion.

6.24. For hydrogen-like systems find the magnetic moment μ_n corresponding to the motion of an electron along the n-th orbit and the ratio of the magnetic and mechanical moments μ_n/M_n. Calculate the magnetic moment of an electron occupying the first Bohr orbit.

6.25. Calculate the magnetic field induction at the centre of a hydrogen atom caused by an electron moving along the first Bohr orbit.

6.26. Calculate and draw on the wavelength scale the spectral intervals in which the Lyman, Balmer, and Paschen series for atomic hydrogen are confined. Show the visible portion of the spectrum.

6.27. To what series does the spectral line of atomic hydrogen belong if its wave number is equal to the difference between the wave numbers of the following two lines of the Balmer series: 486.1 and 410.2 nm? What is the wavelength of that line?

6.28. For the case of atomic hydrogen find:

(a) the wavelengths of the first three lines of the Balmer series;

(b) the minimum resolving power $\lambda/\delta\lambda$ of a spectral instrument capable of resolving the first 20 lines of the Balmer series.

6.29. Radiation of atomic hydrogen falls normally on a diffraction grating of width $l = 6.6$ mm. The 50th line of the Balmer series in the observed spectrum is close to resolution at a diffraction angle θ (in accordance with Rayleigh's criterion). Find that angle.

6.30. What element has a hydrogen-like spectrum whose lines have wavelengths four times shorter than those of atomic hydrogen?

6.31. How many spectral lines are emitted by atomic hydrogen excited to the n-th energy level?

6.32. What lines of atomic hydrogen absorption spectrum fall within the wavelength range from 94.5 to 130.0 nm?

6.33. Find the quantum number n corresponding to the excited state of He^+ ion if on transition to the ground state that ion emits two photons in succession with wavelengths 108.5 and 30.4 nm.

6.34. Calculate the Rydberg constant R if He^{+} ions are known to have the wavelength difference between the first (of the longest wavelength) lines of the Balmer and Lyman series equal to $\Delta\lambda = 133.7$ nm.

6.35. What hydrogen-like ion has the wavelength difference between the first lines of the Balmer and Lyman series equal to 59.3 nm?

6.36. Find the wavelength of the first line of the He^{+} ion spectral series whose interval between the extreme lines is $\Delta\omega = 5.18 \cdot 10^{15}\ s^{-1}$.

6.37. Find the binding energy of an electron in the ground state of hydrogen-like ions in whose spectrum the third line of the Balmer series is equal to 108.5 nm.

6.38. The binding energy of an electron in the ground state of He atom is equal to $E_0 = 24.6$ eV. Find the energy required to remove both electrons from the atom.

6.39. Find the velocity of photoelectrons liberated by electromagnetic radiation of wavelength $\lambda = 18.0$ nm from stationary He^{+} ions in the ground state.

6.40. At what minimum kinetic energy must a hydrogen atom move for its inelastic head-on collision with another, stationary, hydrogen atom to make one of them capable of emitting a photon? Both atoms are supposed to be in the ground state prior to the collision.

6.41. A stationary hydrogen atom emits a photon corresponding to the first line of the Lyman series. What velocity does the atom acquire?

6.42. From the conditions of the foregoing problem find how much (in per cent) the energy of the emitted photon differs from the energy of the corresponding transition in a hydrogen atom.

6.43. A stationary He^{+} ion emitted a photon corresponding to the first line of the Lyman series. That photon liberated a photoelectron from a stationary hydrogen atom in the ground state. Find the velocity of the photoelectron.

6.44. Find the velocity of the excited hydrogen atoms if the first line of the Lyman series is displaced by $\Delta\lambda = 0.20$ nm when their radiation is observed at an angle $\theta = 45°$ to their motion direction.

6.45. According to the Bohr-Sommerfeld postulate the periodic motion of a particle in a potential field must satisfy the following quantization rule:

$$\oint p\, dq = 2\pi\hbar n,$$

where q and p are generalized coordinate and momentum of the particle, n are integers. Making use of this rule, find the permitted values of energy for a particle of mass m moving

(a) in a unidimensional rectangular potential well of width l with infinitely high walls;

(b) along a circle of radius r;

(c) in a unidimensional potential field $U = \alpha x^2/2$, where α is a positive constant;

(d) along a round orbit in a central field, where the potential energy of the particle is equal to $U = -\alpha/r$ (α is a positive constant).

6.46. Taking into account the motion of the nucleus of a hydrogen atom, find the expressions for the electron's binding energy in the ground state and for the Rydberg constant. How much (in per cent) do the binding energy and the Rydberg constant, obtained without taking into account the motion of the nucleus, differ from the more accurate corresponding values of these quantities?

6.47. For atoms of light and heavy hydrogen (H and D) find the difference

(a) between the binding energies of their electrons in the ground state;

(b) between the wavelengths of first lines of the Lyman series.

6.48. Calculate the separation between the particles of a system in the ground state, the corresponding binding energy, and the wavelength of the first line of the Lyman series, if such a system is

(a) a mesonic hydrogen atom whose nucleus is a proton (in a mesonic atom an electron is replaced by a meson whose charge is the same and mass is 207 that of an electron);

(b) a positronium consisting of an electron and a positron revolving around their common centre of masses.

6.2. WAVE PROPERTIES OF PARTICLES. SCHRÖDINGER EQUATION

• The de Broglie wavelength of a particle with momentum p:

$$\lambda = \frac{2\pi\hbar}{p}. \tag{6.2a}$$

• Uncertainty principle:

$$\Delta x \cdot \Delta p_x \geqslant \hbar. \tag{6.2b}$$

• Schrödinger time-dependent and time-independent equations:

$$i\hbar \frac{\partial \Psi}{\partial t} = -\frac{\hbar^2}{2m} \nabla^2 \Psi + U\Psi,$$
$$\nabla^2 \psi + \frac{2m}{\hbar^2}(E-U)\psi = 0, \tag{6.2c}$$

where Ψ is the total wave function, ψ is its coordinate part, ∇^2 is the Laplace operator, E and U are the total and potential energies of the particle. In spherical coordinates:

$$\nabla^2 = \frac{\partial^2}{\partial r^2} + \frac{2}{r}\frac{\partial}{\partial r} + \frac{1}{r^2 \sin\theta}\frac{\partial}{\partial \theta}\left(\sin\theta \frac{\partial}{\partial \theta}\right) + \frac{1}{r^2 \sin^2\theta}\frac{\partial^2}{\partial \varphi^2}. \tag{6.2d}$$

• **Coefficient of transparency of a potential barrier $V(x)$:**

$$D \approx \exp\left[-\frac{2}{\hbar}\int_{x_1}^{x_2}\sqrt{2m(V-E)}\,dx\right], \qquad (6.2e)$$

where x_1 and x_2 are the coordinates of the points between which $V > E$.

6.49. Calculate the de Broglie wavelengths of an electron, proton, and uranium atom, all having the same kinetic energy 100 eV.

6.50. What amount of energy should be added to an electron to reduce its de Broglie wavelength from 100 to 50 pm?

6.51. A neutron with kinetic energy $T = 25$ eV strikes a stationary deuteron (heavy hydrogen nucleus). Find the de Broglie wavelengths of both particles in the frame of their centre of inertia.

6.52. Two identical non-relativistic particles move at right angles to each other, possessing de Broglie wavelengths λ_1 and λ_2. Find the de Broglie wavelength of each particle in the frame of their centre of inertia.

6.53. Find the de Broglie wavelength of hydrogen molecules, which corresponds to their most probable velocity at room temperature.

6.54. Calculate the most probable de Broglie wavelength of hydrogen molecules being in thermodynamic equilibrium at room temperature.

6.55. Derive the expression for a de Broglie wavelength λ of a relativistic particle moving with kinetic energy T. At what values of T does the error in determining λ using the non-relativistic formula not exceed 1% for an electron and a proton?

6.56. At what value of kinetic energy is the de Broglie wavelength of an electron equal to its Compton wavelength?

6.57. Find the de Broglie wavelength of relativistic electrons reaching the anticathode of an X-ray tube if the short wavelength limit of the continuous X-ray spectrum is equal to $\lambda_{sh} = 10.0$ pm?

6.58. A parallel stream of monoenergetic electrons falls normally on a diaphragm with narrow square slit of width $b = 1.0$ μm. Find the velocity of the electrons if the width of the central diffraction maximum formed on a screen located at a distance $l = 50$ cm from the slit is equal to $\Delta x = 0.36$ mm.

6.59. A parallel stream of electrons accelerated by a potential difference $V = 25$ V falls normally on a diaphragm with two narrow slits separated by a distance $d = 50$ μm. Calculate the distance between neighbouring maxima of the diffraction pattern on a screen located at a distance $l = 100$ cm from the slits.

6.60. A narrow stream of monoenergetic electrons falls at an angle of incidence $\theta = 30°$ on the natural facet of an aluminium single crystal. The distance between the neighbouring crystal planes parallel to that facet is equal to $d = 0.20$ nm. The maximum mirror reflection is observed at a certain accelerating voltage V_0. Find V_0

if the next maximum mirror reflection is known to be observed when the accelerating voltage is incresed $\eta = 2.25$ times.

6.61. A narrow beam of monoenergetic electrons falls normally on the surface of Ni single crystal. The reflection maximum of fourth order is observed in the direction forming an angle $\theta = 55°$ with the normal to the surface at the energy of the electrons equal to $T = 180$ eV. Calculate the corresponding value of the interplanar distance.

6.62. A narrow steam of electrons with kinetic energy $T = 10$ keV passes through a polycrystalline aluminium foil, forming a system of diffraction fringers on a screen. Calculate the interplanar distance corresponding to the reflection of third order from a certain system of crystal planes if it is responsible for a diffraction ring of diameter $D = 3.20$ cm. The distance between the foil and the screen is $l = 10.0$ cm.

6.63. A steam of electrons accelerated by a potential difference V falls on the surface of a metal whose inner potential is $V_i = 15$ V Find:

(a) the refractive index of the metal for the electrons accelerated by a potential difference $V = 150$ V;

(b) the values of the ratio V/V_i at which the refractive index differs from unity by not more than $\eta = 1.0\%$.

2.64. A particle of mass m is located in a unidimensional square potential well with infinitely high walls. The width of the well is equal to l. Find the permitted values of energy of the particle taking into account that only those states of the particle's motion are realized for which the whole number of de Broglie half-waves are fitted within the given well.

2.65. Describe the Bohr quantum conditions in terms of the wave theory: demonstrate that an electron in a hydrogen atom can move only along those round orbits which accomodate a whole number of de Broglie waves.

2.66. Estimate the minimum errors in determining the velocity of an electron, a proton, and a ball of mass of 1 mg if the coordinates of the particles and of the centre of the ball are known with uncertainly 1 μm.

2.67. Employing the uncertainly principle, evaluate the indeterminancy of the velocity of an electron in a hydrogen atom if the size of the atom is assumed to be $l = 0.10$ nm. Compare the obtained magnitude with the velocity of an electron in the first Bohr orbit of the given atom.

2.68. Show that for the particle whose coordinate uncertainty is $\Delta x = \lambda/2\pi$, where λ is its de Broglie wavelength, the velocity uncertainty is of the same order of magnitude as the particle's velocity itself.

6.69. A free electron was initially confined within a region with linear dimensions $l = 0.10$ nm. Using the uncertainty principle, evaluate the time over which the width of the corresponding train of waves becomes $\eta = 10$ times as large.

6.70. Employing the uncertainty principle, estimate the minimum kinetic energy of an electron confined within a region whose size is $l = 0.20$ nm.

6.71. An electron with kinetic energy $T \approx 4$ eV is confined within a region whose linear dimension is $l = 1$ μm. Using the uncertainty principle, evaluate the relative uncertainty of its velocity.

6.72. An electron is located in a unidimensional square potential well with infinitely high walls. The width of the well is l. From the uncertainty principle estimate the force with which the electron possessing the minimum permitted energy acts on the walls of the well.

6.73. A particle of mass m moves in a unidimensional potential field $U = kx^2/2$ (harmonic oscillator). Using the uncertainty principle, evaluate the minimum permitted energy of the particle in that field.

6.74. Making use of the uncertainty principle, evaluate the minimum permitted energy of an electron in a hydrogen atom and its corresponding apparent distance from the nucleus.

6.75. A parallel stream of hydrogen atoms with velocity $v = 600$ m/s falls normally on a diaphragm with a narrow slit behind which a screen is placed at a distance $l = 1.0$ m. Using the uncertainty principle, evaluate the width of the slit δ at which the width of its image on the screen is minimum.

6.76. Find a particular solution of the time-dependent Schrödinger equation for a freely moving particle of mass m.

6.77. A particle in the ground state is located in a unidimensional square potential well of length l with absolutely impenetrable walls $(0 < x < l)$. Find the probability of the particle staying within a region $\frac{1}{3} l \leqslant x \leqslant \frac{2}{3} l$.

6.78. A particle is located in a unidimensional square potential well with infinitely high walls. The width of the well is l. Find the normalized wave functions of the stationary states of the particle, taking the midpoint of the well for the origin of the x coordinate.

6.79. Demonstrate that the wave functions of the stationary states of a particle confined in a unidimensional potential well with infinitely high walls are orthogonal, i.e. they satisfy the condition $\int_0^l \psi_n \psi_{n'}\, dx = 0$ if $n' \neq n$. Here l is the width of the well, n are integers.

6.80. An electron is located in a unidimensional square potential well with infinitely high walls. The width of the well equal to l is such that the energy levels are very dense. Find the density of energy levels dN/dE, i.e. their number per unit energy interval, as a function of E. Calculate dN/dE for $E = 1.0$ eV if $l = 1.0$ cm.

6.81. A particle of mass m is located in a two-dimensional square potential well with absolutely impenetrable walls. Find:

(a) the particle's permitted energy values if the sides of the well are l_1 and l_2;

(b) the energy values of the particle at the first four levels if the well has the shape of a square with side l.

6.82. A particle is located in a two-dimensional square potential well with absolutely impenetrable walls ($0 < x < a$, $0 < y < b$). Find the probability of the particle with the lowest energy to be located within a region $0 < x < a/3$.

6.83. A particle of mass m is located in a three-dimensional cubic potential well with absolutely impenetrable walls. The side of the cube is equal to a. Find:

(a) the proper values of energy of the particle;

(b) the energy difference between the third and fourth levels;

(c) the energy of the sixth level and the number of states (the degree of degeneracy) corresponding to that level.

6.84. Using the Schrödinger equation, demonstrate that at the point where the potential energy $U(x)$ of a particle has a finite discontinuity, the wave function remains smooth, i.e. its first derivative with respect to the coordinate is continuous.

6.85. A particle of mass m is located in a unidimensional potential field $U(x)$ whose shape is shown in Fig. 6.2, where $U(0) = \infty$. Find:

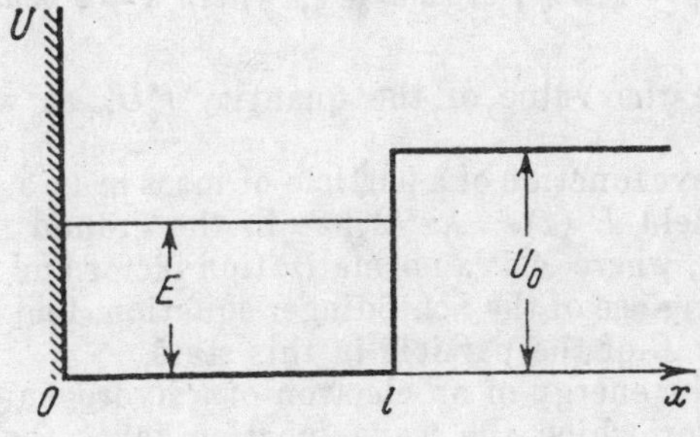

Fig. 6.2.

(a) the equation defining the possible values of energy of the particle in the region $E < U_0$; reduce that equation to the form

$$\sin kl = \pm kl \sqrt{\hbar^2/2ml^2U_0},$$

where $k = \sqrt{2mE}/\hbar$. Solving this equation by graphical means, demonstrate that the possible values of energy of the particle form a discontinuous spectrum;

(b) the minimum value of the quantity l^2U_0 at which the first energy level appears in the region $E < U_0$. At what minimum value of l^2U_0 does the nth level appear?

6.86. Making use of the solution of the foregoing problem, determine the probability of the particle with energy $E = U_0/2$ to be located in the region $x > l$, if $l^2 U_0 = \left(\frac{3}{4}\pi\right)^2 \frac{\hbar^2}{m}$.

6.87. Find the possible values of energy of a particle of mass m located in a spherically symmetrical potential well $U(r) = 0$ for $r < r_0$ and $U(r) = \infty$ for $r = r_0$, in the case when the motion of the particle is described by a wave function $\psi(r)$ depending only on r.

Instruction. When solving the Schrödinger equation, make the substitution $\psi(r) = \chi(r)/r$.

6.88. From the conditions of the foregoing problem find:

(a) normalized eigenfunctions of the particle in the states for which $\psi(r)$ depends only on r;

(b) the most probable value r_{pr} for the ground state of the particle and the probability of the particle to be in the region $r < r_{pr}$.

6.89. A particle of mass m is located in a spherically symmetrical potential well $U(r) = 0$ for $r < r_0$ and $U(r) = U_0$ for $r > r_0$.

(a) By means of the substitution $\psi(r) = \chi(r)/r$ find the equation defining the proper values of energy E of the particle for $E < U_0$, when its motion is described by a wave function $\psi(r)$ depending only on r. Reduce that equation to the form

$$\sin kr_0 = \pm kr_0 \sqrt{\hbar^2/2mr_0^2 U_0}, \text{ where } k = \sqrt{2mE}/\hbar.$$

(b) Calculate the value of the quantity $r_0^2 U_0$ at which the first level appears.

6.90. The wave function of a particle of mass m in a unidimensional potential field $U(x) = kx^2/2$ has in the ground state the form $\psi(x) = Ae^{-\alpha x^2}$, where A is a normalization factor and α is a positive constant. Making use of the Schrödinger equation, find the constant α and the energy E of the particle in this state.

6.91. Find the energy of an electron of a hydrogen atom in a stationary state for which the wave function takes the form $\psi(r) = A(1 + ar)e^{-\alpha r}$, where A, a, and α are constants.

6.92. The wave function of an electron of a hydrogen atom in the ground state takes the form $\psi(r) = Ae^{-r/r_1}$, where A is a certain constant, r_1 is the first Bohr radius. Find:

(a) the most probable distance between the electron and the nucleus;

(b) the mean value of modulus of the Coulomb force acting on the electron;

(c) the mean value of the potential energy of the electron in the field of the nucleus.

6.93. Find the mean electrostatic potential produced by an electron in the centre of a hydrogen atom if the electron is in the ground state for which the wave function is $\psi(r) = Ae^{-r/r_1}$, where A is a certain constant, r_1 is the first Bohr radius.

6.94. Particles of mass m and energy E move from the left to the potential barrier shown in Fig. 6.3. Find:

(a) the reflection coefficient R of the barrier for $E > U_0$;

(b) the effective penetration depth of the particles into the region $x > 0$ for $E < U_0$, i.e. the distance from the barrier boundary to the point at which the probability of finding a particle decreases e-fold.

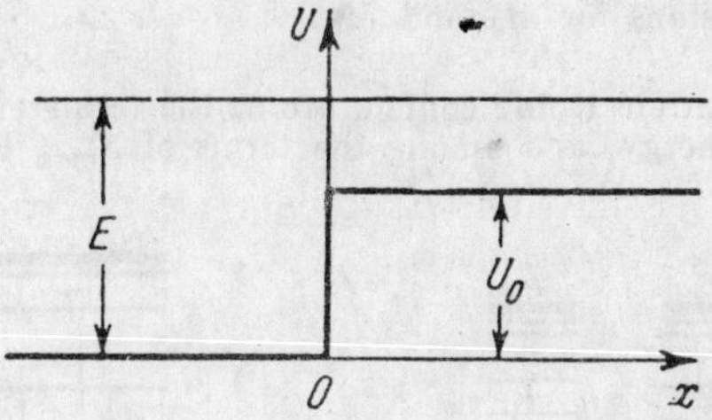

Fig. 6.3.

6.95. Employing Eq. (6.2e), find the probability D of an electron with energy E tunnelling through a potential barrier of width l and height U_0 provided the barrier is shaped as shown:

(a) in Fig. 6.4;

(b) in Fig. 6.5.

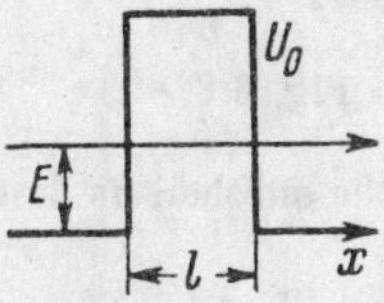

Fig. 6.4.

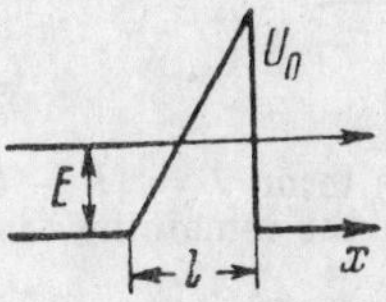

Fig. 6.5.

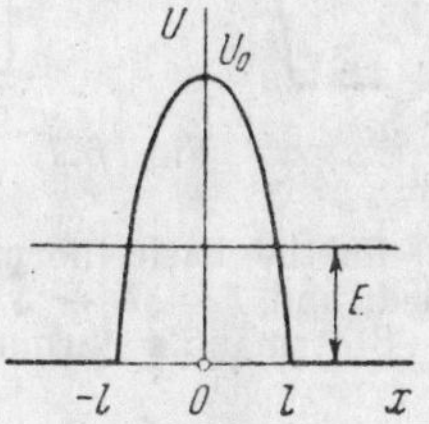

Fig. 6.6.

6.96. Using Eq. (6.2e), find the probability D of a particle of mass m and energy E tunnelling through the potential barrier shown in Fig. 6.6, where $U(x) = U_0 (1 - x^2/l^2)$.

6.3. PROPERTIES OF ATOMS. SPECTRA

• Spectral labelling of terms: $^{\varkappa}(L)_J$, where $\varkappa = 2S + 1$ is the multiplicity, L, S, J are quantum numbers,

$$L = 0,\ 1,\ 2,\ 3,\ 4,\ 5,\ 6, \ldots$$

$$(L):\ S,\ P,\ D,\ F,\ G,\ H,\ I, \ldots$$

• Terms of alkali metal atoms:

$$T = \frac{R}{(n+\alpha)^2}, \tag{6.3a}$$

where R is the Rydberg constant, α is the Rydberg correction.

Fig. 6.7 illustrates the diagram of a lithium atom terms.

• Angular momenta of an atom:

$$M_L = \hbar\sqrt{L(L+1)}, \tag{6.3b}$$

with similar expressions for M_S and M_J.

• Hund rules:

(1) For a certain electronic configuration, the terms of the largest S value are the lowest in energy, and among the terms of S_{max} that of the largest L usually lies lowest;

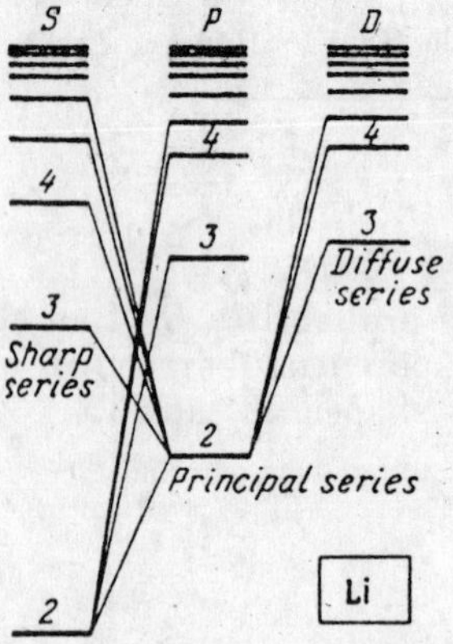

Fig. 6.7.

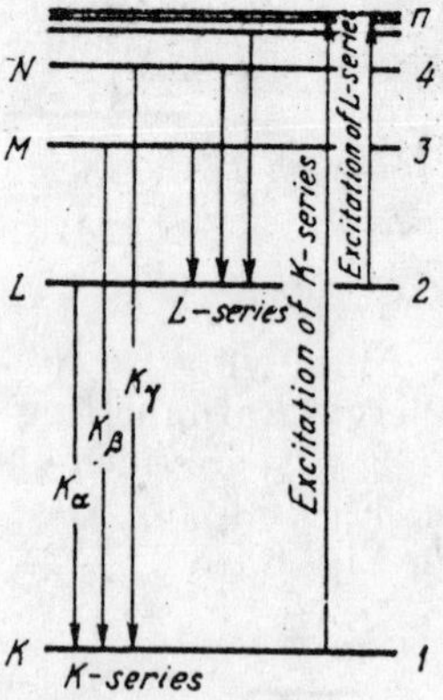

Fig. 6.8.

(2) for the basic (normal) term $J = |L - S|$ if the subshell is less than half-filled, and $J = L + S$ in the remaining cases.

• Boltzmann's formula:

$$\frac{N_2}{N_1} = \frac{g_2}{g_1} e^{-(E_2-E_1)/kT}, \tag{6.3c}$$

where g_1 and g_2 are the statistical weights (degeneracies) of the corresponding levels.

• Probabilities of atomic transitions per unit time between level *1* and a higher level *2* for the cases of spontaneous radiation, induced radiation, and absorption:

$$P_{21}^{sp} = A_{21}, \quad P_{21}^{ind} = B_{21}u_\omega, \quad P_{12}^{abs} = B_{12}u_\omega, \tag{6.3d}$$

where A_{21}, B_{21}, B_{12} are Einstein coefficients, u_ω is the spectral density of radiation corresponding to frequency ω of transition between the given levels.

• Relation between Einstein coefficients:

$$g_1B_{12} = g_2B_{21}, \quad B_{21} = \frac{\pi^2c^3}{\hbar\omega^3} A_{21}. \tag{6.3e}$$

• Diagram showing formation of X-ray spectra (Fig. 6.8).

• Moseley's law for K_α lines:

$$\omega_{K_\alpha} = \frac{3}{4} R (Z-\sigma)^2, \tag{6.3f}$$

where σ is the correction constant which is equal to unity for light elements.

• Magnetic moment of an atom and Landé g factor:

$$\mu = g\sqrt{J(J+1)}\,\mu_B, \qquad g = 1 + \frac{J(J+1)+S(S+1)-L(L+1)}{2J(J+1)}. \quad (6.3g)$$

• Zeeman splitting of spectral lines in a weak magnetic field:

$$\Delta\omega = (m_1 g_1 - m_2 g_2)\,\mu_B B/\hbar. \quad (6.3h)$$

• With radiation directed along the magnetic field, the Zeeman components caused by the transition $m_1 = m_2$ are absent.

6.97. The binding energy of a valence electron in a Li atom in the states $2S$ and $2P$ is equal to 5.39 and 3.54 eV respectively. Find the Rydberg corrections for S and P terms of the atom.

6.98. Find the Rydberg correction for the $3P$ term of a Na atom whose first excitation potential is 2.10 V and whose valence electron in the normal $3S$ state has the binding energy 5.14 eV.

6.99. Find the binding energy of a valence electron in the ground state of a Li atom if the wavelength of the first line of the sharp series is known to be equal to $\lambda_1 = 813$ nm and the short-wave cut-off wavelength of that series to $\lambda_2 = 350$ nm.

6.100. Determine the wavelengths of spectral lines appearing on transition of excited Li atoms from the state $3S$ down to the ground state $2S$. The Rydberg corrections for the S and P terms are -0.41 and -0.04.

6.101. The wavelengths of the yellow doublet components of the resonance Na line caused by the transition $3P \to 3S$ are equal to 589.00 and 589.56 nm. Find the splitting of the $3P$ term in eV units.

6.102. The first line of the sharp series of atomic cesium is a doublet with wavelengths 1358.8 and 1469.5 nm. Find the frequency intervals (in rad/s units) between the components of the sequent lines of that series.

6.103. Write the spectral designations of the terms of the hydrogen atom whose electron is in the state with principal quantum number $n = 3$.

6.104. How many and which values of the quantum number J can an atom possess in the state with quantum numbers S and L equal respectively to

(a) 2 and 3; (b) 3 and 3; (c) 5/2 and 2?

6.105. Find the possible values of total angular momenta of atoms in the states ^4P and ^5D.

6.106. Find the greatest possible total angular momentum and the corresponding spectral designation of the term

(a) of a Na atom whose valence electron possesses the principal quantum number $n = 4$;

(b) of an atom with electronic configuration $1s^2 2p 3d$.

6.107. It is known that in F and D states the number of possible values of the quantum number J is the same and equal to five. Find the spin angular momentum in these states.

6.108. An atom is in the state whose multiplicity is three and the total angular momentum is $\hbar\sqrt{20}$. What can the corresponding quantum number L be equal to?

6.109. Find the possible multiplicities x of the terms of the types (a) $^xD_2$; (b) $^xP_{3/2}$; (c) $^xF_1$.

6.110. A certain atom has three electrons (s, p, and d), in addition to filled shells, and is in a state with the greatest possible total mechanical moment for a given configuration. In the corresponding vector model of the atom find the angle between the spin momentum and the total angular momentum of the given atom.

6.111. An atom possessing the total angular momentum $\hbar\sqrt{6}$ is in the state with spin quantum number $S = 1$. In the corresponding vector model the angle between the spin momentum and the total angular momentum is $\theta = 73.2°$. Write the spectral symbol for the term of that state.

6.112. Write the spectral symbols for the terms of a two-electron system consisting of one p electron and one d electron.

6.113. A system comprises an atom in $^2P_{3/2}$ state and a d electron. Find the possible spectral terms of that system.

6.114. Find out which of the following transitions are forbidden by the selection rules: $^2D_{3/2} \rightarrow {}^2P_{1/2}$, $^3P_1 \rightarrow {}^2S_{1/2}$, $^3F_3 \rightarrow {}^3P_2$, $^4F_{7/2} \rightarrow {}^4D_{5/2}$.

6.115. Determine the overall degeneracy of a $3D$ state of a Li atom. What is the physical meaning of that value?

6.116. Find the degeneracy of the states ^2P, ^3D, and ^4F possessing the greatest possible values of the total angular momentum.

6.117. Write the spectral designation of the term whose degeneracy is equal to seven and the quantum numbers L and S are interrelated as $L = 3S$.

6.118. What element has the atom whose K, L, and M shells and $4s$ subshell are filled completely and $4p$ subshell is half-filled?

6.119. Using the Hund rules, find the basic term of the atom whose partially filled subshell contains

(a) three p electrons; (b) four p electrons.

6.120. Using the Hund rules, find the total angular momentum of the atom in the ground state whose partially filled subshell contains

(a) Three d electrons; (b) seven d electrons.

6.121. Making use of the Hund rules, find the number of electrons in the only partially filled subshell of the atom whose basic term is

(a) $^3F_2$; (b) $^2P_{3/2}$; (c) $^6S_{5/2}$.

6.122. Using the Hund rules, write the spectral symbol of the basic term of the atom whose only partially filled subshell

(a) is filled by 1/3, and $S = 1$;

(b) is filled by 70%, and $S = 3/2$.

6.123. The only partially filled subshell of a certain atom contains three electrons, the basic term of the atom having $L = 3$. Using

The Hund rules, write the spectral symbol of the ground state of the given atom.

6.124. Using the Hund rules, find the magnetic moment of the ground state of the atom whose open subshell is half-filled with five electrons.

6.125. What fraction of hydrogen atoms is in the state with the principal quantum number $\pi = 2$ at a temperature $T = 3000$ K?

6.126. Find the ratio of the number of atoms of gaseous sodium in the state $3P$ to that in the ground state $3S$ at a temperature $T = 2400$ K. The spectral line corresponding to the transition $3P \to \to 3S$ is known to have the wavelength $\lambda = 589$ nm.

6.127. Calculate the mean lifetime of excited atoms if it is known that the intensity of the spectral line appearing due to transition to the ground state diminishes by a factor $\eta = 25$ over a distance $l = 2.5$ mm along the stream of atoms whose velocity is $v = 600$ m/s.

6.128. Rarefied Hg gas whose atoms are practically all in the ground state was lighted by a mercury lamp emitting a resonance line of wavelength $\lambda = 253.65$ nm. As a result, the radiation power of Hg gas at that wavelength turned out to be $P = 35$ mW. Find the number of atoms in the state of resonance excitation whose mean lifetime is $\tau = 0.15$ μs.

6.129. Atomic lithium of concentration $n = 3.6.10^{16}$ cm^{-3} is at a temperature $T = 1500$ K. In this case the power emitted at the resonant lines wavelength $\lambda = 671$ nm ($2P \to 2S$) per unit volume of gas is equal to $P = 0.30$ W/cm^3. Find the mean lifetime of Li atoms in the resonance excitation state.

6.130. Atomic hydrogen is an thermodynamic equilibrium with its radiation. Find:

(a) the ratio of probabilities of induced and spontaneous radiations of the atoms from the level $2P$ at a temperature $T = 3000$ K;

(b) the temperature at which these probabilities become equal.

6.131. A beam of light of frequency ω, equal to the resonant frequency of transition of atoms of gas, passes through that gas heated to temperature T. In this case $h\,\omega >> kT$. Taking into account induced radiation, demonstrate that the absorption coefficient of the gas x varies as $x = x_0\,(1 - e^{-hw/kT})$, where x_0 is the absorption coefficient for $T \to 0$.

6.132. The wavelength of a resonant mercury line is $\lambda = 253.65$ nm. The mean lifetime of mercury atoms in the state of resonance excitation is $\tau = 0.15$ μs. Evaluate the ratio of the Doppler line broadening to the natural linewidth at a gas temperature $T = 300$ K.

6.133. Find the wavelength of the Ka line in copper ($Z = 29$) if the wavelength of the Ka line in iron ($Z = 26$) is known to be equal to 19 pm.

6.134. Proceeding from Moseleys law find:

(a) the wavelength of the Ka line in aluminium and cobalt:

(b) the difference in binding energies of K and L electrons in vanadium.

6.135. How many elements are there in a row between those whose wavelengths of K_α lines are equal to 250 and 179 pm?

6.136. Find the voltage applied to an X-ray tube with nickel anticathode if the wavelength difference between the K_α line and the short-wave cut-off of the continuous X-ray spectrum is equal to 84 pm.

6.137. At a certain voltage applied to an X-ray tube with aluminium anticathode the short-wave cut-off wavelength of the continuous X-ray spectrum is equal to 0.50 nm. Will the K series of the characteristic spectrum whose excitation potential is equal to 1.56 kV be also observed in this case?

6.138. When the voltage applied to an X-ray tube increased from $V_1 = 10$ kV to $V_2 = 20$ kV, the wavelength interval between the K_α line and the short-wave cut-off of the continuous X-ray spectrum increases by a factor $n = 3.0$. Find the atomic number of the element of which the tube's anticathode is made.

6.139. What metal has in its absorption spectrum the difference between the frequencies of X-ray K and L absorption edges equal to $\Delta\omega = 6.85 \cdot 10^{18}$ s^{-1} ?

6.140. Calculate the binding energy of a K electron in vanadium whose L absorption edge has the wavelength $\lambda_L = 2.4$ nm.

6.141. Find the binding energy of an L electron in titanium if the wavelength difference between the first line of the K series and its short-wave cut-off is $\Delta\lambda = 26$ pm.

6.142. Find the kinetic energy and the velocity of the photoelectrons liberated by K_α radiation of zinc from the K shell of iron whose K band absorption edge wavelength is $\lambda_K = 174$ pm.

6.143. Calculate the Landé g factor for atoms
(a) in S states; (b) in singlet states.

6.144. Calculate the Landé g factor for the following terms:
(a) $^6F_{1/2}$; (b) $^4D_{1/2}$; (c) $^5F_2$; (d) $^5P_1$; (e) $^3P_0$.

6.145. Calculate the magnetic moment of an atom (in Bohr magnetons)
(a) in ^1F state;
(b) in $^2D_{3/2}$ state;
(c) in the state in which $S = 1$, $L = 2$, and Landé factor $g = 4/3$.

6.146. Determine the spin angular momentum of an atom in the state D_2 if the maximum value of the magnetic moment projection in that state is equal to four Bohr magnetons.

6.147. An atom in the state with quantum numbers $L = 2$, $S = 1$ is located in a weak magnetic field. Find its magnetic moment if the least possible angle between the angular momentum and the field direction is known to be equal to 30°.

6.148. A valence electron in a sodium atom is in the state with principal quantum number $n = 3$, with the total angular momentum being the greatest possible. What is its magnetic moment in that state?

6.149. An excited atom has the electronic configuration $1s^2 2s^2 2p 3d$ being in the state with the greatest possible total angular momentum. Find the magnetic moment of the atom in that state.

6.150. Find the total angular momentum of an atom in the state with $S = 3/2$ and $L = 2$ if its magnetic moment is known to be equal to zero.

6.151. A certain atom is in the state in which $S = 2$, the total angular momentum $M = \sqrt{2}\hbar$, and the magnetic moment is equal to zero. Write the spectral symbol of the corresponding term.

6.152. An atom in the state $^2P_{3/2}$ is located in the external magnetic field of induction $B = 1.0$ kG. In terms of the vector model find the angular precession velocity of the total angular momentum of that atom.

6.153. An atom in the state $^2P_{1/2}$ is located on the axis of a loop of radius $r = 5$ cm carrying a current $I = 10$ A. The distance between the atom and the centre of the loop is equal to the radius of the latter. How great may be the maximum force that the magnetic field of that current exerts on the atom?

6.154. A hydrogen atom in the normal state is located at a distance $r = 2.5$ cm from a long straight conductor carrying a current $I = 10$ A. Find the force acting on the atom.

6.155. A narrow stream of vanadium atoms in the ground state $^4F_{3/2}$ is passed through a transverse strongly inhomogeneous magnetic field of length $l_1 = 5.0$ cm as in the Stern-Gerlach experiment. The beam splitting is observed on a screen located at a distance $l_2 = 15$ cm from the magnet. The kinetic energy of the atoms is $T = 22$ MeV. At what value of the gradient of the magnetic field induction B is the distance between the extreme components of the split beam on the screen equal to $\delta = 2.0$ mm?

6.156. Into what number of sublevels are the following terms split in a weak magnetic field:

(a) $^3P_0$; (b) $^2F_{5/2}$; (c) $^4D_{1/2}$?

6.157. An atom is located in a magnetic field of induction $B = 2.50$ kG. Find the value of the total splitting of the following terms (expressed in eV units):

(a) ^1D; (b) $^3F_4$.

6.158. What kind of Zeeman effect, normal or anomalous, is observed in a weak magnetic field in the case of spectral lines caused by the following transitions:

(a) $^1P \rightarrow {}^1S$; (b) $^2D_{5/2} \rightarrow {}^2P_{3/2}$; (c) $^3D_1 \rightarrow {}^3P_0$; (d) $^5I_5 \rightarrow {}^5H_4$?

6.159. Determine the spectral symbol of an atomic singlet term if the total splitting of that term in a weak magnetic field of induction $B = 3.0$ kG amounts to $\Delta E = 104$ μeV.

6.160. It is known that a spectral line $\lambda = 612$ nm of an atom is caused by a transition between singlet terms. Calculate the interval $\Delta\lambda$ between the extreme components of that line in the magnetic field with induction $B = 10.0$ kG.

6.161. Find the minimum magnitude of the magnetic field induction B at which a spectral instrument with resolving power $\lambda/\delta\lambda = 1.0.10^5$ is capable of resolving the components of the spectral line $\lambda = 536$ nm caused by a transition between singlet terms. The observation line is at right angles to the magnetic field direction.

6.162. A spectral line caused by the transition $^3D_1 \rightarrow {}^3P_0$ experiences the Zeeman splitting in a weak magnetic field. When observed at right angles to the magnetic field direction, the interval between the neighbouring components of the split line is $\Delta\omega = 1.32.10^{10}$ s^{-1}. Find the magnetic field induction B at the point where the source is located.

6.163. The wavelengths of the Na yellow doublet ($^2P \rightarrow {}^2S$) are equal to 589.59 and 589.00 nm. Find:

(a) the ratio of the intervals between neighbouring sublevels of the Zeeman splitting of the terms $^2P_{3/2}$ and $^2P_{1/2}$ in a weak magnetic field;

(b) the magnetic field induction B at which the interval between neighbouring sublevels of the Zeeman splitting of the term $^2P_{3/2}$ is $\eta = 50$ times smaller than the natural splitting of the term ^2P.

6.164. Draw a diagram of permitted transitions between the terms $^2P_{3/2}$ and $^2S_{1/2}$ in a weak magnetic field. Find the displacements (in rad/s units) of Zeeman components of that line in a magnetic field B = 4.5 kG.

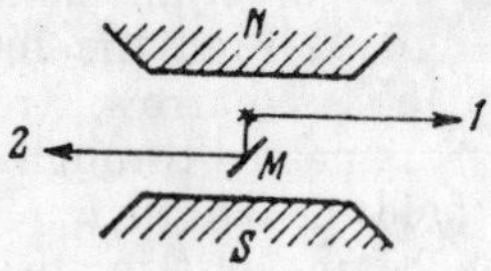

Fig. 6.9.

6.165. The same spectral line undergoing anomalous Zeeman splitting is observed in direction *1* and, after reflection from the mirror M (Fig. 6.9), in direction *2*. How many Zeeman components are observed in both directions if the spectral line is caused by the transition

(a) $^2P_{3/2} \rightarrow {}^2S_{1/2}$; (b) $^3P_2 \rightarrow {}^3S_1$?

6.166. Calculate the total splitting $\Delta\omega$ of the spectral line $^3D_3 \rightarrow {}^3P_2$ in a weak magnetic field with induction $B = 3.4$ kG.

6.4 MOLECULES AND CRYSTALS

- Rotational energy of a diatomic molecule:

$$E_J = \frac{\hbar^2}{2I} J\,(J+1), \tag{6.4a}$$

where I is the molecule's moment of inertia.

- Vibrational energy of a diatomic molecule:

$$E_v = \hbar\omega\left(v + \frac{1}{2}\right), \tag{6.4b}$$

where ω is the natural frequency of oscillations of the molecule.

• Mean energy of a quantum harmonic oscillator at a temperature T:

$$\langle E \rangle = \frac{\hbar\omega}{2} + \frac{\hbar\omega}{e^{\hbar\omega/kT} - 1} \tag{6.4c}$$

• Debye formula for molar vibrational energy of a crystal:

$$U = 9R\Theta \left[\frac{1}{8} + \left(\frac{T}{\Theta}\right)^4 \int_0^{\Theta/T} \frac{x^3\,dx}{e^x - 1} \right] \tag{6.4d}$$

where Θ is the Debye temperature,

$$\Theta = \hbar\omega_{max}/k. \tag{6.4e}$$

• Molar vibrational heat capacity of a vrystal for $T << \Theta$:

$$C = \frac{15}{5}\,\pi^4 R \left(\frac{T}{\Theta}\right)^3 \tag{6.4f}$$

• Distribution of free electrons in metal in the vicinity of the absolute zero:

$$dn = \frac{\sqrt{2}\,m^{3/2}}{\pi^2\hbar^3}\sqrt{E}\;dE, \tag{6.4g}$$

where dn is the concentration of electrons whose energy falls within the interval E, $E + dE$. The energy E is conted off the bottom of the conduction hand.

• Fermi level at $T = 0$:

$$E_F = \frac{\hbar^2}{2m}\,(3\pi^2 n)^{2/3}, \tag{6.4h}$$

where n is the concentration of free electrons in metal.

6.167. Determine the angular rotation velocity of an S_2 molecule promoted to the first excited rotational level if the distance between its nuclei is if = 189 pm.

6.168. For an HCl molecule find the rotational quantum numbers of two neighbouring levels whose energies differ by 7.86 meV. The nuclei of the molecule are separated by the distance of 127.5 pm.

6.169. Find the angular momentum of an oxygen molecule whose rotational energy is E = 2.16 meV and the distance between the nuclei is d = 121 pm.

6.170. Show that the frequency intervals between the neighbouring spectral lines of a true rotational spectrum of a diatomic molecule are equal. Find the moment of inertia and the distance beteen the nuclei of a CH molecule if the intervals between the neighbouring lines of the true rotational spectrum of these molecules are equal to $\Delta\omega = 5.47.10^{12}$ s^{-1}.

6.171. For an HF molecule find the number of rotational levels located between the zeroth and first excited vibrational levels assuming potational states to be independent of vibrational ones. The natural vibration frequency of this molecule is equal to $7.79.10^{14}$ rad/s, and the distance between the nuclei is 91.7 pm.

6.172. Evaluate how many lines there are in a true rotational spectrum of CO molecules whose natural vibration frequency is $\omega = 4.09 \cdot 10^{14}$ s^{-1} and moment of inertia $I = 1.44 \cdot 10^{-39}$ $g \cdot cm^2$.

6.173. Find the number of rotational levels per unit energy interval, dN/dE, for a diatomic molecule as a function of rotational energy E. Calculate that magnitude for an iodine molecule in the state with rotational quantum number $J = 10$. The distance between the nuclei of that molecule is equal to 267 pm.

6.174. Find the ratio of energies required to excite a diatomic molecule to the first vibrational and to the first rotational level. Calculate that ratio for the following molecules:

Molecule	ω, 10^{14} s^{-1}	d, pm
(a) H_2	8.3	74
(b) HI	4.35	160
(c) I_2	0 40	267

Here ω is the natural vibration frequency of a molecule, d is the distance between nuclei.

6.175. The natural vibration frequency of a hydrogen molecule is equal to $8.25 \cdot 10^{14}$ s^{-1}, the distance between the nuclei is 74 pm. Find the ratio of the number of these molecules at the first excited vibrational level ($v = 1$) to the number of molecules at the first excited rotational level ($J = 1$) at a temperature $T = 875$ K. It should be remembered that the degeneracy of rotational levels is equal to $2J + 1$.

6.176. Derive Eq. (6.4c), making use of the Boltzmann distribution. From Eq. (6.4c) obtain the expression for molar vibration heat capacity $C_{V\,vib}$ of diatomic gas. Calculate $C_{V\,vib}$ for Cl_2 gas at the temperature 300 K. The natural vibration frequency of these molecules is equal to $1.064 \cdot 10^{14}$ s^{-1}

6.177. In the middle of the rotation-vibration band of emission spectrum of HCl molecule, where the "zeroth" line is forbidden by the selection rules, the interval between neighbouring lines is $\Delta\omega = 0.79 \cdot 10^{13}$ s^{-1}. Calculate the distance between the nuclei of an HCl molecule.

6.178. Calculate the wavelengths of the red and violet satellites, closest to the fixed line, in the vibration spectrum of Raman scattering by F_2 molecules if the incident light wavelength is equal to $\lambda_0 = 404.7$ nm and the natural vibration frequency of the molecule is $\omega = 2.15 \cdot 10^{14}$ s^{-1}.

6.179. Find the natural vibration frequency and the quasielastic force coefficient of an S_2 molecule if the wavelengths of the red and violet satellites, closest to the fixed line. in the vibration spectrum of Raman scattering are equal to 346.6 and 330.0 nm.

6.180. Find the ratio of intensities of the violet and red satellites, closest to the fixed line, in the vibration spectrum of Raman scattering by Cl_2 molecules at a temperature $T = 300$ K if the natural vibration frequency of these molecules is $\omega = 1.06 \cdot 10^{14}$ s^{-1}. By what factor will this ratio change if the temperature is doubled?

6.181. Consider the possible vibration modes in the following linear molecules:

(a) CO_2 (O—C—O); (b) C_2H_2 (H—C—C—H).

6.182. Find the number of natural transverse vibrations of a string of length l in the frequency interval from ω to $\omega + d\omega$ if the propagation velocity of vibrations is equal to v. All vibrations are supposed to occur in one plane.

6.183. There is a square membrane of area S. Find the number of natural vibrations perpendicular to its plane in the frequency interval from ω to $\omega + d\omega$ if the propagation velocity of vibrations is equal to v.

6.184. Find the number of natural transverse vibrations of a right-angled parallelepiped of volume V in the frequency interval from ω to $\omega + d\omega$ if the propagation velocity of vibrations is equal to v.

6.185. Assuming the propagation velocities of longitudinal and transverse vibrations to be the same and equal to v, find the Debye temperature

(a) for a unidimensional crystal, i.e. a chain of identical atoms, incorporating n_0 atoms per unit length;

(b) for a two-dimensional crystal, i.e. a plane square grid consisting of identical atoms, containing n_0 atoms per unit area;

(c) for a simple cubic lattice consisting of identical atoms, containing n_0 atoms per unit volume.

6.186. Calculate the Debye temperature for iron in which the propagation velocities of longitudinal and transverse vibrations are equal to 5.85 and 3.23 km/s respectively.

6.187. Evaluate the propagation velocity of acoustic vibrations in aluminium whose Debye temperature is $\Theta = 396$ K.

6.188. Derive the formula expressing molar heat capacity of a unidimensional crystal, a chain of identical atoms, as a function of temperature T if the Debye temperature of the chain is equal to Θ. Simplify the obtained expression for the case $T \gg \Theta$.

6.189. In a chain of identical atoms the vibration frequency ω depends on wave number k as $\omega = \omega_{max} \sin (ka/2)$, where ω_{max} is the maximum vibration frequency, $k = 2\pi/\lambda$ is the wave number corresponding to frequency ω, a is the distance between neighbouring atoms. Making use of this dispersion relation, find the dependence of the number of longitudinal vibrations per unit frequency interval on ω, i.e. $dN/d\omega$, if the length of the chain is l. Having obtained $dN/d\omega$, find the total number N of possible longitudinal vibrations of the chain.

6.190. Calculate the zero-point energy per one gram of copper whose Debye temperature is $\Theta = 330$ K.

6.191. Fig. 6.10 shows heat capacity of a crystal vs temperature in terms of the Debye theory. Here C_{cl} is classical heat capacity, Θ is the Debye temperature. Using this plot, find:

(a) the Debye temperature for silver if at a temperature $T = 65$ K its molar heat capacity is equal to 15 J/(mol·K);

(b) the molar heat capacity of aluminium at $T = 80$ K if at $T = 250$ K it is equal to 22.4 J/(mol·K);

(c) the maximum vibration frequency for copper whose heat capacity at $T = 125$ K differs from the classical value by 25%.

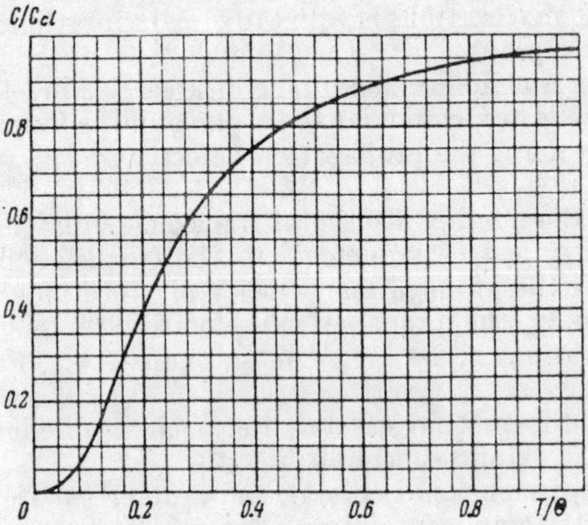

Fig. 6.10.

6.192. Demonstrate that molar heat capacity of a crystal at a temperature $T \ll \Theta$, where Θ is the Debye temperature, is defined by Eq. (6.4f).

6.193. Can one consider the temperatures 20 and 30 K as low for a crystal whose heat capacities at these temperatures are equal to 0.226 and 0.760 J/(mol·K)?

6.194. Calculate the mean zero-point energy per one oscillator of a crystal in terms of the Debye theory if the Debye temperature of the crystal is equal to Θ.

6.195. Draw the vibration energy of a crystal as a function of frequency (neglecting the zero-point vibrations). Consider two cases: $T = \Theta/2$ and $T = \Theta/4$, where Θ is the Debye temperature.

6.196. Evaluate the maximum values of energy and momentum of a phonon (acoustic quantum) in copper whose Debye temperature is equal to 330 K.

6.197. Employing Eq. (6.4g), find at $T = 0$:

(a) the maximum kinetic energy of free electrons in a metal if their concentration is equal to n;

(b) the mean kinetic energy of free electrons if their maximum kinetic energy T_{max} is known.

6.198. What fraction (in per cent) of free electrons in a metal at $T = 0$ has a kinetic energy exceeding half the maximum energy?

6.199. Find the number of free electrons per one sodium atom at $T = 0$ if the Fermi level is equal to $E_F = 3.07$ eV and the density of sodium is 0.97 g/cm^3.

6.200. Up to what temperature has one to heat classical electronic gas to make the mean energy of its electrons equal to that of free electrons in copper at $T = 0$? Only one free electron is supposed to correspond to each copper atom.

6.201. Calculate the interval (in eV units) between neighbouring levels of free electrons in a metal at $T = 0$ near the Fermi level, if the concentration of free electrons is $n = 2.0 \cdot 10^{22}$ cm^{-3} and the volume of the metal is $V = 1.0$ cm^3.

6.202. Making use of Eq. (6.4g), find at $T = 0$:

(a) the velocity distribution of free electrons;

(b) the ratio of the mean velocity of free electrons to their maximum velocity.

6.203. On the basis of Eq. (6.4g) find the number of free electrons in a metal at $T = 0$ as a function of de Broglie wavelengths.

6.204. Calculate the electronic gas pressure in metallic sodium, at $T = 0$, in which the concentration of free electrons is $n = 2.5 \cdot 10^{22}$ cm^{-3}. Use the equation for the pressure of ideal gas.

6.205. The increase in temperature of a cathode in electronic tube by $\Delta T = 1.0$ K from the value $T = 2000$ K results in the increase of saturation current by $\eta = 1.4\%$. Find the work function of electron for the material of the cathode.

6.206. Find the refractive index of metallic sodium for electrons with kinetic energy $T = 135$ eV. Only one free electron is assumed to correspond to each sodium atom.

6.207. Find the minimum energy of electron-hole pair formation in an impurity-free semiconductor whose electric conductance increases $\eta = 5.0$ times when the temperature increases from $T_1 = 300$ K to $T_2 = 400$ K.

6.208. At very low temperatures the photoelectric threshold short wavelength in an impurity-free germanium is equal to $\lambda_{th} = 1.7$ μm. Find the temperature coefficient of resistance of this germanium sample at room temperature.

6.209. Fig. 6.11 illustrates logarithmic electric conductance as a function of reciprocal temperature (T in kK units) for some

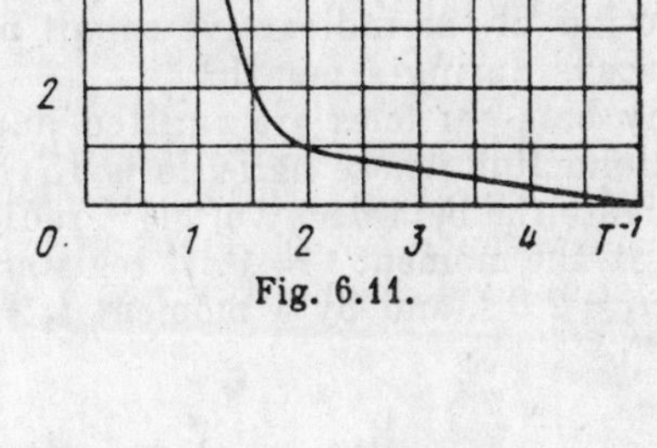

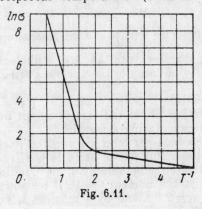

Fig. 6.11.

n-type semiconductor. Using this plot, find the width of the forbidden band of the semiconductor and the activation energy of donor levels.

6.210. The resistivity of an impurity-free semiconductor at room temperature is $\rho = 50\ \Omega\cdot\text{cm}$. It becomes equal to $\rho_1 = 40\ \Omega\cdot\text{cm}$ when the semiconductor is illuminated with light, and $t = 8$ ms after switching off the light source the resistivity becomes equal to $\rho_2 = 45\ \Omega\cdot\text{cm}$. Find the mean lifetime of conduction electrons and holes.

6.211. In Hall effect measurements a plate of width $h = 10$ mm and length $l = 50$ mm made of p-type semiconductor was placed in a magnetic field with induction $B = 5.0$ kG. A potential difference $V = 10$ V was applied across the edges of the plate. In this case the Hall field is $V_H = 50$ mV and resistivity $\rho = 2.5\ \Omega\cdot\text{cm}$. Find the concentration of holes and hole mobility.

6.212. In Hall effect measurements in a magnetic field with induction $B = 5.0$ kG the transverse electric field strength in an impurity-free germanium turned out to be $\eta = 10$ times less than the longitudinal electric field strength. Find the difference in the mobilities of conduction electrons and holes in the given semiconductor.

6.213. The Hall effect turned out to be not observable in a semiconductor whose conduction electron mobility was $\eta = 2.0$ times that of the hole mobility. Find the ratio of hole and conduction electron concentrations in that semiconductor.

6.5. RADIOACTIVITY

- Fundamental law of radioactive decay:

$$N = N_0 e^{-\lambda t}. \tag{6.5a}$$

- Relation between the decay constant λ, the mean lifetime τ, and the half-life T:

$$\lambda = \frac{1}{\tau} = \frac{\ln 2}{T}. \tag{6.5b}$$

- Specific activity is the activity of a unit mass of a radioisotope.

6.214. Knowing the decay constant λ of a nucleus, find:

(a) the probability of decay of the nucleus during the time from 0 to t;

(b) the mean lifetime τ of the nucleus.

6.215. What fraction of the radioactive cobalt nuclei whose half-life is 71.3 days decays during a month?

6.216. How many beta-particles are emitted during one hour by 1.0 µg of Na^{24} radionuclide whose half-life is 15 hours?

6.217. To investigate the beta-decay of Mg^{23} radionuclide, a counter was activated at the moment $t = 0$. It registered N_1 beta-particles by a moment $t_1 = 2.0$ s, and by a moment $t_2 = 3t_1$ the number of registered beta-particles was 2.66 times greater. Find the mean lifetime of the given nuclei.

6.218. The activity of a certain preparation decreases 2.5 times after 7.0 days. Find its half-life.

6.219. At the initial moment the activity of a certain radionuclide totalled 650 particles per minute. What will be the activity of the preparation after half its half-life period?

6.220. Find the decay constant and the mean lifetime of Co^{55} radionuclide if its activity is known to decrease 4.0% per hour. The decay product is nonradioactive.

6.221. A U^{238} preparation of mass 1.0 g emits $1.24 \cdot 10^4$ alpha-particles per second. Find the half-life of this nuclide and the activity of the preparation.

6.222. Determine the age of ancient wooden items if it is known that the specific activity of C^{14} nuclide in them amounts to 3/5 of that in lately felled trees. The half-life of C^{14} nuclei is 5570 years.

6.223. In a uranium ore the ratio of U^{238} nuclei to Pb^{206} nuclei is $\eta = 2.8$. Evaluate the age of the ore, assuming all the lead Pb^{206} to be a final decay product of the uranium series. The half-life of U^{238} nuclei is $4.5 \cdot 10^9$ years.

6.224. Calculate the specific activities of Na^{24} and U^{235} nuclides whose half-lifes are 15 hours and $7.1 \cdot 10^8$ years respectively.

6.225. A small amount of solution containing Na^{24} radionuclide with activity $A = 2.0 \cdot 10^3$ disintegrations per second was injected in the bloodstream of a man. The activity of 1 cm^3 of blood sample taken $t = 5.0$ hours later turned out to be $A' = 16$ disintegrations per minute per cm^3. The half-life of the radionuclide is $T = 15$ hours. Find the volume of the man's blood.

6.226. The specific activity of a preparation consisting of radioactive Co^{58} and nonradioactive Co^{59} is equal to $2.2 \cdot 10^{12}$ dis/(s·g). The half-life of Co^{58} is 71.3 days. Find the ratio of the mass of radioactive cobalt in that preparation to the total mass of the preparation (in per cent).

6.227. A certain preparation includes two beta-active components with different half-lifes. The measurements resulted in the following dependence of the natural logarithm of preparation activity on time t expressed in hours:

t	0	1	2	3	5	7	10	14	20
$\ln A$	4.10	3.60	3.10	2.60	2.06	1.82	1.60	1.32	0.90

Find the half-lifes of both components and the ratio of radioactive nuclei of these components at the moment $t = 0$.

6.228. A P^{32} radionuclide with half-life $T = 14.3$ days is produced in a reactor at a constant rate $q = 2.7 \cdot 10^9$ nuclei per second. How soon after the beginning of production of that radionuclide will its activity be equal to $A = 1.0 \cdot 10^9$ dis/s?

6.229. A radionuclide A_1 with decay constant λ_1 transforms into a radionuclide A_2 with decay constant λ_2. Assuming that at the initial moment the preparation contained only the radionuclide A_1, find:

(a) the equation describing accumulation of the radionuclide A_2 with time;

(b) the time interval after which the activity of radionuclide A_2 reaches the maximum value.

6.230. Solve the foregoing problem if $\lambda_1 = \lambda_2 = \lambda$.

6.231. A radionuclide A_1 goes through the transformation chain $A_1 \rightarrow A_2 \rightarrow A_3$ (stable) with respective decay constants λ_1 and λ_2. Assuming that at the initial moment the preparation contained only the radionuclide A_1 equal in quantity to N_{10} nuclei, find the equation describing accumulation of the stable isotope A_3.

6.232. A Bi^{210} radionuclide decays via the chain

$$Bi^{210} \xrightarrow[\lambda_1]{} Po^{210} \xrightarrow[\lambda_2]{} Pb^{206} \text{ (stable)},$$

where the decay constants are $\lambda_1 = 1.60 \cdot 10^{-6}$ s^{-1}, $\lambda_2 = 5.80 \cdot 10^{-8}$ s^{-1}. Calculate alpha- and beta-activities of the Bi^{210} preparation of mass 1.00 mg a month after its manufacture.

6.233. (a) What isotope is produced from the alpha-radioactive Ra^{226} as a result of five alpha-disintegrations and four β^--disintegrations?

(b) How many alpha- and β^--decays does U^{238} experience before turning finally into the stable Pb^{206} isotope?

6.234. A stationary Pb^{200} nucleus emits an alpha-particle with kinetic energy $T_\alpha = 5.77$ MeV. Find the recoil velocity of a daughter nucleus. What fraction of the total energy liberated in this decay is accounted for by the recoil energy of the daughter nucleus?

6.235. Find the amount of heat generated by 1.00 mg of a Po^{210} preparation during the mean lifetime period of these nuclei if the emitted alpha-particles are known to possess the kinetic energy 5.3 MeV and practically all daughter nuclei are formed directly in the ground state.

6.236. The alpha-decay of Po^{210} nuclei (in the ground state) is accompanied by emission of two groups of alpha-particles with kinetic energies 5.30 and 4.50 MeV. Following the emission of these particles the daughter nuclei are found in the ground and excited states. Find the energy of gamma-quanta emitted by the excited nuclei.

6.237. The mean path length of alpha-particles in air under standard conditions is defined by the formula $R = 0.98 \cdot 10^{-27}\, v_0^3$ cm, where v_0 (cm/s) is the initial velocity of an alpha-particle. Using this formula, find for an alpha-particle with initial kinetic energy 7.0 MeV:

(a) its mean path length;

(b) the average number of ion pairs formed by the given alpha-particle over the whole path R as well as over its first half, assuming the ion pair formation energy to be equal to 34 eV.

6.238. Find the energy Q liberated in β^-- and β^+-decays and in K-capture if the masses of the parent atom M_p, the daughter atom M_d and an electron m are known.

6.239. Taking the values of atomic masses from the tables, find the maximum kinetic energy of beta-particles emitted by Be^{10} nuclei and the corresponding kinetic energy of recoiling daughter nuclei formed directly in the ground state.

6.240. Evaluate the amount of heat produced during a day by a β^--active Na^{24} preparation of mass $m = 1.0$ mg. The beta-particles are assumed to possess an average kinetic energy equal to 1/3 of the highest possible energy of the given decay. The half-life of Na^{24} is $T = 15$ hours.

6.241. Taking the values of atomic masses from the tables, calculate the kinetic energies of a positron and a neutrino emitted by C^{11} nucleus for the case when the daughter nucleus does not recoil.

6.242. Find the kinetic energy of the recoil nucleus in the positronic decay of a N^{13} nucleus for the case when the energy of positrons is maximum.

6.243. From the tables of atomic masses determine the velocity of a nucleus appearing as a result of K-capture in a Be^7 atom provided the daughter nucleus turns out to be in the ground state.

6.244. Passing down to the ground state, excited Ag^{109} nuclei emit either gamma quanta with energy 87 keV or K conversion electrons whose binding energy is 26 keV. Find the velocity of these electrons.

6.245. A free stationary Ir^{191} nucleus with excitation energy $E = 129$ keV passes to the ground state, emitting a gamma quantum. Calculate the fractional change of gamma quanta energy due to recoil of the nucleus.

6.246. What must be the relative velocity of a source and an absorber consisting of free Ir^{191} nuclei to observe the maximum absorption of gamma quanta with energy $\varepsilon = 129$ keV?

6.247. A source of gamma quanta is placed at a height $h = 20$ m above an absorber. With what velocity should the source be displaced upward to counterbalance completely the gravitational variation of gamma quanta energy due to the Earth's gravity at the point where the absorber is located?

6.248. What is the minimum height to which a gamma quanta source containing excited Zn^{67} nuclei has to be raised for the gravitational displacement of the Mössbauer line to exceed the line width itself, when registered on the Earth's surface? The registered gamma quanta are known to have an energy $\varepsilon = 93$ keV and appear on transition of Zn^{67} nuclei to the ground state, and the mean lifetime of the excited state is $\tau = 14$ µs.

6.6. NUCLEAR REACTIONS

• Binding energy of a nucleus:

$$E_b = Zm_H + (A - Z)\,m_n - M, \qquad (6.6a)$$

where Z is the charge of the nucleus (in units of e), A is the mass number, m_H, m_n, and M are the masses of a hydrogen atom, a neutron, and an *atom* corresponding to the given nucleus.

In calculations the following formula is more convenient to use:

$$E_b = Z\Delta_H + (A - Z)\Delta_n - \Delta, \qquad (6.6b)$$

where Δ_H, Δ_n, and Δ are the mass surpluses of a hydrogen atom, a neutron, and an atom corresponding to the given nucleus.

• Energy diagram of a nuclear reaction

$$m + M \rightarrow M^* \rightarrow m' + M' + Q \qquad (6.6c)$$

is illustrated in Fig. 6.12, where $m+M$ and $m'+M'$ are the sums of rest masses of particles before and after the reaction, $\tilde{T}$ and $\tilde{T}'$ are the total kinetic energies of particles before and after the reaction (in the frame of the centre of inertia), E^* is the excitation energy of the transitional nucleus, Q is the energy of the reaction, E and E' are the binding energies of the particles m and m' in the transitional nucleus, *1, 2, 3* are the energy levels of the transitional nucleus.

• Threshold (minimum) kinetic energy of an incoming particle at which an endoergic nuclear reaction

$$T_{th} = \frac{m+M}{M}\,|Q| \qquad (6.6d)$$

becomes possible; here m and M are the masses of the incoming particle and the target nucleus.

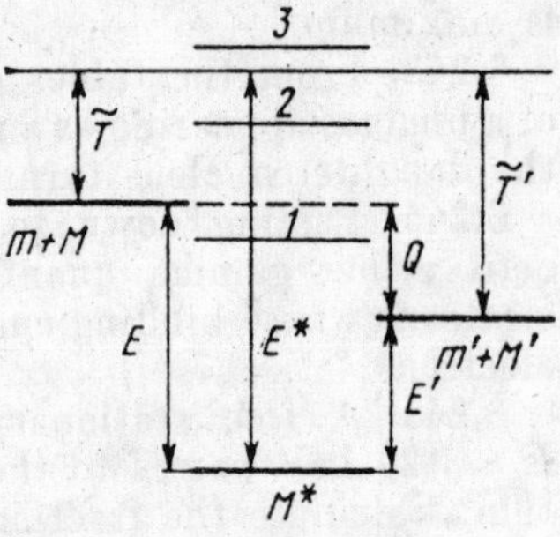

Fig. 6.12.

6.249. An alpha-particle with kinetic energy $T_\alpha = 7.0$ MeV is scattered elastically by an initially stationary Li^6 nucleus. Find the kinetic energy of the recoil nucleus if the angle of divergence of the two particles is $\Theta = 60°$.

6.250. A neutron collides elastically with an initially stationary deuteron. Find the fraction of the kinetic energy lost by the neutron

(a) in a head-on collision;

(b) in scattering at right angles.

6.251. Find the greatest possible angle through which a deuteron is scattered as a result of elastic collision with an initially stationary proton.

6.252. Assuming the radius of a nucleus to be equal to $R = 0.13\sqrt[3]{A}$ pm, where A is its mass number, evaluate the density of nuclei and the number of nucleons per unit volume of the nucleus.

6.253. Write missing symbols, denoted by x, in the following nuclear reactions:

(a) $B^{10}(x, \alpha)Be^8$;

(b) O^{17} (d, n) x;

(c) Na^{23} (p, x) Ne^{20};

(d) x (p, n) Ar^{37}.

6.254. Demonstrate that the binding energy of a nucleus with mass number A and charge Z can be found from Eq. (6.6b).

6.255. Find the binding energy of a nucleus consisting of equal numbers of protons and neutrons and having the radius one and a half times smaller than that of Al^{27} nucleus.

6.256. Making use of the tables of atomic masses, find:

(a) the mean binding energy per one nucleon in O^{16} nucleus;

(b) the binding energy of a neutron and an alpha-particle in a B^{11} nucleus;

(c) the energy required for separation of an O^{16} nucleus into four identical particles.

6.257. Find the difference in binding energies of a neutron and a proton in a B^{11} nucleus. Explain why there is the difference.

6.258. Find the energy required for separation of a Ne^{20} nucleus into two alpha-particles and a C^{12} nucleus if it is known that the binding energies per one nucleon in Ne^{20}, He^4, and C^{12} nuclei are equal to 8.03, 7.07, and 7.68 MeV respectively.

6.259. Calculate in atomic mass units the mass of

(a) a Li^8 atom whose nucleus has the binding energy 41.3 MeV;

(b) a C^{10} nucleus whose binding energy per nucleon is equal to 6.04 MeV.

6.260. The nuclei involved in the nuclear reaction $A_1 + A_2 \rightarrow \rightarrow A_3 + A_4$ have the binding energies E_1, E_2, E_3, and E_4. Find the energy of this reaction.

6.261. Assuming that the splitting of a U^{235} nucleus liberates the energy of 200 MeV, find:

(a) the energy liberated in the fission of one kilogram of U^{235} isotope, and the mass of coal with calorific value of 30 kJ/g which is equivalent to that for one kg of U^{235};

(b) the mass of U^{235} isotope split during the explosion of the atomic bomb with 30 kt trotyl equivalent if the calorific value of trotyl is 4.1 kJ/g.

6.262. What amount of heat is liberated during the formation of one gram of He^4 from deuterium H^2? What mass of coal with calorific value of 30 kJ/g is thermally equivalent to the magnitude obtained?

6.263. Taking the values of atomic masses from the tables, calculate the energy per nucleon which is liberated in the nuclear reaction $Li^6 + H^2 \rightarrow 2He^4$. Compare the obtained magnitude with the energy per nucleon liberated in the fission of U^{235} nucleus.

6.264. Find the energy of the reaction $Li^7 + p \rightarrow 2He^4$ if the binding energies per nucleon in Li^7 and He^4 nuclei are known to be equal to 5.60 and 7.06 MeV respectively.

6.265. Find the energy of the reaction N^{14} (α, p) O^{17} if the kinetic energy of the incoming alpha-particle is $T_\alpha = 4.0$ MeV and the proton outgoing at an angle $\theta = 60°$ to the motion direction of the alpha-particle has a kinetic energy $T_p = 2.09$ MeV.

6.266. Making use of the tables of atomic masses, determine the energies of the following reactions:

(a) Li^7 (p, n) Be^7;
(b) Be^9 (n, γ) Be^{10};
(c) Li^7 (α, n) B^{10};
(d) O^{16} (d, α) N^{14}.

6.267. Making use of the tables of atomic masses, find the velocity with which the products of the reaction B^{10} (n, α) Li^7 come apart; the reaction proceeds via interaction of very slow neutrons with stationary boron nuclei.

6.268. Protons striking a stationary lithium target activate a reaction Li^7 (p, n) Be^7. At what value of the proton's kinetic energy can the resulting neutron be stationary?

6.269. An alpha particle with kinetic energy $T = 5.3$ MeV initiates a nuclear reaction Be^9 (α, n) C^{12} with energy yield $Q = +5.7$ MeV. Find the kinetic energy of the neutron outgoing at right angles to the motion direction of the alpha-particle.

6.270. Protons with kinetic energy $T = 1.0$ MeV striking a lithium target induce a nuclear reaction $p + Li^7 \rightarrow 2He^4$. Find the kinetic energy of each alpha-particle and the angle of their divergence provided their motion directions are symmetrical with respect to that of incoming protons.

6.271. A particle of mass m strikes a stationary nucleus of mass M and activates an endoergic reaction. Demonstrate that the threshold (minimal) kinetic energy required to initiate this reaction is defined by Eq. (6.6d).

6.272. What kinetic energy must a proton possess to split a deuteron H^2 whose binding energy is $E_b = 2.2$ MeV?

6.273. The irradiation of lithium and beryllium targets by a monoergic stream of protons reveals that the reaction $Li^7(p, n)Be^7 - 1.65$ MeV is initiated whereas the reaction $Be^9(p, n)B^9 - 1.85$ MeV does not take place. Find the possible values of kinetic energy of the protons.

6.274. To activate the reaction (n, α) with stationary B^{11} nuclei, neutrons must have the threshold kinetic energy $T_{th} = 4.0$ MeV. Find the energy of this reaction.

6.275. Calculate the threshold kinetic energies of protons required to activate the reactions (p, n) and (p, d) with Li^7 nuclei.

6.276. Using the tabular values of atomic masses, find the threshold kinetic energy of an alpha particle required to activate the nuclear reaction Li^7 (α, n) B^{10}. What is the velocity of the B^{10} nucleus in this case?

6.277. A neutron with kinetic energy $T = 10$ MeV activates a nuclear reaction C^{12} (n, α) Be^9 whose threshold is $T_{th} = 6.17$ MeV. Find the kinetic energy of the alpha-particles outgoing at right angles to the incoming neutrons' direction.

6.278. How much, in per cent, does the threshold energy of gamma quantum exceed the binding energy of a deuteron ($E_b = 2.2$ MeV) in the reaction $\gamma + H^2 \rightarrow n + p$?

6.279. A proton with kinetic energy $T = 1.5$ MeV is captured by a deuteron H^2. Find the excitation energy of the formed nucleus.

6.280. The yield of the nuclear reaction $C^{13}(d, n)N^{14}$ has maximum magnitudes at the following values of kinetic energy T_i of bombarding deuterons: 0.60, 0.90, 1.55, and 1.80 MeV. Making use of the table of atomic masses, find the corresponding energy levels of the transitional nucleus through which this reaction proceeds.

6.281. A narrow beam of thermal neutrons is attenuated $\eta = 360$ times after passing through a cadmium plate of thickness $d = 0.50$ mm. Determine the effective cross-section of interaction of these neutrons with cadmium nuclei.

6.282. Determine how many times the intensity of a narrow beam of thermal neutrons will decrease after passing through the heavy water layer of thickness $d = 5.0$ cm. The effective cross-sections of interaction of deuterium and oxygen nuclei with thermal neutrons are equal to $\sigma_1 = 7.0$ b and $\sigma_2 = 4.2$ b respectively.

6.283. A narrow beam of thermal neutrons passes through a plate of iron whose absorption and scattering effective cross-sections are equal to $\sigma_a = 2.5$ b and $\sigma_s = 11$ b respectively. Find the fraction of neutrons quitting the beam due to scattering if the thickness of the plate is $d = 0.50$ cm.

6.284. The yield of a nuclear reaction producing radionuclides may be described in two ways: either by the ratio w of the number of nuclear reactions to the number of bombarding particles, or by the quantity k, the ratio of the activity of the formed radionuclide to the number of bombarding particles. Find:

(a) the half-life of the formed radionuclide, assuming w and k to be known:

(b) the yield w of the reaction $Li^7(p, n)Be^7$ if after irradiation of a lithium target by a beam of protons (over $t = 2.0$ hours and with beam current $I = 10$ μA) the activity of Be^7 became equal to $A = 1.35 \cdot 10^8$ dis/s and its half-life to $T = 53$ days.

6.285. Thermal neutrons fall normally on the surface of a thin gold foil consisting of stable Au^{197} nuclide. The neutron flux density is $J = 1.0 \cdot 10^{10}$ part./(s·cm²). The mass of the foil is $m = 10$ mg. The neutron capture produces beta-active Au^{198} nuclei with half-life $T = 2.7$ days. The effective capture cross-section is $\sigma = 98$ b. Find:

(a) the irradiation time after which the number of Au^{197} nuclei decreases by $\eta = 1.0\%$;

(b) the maximum number of Au^{198} nuclei that can be formed during protracted irradiation.

6.286. A thin foil of certain stable isotope is irradiated by thermal neutrons falling normally on its surface. Due to the capture of neutrons a radionuclide with decay constant λ appears. Find the law describing accumulation of that radionuclide $N(t)$ per unit area of the foil's surface. The neutron flux density is J, the number of nuclei per unit area of the foil's surface is n, and the effective cross section of formation of active nuclei is σ.

6.287. A gold foil of mas $m = 0.20$ g was irradiated during $t = 6.0$ hours by a thermal neutron flux falling normally on its surface. Following $\tau = 12$ hours after the completion of irradiation the activity of the foil became equal to $A = 1.9.10^7$ dis/s. Find the neutron flux density if the effective cross-section of formation of a radioactive nucleus is $\sigma = 96$ b, and the half-life is equal to $T = 2.7$ days.

6.288. How many neutrons are there in the hundredth generation if the fission process starts with $N_0 = 1000$ neutrons and takes place in a medium with multiplication constant $k = 1.05$?

6.289. Find the number of neutrons generated per unit time in a uranium reactor whose thermal power is $P = 100$ MW if the average number of neutrons liberated in each nuclear splitting is $\upsilon = 2.5$. Each splitting is assumed to release an energy $E = 200$ MeV.

6.290. In a thermal reactor the mean lifetime of one generation of thermal neutrons is $\tau = 0.10$ s. Assuming the multiplication constant to be equal to $k = 1.010$, find:

(a) how many times the number of neutrons in the reactor, and consequently its power, will increase over $t = 1.0$ min;

(b) The period T of the reactor, i.e. the time period over which its power increases e-fold.

6.7. ELEMENTARY PARTICLES

- Total energy and momentum of a relativistic particle:

$$E = m_0c^2 + T, \quad pc = \sqrt{T(T + 2m_0c^2)}, \tag{6.7a}$$

where T is the kinetic energy of the particle.

- When examining collisions of particles it pays to use the invariant:

$$E^2 - p^2c^2 = m_0^2c^4, \tag{6.7b}$$

Where E and p are the total energy and the total momentum of the system prior to collision, m_0 is the rest mass of the formed particle.

- Threshold (minimal) kinetic energy of a particle m striking a stationury particle M and activating the endoergic reaction $m + M\ m_1 + m_2 + \ldots$

$$T_{th} = \frac{(m_1 + m_2 + \cdots)^2 - (m + M)^2}{2M}c^2, \tag{6.7c}$$

here m, M, m_1, m_2, . . . are the rest masses of the respective particles.

- Quantum numbers classifying elementary particles:

Q, electric charge,
L, lepton charge,
B, baryon charge,
T, isotopic spin, T_z, its projection,
S, strangeness, $S = 2(Q) - B$,
Y, hypercharge, $Y = B + S$.

• Relation between quantum numbers of strongly interacting particles:

$$Q = T_z + \frac{Y}{2} = T_z + \frac{B+S}{2}, \qquad (6.7d)$$

• Interactions of particles obey the laws of conservation of the Q, L and B charges. In strong interactions the laws of conservation of S (or Y), T, and its projection T_z are also valid.

6.291. Calculate the kinetic energies of protons whose momenta are 0.10, 1.0, and 10 GeV/c, where c is the velocity of light.

6.292. Find the mean path travelled by poins whose kinetic energy exceeds their rest energy $\eta = 1.2$ times. The mean lifetime of very slow pions is $\tau_0 = 25.5$ ns.

6.293. Negative pions with kinetic energy $T = 100$ MeV travel an average distane $l = 11$ m from their origin to decay. Find the proper lifetime of these pions.

6.294. There is a narrow beam of negatie pions with kintic energy T equal to the rest energy of these particles. Find the ratio of fluxes at the sections of the beam separated by a distance $l = 20$ m. The proper men lifetime of these pions is $\tau_0 = 25.5$ ns.

6.295. A stationary positive pion disintegrated into a muon and a neutrino. Find the kinetic energy of the muon and the energy of the neutrino.

6.296. Find the kinetic energy of a neutron emerging as a result of the decay of a stationary Σ^- hyperon ($\Sigma^- \rightarrow n + \pi^-$).

6.297. A stationary positive muon disintegrated into a positron and two neutrinos. Find the greatest possible kinetic energy of the positron.

6.298. A stationary neutral particle disintegrated into a proton with kinetic energy $T = 5.3$ MeV and a negative pion. Find the mass of that particle. What is its name?

6.299. A negative pion with kinetic energy $T = 50$ MeV disintegrated during its flight into a muon and a neutrino. Find the energy of the neutrino out going at right angles to the pion's motion direction.

6.300. A Σ^+ hyperon with kinetic energy $T_z = 320$ MeV disintegrated during its flight into a neutral particle and a positive pion outgoing with kinetic energy $T_\pi = 42$ MeV at right angles to the hyperon's motion direction. Find the rest mass of the neutral particle (in MeV unit).

6.301. A neutral pion disintegrated during its flight into two gamma quanta with equal energies. The angle of divergence of gamma quanta is $\Theta = 60°$. Find the kinetic energy of the pion and of each gamma quantum.

6.302. A relativistic particle with rest mass m collides with a stationary particle of mass M and activates a reaction leading to formation of new particles; $m + M \rightarrow m_1 + m_2 + \cdots$, where the rest masses of newly formed particles are written on the right hand side. Making use of the invariance of the quantity $E^2 - p^2c^2$, demonstrate that the threshold kinetic energy of the particle m required for this reaction is defined by Eq. (6.7c).

6.303. A positron with kinetic energy $T = 750$ keV strikes a stationary free electron. As a result of annihilation, two gamma quanta with equal energies appear. Find the angle of divergence between them.

6.304. Find the threshold energy of gamma quantum required to form

(a) an electron-positron pair in the field of a stationary electron;
(b) a pair of pions of opposite signs in the field of a stationary proton.

6.305. Protons with kinetic energy T strike a stationary hydrogen target. Find the threshold values of T for the following reactions:
(a) $p + p \to p + p + p + \tilde{p}$; (b) $p + p \to p + p + \pi^0$.

6.306. A hydrogen target is bombarded by pions. Calculate the threshold values of kinetic energies of these pions making possible the following reactions:
(a) $\pi^- + p \to K^+ + \Sigma^-$; (b) $\pi^0 + p \to K^+ + \Lambda^0$.

6.307. Find the strangeness S and the hypercharge Y of a neutral elementary particle whose isotopic spin projection is $T_z = +1/2$ and baryon charge $B = +1$. What particle is this?

6.308. Which of the following processes are forbidden by the law of conservation of lepton charge:

(1) $n \to p + e^- + \nu$; (4) $p + e^- \to n + \nu$;
(2) $\pi^+ \to \mu^+ + e^- + e^+$; (5) $\mu^+ \to e^+ + \nu + \tilde{\nu}$;
(3) $\pi^- \to \mu^- + \nu$; (6) $K^- \to \mu^- + \tilde{\nu}$?

6.309. Which of the following processes are forbidden by the law of conservation of strangeness:

(1) $\pi^- + p \to \Sigma^- + K^+$; (4) $n + p \to \Lambda^0 + \Sigma^+$;
(2) $\pi^- + p \to \Sigma^+ + K^-$; (5) $\pi^- + n \to \Xi^- + K^+ + K^-$;
(3) $\pi^- + p \to K^+ + K^- + n$; (6) $K^- + p \to \Omega^- + K^+ + K^0$?

6.310. Indicate the reasons why the following processes are forbidden:

(1) $\Sigma^- \to \Lambda^0 + \pi^-$; (4) $n + p \to \Sigma^+ + \Lambda^0$;
(2) $\pi^- + p \to K^+ + K^-$; (5) $\pi^- \to \mu^- + e^+ + e^-$;
(3) $K^- + n \to \Omega^- + K^+ + K^0$; (6) $\mu^- \to e^- + \nu_e + \tilde{\nu}_\mu$.

ANSWERS AND SOLUTIONS

1.1. $v = l/2\tau = 3.0$ km per hour.
1.2. $\langle v \rangle = 2v_0(v_1 + v_2)/(2v_0 + v_1 + v_2)$.
1.3. $\Delta t = \tau\sqrt{1 - 4\langle v \rangle / w\tau} = 15$ s.
1.4. (a) 10 cm/s; (b) 25 cm/s; (c) $t_0 = 16$ s.
1.5. $(\mathbf{r}_1 - \mathbf{r}_2)/|\mathbf{r}_1 - \mathbf{r}_2| = (\mathbf{v}_2 - \mathbf{v}_1)/|\mathbf{v}_2 - \mathbf{v}_1|$.
1.6. $v' = \sqrt{v_0^2 + v^2 + 2v_0 v \cos\varphi} \approx 40$ km per hour, $\varphi' = 19°$.
1.7. $u = \dfrac{v_0}{(1 - v_0^2/v'^2)^{-1/2} - 1} = 3.0$ km per hour.
1.8. $\tau_A/\tau_B = \eta/\sqrt{\eta^2 - 1} = 1.8$.
1.9. $\theta = \arcsin(1/n) + \pi/2 = 120°$.
1.10. $l = v_0 t\sqrt{2(1 - \sin\theta)} = 22$ m.
1.11. $l = (v_1 + v_2)\sqrt{v_1 v_2 / g} = 2.5$ m.
1.12. $t = 2a/3v$.
1.13. It is seen from Fig. 1*a* that the points *A* and *B* converge with velocity $v - u\cos\alpha$, where the angle α varies with time. The

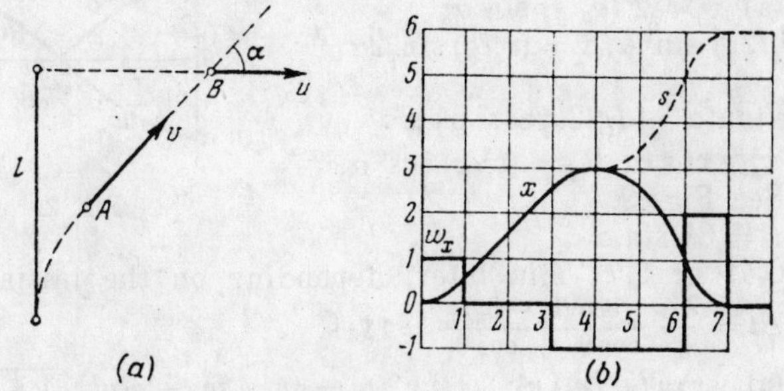

Fig. 1.

points merge provided the following two conditions are met:

$$\int_0^\tau (v - u\cos\alpha)\,dt = l, \qquad \int_0^\tau v\cos\alpha\,dt = u\tau,$$

where τ is the sought time. It follows from these two equations that

$$\tau = vl/(v^2 - u^2).$$

1.14. $x_1 - x_2 = l - w\tau(t + \tau/2) = 0.24$ km. Toward the train with velocity $V = 4.0$ m/s.
1.15. (a) 0.7 s; (b) 0.7 and 1.3 m respectively.

1.16. $t_m = \dfrac{v_1 l_1 + v_2 l_2}{v_1^2 + v_2^2}, \quad l_{min} = \dfrac{|l_1 v_2 - l_2 v_1|}{\sqrt{v_1^2 + v_2^2}}.$

1.17. $CD = l/\sqrt{\eta^2 - 1}$.

1.18. See Fig. 1b.

1.19. (a) $\langle v \rangle = \pi R/\tau = 50$ cm/s; (b) $|\langle \mathbf{v} \rangle| = 2R/\tau = 32$ cm/s; (c) $|\langle \mathbf{w} \rangle| = 2\pi R/\tau^2 = 10$ cm/s^2.

1.20. (a) $\mathbf{v} = \mathbf{a}(1 - 2\alpha t)$, $\mathbf{w} = -2\alpha\mathbf{a} = \text{const}$; (b) $\Delta t = 1/\alpha$, $s = a/2\alpha$.

1.21. (a) $x = v_0 t\,(1 - t/2\tau)$, $x = 0.24$, 0 and -4.0 m; (b) 1.1, 9 and 11 s; (c) $s = \begin{cases} (1 - t/2\tau)\, v_0 t & \text{for } t \leqslant \tau, \\ [1 + (1 - t/\tau)^2]\, v_0 t/2 & \text{for } t \geqslant \tau. \end{cases}$ 24 and 34 cm respectively.

1.22. (a) $v = \alpha^2 t/2$, $w = \alpha^2/2$; (b) $\langle v \rangle = \alpha\sqrt{s}/2$.

1.23. (a) $s = (^2/_3 a)\, v_0^{3/2}$; (b) $t = 2\sqrt{v_0}/a$.

1.24. (a) $y = -x^2 b/a^2$; (b) $\mathbf{v} = a\mathbf{i} - 2bt\mathbf{j}$, $\mathbf{w} = -2b\mathbf{j}$, $v = \sqrt{a^2 + 4b^2t^2}$, $w = 2b$; (c) $\tan\alpha = a/2bt$; (d) $\langle \mathbf{v} \rangle = a\mathbf{i} - bt\mathbf{j}$, $|\langle \mathbf{v} \rangle| = \sqrt{a^2 + b^2t^2}$.

1.25. (a) $y = x - x^2\alpha/a$; (b) $v = a\sqrt{1 + (1 - 2\alpha t)^2}$, $w = 2\alpha a = \text{const}$; (c) $t_0 = 1/\alpha$.

1.26. (a) $s = a\omega\tau$; (b) $\pi/2$.

1.27. $v_0 = \sqrt{(1 + a^2)\, w/2b}$.

1.28. (a) $\mathbf{r} = \mathbf{v}_0 t + \mathbf{g}t^2/2$; (b) $\langle \mathbf{v} \rangle_t = \mathbf{v}_0 + \mathbf{g}t/2$, $\langle \mathbf{v} \rangle = \mathbf{v}_0 - \mathbf{g}\,(\mathbf{v}_0\mathbf{g})/g^2$.

1.29. (a) $\tau = 2\,(v_0/g)\sin\alpha$; (b) $h = (v_0^2/2g)\sin^2\alpha$, $l = (v_0^2/g)\sin 2\alpha$, $\alpha = 76°$; (c) $y = x\tan\alpha - (g/2v_0^2\cos^2\alpha)\, x^2$; (d) $R_1 = v_0^2/g\cos\alpha$, $R_2 = (v_0^2/g)\cos^2\alpha$.

1.30. See Fig. 2.

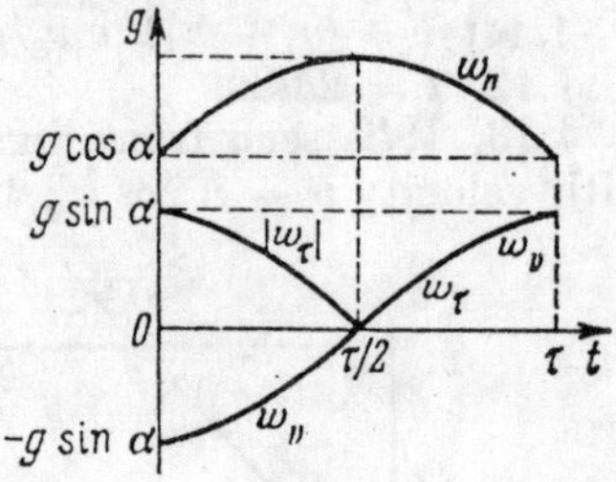

Fig. 2.

1.31. $l = 8h\sin\alpha$.

1.32. 0.41 or 0.71 min later, depending on the initial angle.

1.33. $\Delta t = \dfrac{2v_0}{g}\,\dfrac{\sin(\theta_1 - \theta_2)}{\cos\theta_1 + \cos\theta_2} = 11$ s.

1.34. (a) $x = (a/2v_0)\, y^2$; (b) $w = av_0$, $w_\tau = a^2 y/\sqrt{1 + (ay/v_0)^2}$, $w_n = av_0/\sqrt{1 + (ay/v_0)^2}$.

1.35. (a) $y = (b/2a)\, x^2$; (b) $R = v^2/w_n = v^2/\sqrt{w^2 - w_\tau^2} = (a/b)\,[1 + (xb/a)^2]^{3/2}$.

1.36. $v = \sqrt{2ax}$.

1.37. $w = a\sqrt{1 + (4\pi n)^2} = 0.8$ m/s^2.

1.38. (a) $v = v_0/(1 + v_0 t/R) = v_0 e^{-s/R}$; (b) $w = \sqrt{2}\, v_0^2/Re^{2s/R} = \sqrt{2}\, v^2/R$.

1.39. $\tan\alpha = 2s/R$.

1.40. (a) $w_0 = a^2\omega^2/R = 2.6$ m/s^2, $w_a = a\omega^2 = 3.2$ m/s^2; (b) $w_{min} = a\omega^2\sqrt{1 - (R/2a)^2} = 2.5$ m/s^2, $l_m = \pm a\sqrt{1 - R^2/2a^2} = \pm 0.37$ m.

1.41. $R=a^3/2bs$, $w=a\sqrt{1+(4bs^2/a^3)^2}$.

1.42. (a) $w=2av^2$, $R=\frac{1}{2}a$; (b) $w=bv^2/a^2$, $R=a^2/b$.

1.43. $v=2R\omega=0.40$ m/s, $w=4R\omega^2=0.32$ m/s².

1.44. $w=(v/t)\sqrt{1+4a^2t^4}=0.7$ m/s².

1.45. $\omega=2\pi nv/l=2.0\cdot10^3$ rad/s.

1.46. (a) $\langle\omega\rangle=2a/3=4$ rad/s, $\langle\beta\rangle=\sqrt{3ab}=6$ rad/s²; (b) $\beta=2\sqrt{3ab}=12$ rad/s².

1.47. $t=\sqrt[3]{(4/a)\tan\alpha}=7$ s.

1.48. $\langle\omega\rangle=\omega_0/3$.

1.49. (a) $\varphi=(1-e^{-at})\,\omega_0/a$; (b) $\omega=\omega_0e^{-at}$.

1.50. $\omega_z=\pm\sqrt{2\beta_0\sin\varphi}$, see Fig. 3.

1.51. (a) $y=v^2/\beta x$ (hyperbola); (b) $y=\sqrt{2wx/\omega}$ (parabola).

1.52. (a) $w_A=v^2/R=2.0$ m/s², the vector $\mathbf{w}_A$ is permanently directed to the centre of the wheel; (b) $s=8R=4.0$ m.

1.53. (a) $v_A=2wt=10.0$ cm/s, $v_B=\sqrt{2}\,wt=7.1$ cm/s, $v_0=0$; (b) $w_A=2w\sqrt{1+(wt^2/2R)^2}=5.6$ cm/s², $w_B=w\sqrt{1+(1-wt^2/R)^2}=2.5$ cm/s², $w_O=w^2t^2/R=2.5$ cm/s².

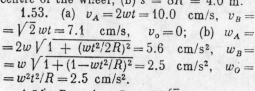

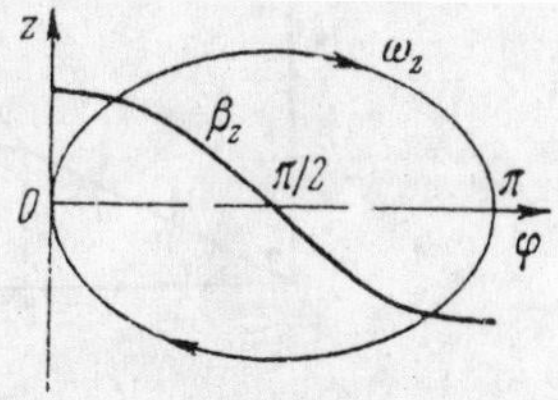

Fig. 3.

1.54. $R_A=4r$, $R_B=2\sqrt{2}\,r$.

1.55. $\omega=\sqrt{\omega_1^2+\omega_2^2}=5$ rad/s, $\beta=\omega_1\omega_2=12$ rad/s².

1.56. (a) $\omega=at\sqrt{1+(bt/a)^2}=8$ rad/s, $\beta=a\sqrt{1+(2bt/a)^2}=1.3$ rad/s²; (b) 17°.

1.57. (a) $\omega=v/R\cos\alpha=2.3$ rad/s, 60°; (b) $\beta=(v/R)^2\tan\alpha=2.3$ rad/s².

1.58. $\omega=\omega_0\sqrt{1+(\beta_0t/\omega_0)^2}=0.6$ rad/s, $\beta=\beta_0\sqrt{1+\omega_0^2t^2}=0.2$ rad/s².

1.59. $\Delta m=2mw/(g+w)$.

1.60. $\mathbf{w}=\dfrac{m_0-k(m_1+m_2)}{m_0+m_1+m_2}\mathbf{g}$, $T=\dfrac{(1+k)\,m_0}{m_0+m_1+m_2}m_2g$.

1.61. (a) $F=\dfrac{(k_1-k_2)\,m_1m_2g\cos\alpha}{m_1+m_2}$; (b) $\tan\alpha_{min}=\dfrac{k_1m_1+k_2m_2}{m_1+m_2}$.

1.62. $k=[(\eta^2-1)/(\eta^2+1)]\tan\alpha=0.16$.

1.63. (a) $m_2/m_1>\sin\alpha+k\cos\alpha$; (b) $m_2/m_1<\sin\alpha-k\cos\alpha$; (c) $\sin\alpha-k\cos\alpha<m_2/m_1<\sin\alpha+k\cos\alpha$.

1.64. $\mathbf{w}_2=\mathbf{g}\,(\eta-\sin\alpha-k\cos\alpha)/(\eta+1)=0.05\,\mathbf{g}$.

1.65. When $t\leqslant t_0$, the accelerations $w_1=w_2=at/(m_1+m_2)$; when $t\geqslant t_0$ $w_1=kgm_2/m_1$, $w_2=(at-km_2g)/m_2$. Here $t_0=kgm_2\,(m_1+m_2)/am$. See Fig. 4.

1.66. $\tan2\alpha=-1/k$, $\alpha=49°$; $t_{min}=1.0$ s.

1.67. $\tan\beta=k$; $T_{min}=mg\,(\sin\alpha+k\cos\alpha)/\sqrt{1+k^2}$.

1.68. (a) $v=\dfrac{mg^2\cos\alpha}{2a\sin^2\alpha}$; (b) $s=\dfrac{m^2g^3\cos\alpha}{6a^2\sin^3\alpha}$.

1.69. $v=\sqrt{(2g/3a)\sin\alpha}$.

1.70. $\tau = \sqrt{2l/(3w + kg)}$.

1.71. (a) $\mathbf{w}_1 = \frac{(m_1 - m_2)\,\mathbf{g} + 2m_2\mathbf{w}_0}{m_1 + m_2}$, $\quad \mathbf{w}_1' = \frac{m_1 - m_2}{m_1 + m_2}(\mathbf{g} - \mathbf{w}_0)$;
(b) $\mathbf{F} = \frac{4m_1m_2}{m_1 + m_2}(\mathbf{g} - \mathbf{w}_0)$.

1.72. $\mathbf{w} = 2\mathbf{g}\,(2\eta - \sin\alpha)/(4\eta + 1)$.

1.73. $\mathbf{w}_1 = \frac{4m_1m_2 + m_0(m_1 - m_2)}{4m_1m_2 + m_0(m_1 + m_2)}\,\mathbf{g}$.

1.74. $F_{fr} = 2lmM/(M - m)\,t^2$.

1.75. $t = \sqrt{2l\,(4 + \eta)/3g\,(2 - \eta)} = 1.4$ s.

1.76. $H = 6h\eta\,/(\eta + 4) = 0.6$ m.

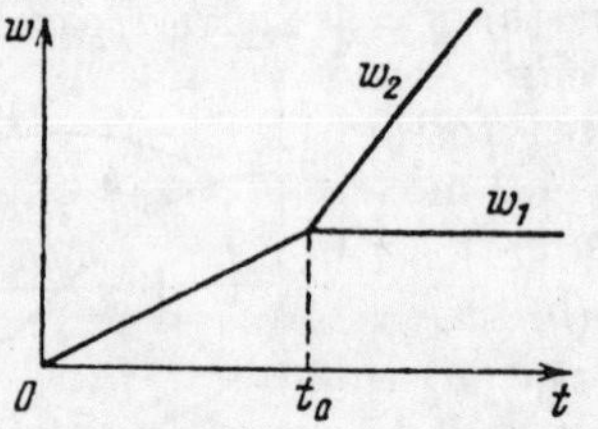

Fig. 4.

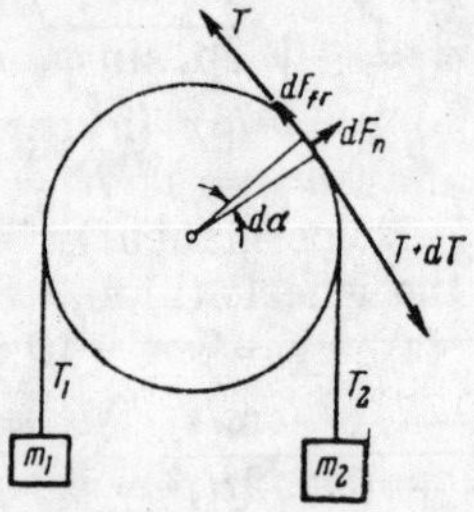

Fig. 5.

1.77. $w_A = g/(1 + \eta\cot^2\alpha)$, $w_B = g/(\tan\alpha + \eta\cot\alpha)$.

1.78. $w = g\sqrt{2}/(2 + k + M/m)$.

1.79. $w_{min} = g\,(1 - k)/(1 + k)$.

1.80. $w_{max} = g\,(1 + k\cot\alpha)/(\cot\alpha - k)$.

1.81. $w = g\sin\alpha\cos\alpha/(\sin^2\alpha + m_1/m_2)$.

1.82. $w = \frac{mg\sin\alpha}{M + 2m\,(1 - \cos\alpha)}$.

1.83. (a) $|\langle\mathbf{F}\rangle| = 2\sqrt{2}\,mv^2/\pi R$; (b) $|\langle\mathbf{F}\rangle| = mw_\tau$.

1.84. 2.1, 0.7 and 1.5 kN.

1.85. (a) $w = g\sqrt{1 + 3\cos^2\theta}$, $T = 3mg\cos\theta$;
(b) $T = mg\sqrt{3}$; (c) $\cos\theta = 1/\sqrt{3}$, $\theta = 54.7°$.

1.86. $\approx 53°$.

1.87. $\theta = \arccos(2/3) \approx 48°$, $v = \sqrt{2gR/3}$.

1.88. $\varepsilon = 1/(\varkappa/m\omega^2 - 1)$. Is independent of the rotation direction.

1.89. $r = R/2$, $v_{max} = \frac{1}{2}\sqrt{kgR}$.

1.90. $s = \frac{1}{2}R\sqrt{(kg/w_\tau)^2 - 1} = 60$ m.

1.91. $v \leqslant \alpha\sqrt{kg/a}$.

1.92. $T = (\cot\theta + \omega^2R/g)\,mg/2\pi$.

1.93. (a) Let us examine a small element of the thread in contact with the pulley (Fig. 5). Since the element is weightless, $dT = dF_{fr} = k\,dF_n$ and $dF_n = T\,d\alpha$. Hence, $dT/T = k\,d\alpha$. Integrating this equation, we obtain $k = (\ln \eta_0)/\pi$; (b) $w = g(\eta - \eta_0)/(\eta + \eta_0)$.

1.94. $F = (mv_0^2/R)\cos^2\alpha$.

1.95. $\mathbf{F} = -m\omega^2\mathbf{r}$, where $\mathbf{r}$ is the radius vector of the particle relative to the origin of coordinates; $F = m\omega^2\sqrt{x^2+y^2}$.

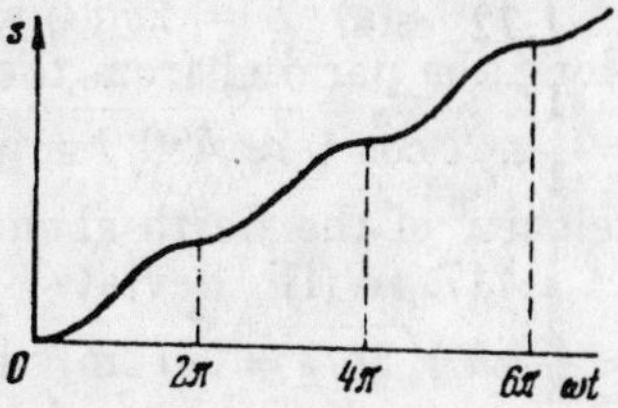

Fig. 6.

1.96. (a) $\Delta\mathbf{p} = m\mathbf{g}t$; (b) $|\Delta\mathbf{p}| = -2m(\mathbf{v}_0\mathbf{g})/g$.

1.97. (a) $\mathbf{p} = \mathbf{a}\tau^3/6$; (b) $s = a\tau^4/12m$.

1.98. $s = (\omega t - \sin\omega t)\,F_0/m\omega^2$, see Fig. 6.

1.99. $t = \pi/\omega$; $s = 2F_0/m\omega^2$; $v_{max} = F_0/m\omega$.

1.100. (a) $v = v_0 e^{-tr/m}$, $t \to \infty$; (b) $v = v_0 - sr/m$, $s_{total} = \dfrac{mv_0}{r}$; (c) $\langle v\rangle = v_0\,\dfrac{\eta - 1}{\eta\ln\eta}$.

1.101. $t = \dfrac{h(v_0 - v)}{v_0 v \ln(v_0/v)}$

1.102. $s = \dfrac{2}{a}\tan\alpha$, $v_{max} = \sqrt{\dfrac{g}{a}\sin\alpha\tan\alpha}$.

Instruction. To reduce the equation to the form which is convenient to integrate, the acceleration must be represented as dv/dt and then a change of variables made according to the formula $dt = dx/v$.

1.103. $s = {}^1/_6\, a(t - t_0)^3/m$, where $t_0 = kmg/a$ is the moment of time at which the motion starts. At $t \leqslant t_0$ the distance is $s = 0$.

1.104. $v' = v_0/\sqrt{1 + kv_0^2/mg}$.

1.105. (a) $v = (2F/m\omega)\,|\sin(\omega t/2)|$; (b) $\Delta s = 8F/m\omega^2$, $\langle v\rangle = 4F/\pi m\omega$.

1.106. $v = v_0/(1 + \cos\varphi)$. **Instruction.** Here $w_\tau = -w_x$, and therefore $v = -v_x + \text{const}$. From the initial condition it follows that const $= v_0$. Besides, $v_x = v\cos\varphi$.

1.107. $w = [1 - \cos(l/R)]\,Rg/l$.

1.108. (a) $v = \sqrt{2gR/3}$; (b) $\cos\theta_0 = \dfrac{2 + \eta\sqrt{5 + 9\eta^2}}{3(1+\eta^2)}$, where $\eta = w_0/g$, $\theta_0 \approx 17°$.

1.109. For $n < 1$, including negative values.

1.110. When $\omega^2 R > g$, there are two steady equilibrium positions: $\theta_1 = 0$ and $\theta_2 = \arccos(g/\omega^2 R)$. When $\omega^2 R < g$, there is only one equilibrium position: $\theta_1 = 0$. As long as there is only one lower equilibrium position, it is steady. Whenever the second equilibrium position appears (which is permanently steady) the lower one becomes unsteady.

1.111. $h \approx (\omega s^2/v)\sin\varphi = 7$ **cm**, where ω is the angular velocity of the Earth's rotation.

1.112. $F = m\sqrt{g^2 + \omega^4 r^2 + (2v'\omega)^2} = 8$ N.

1.113. $F_{cor} = 2m\omega^2 r\sqrt{1 + (v_0/\omega r)^2} = 2.8$ N.

1.114. (a) $w' = \omega^2 R$; (b) $F_{in} = m\omega^2 r \sqrt{(2R/r)^2 - 1}$.

1.115. $F_{cf} = m\omega^2 R \sqrt{5/9} = 8$ N, $F_{cor} = {}^2/_3 m\omega^2 R \sqrt{5 + 8g/3\omega^2 R} = 17$ N.

1.116. (a) $F = 2mv\omega \sin\varphi = 3.8$ kN, on the right rail; (b) along the parallel from the east to the west with the velocity $v = \frac{1}{2}\omega R \cos\varphi \approx 420$ km per hour. Here ω is the angular rotation velocity of the Earth about its axis, R is its radius.

1.117. Will deviate to the east by the distance $x \approx \frac{2}{3}\omega h \sqrt{2h/g} = 24$ cm. Here ω is the angular velocity of the Earth's rotation about its axis.

1.118. $A = \mathbf{F}(\mathbf{r}_2 - \mathbf{r}_1) = -17$ J.

1.119. $A = ma^4 t^2/8$.

1.120. $F = 2as\sqrt{1 + (s/R)^2}$.

1.121. $A = mg(h + kl)$.

1.122. $A = -kmgl/(1 - k\cot\alpha) = -0.05$ J

1.123. $F_{min} = (m_1 + m_2/2)kg$.

1.124. $A = -(1 - \eta)\eta mgl/2 = -1.3$ J.

1.125. $\langle P \rangle = 0$, $P = mg(gt - v_0 \sin\alpha)$.

1.126. $P = mRat$, $\langle P \rangle = mRat/2$.

1.127. (a) $\langle P \rangle = -kmgv_0/2 = -2$ W; (b) $P_{max} = -{}^1/_2 mv_0^2 \sqrt{\alpha g}$.

1.128. $A = {}^1/_2 m\omega^2 (r_2^2 - r_1^2) = 0.20$ J.

1.129. $A_{min} = {}^1/_2 k(\Delta l)^2$, where $k = k_1 k_2/(k_1 + k_2)$.

1.130. $A = 3mg/4a$, $\Delta U = mg/2a$.

1.131. (a) $r_0 = 2a/b$, steady; (b) $F_{max} = b^3/27a^2$, see Fig. 7.

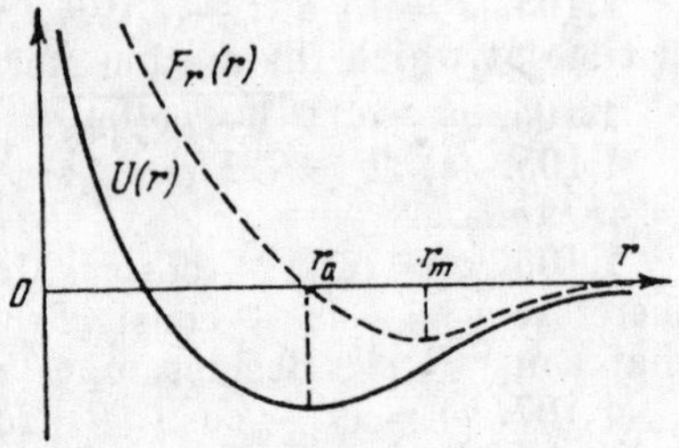

Fig. 7.

1.132. (a) No; (b) ellipses whose ratio of semiaxes is $a/b = \sqrt{\beta/\alpha}$; also ellipses, but with $a/b = \beta/\alpha$.

1.133. The latter field is potential.

1.134. $s = v_0^2/2g(\sin\alpha + k\cos\alpha)$, $A = -mv_0^2 k/2(k + \tan\alpha)$.

1.135. $h = H/2$; $s_{max} = H$.

1.136. $v = {}^2/_3\sqrt{gh/3}$.

1.137. $v_{min} = \sqrt{5gl}$; $T = 3mg$.

1.138. $t = l_0^2/2v_0 R$.

1.139. $\Delta l = (1 + \sqrt{1 + 2kl/mg})\, mg/k$.

1.140. $v = \sqrt{19gl_0/32} = 1.7$ m/s.

1.141. $A = \dfrac{kmgl_0}{2} \dfrac{1 - \cos\theta}{(\sin\theta + k\cos\theta)\cos\theta} = 0.09$ J.

1.142. $A = \varkappa l_0^2 \eta(1 + \eta)/2(1 - \eta)^2$, where $\eta = m\omega^2/\varkappa$.

1.143. $\mathbf{w}_C = \mathbf{g}(m_1 - m_2)^2/(m_1 + m_2)^2$.

1.145. $r = (g/\omega^2)\tan\theta = 0.8$ cm, $T = mg/\cos\theta = 5$ N.

1.146. (a) $F_{fr} = mg[\sin\alpha + (\omega^2 l/g)\cos\alpha] = 6$ N. (b) $\omega < \sqrt{g(k - \tan\alpha)/l(1 + k\tan\alpha)} = 2$ rad/s.

1.147. (a) $\mathbf{V} = (m_1\mathbf{v}_1 + m_2\mathbf{v}_2)/(m_1 + m_2)$; (b) $T = \mu(\mathbf{v}_1 - \mathbf{v}_2)^2/2$, where $\mu = m_1 m_2 (m_1 + m_2)$.

1.148. $E = \tilde{E} + mV^2/2$.

1.149. $\tilde{E} = \mu(v_1^2 + v_2^2)/2$, where $\mu = m_1 m_2/(m_1 + m_2)$.

1.150. $\mathbf{p} = \mathbf{p}_0 + m\mathbf{g}t$, where $\mathbf{p}_0 = m\mathbf{v}_1 + m_2\mathbf{v}_2$, $m = m_1 + m_2$; $\mathbf{r}_C = \mathbf{v}_0 t + \mathbf{g}t^2/2$, where $\mathbf{v}_0 = (m_1\mathbf{v}_1 + m_2\mathbf{v}_2)/(m_1 + m_2)$.

1.151. $v_C = x\sqrt{\varkappa m_2/(m_1 + m_2)}$.

1.152. (a) $l_{max} = l_0 + F/\varkappa$, $l_{min} = l_0$; (b) $l_{max} = l_0 + 2m_1 F/\varkappa(m_1 + m_2)$, $l_{min} = l_0$.

1.153. (a) $\Delta l > 3mg/\varkappa$; (b) $h = (1 + \varkappa\Delta l/mg)^2 mg/8\varkappa = 8mg/\varkappa$.

1.154. $\mathbf{v}_1 = -m\mathbf{v}/(M - m)$, $\mathbf{v}_2 = M\mathbf{v}/(M - m)$.

1.155. $\mathbf{v}_{rear} = \mathbf{v}_0 - \dfrac{m}{M+m}\mathbf{u}$; $\mathbf{v}_{form} = \mathbf{v}_0 + \dfrac{mM}{(M+m)^2}\mathbf{u}$.

1.156. (1) $\mathbf{v}_1 = -\dfrac{2m}{M+2m}\mathbf{u}$; (2) $\mathbf{v}_2 = -\dfrac{m(2M+3m)}{(M+m)(M+2m)}\mathbf{u}$, $v_2/v_1 = 1 + m/2(M+m) > 1$.

1.158. $\Delta p = m\sqrt{2gh}(\eta + 1)/(\eta - 1) = 0.2$ kg·m/s.

1.159. (a) $\mathbf{l} = -\dfrac{m}{M+m}\mathbf{l}'$; (b) $\mathbf{F} = -\dfrac{mM}{M+m}\dfrac{d\mathbf{v}'}{dt}$.

1.160. $\mathbf{l} = m\mathbf{l}'/2M$.

1.161. $\tau = (p\cos\alpha - M\sqrt{2gl\sin\alpha})/Mg\sin\alpha$.

1.162. (a) $v = (2M/m)\sqrt{gl}\sin(\theta/2)$; (b) $\eta \approx 1 - m/M$.

1.163. $h = Mv^2/2g(M + m)$.

1.164. (1) $A = -\mu gh$, where $\mu = mM/(m + M)$; (2) Yes.

1.166. $\mathbf{v} = 1.0\mathbf{i} + 2.0\mathbf{j} - 4.0\mathbf{k}$, $v \approx 4.6$ m/s.

1.167. $\Delta T = -\mu(\mathbf{v}_1 - \mathbf{v}_2)^2/2$, where $\mu = m_1 m_2/(m_1 + m_2)$.

1.168. (a) $\eta = 2m_1/(m_1 + m_2)$; (b) $\eta = 4m_1 m_2/(m_1 + m_2)^2$.

1.169. (a) $m_1/m_2 = 1/3$; (b) $m_1/m_2 = 1 + 2\cos\Theta = 2.0$.

1.170. $\eta = {}^1/_2\cos^2\alpha = 0.25$.

1.171. $v_{max} = v(1 + \sqrt{2(\eta - 1)}) = 1.0$ km per second.

1.172. Will continue moving in the same direction, although this time with the velocity $v' = (1 - \sqrt{1 - 2\eta})v/2$. For $\eta \ll 1$ the velocity $v' \approx \eta v/2 = 5$ cm/s.

1.173. $\Delta T/T = (1 + m/M)\tan^2\theta + m/M - 1 = -40\%$.

1.174. (a) $p = \mu\sqrt{v_1^2 + v_2^2}$; (b) $T = {}^1/_2\mu(v_1^2 + v_2^2)$. Here $\mu = m_1 m_2/(m_1 + m_2)$.

1.175. $\sin\theta_{max} = m_2/m_1$.

1.176. $\mathbf{v}' = -\mathbf{v}(2 - \eta^2)/(6 - \eta^2)$. Respectively at smaller η, equal, or greater than $\sqrt{2}$.

1.178. Suppose that at a certain moment t the rocket has the mass m and the velocity $\mathbf{v}$ relative to the reference frame employed. Consider the inertial reference frame moving with the same velocity as the rocket has at a *given* moment. In this reference frame the momentum increment that the system "rocket-ejected portion of gas" acquires during the time dt is equal to $d\mathbf{p} = m\,d\mathbf{v} + \mu\,dt\cdot\mathbf{u} = \mathbf{F}\,dt$. What follows is evident.

1.179. $\mathbf{v} = -\mathbf{u}\ln(m_0/m)$.

1.180. $m = m_0 e^{-wt/u}$.

1.181. $\alpha = (u/v_0)\ln(m_0/m)$.

1.182. $\mathbf{v} = \frac{\mathbf{F}}{\mu}\ln\frac{m_0}{m_0-\mu t}$, $\mathbf{w} = \frac{\mathbf{F}}{m_0-\mu t}$.

1.183. $\mathbf{v} = \mathbf{F}t/m_0(1+\mu t/m_0)$, $\mathbf{w} = \mathbf{F}/m_0(1+\mu t/m_0)^2$.

1.184. $v = \sqrt{2gh\ln(l/h)}$.

1.185. $\mathbf{N} = 2\mathbf{b}\sqrt{a/b}$.

1.186. $M = {}^1/_2 mgv_0 t^2\cos\alpha$; $M = (mv_0^3/2g)\sin^2\alpha\cos\alpha = 37\ \text{kg}\cdot\text{m}^2/\text{s}$.

1.187. (a) Relative to all points of the straight line drawn at right angles to the wall through the point O;
(b) $|\Delta\mathbf{M}| = 2\,mvl\cos\alpha$.

1.188. Relative to the centre of the circle.
$|\Delta\mathbf{M}| = 2\sqrt{1-(g/\omega^2 l)^2}\,mgl/\omega$.

1.189. $|\Delta\mathbf{M}| = hmV$.

1.190. $M = m\omega v_0^2 t^2$.

1.191. $m = 2kr_1^2/v_2^2$.

1.192. $v_0 = \sqrt{2gl/\cos\theta}$.

1.193. $F = m\omega_0^2 r_0^4/r^3$.

1.194. $M_z = Rmgt$.

1.195. $M = Rmgt\sin\alpha$. Will not change.

1.196. $\mathbf{M}' = \mathbf{M} - [\mathbf{r}_0\mathbf{p}]$. In the case when $\mathbf{p} = 0$, i.e. in the frame of the centre of inertia.

1.198. $\tilde{M} = {}^1/_3\ lmv_0$.

1.199. $\varepsilon_{max} \approx mv_0^2/\varkappa l_0^2$. The problem is easier to solve in the frame of the centre of inertia.

1.200. $T = 2\pi\gamma M/v^3 = 225$ days.

1.201. (a) 5.2 times; (b) 13 km/s, $2.2\cdot10^{-4}$ m/s².

1.202. $T = \pi\sqrt{(r+R)^3/2\gamma M}$. It is sufficient to consider the motion along the circle whose radius is equal to the major semi-axis of the given ellipse, i.e. $(r+R)/2$, since in accordance with Kepler's laws the period of revolution is the same.

1.203. Falling of the body on the Sun can be considered as the motion along a very elongated (in the limit, degenerated) ellipse whose major semi-axis is practically equal to the radius R of the Earth's orbit. Then from Kepler's laws, $(2\tau/T)^2 = [(R/2)/R]^3$, where τ is the falling time (the time needed to complete half a revolution along the elongated ellipse), T is the period of the Earth's revolution around the Sun. Hence, $\tau = T/4\sqrt{2} = 65$ days.

1.204. Will not change.

1.205. $l = \sqrt[3]{\gamma M(T/2\pi)^2}$.

1.206. (a) $U = -\gamma m_1 m_2/r$; (b) $U = -\gamma(mM/l)\ln(1+l/a)$; $F = \gamma mM/a(a+l)$.

1.207. $M = m\sqrt{2\gamma m_S r_1 r_2/(r_1+r_2)}$, where m_S is the mass of the Sun.

1.208. $E = T + U = -\gamma m m_S/2a$, where m_S is the mass of the Sun.

1.209. $r_m = \frac{r_0}{2-\eta}\left[1 \pm \sqrt{1-(2-\eta)\eta \sin^2\alpha}\right]$, where $\eta = r_0 v_0^2/\gamma m_S$, m_S being the mass of the Sun.

1.210. $r_{min} = (\gamma m_S/v_0^2)\left[\sqrt{1+(l v_0^2/\gamma m_S)^2} - 1\right]$, where m_S is the mass of the Sun.

1.211. (a) First let us consider a thin spherical layer of radius ρ and mass δM. The energy of interaction of the particle with an elementary belt δS of that layer is equal to (Fig. 8)

$$dU = -\gamma\,(m\delta M/2l)\sin\theta\,d\theta. \qquad (*)$$

According to the cosine theorem in the triangle OAP $l^2 = \rho^2 + r^2 - 2\rho r\cos\theta$. Having determined the differential of this expression, we can reduce Eq. (*) to the form that is convenient for integration. After integrating over the whole layer we obtain $\delta U = -\gamma m\,\delta M/r$. And finally, integrating over all layers of the sphere, we obtain $U = -\gamma m M/r$; (b) $F_r = -\partial U/\partial r = -\gamma m M/r^2$.

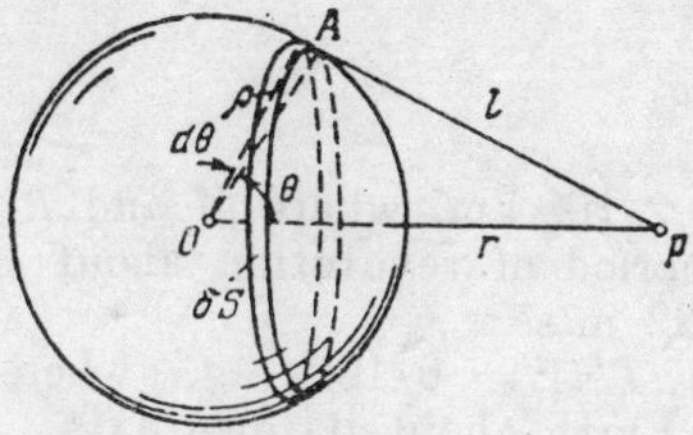

Fig. 8.

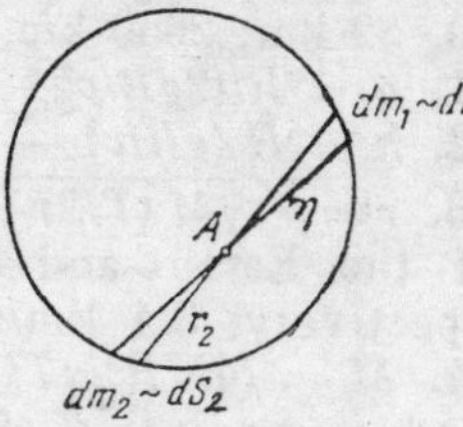

Fig. 9.

1.212. First let us consider a thin spherical layer of substance (Fig. 9). Construct a cone with a small angle of taper and the vertex at the point A. The ratio of the areas cut out by the cone in the layer is $dS_1 : dS_2 = r_1^2 : r_2^2$. The masses of the cut volumes are proportional to their areas. Therefore these volumes will attract the particle A with forces equal in magnitude and opposite in direction. What follows is obvious.

1.213. $A = -{}^3/_2\gamma m M/R$.

1.214. $\mathbf{G} = \begin{cases} -(\gamma M/R^3)\,\mathbf{r} & \text{for } r \leqslant R, \\ -(\gamma M/r^3)\,\mathbf{r} & \text{for } r \geqslant R; \end{cases}$

$\varphi = \begin{cases} -{}^3/_2(1-r^2/3R^2)\gamma M/R & \text{for } r \leqslant R, \\ -\gamma M/r & \text{for } r \geqslant R. \end{cases}$ See Fig. 10.

1.215. $\mathbf{G} = -{}^4/_3\pi\gamma\rho\mathbf{l}$. The field inside the cavity is uniform.

1.216. $p = {}^3/_8(1 - r^2/R^2)\gamma M^2/\pi R^4$. About $1.8\cdot10^6$ atmospheres.

1.217. (a) Let us subdivide the spherical layer into small elements, each of mass δm. In this case the energy of interaction of each element with all others is $\delta U = -\gamma m\, \delta m/R$. Summing over all

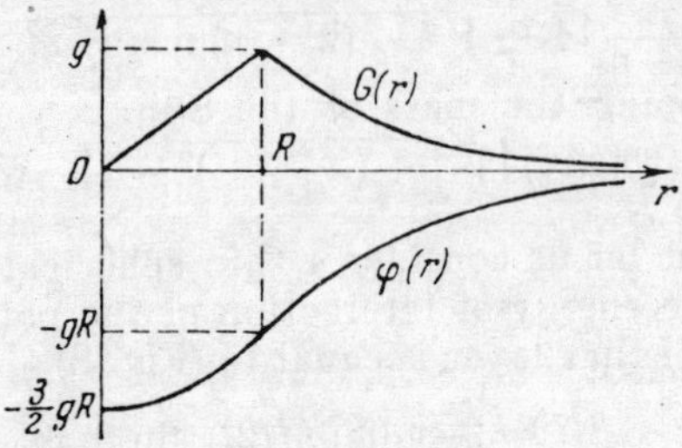

Fig. 10.

elements and taking into account that each pair of interacting elements appears twice in the result, we obtain $U = -\gamma m^2/2R$; (b) $U = -3\gamma m^2/5R$.

1.218. $\Delta t \approx \frac{2\pi}{\sqrt{\gamma M}} \frac{r^{3/2}}{3\Delta r/2r+\delta} = \begin{cases} 4.5 \text{ days } (\delta=0), \\ 0.84 \text{ hour } (\delta=2). \end{cases}$

1.219. $w_1 : w_2 : w_3 = 1 : 0.0034 : 0.0006$.

1.220. 32 km; 2650 km.

1.221. $h = R/(2gR/v_0^2 - 1)$.

1.222. $h = R\,(gR/v^2 - 1)$.

1.223. $r = \sqrt[3]{\gamma M\,(T/2\pi)^2} = 4.2 \cdot 10^4$ km, where M and T are the mass of the Earth and its period of revolution about its own axis respectively; 3.1 km/s, 0.22 m/s².

1.224. $M = (4\pi^2 R^3/\gamma T^2)\,(1 + T/\tau)^2 = 6 \cdot 10^{24}$ kg, where T is the period of revolution of the Earth about its own axis.

1.225. $v' = \frac{2\pi R}{T} + \sqrt{\frac{\gamma M}{R}} = 7.0$ km/s, $w' = \frac{\gamma M}{R^2}\left(1 + \frac{2\pi R}{T} \times \sqrt{\frac{R}{\gamma M}}\right) = 4.9$ m/s². Here M is the mass of the Earth, T is its period of revolution about its own axis.

1.226. 1.27 times.

1.227. The decrease in the total energy E of the satellite over the time interval dt is equal to $-dE = Fv\,dt$. Representing E and v as functions of the distance r between the satellite and the centre of the Moon, we can reduce this equation to the form convenient for integration. Finally, we get $\tau \approx (\sqrt{\eta} - 1)\, m/\alpha\sqrt{gR}$

1.228. $v_1 = 1.67$ km/s, $v_2 = 2.37$ km/s.

1.229. $\Delta v = \sqrt{\gamma M/R}\,(1 - \sqrt{2}) = -0.70$ km/s, where M and R are the mass and the radius of the Moon.

1.230. $\Delta v = \sqrt{gR}\,(\sqrt{2} - 1) = 3.27$ km/s, where g is the standard free-fall acceleration, R is the radius of the Earth.

1.231. $r = nR/(1 + \sqrt{\eta}) = 3.8 \cdot 10^4$ km.

1.232. $A \approx \gamma m\,(M_1/R_1 + M_2/R_2) = 1.3 \cdot 10^8$ kJ, where M and R are the mass and the radius of the Earth and the Moon.

1.233. $v_3 \approx \sqrt{2v_1^2 + (\sqrt{2} - 1)^2\,V_1^2} \approx 17$ km/s. Here $v_1^2 = \gamma M_E/R$, M_E and R are the mass and the radius of the Earth; $V_1^2 = \gamma M_S/r$, M_S is the mass of the Sun, r is the radius of the Earth's orbit.

1.234. $l = 2aF_2/mw = 1.0$ m.

1.235. $\mathbf{N} = (aB - bA)\,\mathbf{k}$, where $\mathbf{k}$ is the unit vector of the z axis; $l = |aB - bA|/\sqrt{A^2 + B^2}$.

1.236. $l = |aA - bB|/\sqrt{A^2 + B^2}$.

1.237. $F_{res} = 2F$. This force is parallel to the diagonal AC and is applied at the midpoint of the side BC.

1.238. (a) $I = {}^1/_3 ml^2$; (b) $I = {}^1/_3 m\,(a^2 + b^2)$.

1.239. (a) $I = {}^1/_2\,\pi\rho b R^4 = 2.8$ g$\cdot$m^2; (b) $I = {}^3/_{10}\,mR^2$.

1.240. $I = {}^1/_4 mR^2$.

1.241. $I = (37/72)\,mR^2 = 0.15$ kg$\cdot$m^2.

1.242. $I = {}^2/_3\,mR^2$.

1.243. (a) $\omega = gt/R\,(1 + M/2m)$; (b) $T = mg^2t^2/2(1 + M/2m)$.

1.244. $T = {}^1/_2 mg$, $w_0 = gmr^2/I$.

1.245. $\omega = \sqrt{6F \sin\varphi/ml}$.

1.246. $\beta = \dfrac{|m_2 - m_1|g}{(m_1 + m_2 + m/2)\,R}$, $\dfrac{T_1}{T_2} = \dfrac{m_1\,(m + 4m_2)}{m_2\,(m + 4m_1)}$.

1.247. $A = -\dfrac{(m_2 - km_1)\,km_1g^2t^2}{m + 2\,(m_1 + m_2)}$.

1.248. $n = (1 + k^2)\,\omega_0^2R/8\pi k\,(k + 1)\,g$.

1.249. $t = {}^3/_4\,\omega R/kg$.

1.250. $\langle\omega\rangle = {}^1/_3\,\omega_0$.

1.251. $\beta = 2mgx/Rl\,(M + 2m)$.

1.252. (a) $k \geqslant {}^2/_7 \tan\alpha$; (b) $T = {}^5/_{14}\,mg^2t^2 \sin^2\alpha$.

1.253. (a) $T = {}^1/_6\,mg = 13$ N, $\beta = {}^2/_3\,g/R = 5 \cdot 10^2$ rad/s^2; (b) $P = {}^2/_3\,mg^2t$.

1.254. $\mathbf{w}' = {}^2/_3\,(\mathbf{g} - \mathbf{w}_0)$, $\mathbf{F} = {}^1/_3\,m\,(\mathbf{g} - \mathbf{w}_0)$.

1.255. $w = g \sin\alpha/(1 + I/mr^2) = 1.6$ m/s^2.

1.256. $F_{max} = 3kmg/(2 - 3k)$; $w_{max} = 2kg/(2 - 3k)$.

1.257. (a) $w_x = \dfrac{F\,(\cos\alpha - r/R)}{m\,(1 + \gamma)}$; (b) $A = \dfrac{F^2t^2\,(\cos\alpha - r/R)^2}{2m\,(1 + \gamma)}$.

1.258. $T = {}^1/_{10}\,mg$.

1.259. $\mathbf{w} = 3\mathbf{g}\,(M + 3m)/(M + 9m + I/R^2)$.

1.260. (a) $w = \dfrac{F\,(3m_1 + 2m_2)}{m_1\,(m_1 + m_2)}$; (b) $T = \dfrac{F^2t^2\,(3m_1 + 2m_2)}{2m_1\,(m_1 + m_2)}$.

1.261. $w_1 = F/(m_1 + {}^2/_7 m_2)$; $w_2 = {}^2/_7\,w_1$.

1.262. (a) $t = {}^1/_3\,\omega_0R/kg$; (b) $A = -{}^1/_6 m\omega_0^2R^2$.

1.263. $\omega = \sqrt{10g\,(R + r)/17r^2}$.

1.264. $v_0 = \sqrt{{}^1/_3 gR\,(7\cos\alpha - 4)} = 1.0$ m/s.

1.265. $v_0 = \sqrt{8gR}$.

1.266. $T = mv^2$.

1.267. $T = {}^7/_{10}\,mv^2\,(1 + {}^2/_7 r^2/R^2)$.

1.269. $N = {}^1/_{24} m\omega^2 l^2 \sin 2\theta$.
1.270. $\cos\theta = {}^3/_2\, g/\omega^2 l$.
1.271. $\Delta x = {}^1/_2\, ka$.
1.272. $v' = \omega_0 l/\sqrt{1 + 3m/M}$.
1.273. $F = {}^9/_2 J^2/ml = 9$ N.
1.274. (a) $v' = \dfrac{3m - 4M}{3m + 4M} v$; (b) $F = \dfrac{8Mv^2}{l(1 + 4M/3m)^2}$.
1.275. (a) $v = (M/m)\sqrt{{}^2/_3 gl}\, \sin(\alpha/2)$; (b) $\Delta p = M\sqrt{{}^1/_6 gl} \sin(\alpha/2)$; (c) $x \approx {}^2/_3 l$.
1.276. (a) $\omega = (1 + 2m/M)\,\omega_0$; (b) $A = {}^1/_2 m\omega_0^2 R^2 (1 + 2m/M)$.
1.277. (a) $\varphi = -\dfrac{2m_1}{2m_1 + m_2}\varphi'$; (b) $N_z = -\dfrac{m_1 m_2 R}{2m_1 + m_2}\dfrac{dv'}{dt}$.
1.278. (a) $\omega = \dfrac{I_1\omega_1 + I_2\omega_2}{I_1 + I_2}$; (b) $A = -\dfrac{I_1 I_2}{2(I_1 + I_2)}(\omega_1 - \omega_2)^2$.
1.279. $v' = v(4 - \eta)/(4 + \eta)$, $\omega = 12v/l\,(4 + \eta)$. For $\eta = 4$ and $\eta > 4$.
1.280. (a) $A_{90^\circ} = {}^1/_2 I_0^2\omega_0^2/(I + I_0)$, $A_{180^\circ} = 2I_0^2\omega_0^2/I$; (b) $N = I_0^2\omega_0^2/(I + I_0)$.
1.281. $\omega = \sqrt{2g/l} = 6.0$ rad/s; $F = mgl_0/l = 25$ N.
1.282. (a) $M = {}^1/_{12}\, m\omega l^2 \sin\theta$, $M_z = M\sin\theta$. (b) $|\Delta \mathbf{M}| = {}^1/_{12} m\omega l^2 \sin 2\theta$; (c) $N = {}^1/_{24} m\omega^2 l^2 \times \sin 2\theta$.
1.283. (a) $\omega' = mgl/I\omega = 0.7$ rad/s; (b) $F = m\omega'^2 l \sin\theta = 10$ mN. See Fig. 11.

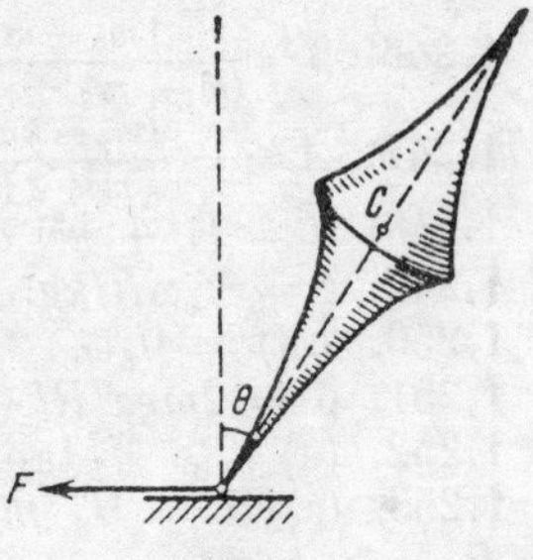

Fig. 11.

1.284. $\omega = (g + w)\, l/\pi n R^2 = 3 \times 10^2$ rad/s.
1.285. $\omega' = ml\sqrt{g^2 + w^2}/I\omega = 0.8$ rad/s. The vector ω' forms the angle $\theta = \arctan(w/g) = 6^\circ$ with the vertical.
1.286. $F' = {}^2/_5\, mR^2\omega\omega'/l = 0.30$ kN.
1.287. $F_{max} = \pi m r^2 \varphi_m \omega/lT = 0.09$ kN.
1.288. $N = 2\pi n I v/R = 6$ kN·m.
1.289. $F_{add} = 2\pi n I v/Rl = 1.4$ kN. The force exerted on the outside rail increases by this value while that exerted on the inside one decreases by the same value.
1.290. $p = \alpha E \Delta T = 2.2 \cdot 10^3$ atm, where α is the thermal expansion coefficient.
1.291. (a) $p \approx \sigma_m \Delta r/r = 20$ atm; (b) $p \approx 2\sigma_m \Delta r/r = 40$ atm. Here σ_m is the glass strength.
1.292. $n = \sqrt{2\sigma_m/\rho}/\pi l = 0.8 \cdot 10^2$ rps, where σ_m is the tensile strength, and ρ is the density of copper.
1.293. $n = \sqrt{\sigma_m/\rho}/2\pi R = 23$ rps, where σ_m is the tensile strength, and ρ is the density of lead.
1.294. $x \approx l\sqrt[3]{mg/2\pi d^2 E} = 2.5$ cm
1.295. $\varepsilon = {}^1/_2 F_0/ES$.

1.296. $T = \frac{1}{2}m\omega^2 l\,(1 - r^2/l^2)$, $\Delta l = \frac{1}{3}\,\rho\omega^2 l^3/E$, where ρ is the density of copper.

1.297. $\Delta V = (1 - 2\mu)\,Fl/E = 1.6$ mm^3, where μ is Poisson's ratio for copper.

1.298. (a) $\Delta l = \frac{1}{2}\,\rho g l^2/E$; (b) $\Delta V/V = (1 - 2\mu)\,\Delta l/l$, where ρ is the density, and μ is Poisson's ratio for copper.

1.299. (a) $\Delta V/V = -3\,(1 - 2\mu)\,p/E$; (b) $\beta = 3\,(1 - 2\mu)/E$.

1.300. $R = \frac{1}{6}\,Eh^2/\rho g l^2 = 0.12$ km, where ρ is the density of steel.

1.301. (a) Here N is independent of x and equal to N_0. Integrating twice the initial equation with regard to the boundary conditions $dy/dx\,(0) = 0$ and $y\,(0) = 0$, we obtain $y = (N_0/2EI)\,x^2$. This is the equation of a parabola. The bending deflection is $\lambda = N_0 l^2/2EI$, where $I = a^4/12$.

(b) In this case $N\,(x) = F\,(l - x)$ and $y = (F/2EI)\,(l - x/3)\,x^2$; $\lambda = Fl^3/3EI$, where I is of the same magnitude as in (a).

1.302. $\lambda = Fl^3/48EI$.

1.303. (a) $\lambda = \frac{3}{2}\,\rho g l^4/Eh^2$; (b) $\lambda = \frac{5}{2}\,\rho g l^4/Eh^2$. Here ρ is the density of steel.

1.304. $\lambda = \frac{9}{5}\beta\rho l^5/Eh^2$, where ρ is the density of steel.

1.305. (a) $\varphi = (l/2\pi r^3\,\Delta r G)\cdot N$; (b) $\varphi = (2l/\pi r^4 G)\cdot N$.

1.306. $N = \pi\,(d_2^4 - d_1^4)\,G\varphi/32l = 0.5$ kN·m.

1.307. $P = \frac{1}{2}\,\pi r^4 G\varphi\omega = 17$ kW.

1.308. $N = \frac{1}{2}\,\beta m\,(r_2^4 - r^4)/(r_2^2 - r_1^2)$.

1.309. $U = \frac{1}{2}mE\varepsilon^2/\rho = 0.04$ kJ, where ρ is the density of steel.

1.310. (a) $U = \frac{1}{6}\pi r^2 l^3\rho^2 g^2/E$; (b) $U = \frac{2}{3}\,\pi r^2 lE\,(\Delta l/l)^2$. Here ρ is the density of steel.

1.311. $A \approx \frac{1}{6}\,\pi^2 h\delta^3 E/l = 0.08$ kJ.

1.312. $U = \frac{1}{4}\,\pi r^4 G\varphi^2/l = 7$ J.

1.313. $u = \frac{1}{2}\,G\varphi^2 r^2/l^2$.

1.314. $u = \frac{1}{2}\beta\,(\rho g h)^2 = 23.5$ kJ/m^3, where β is the compressibility.

1.315. $p_1 > p_2$, $v_1 < v_2$. The density of streamlines grows on transition from point *1* to point *2*.

1.316. $Q = S_1 S_2 \sqrt{2g\Delta h/(S_2^2 - S_1^2)}$.

1.317. $Q = S\sqrt{2g\Delta h\rho_0/\rho}$.

1.318. $v = \sqrt{2g\,(h_1 + h_2\rho_2/\rho_1)} = 3$ m/s, where ρ_1 and ρ_2 are the densities of water and kerosene.

1.319. $h = 25$ cm; $l_{max} = 50$ cm.

1.320. $h = \frac{1}{2}\,v^2/g - h_0 = 20$ cm.

1.321. $p = p_0 + \rho g h\,(1 - R_1^2/r^2)$, where $R_1 < r < R_2$, p_0 is the atmospheric pressure.

1.322. $A = \frac{1}{2}\rho V^3/s^2 t^2$, where ρ is the density of water.

1.323. $\tau = \sqrt{2h/g}\;S/s$.

1.324. $v = \omega h\sqrt{2l/h - 1}$.

1.326. $F = 2\rho g S\,\Delta h = 0.50$ N.

1.327. $F = \rho g b l\,(2h - l) = 5$ N.

1.328. $N = \rho l Q^2/\pi r^2 = 0.7$ N·m.

1.329. $F = \rho g h (S - s)^2/S = 6$ N

1.330. (a) The paraboloid of revolution: $z = (\omega^2/2g)\, r^2$, where z is the height measured from the surface of the liquid along the axis of the vessel, r is the distance from the rotation axis; (b) $p = p_0 + {}^1/_2 \rho\omega^2 r^2$.

1.331. $P = \pi\eta\omega^2 R^4/h = 9$ W.

1.332. $v = v_0 \dfrac{\ln (r/R_2)}{\ln (R_1/R_2)}$.

1.333. (a) $\omega = \omega_2 \dfrac{R_1^2 R_2^2}{R_2^2 - R_1^2}\left(\dfrac{1}{R_1^2} - \dfrac{1}{r^2}\right)$; (b) $N = 4\pi\eta\omega_2 \dfrac{R_1^2 R_2^2}{R_2^2 - R_1^2}$

1.334. (a) $Q = {}^1/_2\, \pi v_0 R^2$; (b) $T = {}^1/_6\, \pi l R^2 \rho v_0^2$; (c) $F_{fr} = 4\pi\eta l v_0$; (d) $\Delta p = 4\eta l v_0/R^2$.

1.335. The additional head $\Delta h = 5$ cm at the left-hand end of the tube imparts kinetic energy to the liquid flowing into the tube. From the condition $\rho v^2/2 = \rho g \Delta h$ we get $v = \sqrt{2g\,\Delta h} = 1.0$ m/s.

1.336. $e^{\alpha\Delta x} = 5$.

1.337. $v_2 = v_1 \dfrac{r_1 \rho_1 \eta_2}{r_2 \rho_2 \eta_1} = 5$ μm/s.

1.338. $d = \sqrt[3]{\dfrac{18\,\mathrm{Re}\,\eta^2}{(\rho - \rho_0)\rho_0 g}} = 5$ mm, where ρ_0 and ρ are the densities of glycerin and lead.

1.339. $t = -\dfrac{\rho d^2}{18\eta} \ln n = 0.20$ s.

1.340. $v = c\sqrt{\eta(2-\eta)} = 0.1c$, where c is the velocity of light.

1.341. (a) $P = a(1 + \sqrt{4 - 3\beta^2})$; (b) $P = a(\sqrt{1-\beta^2} + \sqrt{4-\beta^2})$. Here $\beta = V/c$.

1.342. $l_0 = l\sqrt{(1 - \beta^2 \sin^2\theta)/(1-\beta^2)} = 1.08$ m, where $\beta = v/c$.

1.343. (a) $\tan\theta' = \dfrac{\tan\theta}{\sqrt{1-\beta^2}}$. Hence $\theta' = 59°$; (b) $S = S_0\sqrt{1 - \beta^2\cos^2\theta} = 3.3$ m². Here $\beta = v/c$.

1.344. $v = c\sqrt{\left(2 - \dfrac{\Delta t}{t}\right)\dfrac{\Delta t}{t}} = 0.6\cdot 10^8$ m/s.

1.345. $l_0 = c\Delta t'\sqrt{1 - (\Delta t/\Delta t')^2} = 4.5$ m.

1.346. $s = c\Delta t\sqrt{1 - (\Delta t_0/\Delta t)^2} = 5$ m.

1.347. (a) $\Delta t_0 = (l/v)\sqrt{1 - (v/c)^2} = 1.4$ μs; (b) $l' = l\sqrt{1 - (v/c)^2} = 0.42$ km.

1.348. $l_0 = v\Delta t/\sqrt{1 - (v/c)^2} = 17$ m.

1.349. $l_0 = \sqrt{\Delta x_1 \Delta x_2} = 6.0$ m, $v = c\sqrt{1 - \Delta x_1/\Delta x_2} = 2.2\cdot 10^8$ m/s.

1.350. $v = \dfrac{2l_0/\Delta t}{1 + (l_0/c\Delta t)^2}$.

1.351. The forward particle decayed $\Delta t = l\beta/c\,(1 - \beta^2) = 20$ μs later, where $\beta = v/c$.

1.352. (a) $l_0 = \dfrac{x_A - x_B - v(t_A - t_B)}{\sqrt{1 - (v/c)^2}}$;

(b) $t_A - t_B = (1 - \sqrt{1-(v/c)^2})\, l_0/v$ or $t_B - t_A = (1 + \sqrt{1-(v/c)^2})\, l_0/v$.

1.353. (a) $t(B) = l_0/v$, $t(B') = (l_0/v)\sqrt{1-(v/c)^2}$; (b) $t(A) = (l_0/v)\sqrt{1-(v/c)^2}$, $t(A') = l_0/v$.

1.354. See Fig. 12 showing the positions of hands "in terms of K clocks".

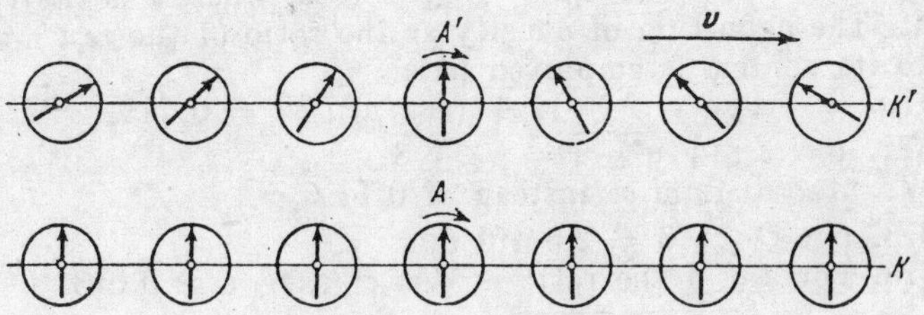

Fig. 12.

1.355. $x = (1 - \sqrt{1-\beta^2})\, c/\beta$, where $\beta = V/c$.

1.356. It should be shown first that if $\Delta t = t_2 - t_1 > 0$, then $\Delta t' = t_2' - t_1' > 0$.

1.357. (a) 13 ns; (b) 4.0 m. **Instruction.** Employ the invariance of the interval.

1.358. $v' = \dfrac{\sqrt{(v_x - V)^2 + v_y^2(1 - V^2/c^2)}}{1 - v_x V/c^2}$.

1.359. (a) $v = v_1 + v_2 = 1.25c$; (b) $v = (v_1 + v_2)/(1 + v_1 v_2/c^2) = 0.91c$.

1.360. $l = l_0(1 - \beta^2)/(1 + \beta^2)$, where $\beta = v/c$.

1.361. $v = \sqrt{v_1^2 + v_2^2 - (v_1 v_2/c^2)}$.

1.362. $s = \Delta t_0 \sqrt{\dfrac{V^2 + (1-\beta^2)\, v'^2}{(1-\beta^2)(1 - v'^2/c^2)}}$, where $\beta = V/c$.

1.363. $\tan\theta' = \dfrac{\sqrt{1-\beta^2}\sin\theta}{\cos\theta - V/c}$, where $\beta = V/c$.

1.364. $\tan\theta = v'V/c^2\sqrt{1-(V/c)^2}$.

1.365. (a) $w' = w(1-\beta^2)^{3/2}/(1 - \beta v/c)^3$; (b) $w' = w(1-\beta^2)$. Here $\beta = V/c$.

1.366. Let us make use of the relation between the acceleration w' and the acceleration w in the reference frame fixed to the Earth:

$$w' = (1 - v^2/c^2)^{-3/2}\, \frac{dv}{dt}$$

This formula is given in the solution of the foregoing problem (item (a)) where it is necessary to assume $V = v$. Integrating the given equation (for $w' = \text{const}$), we obtain $v = w't/\sqrt{1 + (w't/c)^2}$. The sought distance is $l = (\sqrt{1 + (w't/c)^2} - 1)\, c^2/w' = 0.91$ light-year; $(c - v)/c = 1/2\,(c/w't)^2 = 0.47\%$.

1.367. Taking into account that $v = w't/\sqrt{1+(w't/c)^2}$, we get

$$\tau_0 = \int_0^{\tau} \frac{dt}{\sqrt{1+(w't/c)^2}} = \frac{c}{w'} \ln\left[\frac{w'\tau}{c} + \sqrt{1+\left(\frac{w'\tau}{c}\right)^2}\right] = 3.5 \text{ months}.$$

1.368. $m/m_0 \approx 1/\sqrt{2(1-\beta)} \approx 70$, where $\beta = v/c$.

1.369. $v = c\sqrt{\eta(2+\eta)}/(1+\eta) = 0.6c$, where c is the velocity of light. The definition of density as the ratio of the *rest* mass of a body to its volume is employed here.

1.370. $(c-v)/c = 1 - [1+(m_0c/p)^2]^{-1/2} = 0.44\%$.

1.371. $v = (c/\eta)\sqrt{\eta^2-1} = {}^1/_2 c\sqrt{3}$.

1.372. $A = 0.42\ m_0c^2$ instead of $0.14\ m_0c^2$.

1.373. $v = {}^1/_2 c\sqrt{3} = 2.6 \cdot 10^8$ m/s.

1.374. For $\varepsilon \ll 1$ the ratio is $T/m_0c^2 \lesssim {}^4/_3\ \varepsilon \approx 0.013$.

1.375. $p = \sqrt{T(T+2m_0c^2)}/c = 1.09$ GeV/c, where c is the velocity of light.

1.376. $F = (I/ec)\sqrt{T(T+2m_0c^2)}$, $P = TI/e$.

1.377. $p = 2nmv^2/(1-v^2/c^2)$.

1.378. $v = Fct/\sqrt{m_0^2c^2+F^2t^2}$, $l = \sqrt{(m_0c^2/F)^2+c^2t^2} - m_0c^2/F$.

1.379. $F = m_0c^2/a$.

1.380. (a) In two cases: $\mathbf{F} \parallel \mathbf{v}$ and $\mathbf{F} \perp \mathbf{v}$; (b) $\mathbf{F}_\perp = m_0\mathbf{w}\sqrt{1-\beta^2}$, $\mathbf{F}_\parallel = m_0\mathbf{w}/(1-\beta^2)^{3/2}$, where $\beta = v/c$.

1.382. $\varepsilon' = \varepsilon\sqrt{(1-\beta)/(1+\beta)}$, where $\beta = V/c$, $V = {}^3/_5 c$.

1.383. $E^2 - p^2c^2 = m_0^2c^4$, where m_0 is the rest mass of the particle.

1.384. (a) $\tilde{T} = 2m_0c^2(\sqrt{1+T/2m_0c^2}-1) = 777$ MeV, $\tilde{p} = \sqrt{{}^1/_2 m_0T} = 940$ MeV/c; (b) $V = c\sqrt{T/(T+2m_0c^2)} = 2.12 \cdot 10^8$ m/s.

1.385. $M_0 = \sqrt{2m_0(T+2m_0c^2)}/c$, $V = c\sqrt{T/(T+2m_0c^2)}$.

1.386. $T' = 2T(T+2m_0c^2)/m_0c^2 = 1.43 \cdot 10^3$ GeV.

1.387. $E_{1\,max} = \dfrac{m_0^2+m_1^2-(m_2+m_3)^2}{2m_0}c^2$. The particle m_1 has the highest energy when the energy of the system of the remaining two particles m_2 and m_3 is the lowest, i.e. when they move as a single whole.

1.388. $v/c = \dfrac{1-(m/m_0)^{2u/c}}{1+(m/m_0)^{2u/c}}$. Use the momentum conservation law (as in solving Problem 1.178) and the relativistic formula for velocity transformation.

2.1. $m = \rho V\,\Delta p/p_0 = 30$ g, where p_0 is the standard atmospheric pressure.

2.2. $p = {}^1/_2\,(p_1T_2/T_1 - \Delta p) = 0.10$ atm.

2.3. $m_1/m_2 = (1-a/M_2)/(a/M_1-1) = 0.50$, where $a = mRT/pV$.

2.4. $\rho = \dfrac{p_0(m_1+m_2)}{RT(m_1/M_1+m_2/M_2)} = 1.5$ g/l.

2.5. (a) $p = (\nu_1 + \nu_2 + \nu_3)\, RT/V = 2.0$ atm; (b) $M = (\nu_1 M_1 + \nu_2 M_2 + \nu_3 M_3)/(\nu_1 + \nu_2 + \nu_3) = 36.7$ g/mol.

2.6. $T = T_0 \eta' (\eta^2 - 1)/\eta (\eta'^2 - 1) = 0.42$ kK.

2.7. $n = \frac{\ln \eta}{\ln (1 + \Delta V/V)}$.

2.8. $p = p_0 e^{-Ct/V}$.

2.9. $t = (V/C) \ln \eta = 1.0$ min.

2.10. $\Delta T = (mg + p_0\, \Delta S)\, l/R = 0.9$ K.

2.11. (a) $T_{max} = {}^2/_3 (p_0/R) \sqrt{p_0/3\alpha}$; (b) $T_{max} = p_0/e\beta R$.

2.12. $p_{min} = 2R\sqrt{\alpha T_0}$.

2.13. $dT/dh = -Mg/R = -33$ mK/m.

2.14. $dT/dh = -Mg\,(n-1)/nR$.

2.15. 0.5 and 2 atm.

2.16. (a) $h = RT/Mg = 8.0$ km; (b) $h \approx \eta RT/Mg = 0.08$ km.

2.17. $m = (1 - e^{-Mgh/RT})\, p_0 S/g$.

2.18. $h_C = \int_0^\infty h\rho\, dh \Big/ \int_0^\infty \rho\, dh = RT/Mg$.

2.19. (a) $p = p_0 (1 - ah)^n$, $h < 1/a$; (b) $p = p_0/(1 + ah)^n$. Here $n = Mg/aRT_0$.

2.20. $p = p_0 e^{M\omega^2 r^2/2RT}$.

2.21. $p_{id} = \rho RT/M = 280$ atm; $p = \rho RT/(M - \rho b) - a\rho^2/M^2 = 80$ atm.

2.22. (a) $T = a\,(V - b)\,(1 + \eta)/RV\,(\eta V + b) = 133$ K; (b) $p = RT/(V - b) - a/V^2 = 9.9$ atm.

2.23. $a = V^2\,(T_1 p_2 - T_2 p_1)/(T_2 - T_1) = 185$ atm·l²/mol², $b = V - R\,(T_2 - T_1)/(p_2 - p_1) = 0.042$ l/mol.

2.24. $\varkappa = V^2\,(V - b)^2/[RTV^3 - 2a\,(V - b)^2]$.

2.25. $T > a/bR$.

2.26. $U = pV/(\gamma - 1) = 10$ MJ.

2.27. $\Delta T = {}^1/_2 Mv^2\,(\gamma - 1)/R$.

2.28. $T = T_1 T_2\,(p_1 V_1 + p_2 V_2)/(p_1 V_1 T_2 + p_2 V_2 T_1)$; $p = (p_1 V_1 + p_2 V_2)/(V_1 + V_2)$.

2.29. $\Delta U = -p_0 V \Delta T/T_0\,(\gamma - 1) = -0.25$ kJ, $Q' = -\Delta U$.

2.30. $Q = A\gamma/(\gamma - 1) = 7$ J.

2.31. $A = R\Delta T = 0.60$ kJ, $\Delta U = Q - R\Delta T = 1.00$ kJ, $\gamma = Q/(Q - R\Delta T) = 1.6$.

2.32. $Q = \nu RT_0\,(1 - 1/n) = 2.5$ kJ.

2.33. $\gamma = \frac{\nu_1\gamma_1(\gamma_2 - 1) + \nu_2\gamma_2(\gamma_1 - 1)}{\nu_1(\gamma_2 - 1) + \nu_2(\gamma_1 - 1)} = 1.33$.

2.34. $c_V = 0.42$ J/(g·K), $c_p = 0.65$ J/(g·K).

2.35. $A = RT\,(n - 1 - \ln n)$.

2.36. $A' = p_0 V_0 \ln [(\eta + 1)^2/4\eta]$.

2.37. $\gamma = 1 + (n - 1)/(Q/\nu RT_0 - \ln n) = 1.4$.

2.38. See Fig. 13 where V is an isochore, p is an isobaric line, T is an isothermal line, and S is an adiabatic line.

2.39. (a) $T = T_0 \eta^{(\gamma-1)/\gamma} = 0.56$ kK; (b) $A' = RT_0(\eta^{(\gamma-1)/\gamma} - 1)/(\gamma - 1) = 5.6$ kJ

2.40. The work in the adiabatic process is $n = (\eta^{\gamma-1} - 1)/(\gamma - 1) \ln \eta = 1.4$ times greater.

2.41. $T = T_0 [(\eta + 1)^2/4\eta]^{(\gamma-1)/2}$.

2.42. $v = \sqrt{2\gamma RT/(\gamma - 1) M} = 3.3$ km/s.

2.43. $Q = R\Delta T (2 - \gamma)/(\gamma - 1)$.

2.45. $C_n = R (n - \gamma)/(n - 1) (\gamma - 1)$; $C_n < 0$ for $1 < n < \gamma$.

2.46. $C = R(n - \gamma)/(n - 1)(\gamma - 1) = -4.2$ J/(K·mol), where $n = \ln \beta/\ln \alpha$.

2.47. (a) $Q = R (n - \gamma) \Delta T/(n - 1)(\gamma - 1) = 0.11$ kJ; (b) $A = -R\Delta T/(n - 1) = 0.43$ kJ.

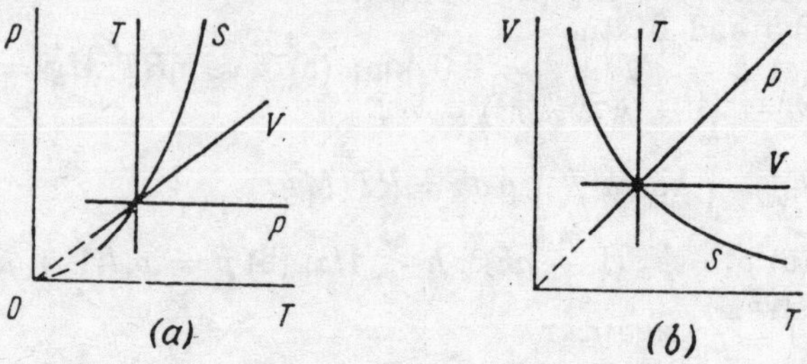

Fig. 13.

2.48. (a) $\Delta U = \alpha V_0^2(\eta^2 - 1)/(\gamma - 1)$; (b) $A = {}^1/_2 \alpha V_0^2 (\eta^2 - 1)$; (c) $C = {}^1/_2 R (\gamma + 1)/(\gamma - 1)$.

2.49. (a) $C = -R/(\gamma - 1)$; (b) $TV^{(\gamma-1)/2} = \text{const}$; (c) $A = 2RT_0 (1 - \eta^{(1-\gamma)/2})/(\gamma - 1)$.

2.50. (a) $A = (1 - \alpha) R\Delta T$; (b) $C = R/(\gamma - 1) + R (1 - \alpha)$; $C < 0$ for $\alpha > \gamma/(\gamma - 1)$.

2.51. (a) $A = \Delta U (\gamma - 1)/\alpha$; $Q = \Delta U [1 + (\gamma - 1)/\alpha]$; (b) $C = R/(\gamma - 1) + R/\alpha$.

2.52. (a) $C = C_V + R/\alpha V$; (b) $C = C_V + R/(1 + \alpha V)$.

2.53. (a) $C = \gamma R/(\gamma - 1) + \alpha R/p_0 V$; (b) $\Delta U = p_0 (V_2 - V_1)/(\gamma - 1)$; $A = p_0 (V_2 - V_1) + \alpha \ln (V_2/V_1)$; $Q = \gamma p_0 (V_2 - V_1)/(\gamma - 1) + \alpha \ln (V_2/V_1)$.

2.54. (a) $C = C_p + RT_0/\alpha V$; (b) $Q = \alpha C_p (V_2 - V_1) + RT_0 \ln (V_2/V_1)$.

2.55. (a) $Ve^{-\alpha T/R} = \text{const}$; (b) $Te^{R/\beta V} = \text{const}$; (c) $V - aT = \text{const}$.

2.56. (a) $A = \alpha \ln \eta - RT_0 (\eta - 1)/(\gamma - 1)$; (b) $pV^\gamma e^{\alpha(\gamma-1)/pV} = \text{const}$.

2.57. $A = RT \ln \frac{V_2 - b}{V_1 - b} + a \left(\frac{1}{V_2} - \frac{1}{V_1}\right)$, where a and b are Van der Waals constants.

2.58. (a) $\Delta U = a/V_1 - a/V_2 = 0.11$ kJ; (b) $Q = RT \ln \frac{V_2 - b}{V_1 - b} = 3.8$ kJ.

2.59. (a) $T(V-b)^{R/C_V} = \text{const}$;
(b) $C_p - C_V = \dfrac{R}{1-2a(V-b)^2/RTV^3}$.

2.60. $\Delta T = -\dfrac{\nu a V_2(\gamma-1)}{RV_1(V_1+V_2)} = -3.0$ K.

2.61. $Q = \nu^2 a(V_2 - V_1)/V_1V_2 = 0.33$ kJ.

2.62. $n = p/kT = 1\cdot 10^5$ cm^{-3}; $\langle l\rangle = 0.2$ mm.

2.63. $p = (1+\eta)\,mRT/MV = 1.9$ atm, where M is the mass of an N_2 mole.

2.64. $n = (p/kT - \rho/m_2)/(1 - m_1/m_2) = 1.6\cdot 10^{19}$ cm^{-3}, where m_1 and m_2 are the masses of helium and nitrogen molecules.

2.65. $p = 2nmv^2\cos^2\theta = 1.0$ atm, where m is the mass of a nitrogen molecule.

2.66. $i = 2/(\rho v^2/p - 1) = 5$.

2.67. $v/v_{sq} = \sqrt{(i+2)/3i}$; (a) 0.75; (b) 0.68.

2.68. $\langle\varepsilon\rangle = \begin{cases} (3N-3)\,kT & \text{for volume molecules.} \\ (3N-5/2)\,kT & \text{for linear molecules.}\end{cases}$

$1/2(N-1)$ and $1/(2N-5/3)$ respectively.

2.69. (a) $C_V = {}^7/_2 R$, $\gamma = 9/7$; (b) $C_V = (3N - 5/2)\,R$, $\gamma = (6N-3)/(6N-5)$; (c) $C_V = 3(N-1)\,R$, $\gamma = (N - {}^2/_3)/(N-1)$.

2.70. $A/Q = \begin{cases} 1/(3N-2) & \text{for volume molecules,} \\ 1/(3N-3/2) & \text{for linear molecules.}\end{cases}$

For monoatomic molecules $A/Q = 2/5$.

2.71. $M = R/(c_p - c_V) = 32$ g/mol. $i = 2/(c_p/c_V - 1) = 5$.

2.72. (a) $i = 2(C_p/R - 1) = 5$; (b) $i = 2[C/R + 1/(n-1)] = 3$, where $n = 1/2$ is the polytropic index.

2.73. $\gamma = (5\nu_1 + 7\nu_2)/(3\nu_1 + 5\nu_2)$.

2.74. Increases by $\Delta p/p = Mv^2/iRT = 2.2\%$, where $i = 5$.

2.75. (a) $v_{sq} = \sqrt{3RT/M} = 0.47$ km/s, $\langle\varepsilon\rangle = {}^3/_2 kT = 6.0\cdot 10^{-21}$ J;
(b) $v_{sq} = 3\sqrt{2kT/\pi\rho d^3} = 0.15$ m/s.

2.76. $\eta^i = 7.6$ times.

2.77. $Q = {}^1/_2(\eta^2 - 1)\,imRT/M = 10$ kJ.

2.78. $\omega_{sq} = \sqrt{2kT/I} = 6.3\cdot 10^{12}$ rad/sec.

2.79. $\langle\varepsilon\rangle_{rot} = kT_0\eta^{2/i} = 0.7\cdot 10^{-20}$ J.

2.80. Decreases $\eta^{(i+1)/i}$ times, where $i = 5$.

2.81. Decreases $\eta^{(i-1)/(i-2)} = 2.5$ times.

2.82. $C = {}^1/_2 R(i+1) = 3R$.

2.83. $v_{pr} = \sqrt{2p/\rho} = 0.45$ km/s, $\langle v\rangle = 0.51$ km/s, $v_{sq} = 0.55$ km/s.

2.84. (a) $\delta N/N = (8/\sqrt{\pi})\,e^{-1}\delta\eta = 1.66\%$;
(b) $\delta N/N = 12\sqrt{3/2\pi}\,e^{-3/2}\delta\eta = 1.85\%$.

2.85. (a) $T = \dfrac{m(\Delta v)^2}{k(\sqrt{3}-\sqrt{2})^2} = 380$ K; (b) $T = \dfrac{mv^2}{2k} = 340$ K.

2.86. (a) $T = \dfrac{m(v_2^2 - v_1^2)}{4k\ln(v_2/v_1)} = 330$ K; (b) $v = \sqrt{\dfrac{3kT_0}{m}\dfrac{\eta\ln\eta}{\eta-1}}$.

2.87. $T = \dfrac{m_N (\Delta v)^2}{2k\left(1-\sqrt{m_N/m_0}\right)^2} = 0.37$ kK.

2.88. $v = \sqrt{\dfrac{3kT \ln (m_2/m_1)}{m_2 - m_1}} = 1.61$ km/s.

2.89. $T = {}^1/_3 mv^2/k$.

2.90. $dN/N = \left(\dfrac{m}{2\pi kT}\right)^{3/2} e^{-mv^2/2kT}\, 2\pi v_\perp\, dv_\perp\, dv_x$.

2.91. $\langle v_x \rangle = 0$, $\langle |v_x| \rangle = \sqrt{2kT/\pi m}$.

2.92. $\langle v_x^2 \rangle = kT/m$.

2.93. $\nu = {}^1/_4 n \langle v \rangle$, where $\langle v \rangle = \sqrt{8kT/\pi m}$.

2.94. $p = \int\limits_0^\infty 2mv_x \cdot v_x\, dn(v_x) = nkT$, where $dn(v_x) = (m/2\pi kT)^{1/2} n \cdot e^{-mv_x^2/2kT}\, dv_x$.

2.95. $\langle 1/v \rangle = \sqrt{2m/\pi kT} = 4\pi \langle v \rangle$.

2.96. $dN/N = 2\pi (\pi kT)^{-3/2} e^{-\varepsilon/kT} \sqrt{\varepsilon}\, d\varepsilon$; $\varepsilon_{pr} = {}^1/_2 kT$; no.

2.97. $\delta N/N = 3\sqrt{6\pi}\, e^{-3/2} \delta\eta = 0.9\%$.

2.98. $\dfrac{\Delta N}{N} = \dfrac{2\pi}{(\pi kT)^{3/2}} \int\limits_{\varepsilon_0}^\infty \sqrt{\varepsilon}\, e^{-\varepsilon/kT} d\varepsilon$.

The principal contribution to the value of the integral is provided by the smallest values of ε, namely $\varepsilon \approx \varepsilon_0$. The slowly varying factor $\sqrt{\varepsilon}$ can be taken from under the radical sign if ascribed the constant value $\sqrt{\varepsilon_0}$. Then

$$\Delta N/N = 2\sqrt{\varepsilon_0/\pi kT}\, e^{-\varepsilon_0/kT}.$$

2.99. (a) $v_{pr} = \sqrt{3kT/m}$; (b) $\varepsilon_{pr} = kT$.

2.100. $d\nu = \int\limits_{v=0}^\infty dn\, (d\Omega/4\pi)\, v \cos\theta = n\, (2kT/\pi m)^{1/2} \sin\theta \cos\theta\, d\theta$.

2.101. $d\nu = \int\limits_{\theta=0}^{\pi/2} dn\, (d\Omega/4\pi)\, v \cos\theta = \pi\, (m/2\pi kT)^{3/2}\, e^{-mv^2/2kT} v^3\, dv$.

2.102. $F = (kT/\Delta h) \ln \eta = 0.9 \cdot 10^{-19}$ N.

2.103. $N_A = (6RT/\pi d^3 \Delta\rho g h) \ln \eta \approx 6.4 \cdot 10^{23}$ mol^{-1}.

2.104. $\eta/\eta_0 = e^{(M_2 - M_1) gh/RT} = 1.39$.

2.105. $h = \dfrac{kT \ln (n_2/n_1)}{(m_2 - m_1)\, g}$.

2.106. Will not change.

2.107. $\langle U \rangle = kT$. Does not depend.

2.108. $w \approx \eta RT/Ml \approx 70$ g.

2.109. $M = \dfrac{2RT\rho \ln \eta}{(\rho - \rho_0)(r_2^2 - r_1^2)\, \omega^2}$.

2.110. $\omega = \sqrt{(2RT/Ml^2) \ln \eta} = 280$ rad/s.

2.111. (a) $dN = n_0\, e^{-ar^2/kT} 4\pi r^2\, dr$; (b) $r_{pr} = \sqrt{kT/a}$; (c) $dN/N = (a/\pi kT)^{3/2}\, e^{-ar^2/kT} 4\pi r^2\, dr$; (d) Will increase $\eta^{3/2}$-fold.

2.112. (a) $dN = (2\pi n_0/a^{3/2})\, e^{-U/kT}\sqrt{U}\,dU$; (b) $U_{pr} = \frac{1}{2}kT$.
2.113. In the latter case.
2.114. (a) $\eta = 1 - n^{1-\gamma} = 0.25$; (b) $\eta = 1 - n^{1/\gamma - 1} = 0.18$.
2.115. $\varepsilon = (1 - \eta)/\eta = 9$.
2.116. $\eta = 1 - 2T_2/(T_1 + T_2)$.
2.117. $\eta = 1 - n^{1-\gamma} = 60\%$.
2.118. $\eta = 1 - n^{-(1-1/\gamma)}$.
2.119. $\eta = 1 - (n + \gamma)/(1 + \gamma n)$
2.120. In both cases $\eta = 1 - \dfrac{\ln n}{n-1}$.
2.121. In both cases $\eta = 1 - \dfrac{n-1}{n \ln n}$.
2.122. $\eta = 1 - \dfrac{n-1}{n \ln n}$.
2.123. (a) $\eta = 1 - \gamma \dfrac{n-1}{n^\gamma - 1}$; (b) $\eta = 1 - \dfrac{n^\gamma - 1}{\gamma (n-1) n^{\gamma - 1}}$
2.124. (a) $\eta = 1 - \dfrac{\gamma(n-1)}{n - 1 + (\gamma - 1) n \ln n}$;
(b) $\eta = 1 - \dfrac{n - 1 + (\gamma - 1)\ln n}{\gamma (n-1)}$.
2.125. $\eta = \dfrac{(\tau - 1)\ln \nu}{\tau \ln \nu + (\tau - 1)/(\gamma - 1)}$.
2.126. $\eta = \dfrac{(\tau - 1)\ln n}{\tau \ln n + (\tau - 1)\gamma/(\gamma - 1)}$.
2.127. $\eta = 1 - 2\dfrac{\gamma + \sqrt{\tau}}{(1+\gamma)(1+\sqrt{\tau})}$.

2.128. The inequality $\int \dfrac{\delta Q_1}{T_1} - \int \dfrac{\delta Q_2'}{T_2} \leqslant 0$ becomes even stronger when T_1 is replaced by T_{max} and T_2 by T_{min}. Then $Q_1/T_{max} - Q_2'/T_{min} < 0$. Hence

$$\frac{Q_1 - Q_2'}{Q_1} < \frac{T_{max} - T_{min}}{T_{max}}, \text{ or } \eta < \eta_{Carnot}.$$

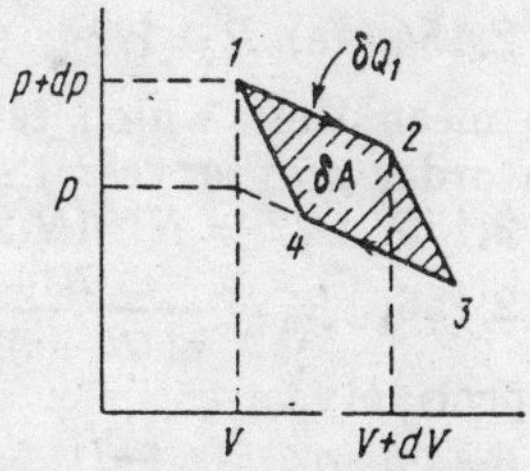

Fig. 14.

2.129. According to the Carnot theorem $\delta A/\delta Q_1 = dT/T$. Let us find the expressions for δA and δQ_1. For an infinitesimal Carnot cycle (e.g. parallelogram *1234* shown in Fig. 14)

$$\delta A = dp \cdot dV = (\partial p/\partial T)_V dT \cdot dV,$$
$$\delta Q_1 = dU_{12} + p\,dV = [(\partial U/\partial V)_T + p]\,dV.$$

It remains to substitute the two latter expressions into the former one.

2.130. (a) $\Delta S = \dfrac{R \ln n}{\gamma - 1} = 19$ J/(K·mol); (b) $\Delta S = \dfrac{\gamma R \ln n}{\gamma - 1} = 25$ J/(K·mol).
2.131. $n = e^{\Delta S/\nu R} = 2.0$.
2.132. $\Delta S = \nu R \ln n = 20$ J/K.
2.133. $\Delta S = -\dfrac{m}{M}\dfrac{\gamma R}{\gamma - 1}\ln n = -10$ J/K.
2.134. $\Delta S = (\gamma \ln \alpha - \ln \beta)\,\nu R/(\gamma - 1) = -11$ J/K.

2.135. $S_2 - S_1 = \nu R\left(\ln \alpha - \frac{\ln \beta}{\gamma - 1}\right) = 1.0$ J/K.

2.136. $\Delta S = \frac{(n-\gamma) R}{(n-1)(\gamma-1)} \ln \tau$.

2.137. $\Delta S = \frac{\nu(\gamma+1) R}{\gamma-1} \ln \alpha = 46$ J/K.

2.138. $V_m = \gamma p_0/\alpha\,(1+\gamma)$.

2.139. $T = T_0 + (R/a) \ln (V/V_0)$.

2.140. $\Delta S = R \ln [(V_2 - b)/(V_1 - b)]$.

2.141. $\Delta S = C_V \ln (T_2/T_1) + R \ln [(V_2 - b)/(V_1 - b)]$.

2.142. $S = aT^3/3$.

2.143. $\Delta S = m\,[a \ln (T_2/T_1) + b\,(T_2 - T_1)] = 2.0$ kJ/K.

2.144. $C = S/n$; $C < 0$ for $n < 0$.

2.145. $T = T_0 e^{(S-S_0)/C}$. See Fig. 15.

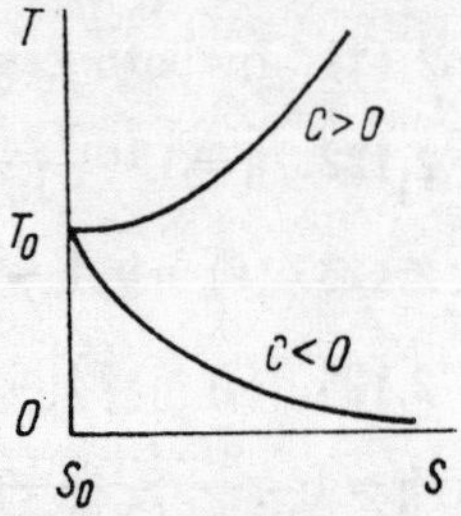

Fig. 15.

2.146. (a) $C = -\alpha/T$; (b) $Q = \alpha \ln (T_1/T_2)$; (c) $A = \alpha \ln (T_1/T_2) + C_V\,(T_1 - T_2)$.

2.147. (a) $\eta = (n-1)/2n$; (b) $\eta = (n-1)/(n+1)$.

2.148. $\Delta S = \nu R \ln n = 20$ J/K.

2.149. $\Delta U = (2^{\gamma-1} - 1)\,RT_0/(\gamma - 1)$, $\Delta S = R \ln 2$.

2.150. The pressure will be higher after the fast expansion.

2.151. $\Delta S = \nu_1 R \ln (1+n) + \nu_2 R \ln (1 + 1/n) = 5.1$ J/K.

2.152. $\Delta S = m_1 c_1 \ln (T/T_1) + m_2 c_2 \ln (T/T_2) = 4.4$ J/K, where $T = (m_1 c_1 T_1 + m_2 c_2 T_2)/(m_1 c_1 + m_2 c_2)$, c_1 and c_2 are the specific heat capacities of copper and water.

2.153. $\Delta S = C_V \ln \frac{(T_1+T_2)^2}{4T_1T_2} > 0$.

2.154. (a) $P = 1/2^N$; (b) $N = \frac{\log (t/\tau)}{\log 2} \approx 80$, where $\tau \approx 10^{-5}$ s is the mean time which takes a helium atom to cover distances of the order of the vessel's dimensions.

2.155. $\Omega_{pr} = N!/[(N/2)!]^2 = 252$. $P_{N/2} = \Omega_{pr}/2^N = 24.6\%$.

2.156. $P_n = \frac{N!}{n!\,(N-n)!\,2^N}$; 1/32, 5/32, 10/32, 10/32, 5/32, 1/32 respectively.

2.157. $P_n = \frac{N!}{n!\,(N-n)!}\,p^n\,(1-p)^{N-n}$, where $p = V/V_0$.

2.158. $d = \sqrt[3]{6/\pi n_0 \eta^2} = 0.4$ μm, where n_0 is Loschmidt's number; $\langle n \rangle = 1/\eta^2 = 1.0 \cdot 10^6$.

2.159. Will increase $\Omega/\Omega_0 = (1 + \Delta T/T_0)^{iN_A/2} = 10^{1.31 \cdot 10^{21}}$ times.

2.160. (a) $\Delta p = 4\alpha/d = 13$ atm; (b) $\Delta p = 8\alpha/d = 1.2 \cdot 10^{-3}$ atm.

2.161. $h = 4\alpha/\rho g d = 21$ cm.

2.162. $\alpha = {}^1/_8 p_0 d\,(1 - \eta^3/n)/(\eta^2 - 1)$.

2.163. $p = p_0 + \rho g h + 4\alpha/d = 2.2$ atm.

2.164. $h = [p_0\,(n^3 - 1) + 4\alpha\,(n^2 - 1)/d]/\rho g = 5$ m.

2.165. $\Delta h = 4\alpha\,|\cos \theta|\,(d_2 - d_1)/d_1 d_2 \rho g = 11$ mm.

2.166. $R = 2\alpha/\rho g h = 0.6$ mm.
2.167. $x = l/(1 + p_0 d/4\alpha) = 1.4$ cm.
2.168. $\alpha = [\rho g h + p_0 l/(l - h)]\, d/4 \cos\theta$.
2.169. $h = 4\alpha/\rho g\,(d_2 - d_1) = 6$ cm.
2.170. $h = 2a\cos\theta/\rho g x \delta\varphi$.
2.171. $V_1 = {}^1/_4 \pi d^2 \sqrt{\frac{2gl - 4\alpha(n-1)/\rho d}{n^4 - 1}} = 0.9\ \text{cm}^3/\text{s}$.
2.172. $R_2 - R_1 \approx {}^1/_8 \rho g h^3/\alpha = 0.20$ mm.
2.173. $m \approx 2\pi R^2 \alpha |\cos\theta| (n^2 - 1)/gh = 0.7$ kg.
2.174. $F \approx 2\alpha m/\rho h^2 = 1.0$ N.
2.175. $F = 2\pi R^2 \alpha/h = 0.6$ kN.
2.176. $F = 2\alpha^2 l/\rho g d^2 = 13$ N.
2.177. $t = 2l\eta R^4/a r^4$.
2.178. $Q = 2\pi\alpha^2/\rho g$.
2.179. (a) $F = \pi\alpha d^2 = 3\ \mu$J; (b) $F = 2\pi\alpha d^2 = 10\ \mu$J.
2.180. $\Delta F = 2\pi\alpha d^2 (2^{-1/3} - 1) = -1.5\ \mu$J.
2.181. $A' = F + pV\ln(p/p_0)$, where $F = 8\pi R^2\alpha$, $p = p_0 + 4\alpha/R$, $V = {}^4/_3 \pi R^3$.
2.182. $C - C_p = {}^1/_2 R/(1 + {}^3/_8 p_0 r/\alpha)$.
2.184. (a) $\Delta S = -2\,(d\alpha/dT)\,\Delta\sigma$; (b) $\Delta U = 2\,(\alpha - T\,d\alpha/dT) \times \Delta\sigma$.
2.185. $A = \Delta m RT/M = 1.2$ J.
2.186. $m_v = (V - mV'_l)/(V'_v - V'_l) = 20$ g, $V_v = 1.0$ l. Here V'_l is the specific volume of water.
2.187. $m_l \approx M p_0 (V_0 - V)/RT = 2.0$ g, where p_0 is the standard atmospheric pressure.
2.188. $\eta = (n - 1)/(N - 1)$; $\eta = 1/(N + 1)$.
2.189. $\Delta S = mq/T = 6.0$ kJ/K; $\Delta U = m(q - RT/M) = 2.1$ MJ, where $T = 373$ K.
2.190. $h \approx \frac{(Q - mc\Delta T)}{p_0 S(1 + qM/RT)} = 20$ cm, where c is the specific heat capacity of water, $\Delta T = 100$ K, q is the specific heat of vaporization of water, T is its boiling temperature.
2.191. $A = mc\,(T - T_0)\,RT/qM = 25$ J, where c is the specific heat capacity of water, T is the initial vapour temperature equal to the water boiling temperature, as is seen from the hypothesis, q is the specific heat of vapour condensation.
2.192. $d \approx 4\alpha M/\eta\rho RT = 0.2\ \mu$m, where ρ is the density of water.
2.193. $\mu = \eta p_0 \sqrt{M/2\pi RT} = 0.35\ \text{g/(s}\cdot\text{cm}^2)$, where p_0 is the standard atmospheric pressure.
2.194. $p = \mu\sqrt{2\pi RT/M} = 0.9$ nPa.
2.195. $\Delta p = a/V^2 M = 1.7\cdot 10^4$ atm.
2.196. $p_i \approx \rho q$. About $2\cdot 10^4$ atm.
2.198. $a = {}^{27}/_{64} R^2 T_{cr}^2/p_{cr} = 3.6\ \text{atm}\cdot\text{l}^2/\text{mol}^2$, $b = {}^1/_8 RT_{cr}/p_{cr} = 0.043$ l/mol.
2.199. $V'_{cr} = {}^3/_8 RT_{cr}/Mp_{cr} = 4.7\ \text{cm}^3/\text{g}$.
2.200. $(\pi + 3/\nu^2)(3\nu - 1) = 8\tau$, $\tau = 1.5$.

2.201. (a) $V_{max} = 3bm/M = 5.0$ l; (b) $p_{max} = a/27b^2 = 230$ atm.

2.202. $T_{cr} = {}^8/_{27}\, a/bR = 0.30$ kK, $\rho_{cr} = {}^1/_3\, M/b = 0.34$ g/cm³.

2.203. $\eta = {}^8/_3\, Mp_{cr}/\rho RT_{cr} = 0.25$, where ρ is the density of ether at room temperature.

2.204. Let us apply Eq. (2.4e) to the reversible isothermic cycle *1-2-3-4-5-3-1*:

$$T \oint dS = \oint dU + \oint p dV.$$

Since the first two integrals are equal to zero, $\oint p\, dV = 0$ as well. The latter equality is possible only when areas *I* and *II* are equal.

Note that this reasoning is inapplicable to the cycle *1-2-3-1*, for example. It is irreversible since it involves the irreversible transition at point *3* from a single-phase to a diphase state.

2.205. $\eta = c \mid t \mid /q = 0.25$, where q is the specific heat of melting of ice; at $t = -80°C$.

2.206. $\Delta T = -(T\Delta V'/q)\, \Delta p = -7.5$ mK, where q is the specific heat of melting of ice.

2.207. $V'_{sv} \approx q\Delta T/T\Delta p = 1.7$ m³/kg, where q is the specific heat of vaporization, $T = 373$ K.

2.208. $p_{sv} \approx p_0\,(1 + qM\Delta T/RT^2) = 1.04$ atm where q is the specific heat of vaporization, p_0 is the standard atmospheric pressure, $\Delta T = 1.1$ K.

2.209. $\Delta m/m = (qM/RT - 1)\, \Delta T/T = 5\%$.

2.210. $p = p_0 \exp\left[\frac{qM}{R}\left(\frac{1}{T_0} - \frac{1}{T}\right)\right]$. These assumptions are admissible in the case of a vapour narrow temperature interval, far below the critical temperature.

2.211. $\eta \approx cpT\Delta V'/q^2 = 0.03$, where c is the specific heat capacity of ice, $T \approx 273$ K, q is the specific heat of melting.

2.212. (a) 216 *K*, 5.1 atm; (b) 0.78, 0.57, and 0.21 kJ/g.

2.213. $\Delta S \approx m\,[c \ln (T_2/T_1) + q/T_2] = 7.2$ kJ/K.

2.214. $\Delta s \approx q_m/T_1 + c \ln (T_2/T_1) + q_v/T_2 = 8.6$ J/(g·K).

2.215. $\Delta S = mc \ln (T/T_1) = -10$ J/K, where c is the specific heat capacity of copper, $T = 273$ K (under these conditions only a part of the ice will melt).

2.216. (a) When $m_2c_2t_2 < m_1q$, not all the ice will melt and

$$\Delta S = m_2c_2\left(\frac{T_2}{T_1} - 1 - \ln\frac{T_2}{T_1}\right) = 9.2 \text{ J/K};$$

(b) When $m_2c_2t_2 > m_1q$, the ice will melt completely and

$$\Delta S = \frac{m_1q}{T_1} + c_2\left(m_1 \ln\frac{T}{T_1} - m_2 \ln\frac{T_2}{T}\right) = 18 \text{ J/K},$$

where $T = \dfrac{m_1T_1 + m_2T_2 - m_1q/c_2}{m_1 + m_2}$.

2.217. $\Delta S = mq\left(\frac{1}{T_1} - \frac{1}{T_2}\right) + mc\left(\frac{T_2}{T_1} - 1 - \ln\frac{T_2}{T_1}\right) = 0.48$ J/K.

2.218. $C = C_p - qM/T = -74$ J/(K·mol), where $C_p = R\gamma/(\gamma - 1)$.

2.219. $\Delta S = qM/T_2 + C_p \ln (T_2/T_1)$.

2.220. (a) $\eta \approx 0.37$; (b) $\eta \approx 0.23$.

2.221. $\lambda = \Delta l/\ln \eta$.

2.222. (a) $P = e^{-\alpha t}$; (b) $\langle t \rangle = 1/\alpha$.

2.223. (a) $\lambda = 0.06$ μm, $\tau = 0.13$ ns; (b) $\lambda = 6$ Mm, $\tau = 3.8$ hours.

2.224. 18 times.

2.225. $\lambda = (2\pi N_A/3b)^{2/3} (kT_0/\sqrt{2}\pi p_0) = 84$ nm.

2.226. $\nu = \pi d^2 p_0 N_A \sqrt{2\gamma/MRT_0} = 5.5$ GHz.

2.227. (a) 0.7 Pa; (b) $2 \cdot 10^{14}$ cm^{-3}, 0.2 μm.

2.228. (a) $\nu = \sqrt{2}\pi d^2 n \langle v \rangle = 0.74 \cdot 10^{10}$ s^{-1}; (b) $\nu = {}^1/_2 \sqrt{2}\pi d^2 n^2 \langle v \rangle = 1.0 \times 10^{29}$ s$^{-1}\cdot$cm^{-3}, where $n = p_0/kT_0$, $\langle v \rangle = \sqrt{8RT/\pi M}$.

2.229. (a) $\lambda = \text{const}$, $\nu \propto \sqrt{T}$; (b) $\lambda \propto T$, $\nu \propto 1/\sqrt{T}$.

2.230. (a) $\lambda = \text{const}$, ν increases $\sqrt{n}$ times; (b) λ decreases n times, ν increases n times.

2.231. (a) $\lambda \propto V$, $\nu \propto V^{-6/5}$; (b) $\lambda \propto p^{-5/7}$, $\nu \propto p^{6/7}$; (c) $\lambda \propto T^{-5/2}$, $\nu \propto T^3$.

2.232. (a) $\lambda \propto V$, $\nu \propto V^{-(n+1)/2}$; (b) $\lambda \propto p^{-1/n}$, $\nu \propto p^{(n+1)/2n}$; (c) $\lambda \propto T^{1/(1-n)}$, $\nu \propto T^{(n+1)/2(n-1)}$.

2.233. (a) $C = {}^1/_4 R(1 + 2i) = 23$ J/(K·mol); (b) $C = {}^1/_2 R(i + 2) = 29$ J/(K·mol).

2.234. $n = n_0 e^{-t/\tau}$, where $\tau = 4V/S\langle v \rangle$, $\langle v \rangle = \sqrt{8RT/\pi M}$.

2.235. Increases $(1 + \eta)/(1 + \sqrt{\eta})$ times.

2.236. Increases $\alpha^3/\beta = 2$ times.

2.237. (a) D increases n times, $\eta = \text{const}$; (b) D increases $n^{3/2}$ times, η increases $\sqrt{n}$ times.

2.238. D decreases $n^{4/5} \approx 6.3$ times, η increases $n^{1/5} \approx 1.6$ times.

2.239. (a) $n = 3$; (b) $n = 1$; (c) $n = 1$.

2.240. 0.18 nm.

2.241. $d_{Ar}/d_{He} = 1.7$.

2.242. $N_1 \approx 2\pi\eta\omega R^3/\Delta R$; $p = \sqrt{2}\, kT/\pi d^2 n \Delta R = 0.7$ Pa.

2.243. $\eta = (1/R_1^2 - 1/R_2^2) N_1/4\pi\omega$.

2.244. $N = {}^1/_2 \pi\eta\omega a^4/h$.

2.245. $N = {}^1/_3 \omega a^4 p \sqrt{\pi M/2RT}$.

2.246. $\mu = \dfrac{\pi a^4 M}{16\eta RT} \dfrac{|p_2^2 - p_1^2|}{l}$.

2.247. $T = (\varkappa_1 T_1/l_1 + \varkappa_2 T_2/l_2)/(\varkappa_1/l_1 + \varkappa_2/l_2)$.

2.248. $\varkappa = (l_1 + l_2)/(l_1/\varkappa_1 + l_2/\varkappa_2)$.

2.249. $T(x) = T_1 (T_2/T_1)^{x/l}$; $q = (\alpha/l) \ln (T_2/T_1)$.

2.250. $\Delta T = (\Delta T)_0 e^{-\alpha t}$, where $\alpha = (1/C_1 + 1/C_2) S\varkappa/l$.

2.251. $T = T_1 \{1 + (x/l) [(T_2/T_1)^{3/2} - 1]\}^{2/3}$, where x is the distance from the plate maintained at the temperature T_1.

2.252. $q=\frac{2iR^{3/2}(T_2^{3/2}-T_1^{3/2})}{9\pi^{3/2}l\,d^2N_A\sqrt{M}}=40$ W/m², where $i=3$, d is the effective diameter of helium atom.

2.253. $\lambda = 23$ mm $> l$, consequently, the gas is ultra-thin; $q = p\,\langle v\rangle\,(t_2 - t_1)/6T\,(\gamma - 1) = 22$ W/m², where $\langle v\rangle = \sqrt{8RT/\pi M}$, $T = {}^1/_2\,(T_1 + T_2)$.

2.254. $T=T_1+\frac{T_2-T_1}{\ln(R_2/R_1)}\ln\frac{r}{R_1}$.

2.255. $T=T_1+\frac{T_2-T_1}{1/R_1-1/R_2}\left(\frac{1}{R_1}-\frac{1}{r}\right)$.

2.256. $T = T_0 + (R^2 - r^2)\,w/4\varkappa$.

2.257. $T = T_0 + (R^2 - r^2)\,w/6\varkappa$.

3.1. The ratio F_{el}/F_{gr} is equal to $4\cdot 10^{42}$ and $1\cdot 10^{36}$ respectively; $q/m = 0.86\cdot 10^{-10}$ C/kg.

3.2. About $2\cdot 10^{15}$ N.

3.3. $dq/dt = {}^3/_2 a\sqrt{2\pi\varepsilon_0 mg/l}$.

3.4. $q_3=-\frac{q_1q_2}{(\sqrt{q_1}+\sqrt{q_2})^2}$, $\mathbf{r}_3=\frac{\mathbf{r}_1\sqrt{q_2}+\mathbf{r}_2\sqrt{q_1}}{\sqrt{q_1}+\sqrt{q_2}}$.

3.5. $\Delta T=\frac{qq_0}{8\pi^2\varepsilon_0 r^2}$.

3.6. $\mathbf{E} = 2.7\mathbf{i} - 3.6\mathbf{j}$, $E = 4.5$ kV/m.

3.7. $E=\frac{ql}{\sqrt{2}\pi\varepsilon_0(l^2+x^2)^{3/2}}$.

3.8. $E=\frac{q}{2\pi^2\varepsilon_0 R^2}=0.10$ kV/m.

3.9. $E=\frac{ql}{4\pi\varepsilon_0(r^2+l^2)^{3/2}}$. For $l \gg r$ the strength $E\approx\frac{q}{4\pi\varepsilon_0 l^2}$, as in the case of a point charge. $E_{max}=\frac{q}{6\sqrt{3}\pi\varepsilon_0 r^2}$ for $l=r/\sqrt{2}$.

3.10. $E=\frac{3qR^2}{4\pi\varepsilon_0 x^4}$.

3.11. $F=\frac{q\lambda}{4\pi\varepsilon_0 R}$.

3.12. (a) $E=\frac{\lambda_0}{4\varepsilon_0 R}$; (b) $E=\frac{\lambda_0 R^2}{4\varepsilon_0(x^2+R^2)^{3/2}}$. For $x \gg R$ the strength $E\approx\frac{p}{4\pi\varepsilon_0 x^3}$, where $p=\pi R^2\lambda_0$.

3.13. (a) $E=\frac{q}{4\pi\varepsilon_0 r\sqrt{a^2+r^2}}$; (b) $E=\frac{q}{4\pi\varepsilon_0(r^2-a^2)}$. In both cases $E\approx\frac{q}{4\pi\varepsilon_0 r^2}$ for $r \gg a$.

3.14. $E=\frac{\lambda\sqrt{2}}{4\pi\varepsilon_0 y}$. The vector $\mathbf{E}$ is directed at the angle 45° to the thread.

3.15. (a) $E=\frac{\lambda\sqrt{2}}{4\pi\varepsilon_0 R}$; (b) $E=0$.

3.16. $\mathbf{E} = -{}^1/_3\mathbf{a}r/\varepsilon_0$.

3.17. $\mathbf{E} = -{}^1/_3\mathbf{k}\sigma_0/\varepsilon_0$, where $\mathbf{k}$ is the unit vector of the z axis with respect to which the angle θ is read off. Clearly, the field inside the given sphere is uniform.

3.18. $\mathbf{E} = -{}^1/_6\mathbf{a}R^2/\varepsilon_0$.

3.19. $|\Phi| = {}^1/_2\lambda R/\varepsilon_0$. The sign of Φ depends on how the direction of the normal to the circle is chosen.

3.20. $|\Phi| = \frac{q}{\varepsilon_0}\left(1 - \frac{1}{\sqrt{1+(R/l)^2}}\right)$. The sign of Φ depends on how the direction of the normal to the circle is chosen.

3.21. $|\Phi| = {}^1/_3\pi\rho r_0 (R^2 - r_0^2)/\varepsilon_0$.

3.22. $E_{max} = \lambda/\pi\varepsilon_0 l$.

3.23. $E = {}^1/_2\,\sigma_0/\varepsilon_0$, with the direction of the vector $\mathbf{E}$ corresponding to the angle $\varphi = \pi$.

3.24. $\Phi = 4\pi Ra$.

3.25. (a) $E = \frac{\rho_0 r}{3\varepsilon_0}\left(1 - \frac{3r}{4R}\right)$ for $r \leqslant R$, $E = \frac{\rho_0 R^3}{12\varepsilon_0 r^2}$ for $r \geqslant R$; (b) $E_{max} = {}^1/_9\,\rho_0 R/\varepsilon_0$ for $r_m = {}^2/_3\,R$.

3.26. $q = 2\pi R^2\alpha$, $E = {}^1/_2\alpha/\varepsilon_0$.

3.27. $E = \frac{\rho_0}{3\varepsilon_0\alpha r^2}(1 - e^{-\alpha r^3})$. Accordingly, $E \approx \frac{\rho_0 r}{3\varepsilon_0}$ and $E \approx \approx \frac{\rho_0}{3\varepsilon_0\alpha r^2}$.

3.28. $\mathbf{E} = {}^1/_3\,\mathbf{a}\rho/\varepsilon_0$.

3.29. $\mathbf{E} = {}^1/_2\mathbf{a}\rho/\varepsilon_0$, where the vector $\mathbf{a}$ is directed toward the axis of the cavity.

3.30. $\Delta\varphi = \frac{q}{2\pi\varepsilon_0 R}\left(1 - \frac{1}{\sqrt{1+(a/R)^2}}\right)$.

3.31. $\varphi_1 - \varphi_2 = \frac{\lambda}{2\pi\varepsilon_0}\ln\eta = 5$ kV.

3.32. $\varphi = {}^1/_2\,\sigma R/\varepsilon_0$, $E = {}^1/_4\,\sigma/\varepsilon_0$.

3.33. $\varphi = \frac{\sigma l}{2\varepsilon_0}\left(\sqrt{1+(R/l)^2} - 1\right)$, $E = \frac{\sigma}{2\varepsilon_0}\left(1 - \frac{l}{\sqrt{l^2+R^2}}\right)$. When $l \to 0$, then $\varphi = \frac{\sigma R}{2\varepsilon_0}$, $E = \frac{\sigma}{2\varepsilon_0}$; when $l \gg R$, then $\varphi \approx \frac{q}{4\pi\varepsilon_0 l}$, $E \approx \frac{q}{4\pi\varepsilon_0 l^2}$, where $q = \sigma\pi R^2$.

3.34. $\varphi = \sigma R/\pi\varepsilon_0$.

3.35. $\mathbf{E} = -\mathbf{a}$, i.e. the field is uniform.

3.36. (a) $\mathbf{E} = -2a(x\mathbf{i} - y\mathbf{j})$; (b) $\mathbf{E} = -a(y\mathbf{i} - x\mathbf{j})$. Here $\mathbf{i}$, $\mathbf{j}$ are the unit vectors of the x and y axes. See Fig. 16 illustrating the case $a > 0$.

3.37. $\mathbf{E} = -2(ax\mathbf{i} + ay\mathbf{j} + bz\mathbf{k})$, $E = 2\sqrt{a^2(x^2+y^2) + b^2z^2}$. (a) An ellipsoid of revolution with semiaxes $\sqrt{\varphi/a}$ and $\sqrt{\varphi/b}$. (b) In the case of $\varphi > 0$, a single-cavity hyperboloid of revolution; when $\varphi = 0$, a right round cone; when $\varphi < 0$, a two-cavity hyperboloid of revolution.

3.38. (a) $\varphi_0 = \frac{3q}{8\pi\varepsilon_0 R}$; (b) $\varphi = \varphi_0\left(1 - \frac{r^2}{3R^2}\right)$, $r \leqslant R$.

3.39. $E=\sqrt{E_r^2+E_\theta^2}=\frac{p}{4\pi\varepsilon_0 r^3}\sqrt{1+3\cos^2\theta}$, where E_r is the radial component of the vector **E**, and E_θ is its component perpendicular to E_r.

3.40. $E_z=\frac{p}{4\pi\varepsilon_0}\,\frac{3\cos^2\theta-1}{r^3}$, $E_\perp=\frac{p}{4\pi\varepsilon_0}\,\frac{3\sin\theta\cos\theta}{r^3}$;
$\mathbf{E}\perp\mathbf{p}$ at the points located on the lateral surface of a cone whose axis is directed along the z axis and whose semi-vertex angle θ is found

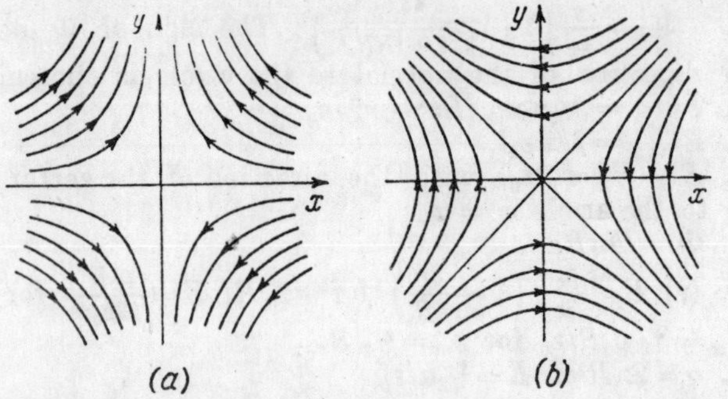

Fig. 16.

from the relation $\cos\theta = 1/\sqrt{3}$ ($\theta_1 = 54.7°$, $\theta_2 = 123.5°$). At these points $E = E_\perp = \frac{p\sqrt{2}}{4\pi\varepsilon_0 r^3}$.

3.41. $R=\sqrt[3]{\frac{p}{4\pi\varepsilon_0 E_0}}$.

3.42. $\varphi\approx\frac{\lambda l}{2\pi\varepsilon_0 r}\cos\theta$, $E\approx\frac{\lambda l}{2\pi\varepsilon_0 r^2}$.

3.43. $\varphi=\frac{ql}{4\pi\varepsilon_0}\,\frac{x}{(R^2+x^2)^{3/2}}$, $E_x=-\frac{ql}{4\pi\varepsilon_0}\,\frac{R^2-2x^2}{(R^2+x^2)^{5/2}}$, where

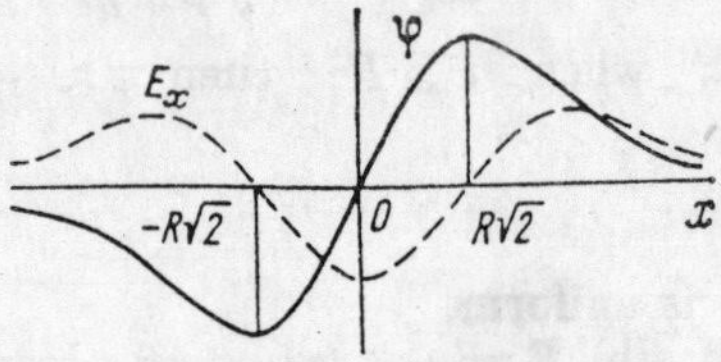

Fig. 17.

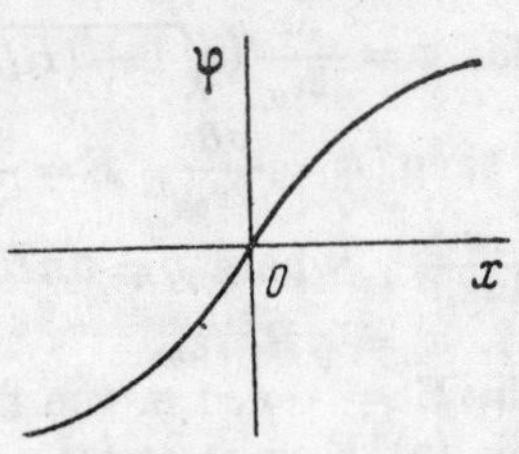

Fig. 18.

E_x is the projection of the vector **E** on the x axis. The functions are plotted in Fig. 17. If $|x|\gg R$, then $\varphi\approx\frac{ql}{4\pi\varepsilon_0 x^2}$ and $E_x\approx\frac{ql}{2\pi\varepsilon_0 x^3}$.

3.44. $\varphi=\frac{\sigma l}{2\varepsilon_0}\,\frac{x}{\sqrt{x^2+R^2}}$, $E_x=-\frac{\sigma l R^2}{2\varepsilon_0(x^2+R^2)^{3/2}}$. See Fig. 18.

3.45. $\varphi \approx \pm \frac{\sigma l}{2\varepsilon_0}\left(1-\frac{x}{\sqrt{x^2+R^2}}\right)$, $E \approx \frac{\sigma l R^2}{2\varepsilon_0 (x^2+R^2)^{3/2}}$. If $x \gg R$, then $\varphi \approx \pm \frac{p}{4\pi\varepsilon_0 x^2}$ and $E \approx \frac{p}{2\pi\varepsilon_0 x^3}$, where $p=\pi R^2 \sigma l$. In the formulas for the potential φ the plus sign corresponds to the space adjoining the positively charged plate and the minus sign to the space adjoining the negatively charged plate.

3.46. (a) $\mathbf{F}=0$; (b) $\mathbf{F}=-\frac{\lambda \mathbf{p}}{2\pi\varepsilon_0 r^2}$; (c) $\mathbf{F}=\frac{\lambda \mathbf{p}}{2\pi\varepsilon_0 r^2}$.

3.47. $F=\frac{3p^2}{2\pi\varepsilon_0 l^4}=2.1\cdot 10^{-16}$ N.

3.48. $\varphi=-axy+\text{const.}$

3.49. $\varphi=ay\left(\frac{y^2}{3}-x^2\right)+\text{const.}$

3.50. $\varphi=-y(ax+bz)+\text{const.}$

3.51. $\rho=6\varepsilon_0 ax$.

3.52. $\rho=2\varepsilon_0\Delta\varphi/d^2$; $E=\rho d/\varepsilon_0$.

3.53. $\rho=-6\varepsilon_0 a$.

3.54. $q=4l\sqrt{\pi\varepsilon_0 kx}$.

3.55. $A=\frac{q^2}{16\pi\varepsilon_0 l}$.

3.56. (a) $F=\frac{(2\sqrt{2}-1)q^2}{8\pi\varepsilon_0 l^2}$; (b) $E=2\left(1-\frac{1}{5\sqrt{5}}\right)\frac{q}{\pi\varepsilon_0 l^2}$.

3.57. $F=\frac{(2\sqrt{2}-1)q^2}{32\pi\varepsilon_0 l^2}$.

3.58. $F=\frac{3p^2}{32\pi\varepsilon_0 l^4}$.

3.59. $\sigma=-\frac{ql}{2\pi(l^2+r^2)^{3/2}}$, $q_{ind}=-q$.

3.60. (a) $F_1=\frac{\lambda^2}{4\pi\varepsilon_0 l}$; (b) $\sigma=\frac{l\lambda}{\pi(l^2+x^2)}$.

3.61. (a) $\sigma=\frac{\lambda}{2\pi l}$; (b) $\sigma(r)=\frac{\lambda}{2\pi\sqrt{l^2+r^2}}$.

3.62. (a) $\sigma=\frac{lq}{2\pi(l^2+R^2)^{3/2}}$; (b) $E=\frac{1}{4\pi\varepsilon_0}\frac{q}{4l^2[1+{}^1/_4(R/l)^2]^{3/2}}$,

$$\varphi=\frac{1}{4\pi\varepsilon_0}\frac{q}{R}\left(1-\frac{1}{\sqrt{1+4(l/R)^2}}\right).$$

3.63. $\varphi=\frac{q}{4\pi\varepsilon_0 l}$.

3.64. $\varphi=\frac{q}{4\pi\varepsilon_0}\left(\frac{1}{r}-\frac{1}{R_1}+\frac{1}{R_2}\right)$.

3.65. $q_2=-\frac{b}{a}q_1$; $\varphi=\frac{q_1}{4\pi\varepsilon_0}\times\begin{cases}1/r-1/a & \text{if } a\leqslant r\leqslant b,\\ (1-b/a)r & \text{if } r\geqslant b.\end{cases}$

3.66. (a) $E_{23}=\Delta\varphi/d$, $E_{12}=E_{34}={}^1/_2 E_{23}$; (b) $|\sigma_1|=\sigma_4={}^1/_2\varepsilon_0\Delta\varphi/d$, $\sigma_2=|\sigma_3|={}^3/_2\varepsilon_0\Delta\varphi/d$.

3.67. $q_1=-q(l-x)/l$, $q_2=-qx/l$. **Instruction.** If the charge q is imagined to be uniformly spread over the plane passing through that charge and parallel to the plates, the charges q_1 and q_2 remain, obviously, unchanged. What changes is only their distribution, and the electric field becomes easy to calculate.

3.68. $dF/dS = {}^1/_2\sigma^2/\varepsilon_0$.

3.69. $F = \frac{q^2}{32\pi\varepsilon_0 R^2} = 0.5$ kN.

3.70. $F = {}^1/_4\pi R^2\sigma_0^2/\varepsilon_0$.

3.71. $N = \frac{n_0 p}{(\varepsilon - 1)\varepsilon_0 E} = 3\cdot 10^3$,

where n_0 is the concentration of molecules.

3.72. $F = \frac{3\beta p^2}{4\pi^2\varepsilon_0 l^7}$.

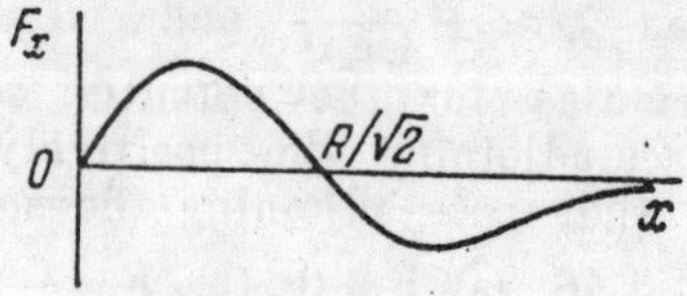

Fig. 19.

3.73. (a) $x = R/\sqrt{2}$; (b) $x = \begin{cases} 1.1R \text{ (attraction)} \\ 0.29R \text{ (repulsion)}. \end{cases}$ See Fig. 19.

3.74. $\mathbf{P} = \frac{\varepsilon - 1}{\varepsilon}\frac{q}{4\pi r^3}\mathbf{r}$, $q' = -\frac{\varepsilon - 1}{\varepsilon}q$.

3.76. $q_{inn}' = -q(\varepsilon - 1)/\varepsilon$, $q_{out}' = q(\varepsilon - 1)/\varepsilon$.

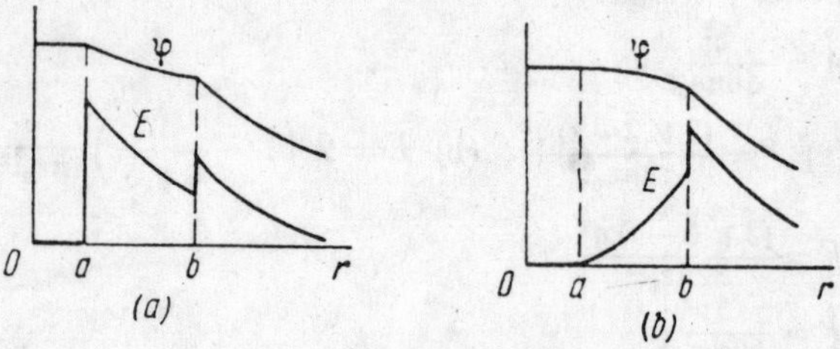

Fig. 20.

3.77. See Fig. 20.

3.78. $E = \frac{E_0}{\varepsilon}\sqrt{\cos^2\alpha_0 + \varepsilon^2\sin^2\alpha_0} = 5.2$ V/m;

$\tan\alpha = \varepsilon\tan\alpha_0$, hence, $\alpha = 74°$; $\sigma' = \frac{\varepsilon_0(\varepsilon - 1)}{\varepsilon}E_0\cos\alpha_0 = 64$ pC/m².

3.79. (a) $\oint \mathbf{E}\,d\mathbf{S} = \frac{\varepsilon - 1}{\varepsilon}\pi R^2 E_0\cos\theta$; (b) $\oint \mathbf{D}\,d\mathbf{r} = -\varepsilon_0(\varepsilon - 1)\times$ $\times lE_0\sin\theta$.

3.80. (a) $E = \begin{cases} \rho l/\varepsilon\varepsilon_0 & \text{for } l < d, \\ \rho d/\varepsilon_0 & \text{for } l > d, \end{cases}$ $\varphi = \begin{cases} -\rho l^2/2\varepsilon\varepsilon_0 & \text{for } l \leqslant d, \\ -(d/2\varepsilon + l - d)\rho d/\varepsilon_0 & \text{for } l \geqslant d. \end{cases}$

The plots $E_x(x)$ and $\varphi(x)$ are shown in Fig. 21. (b) $\sigma' = \rho d(\varepsilon - 1)/\varepsilon$, $\rho' = -\rho(\varepsilon - 1)/\varepsilon$.

3.81. (a) $E = \begin{cases} \rho r/3\varepsilon_0\varepsilon & \text{for } r < R, \\ \rho R^3/3\varepsilon_0 r^2 & \text{for } r > R; \end{cases}$

(b) $\rho' = -\rho(\varepsilon - 1)/\varepsilon$, $\sigma' = \rho R(\varepsilon - 1)/3\varepsilon$. See Fig. 22.

3.82. $\mathbf{E} = -d\mathbf{P}/4\varepsilon_0 R$.

3.83. $\mathbf{E} = -\mathbf{P}_0(1 - x^2/d^2)/\varepsilon_0$, $U = 4dP_0/3\varepsilon_0$.

3.84. (a) $E_1 = 2\varepsilon E_0/(\varepsilon+1)$, $E_2 = 2E_0/(\varepsilon+1)$, $D_1 = D_2 = 2\varepsilon\varepsilon_0 E_0/(\varepsilon+1)$; (b) $E_1 = E_0$, $E_2 = E_0/\varepsilon$, $D_1 = D_2 = \varepsilon_0 E_0$.

3.85. (a) $E_1 = E_2 = E_0$, $D_1 = \varepsilon_0 E_0$, $D_2 = \varepsilon D_1$; (b) $E_1 = E_2 = 2E_0/(\varepsilon+1)$, $D_1 = 2\varepsilon_0 E_0/(\varepsilon+1)$, $D_2 = \varepsilon D_1$.

3.86. $E = q/2\pi\varepsilon_0(\varepsilon+1)r^2$.

3.87. $\rho = \rho_0\varepsilon/(\varepsilon-1) = 1.6\ \text{g/cm}^3$, where ε and ρ_0 are the permittivity and density of kerosene.

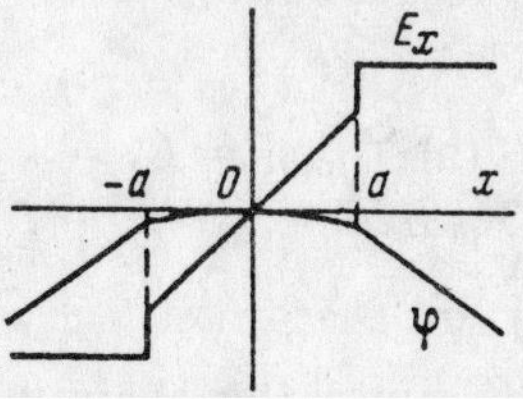

Fig. 21.

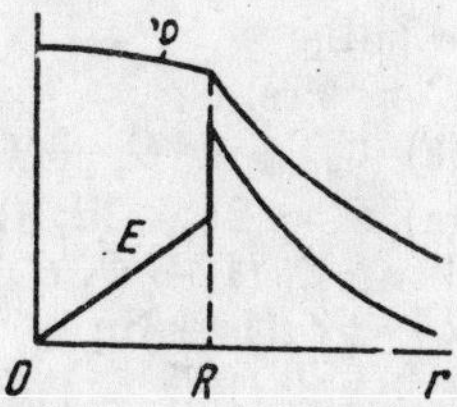

Fig. 22.

3.88. $\sigma'_{max} = (\varepsilon-1)\varepsilon_0 E = 3.5\ \text{nC/m}^2$, $q' = \pi R^2(\varepsilon-1)\varepsilon_0 E = 10\ \text{pC}$.

3.89. (a) Since the normal component of the vector **D** is continuous at the dielectric interface, we obtain

$$\sigma' = -ql(\varepsilon-1)/2\pi r^3(\varepsilon+1), \text{ for } l \to 0 \text{ and } \sigma' \to 0;$$

(b) $q' = -q(\varepsilon-1)/(\varepsilon+1)$.

3.90. $F = q^2(\varepsilon-1)/16\pi\varepsilon_0 l^2(\varepsilon+1)$.

3.91. $D = \begin{cases} q/2\pi(1+\varepsilon)r^2 & \text{in vacuum,} \\ \varepsilon q/2\pi(1+\varepsilon)r^2 & \text{in dielectric;} \end{cases}$

$$\left.\begin{aligned} E &= q/2\pi\varepsilon_0(1+\varepsilon)r^2 \\ \varphi &= q/2\pi\varepsilon_0(1+\varepsilon)r \end{aligned}\right\} \text{ both in vacuum and in dielectric.}$$

3.92. $\sigma' = ql(\varepsilon-1)/2\pi r^3\varepsilon(\varepsilon+1)$; for $l \to 0$ and $\sigma' \to 0$.

3.93. $\sigma' = ql(\varepsilon-1)/2\pi r^3\varepsilon$.

3.94. $\mathbf{E}_1 = \mathbf{P}h/\varepsilon_0 d$ (between the plates), $\mathbf{E}_2 = -(1-h/d)\mathbf{P}/\varepsilon_0$, $\mathbf{D}_1 = \mathbf{D}_2 = \mathbf{P}h/d$.

3.95. $\rho' = -2\alpha$, i.e. is independent of r.

3.96. (a) $\mathbf{E} = -\mathbf{P}/3\varepsilon_0$.

3.97. $\mathbf{E}_0 = \mathbf{E} - \mathbf{P}/3\varepsilon_0$.

3.98. $\mathbf{E} = 3\mathbf{E}_0/(\varepsilon+2)$, $\mathbf{P} = 3\varepsilon_0\mathbf{E}_0(\varepsilon-1)/(\varepsilon+2)$.

3.99. $\mathbf{E} = -\mathbf{P}/2\varepsilon_0$.

3.100. $\mathbf{E} = 2\mathbf{E}_0/(\varepsilon+1)$; $\mathbf{P} = 2\varepsilon_0\mathbf{E}_0(\varepsilon-1)/(\varepsilon+1)$.

3.101. $C = \dfrac{4\pi\varepsilon_0\varepsilon R_1}{1+(\varepsilon-1)R_1/R_2}$.

3.102. The strength decreased $\frac{1}{2}(\varepsilon+1)$ times; $q = \frac{1}{2}C\mathscr{E}(\varepsilon-1)/(\varepsilon+1)$.

3.103. (a) $C = \dfrac{\varepsilon_0 S}{d_1/\varepsilon_1 + d_2/\varepsilon_2}$; (b) $\sigma' = \varepsilon_0 V \dfrac{\varepsilon_1-\varepsilon_2}{\varepsilon_1 d_2 + \varepsilon_2 d_1}$.

3.104. (a) $C = \varepsilon_0(\varepsilon_2-\varepsilon_1)S/d\ln(\varepsilon_2/\varepsilon_1)$; (b) $\rho' = -q(\varepsilon_2-\varepsilon_1)/dS\varepsilon^2$.

3.105. $C = 4\pi\varepsilon_0 a/\ln (R_2/R_1)$.
3.106. When $\varepsilon_1 R_1 E_{1m} = \varepsilon_2 R_2 E_{2m}$.
3.107. $V = R_1 E_1 [\ln (R_2/R_1) + (\varepsilon_1/\varepsilon_2) \ln (R_3/R_2)]$.
3.108. $C \approx \pi\varepsilon_0 \ln (b/a)$.
3.109. $C \approx 2\pi\varepsilon_0/\ln (2b/a)$.
3.110. $C \approx 2\pi\varepsilon_0 \varepsilon a$. **Instruction.** When $b \gg a$, the charges can be assumed to be distributed practically uniformly over the surfaces of the balls.
3.111. $C \approx 4\pi\varepsilon_0 a$.
3.112. (a) $C_{total} = C_1 + C_2 + C_3$; (b) $C_{total} = C$.
3.113. (a) $C = 2\varepsilon_0 S/3d$; (b) $C = 3\varepsilon_0 S/2d$.
3.114. $V \leqslant V_1 (1 + C_1/C_2) = 9$ kV.
3.115. $U = \mathscr{E}/(1 + 3\eta + \eta^2) = 10$ V.
3.116. $C_x = C (\sqrt{5} - 1)/2 = 0.62C$. Since the chain is infinite, all the links beginning with the second can be replaced by the capacitance C_x equal to the sought one.
3.117. $V_1 = q/C_1 = 10$ V, $V_2 = q/C_2 = 5$ V, where $q = (\varphi_A - \varphi_B + \mathscr{E}) C_1 C_2/(C_1 + C_2)$.
3.118. $V_1 = (\mathscr{E}_2 - \mathscr{E}_1)/(1 + C_1/C_2)$, $V_2 = (\mathscr{E}_1 - \mathscr{E}_2)/(1 + C_2/C_1)$.
3.119. $q = |\mathscr{E}_1 - \mathscr{E}_2| C_1 C_2/(C_1 + C_2)$.
3.120. $\varphi_A - \varphi_B = \mathscr{E} \dfrac{C_2 C_3 - C_1 C_4}{(C_1 + C_2)(C_3 + C_4)}$. In the case when $C_1/C_2 = C_3/C_4$.
3.121. $q = \dfrac{V}{1/C_1 + 1/C_2 + 1/C_3} = 0.06$ mC.
3.122. $q_1 = \mathscr{E} C_2$, $q_2 = -\mathscr{E} C_1 C_2/(C_1 + C_2)$.
3.123. $q_1 = \mathscr{E} C_1 (C_1 - C_2)/(C_1 + C_2) = -24\ \mu$C, $q_2 = \mathscr{E} C_2 (C_1 - C_2)/(C_1 + C_2) = -36\ \mu$C, $q_3 = \mathscr{E} (C_2 - C_1) = +60\ \mu$ C.
3.124. $\varphi_A - \varphi_B = (C_2 \mathscr{E}_2 - C_1 \mathscr{E}_1)/(C_1 + C_2 + C_3)$.
3.125. $\varphi_1 = \dfrac{\mathscr{E}_2 C_2 + \mathscr{E}_3 C_3 - \mathscr{E}_1 (C_2 + C_3)}{C_1 + C_2 + C_3}$,
$\varphi_2 = \dfrac{\mathscr{E}_1 C_1 + \mathscr{E}_3 C_3 - \mathscr{E}_2 (C_1 + C_3)}{C_1 + C_2 + C_3}$, $\varphi_3 = \dfrac{\mathscr{E}_1 C_1 + \mathscr{E}_2 C_2 - \mathscr{E}_3 (C_1 + C_2)}{C_1 + C_2 + C_3}$.
3.126. $C_{total} = \dfrac{2C_1 C_2 + C_3 (C_1 + C_2)}{C_1 + C_2 + 2C_3}$.
3.127. (a) $W = (\sqrt{2} + 4) q^2/4\pi\varepsilon_0 a$; (b) $W = (\sqrt{2} - 4) q^2/4\pi\varepsilon_0 a$; (c) $W = -\sqrt{2} q^2/4\pi\varepsilon_0 a$.
3.128. $W = -\dfrac{2 \ln 2}{4\pi\varepsilon_0} \dfrac{q^2}{a}$.
3.129. $W = -q^2/8\pi\varepsilon_0 l$.
3.130. $W = q_1 q_2/4\pi\varepsilon_0 l$.
3.131. $\Delta W = -\frac{1}{2} V^2 C_1 C_2/(C_1 + C_2) = -0.03$ mJ.
3.132. $Q = \mathscr{E}^2 C C_0/(2C + C_0)$.
3.133. $Q = \frac{1}{2} C \mathscr{E}_2^2$. It is remarkable that the result obtained is independent of $\mathscr{E}_1$.
3.134. $W = W_1 + W_2 + W_{12} = \dfrac{1}{4\pi\varepsilon_0} \left(\dfrac{q_1^2}{2R_1} + \dfrac{q_2^2}{2R_2} + \dfrac{q_1 q_2}{R_2} \right)$.

3.135. (a) $W = 3q^2/20\pi\varepsilon_0 R$; (b) $W_1/W_2 = 1/5$.

3.136. $W = (q^2/8\pi\varepsilon_0\varepsilon)(1/a - 1/b) = 27$ mJ.

3.137. $A = (q^2/8\pi\varepsilon_0)(1/R_1 - 1/R_2)$.

3.138. $A = \frac{q(q_0 + q/2)}{4\pi\varepsilon_0}\left(\frac{1}{R_1} - \frac{1}{R_2}\right)$.

3.139. $F_1 = \sigma^2/2\varepsilon_0$.

3.140. $A = (q^2/8\pi\varepsilon_0)(1/a - 1/b)$.

3.141. (a) $A = q^2(x_2 - x_1)/2\varepsilon_0 S$;
(b) $A = \varepsilon_0 SV^2(x_2 - x_1)/2x_1x_2$.

3.142. (a) $A = {}^1/_2 CV^2\eta/(1-\eta)^2 = 1.5$ mJ;
(b) $A = {}^1/_2 CV^2\eta\varepsilon(\varepsilon - 1)/[\varepsilon - \eta(\varepsilon - 1)]^2 = 0.8$ mJ.

3.143. $\Delta p = \varepsilon_0\varepsilon(\varepsilon - 1)V^2/2d^2 = 7$ kPa $= 0.07$ atm.

3.144. $h = (\varepsilon - 1)\sigma^2/2\varepsilon_0\varepsilon\rho g$.

3.145. $F = \pi R\varepsilon_0(\varepsilon - 1)V^2/d$.

3.146. $N = (\varepsilon - 1)\varepsilon_0 R^2 V^2/4d$.

3.147. $I = 2\pi\varepsilon_0 aEv = 0.5$ μA.

3.148. $I \approx 2\pi\varepsilon_0(\varepsilon - 1)rvV/d = 0.11$ μA.

3.149. (a) $\alpha = (\alpha_1 + \eta\alpha_2)/(1+\eta)$; (b) $\alpha \approx (\alpha_2 + \eta\alpha_1)/(1+\eta)$.

3.150. (a) ${}^5/_6 R$; (b) ${}^7/_{12} R$; (c) ${}^3/_4 R$.

3.151. $R_x = R(\sqrt{3} - 1)$.

3.152. $R = (1 + \sqrt{1 + 4R_2/R_1})R_1/2 = 6\ \Omega$. **Instruction.** Since the chain is infinite, all the links beginning with the second can be replaced by the resistance equal to the sought resistance R.

3.153. Imagine the voltage V to be applied across the points A and B. Then $V = IR = I_0R_0$, where I is the current carried by the lead wires, I_0 is the current carried by the conductor AB.

The current I_0 can be represented as a superposition of two currents. If the current I flowed into point A and spread all over the infinite wire grid, the conductor AB would carry (because of symmetry) the current $I/4$. Similarly, if the current I flowed into the grid from infinity and left the grid through point B, the conductor AB would also carry the current $I/4$. Superposing both of these solutions, we obtain $I_0 = I/2$. Therefore, $R = R_0/2$.

3.154. $R = (\rho/2\pi l)\ln(b/a)$.

3.155. $R = \rho(b - a)/4\pi ab$. In the case of $b \to \infty$ $R = \rho/4\pi a$.

3.156. $\rho = 4\pi\Delta t ab/(b - a)C\ln\eta$.

3.157. $R = \rho/2\pi a$.

3.158. (a) $j = 2alV/\rho r^3$; (b) $R = \rho/4\pi a$.

3.159. (a) $j = lV/2\rho r^2\ln(l/a)$; (b) $R_1 = (\rho/\pi)\ln(l/a)$.

3.160. $I = VC/\rho\varepsilon\varepsilon_0 = 1.5$ μA.

3.161. $RC = \rho\varepsilon\varepsilon_0$.

3.162. $\sigma = D_n = D\cos\alpha$; $j = D\sin\alpha/\varepsilon\varepsilon_0\rho$.

3.163. $I = VS(\sigma_2 - \sigma_1)/d\ln(\sigma_2/\sigma_1) = 5$ nA.

3.165. $q = \varepsilon_0(\rho_2 - \rho_1)I$.

3.166. $\sigma = \varepsilon_0 V(\varepsilon_2\rho_2 - \varepsilon_1\rho_1)/(\rho_1 d_1 + \rho_2 d_2)$, $\sigma = 0$ if $\varepsilon_1\rho_1 = \varepsilon_2\rho_2$.

3.167. $q = \varepsilon_0 I(\varepsilon_2\rho_2 - \varepsilon_1\rho_1)$.

3.168. $\rho = 2\varepsilon_0 V(\eta - 1)/d^2(\eta + 1)$.

3.169. (a) $R_1 = 2\pi\alpha/S^2$; (b) $E = 2\pi\alpha I/S^2$.
3.170. $t = -RC \ln (I - V/V_0) = 0.6$ μs.
3.171. $\rho = \tau/\varepsilon_0\varepsilon \ln 2 = 1.4 \cdot 10^{13}$ Ω·m.
3.172. $I = [(\eta - 1)\mathscr{E}/R]\, e^{-\eta t/RC}$.
3.173. $V = \mathscr{E}/(\eta + 1) = 2.0$ V.
3.174. $\varphi_1 - \varphi_2 = (\mathscr{E}_1 - \mathscr{E}_2) R_1/(R_1 + R_2) - \mathscr{E}_1 = -4$ V.
3.175. $R = R_2 - R_1$, $\Delta\varphi = 0$ in the source of current with internal resistance R_2.
3.176. (a) $I = \alpha$; (b) $\varphi_A - \varphi_B = 0$.
3.177. $\varphi_A - \varphi_B = (\mathscr{E}_1 - \mathscr{E}_2) R_1/(R_1 + R_2) = -0.5$ V.
3.178. $I_1 = \mathscr{E}R_2/(RR_1 + R_1R_2 + R_2R) = 1.2$ A, $I_2 = I_1R_1/R_2 = 0.8$ A.
3.179. $V = V_0Rx/[Rl + R_0 (l - x)\, x/l]$; for $R \gg R_0$ $V \approx V_0x/l$.
3.180. $\mathscr{E} = (\mathscr{E}_1R_2 + \mathscr{E}_2R_1)/(R_1 + R_2)$, $R_i = R_1R_2/(R_1 + R_2)$.
3.181. $I = (R_1\mathscr{E}_2 - R_2\mathscr{E}_1)/(RR_1 + R_1R_2 + R_2R) = 0.02$ A, the current is directed from the left to the right (see Fig. 3.44).
3.182. (a) $I_1 = [R_3 (\mathscr{E}_1 - \mathscr{E}_2) + R_2(\mathscr{E}_1 + \mathscr{E}_3)]/(R_1R_2 + R_2R_3 + R_3R_1) = 0.06$ A; (b) $\varphi_A - \varphi_B = \mathscr{E}_1 - I_1R_1 = 0.9$ V.
3.183. $I = [\mathscr{E} (R_2 + R_3) + \mathscr{E}_0R_3]/[R (R_2 + R_3) + R_2R_3]$.
3.184. $\varphi_A - \varphi_B = [\mathscr{E}_2R_3 (R_1 + R_2) - \mathscr{E}_1R_1 (R_2 + R_3)]/(R_1R_2 + R_2R_3 + R_3R_1) = -1.0$ V.
3.185. $I_1 = [R_3 (\varphi_1 - \varphi_2) + R_2 (\varphi_1 - \varphi_3)]/(R_1R_2 + R_2R_3 + R_3R_1) = 0.2$ A.
3.186. $I = \frac{V}{R_2}\left(\frac{R_1 + R_2}{R_1 [1 + R_2R_4 (R_1 + R_3)/R_1R_3 (R_2 + R_4)]} - 1\right) = 1.0$ A.
The current flows from point C to point D.
3.187. $R_{AB} = r (r + 3R)/(R + 3r)$.
3.188. $V = {}^1/_2\mathscr{E} (1 - e^{-2t/RC})$.
3.189. (a) $Q = {}^4/_3\, q^2R/\Delta t$; (b) $Q = {}^1/_2 \ln 2 \cdot q^2R/\Delta t$.
3.190. $R = 3R_0$.
3.192. $Q = I (\mathscr{E} - V) = 0.6$ W, $P = -IV = -2.0$ W.
3.193. $I = V/2R$; $P_{max} = V^2/4R$; $\eta = 1/2$.
3.194. By $2\eta = 2\%$.
3.195. $T - T_0 = (1 - e^{-kt/C})\, V^2/kR$.
3.196. $R_x = R_1R_2/(R_1 + R_2) = 12$ Ω.
3.197. $R = R_1R_2/(R_1 + R_2)$;
$Q_{max} = (\mathscr{E}_1R_2 + \mathscr{E}_2R_1)^2/4R_1R_2 (R_1 + R_2)$.
3.198. $n = \sqrt{Nr/R} = 3$.
3.199. $Q = {}^1/_2 C\mathscr{E}^2R_1/(R_1 + R_2) = 60$ mJ.
3.200. (a) $\Delta W = -{}^1/_2 CV^2\eta/(1 - \eta) = -0.15$ mJ; (b) $A = {}^1/_2 CV^2\eta/(1 - \eta) = 0.15$ mJ.
3.201. $\Delta W = -{}^1/_2 (\varepsilon - 1)\, CV^2 = -0.5$ mJ, $A_{mech} = {}^1/_2 (\varepsilon - 1)\, CV^2 = 0.5$ mJ.
3.202. $h \approx {}^1/_2 \varepsilon_0 (\varepsilon - 1)\, V^2/\rho g d^2$, where ρ is the density of water.
3.203. (a) $q = q_0 e^{-t/\varepsilon_0\varepsilon\rho}$; (b) $Q = (1/a - 1/b)\, q_0^2/8\pi\varepsilon_0\varepsilon$.
3.204. (a) $q = q_0 (1 - e^{-\tau/RC}) = 0.18$ mC; (b) $Q = (1 - e^{-2\tau/RC})\, q_0^2/2C = 82$ mJ.

3.205. (a) $I = (V_0/R)\,e^{-2t/RC}$; (b) $Q = {}^1/_4\,CV_0^2$.
3.206. $e/m = l\omega r/qR = 1.8\cdot10^{11}$ C/kg.
3.207. $p = lIm/e = 0.40$ μN·s.
3.208. $s = enl\,\langle v\rangle/j \sim 10^7$ m, where n is the concentration of free electrons, $\langle v\rangle$ is the mean velocity of thermal motion of an electron.
3.209. (a) $t = enlS/I = 3$ Ms; (b) $F = enl\rho I = 1.0$ MN, where ρ is the resistivity of copper.
3.210. $E = (I/2\pi\varepsilon_0 r)\sqrt{m/2eV} = 32$ V/m, $\Delta\varphi = (I/4\pi\varepsilon_0)\sqrt{m/2eV} = 0.80$ V.
3.211. (a) $\rho(x) = -{}^4/_9\varepsilon_0 a x^{-2/3}$; (b) $j = {}^4/_9\varepsilon_0 a^{3/2}\sqrt{2e/m}$.
3.212. $n = Id/e\,(u_0^+ + u_0^-)\,VS = 2.3\cdot10^8$ cm^{-3}.
3.213. $u_0 = \omega_0 l^2/2V_0$.
3.214. (a) $\dot{n}_i = I_{sat}/eV = 6\cdot10^9$ cm$^{-3}\cdot$s^{-1}; (b) $n = \sqrt{\dot{n}_i/r} = 6\cdot10^7$ cm^{-3}.
3.215. $t = (\eta - 1)\big/\sqrt{r\dot{n}_i} = 13$ ms.
3.216. $t = \varepsilon_0\eta U/e\dot{n}_i d^2 = 4.6$ days.
3.217. $I = ev_0 e^{\alpha d}$.
3.218. $j = (e^{\alpha d} - 1)\,e\dot{n}_i/\alpha$.
3.219. (a) $B = \mu_0 I/2R = 6.3$ μT; (b) $B = \mu_0 R^2 I/2(R^2 + x^2)^{3/2} = 2.3$ μT.
3.220. $B = n\mu_0 I\tan(\pi/n)/2\pi R$, for $n \to \infty$ $B = \mu_0 I/2R$
3.221. $B = 4\mu_0 I/\pi d\sin\varphi = 0.10$ mT.
3.222. $B = (\pi - \varphi + \tan\varphi)\,\mu_0 I/2\pi R = 28$ μT.
3.223. (a) $B = \dfrac{\mu_0 I}{4\pi}\left(\dfrac{2\pi-\varphi}{a} + \dfrac{\varphi}{b}\right)$; (b) $B = \dfrac{\mu_0 I}{4\pi}\left(\dfrac{3\pi}{4a} + \dfrac{\sqrt{2}}{b}\right)$.
3.224. $B \approx \mu_0 hI/4\pi^2 Rr$, where r is the distance from the cut.
3.225. $B = \mu_0 I/\pi^2 R$.
3.226. (a) $B = (\mu_0/4\pi)(\pi I/R)$; (b) $B = (\mu_0/4\pi)(1 + 3\pi/2)\,I/R$; (c) $B = (\mu_0/4\pi)(2 + \pi)\,I/R$.
3.227. $B = (\mu_0/4\pi)\,I\sqrt{2}/l = 2.0$ μT.
3.228. (a) $B = (\mu_0/4\pi)\sqrt{4+\pi^2}\,I/R = 0.30$ μT; (b) $B = (\mu_0/4\pi)\times\sqrt{2+2\pi+\pi^2}\,I/R = 0.34$ μT; (c) $B = (\mu_0/4\pi)\sqrt{2}\,I/R = 0.11$ μT.
3.229. (a) $B = \mu_0 i/2$; (b) $B = \mu_0 i$ between the planes and $B = 0$ outside the planes.
3.230. $B = \begin{cases}\mu_0 jx \text{ inside the plate,}\\ \mu_0 jd \text{ outside the plate.}\end{cases}$
3.231. In the half-space with the straight wire, $B = \mu_0 I/2\pi r$, r is the distance from the wire. In the other half-space $B \equiv 0$.
3.232. The given integral is equal to $\mu_0 I$.
3.233. $\mathbf{B} = \begin{cases}{}^1/_2\mu_0\,[\mathbf{jr}] \text{ for } r \leqslant R,\\ {}^1/_2\mu_0\,[\mathbf{jr}]\,R^2/r^2 \text{ for } r \geqslant R.\end{cases}$
3.234. $\mathbf{B} = {}^1/_2\mu_0\,[\mathbf{jl}]$, i.e. field inside the cavity is uniform.
3.235. $j(r) = (b/\mu_0)(1 + \alpha)\,r^{\alpha-1}$.

3.236. $B = \mu_0 nI/\sqrt{1+(2R/l)^2}$.

3.237. (a) $B = {}^1/_2\mu_0 nI\,(1 - x/\sqrt{x^2+R^2})$, where $x > 0$ outside the solenoid and $x < 0$ inside the solenoid; see Fig. 23; (b) $x_0 = R\,(1-2\eta)/2\sqrt{\eta\,(1-\eta)} \approx 5R$.

3.238. $B = \begin{cases} (\mu_0 I/h)\sqrt{1-(h/2\pi R)^2} = 0.3 \text{ mT}, & r < R, \\ (\mu_0/4\pi)\,2I/r, & r > R. \end{cases}$

3.239. $\eta \approx N/\pi = 8\cdot 10^2$.

3.240. $\Phi = (\mu_0/4\pi)\,I = 1.0\ \mu\text{Wb/m}$.

3.241. $\Phi = \Phi_0/2 = \mu_0 nIS/2$, where Φ_0 is the flux of the vector **B** through the cross-section of the solenoid far from its ends.

3.242. $\Phi = (\mu_0/4\pi)\,2INh\ln\eta = 8\ \mu\text{Wb}$.

3.243. $p_m = 2\pi R^3 B/\mu_0 = 30\ \text{mA}\cdot\text{m}^2$.

3.244. $p_m = {}^1/_2 NI\,d^2 = 0.5\ \text{A}\cdot\text{m}^2$.

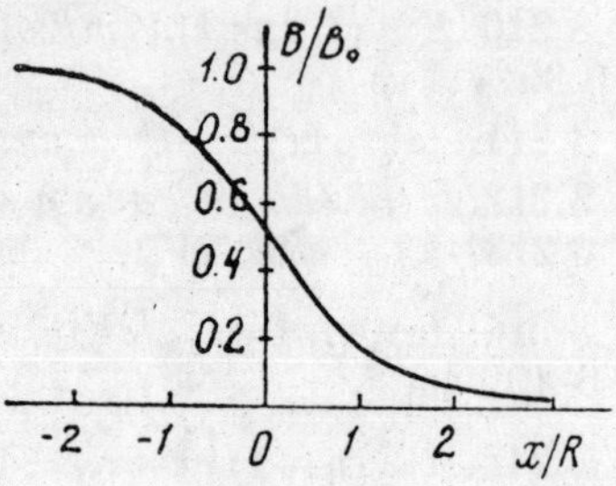

Fig. 23.

3.245. (a) $B = \dfrac{\mu_0 IN\ln(b/a)}{2(b-a)} = 7\ \mu\text{T}$; (b) $p_m = {}^1/_3\pi IN\,(a^2+ab+b^2) = 15\ \text{mA}\cdot\text{m}^2$.

3.246. (a) $B = {}^1/_2\mu_0\sigma\omega R$; (b) $p_m = {}^1/_4\pi\sigma\omega R^4$.

3.247. $B = {}^2/_3\mu_0\sigma\omega R = 29$ pT.

3.248. $p_m = {}^1/_5 qR^2\omega$: $p_m/M = q/2m$.

3.249. $\mathbf{B} = 0$.

3.250. $F_m/F_e = \mu_0\varepsilon_0 v^2 = (v/c)^2 = 1.00\cdot 10^{-6}$.

3.251. (a) $F_1 = \mu_0 I^2/4R = 0.20$ mN/m; (b) $F_1 = \mu_0 I^2/\pi l = 0.13$ mN/m.

3.252. $B = \pi d^2\sigma_m/4RI = 8$ kT, where σ_m is the strength of copper.

3.253. $B = (2\rho gS/I)\tan\theta = 10$ mT, where ρ is the density of copper.

3.254. $B = \Delta mgl/NIS = 0.4$ T.

3.255. (a) $F = 2\mu_0 II_0/\pi\,(4\eta^2-1) = 0.40\ \mu\text{N}$; (b) $A = (\mu_0 aII_0/\pi)\ln[(2\eta+1)/(2\eta-1)] = 0.10\ \mu\text{J}$.

3.256. $R \approx \sqrt{\mu_0/\varepsilon_0}\,(\ln\eta)/\pi = 0.36\ \text{k}\Omega$.

3.257. $F_1 = \mu_0 I^2/\pi^2 R$.

3.258. $F_1 = \dfrac{\mu_0}{4\pi}\,\dfrac{2I_1I_2}{b}\ln(1+b/a)$.

3.259. $F_1 = B^2/2\mu_0$.

3.260. In all three cases $F_1 = (B_1^2 - B_2^2)/2\mu_0$. The force is directed to the right. The current in the conducting plane is directed beyond the drawing.

3.261. $\Delta p = IB/a = 0.5$ kPa.

3.262. $p = \mu_0 I^2/8\pi^2R^2$.

3.263. $p = {}^1/_2\mu_0 n^2 I^2$.

3.264. $I_{lim} = \sqrt{2F_{lim}/\mu_0 nR}$.

3.265. $P = v^2B^2d^2R/(R + \rho d/S)^2$; when $R = \rho d/S$, the power is $P = P_{max} = {}^1/_4 v^2B^2dS/\rho$.

3.266. $U = {}^1/_4 \mu_0 I^2/\pi^2R^2ne = 2$ pV.

3.267. $n = jB/eE = 2.5\cdot 10^{28}$ m^{-1}; almost 1 : 1.

3.268. $u_0 = 1/\eta B = 3.2\cdot 10^{-3}$ $m^2/(V\cdot s)$.

3.269. (a) $F = 0$; (b) $F = (\mu_0/4\pi)\, 2Ip_m/r^2$, $\mathbf{F} \uparrow\downarrow \mathbf{B}$; (c) $F = (\mu_0/4\pi)\, 2Ip_m/r^2$, $\mathbf{F} \uparrow\downarrow \mathbf{r}$.

3.270. $F = (\mu_0/4\pi)\, 6\pi R^2 Ip_m x/(R^2 + x^2)^{5/2}$.

3.271. $F = {}^3/_2 \mu_0 p_{1m} p_{2m}/\pi l^4 = 9$ nN.

3.272. $I' \approx 2Bx^3/\mu_0 R^2 = 0.5$ kA.

3.273. $B' = B\sqrt{\mu^2 \sin^2\alpha + \cos^2\alpha}$.

3.274. (a) $\oint \mathbf{H}\, d\mathbf{S} = \pi R^2 B \cos\theta \cdot (\mu - 1)/\mu\mu_0$;

(b) $\oint \mathbf{B}\, d\mathbf{r} = (1 - \mu)\, Bl \sin\theta$.

3.275. (a) $I'_{sur} = \chi I$; (b) $I'_{vol} = \chi I$; in opposite directions.

3.276. See Fig. 24.

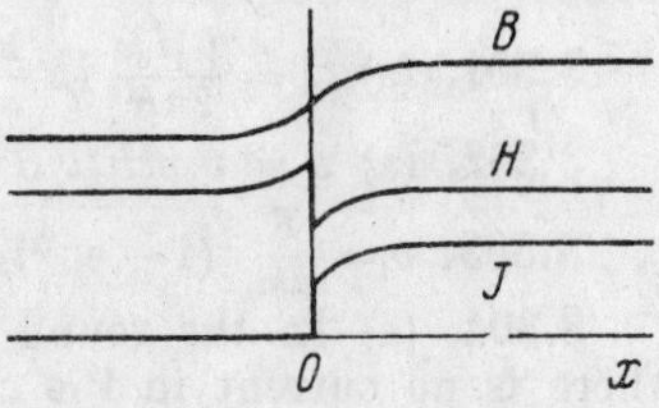

Fig. 24.

3.277. $B = \dfrac{\mu_0\mu_1\mu_2}{\mu_1 + \mu_2}\dfrac{I}{\pi r}$.

3.278. $\mathbf{B} = 2\mathbf{B}_0\mu/(1 + \mu)$.

3.279. $\mathbf{B} = 3\mathbf{B}_0\mu/(2 + \mu)$.

3.280. $H_c = NI/l = 6$ kA/m.

3.281. $H \approx bB/\mu_0\pi d = 0.10$ kA/m.

3.282. When $b \ll R$, the permeability is $\mu \approx 2\pi RB/(\mu_0 NI - bB) = 3.7\cdot 10^3$.

3.283. $H = 0.06$ kA/m, $\mu_{max} \approx 1.0\cdot 10^4$.

3.284. From the theorem on circulation of the vector **H** we obtain

$$B \approx \frac{\mu_0 NI}{b} - \frac{\mu_0 \pi d}{b} H = 1.51 - 0.987H \text{ (kA/m)}.$$

Besides, B and H are interrelated as shown in Fig. 3.76. The required values of H and B must simultaneously satisfy both relations. Solving this system of equations by means of plotting, we obtain $H \approx 0.26$ kA/m, $B \approx 1.25$ T, and $\mu = B/\mu_0 H \approx 4\cdot 10^3$.

3.285. $F \approx {}^1/_2 \chi SB^2/\mu_0$.

3.286. (a) $x_m = 1/\sqrt{4a}$; (b) $\chi = \mu_0 F_{max}\sqrt{e/a}/VB_0^2 = 3.6\cdot 10^{-4}$.

3.287. $A \approx {}^1/_2 \chi VB^2/\mu_0$.

3.288. $\mathscr{E}_i = By\sqrt{8w/a}$.

3.289. $I = Bvl/(R + R_\mu)$, where $R_\mu = R_1R_2/(R_1 + R_2)$.

3.290. (a) $\Delta\varphi = {}^1/_2 \omega^2a^2m/e = 3.0$ nV; (b) $\Delta\varphi \approx {}^1/_2 \omega Ba^2 = 20$ mV.

3.291. $\int_A^C \mathbf{E}\, d\mathbf{r} = -{}^1/_2 \omega Bd^2 = -10$ mV.

3.292. $\mathscr{E}_i = {}^1/_2(-1)^n\ Ba\beta t$, where $n = 1,\ 2, \ldots$ is the number of the half-revolution that the loop performs at the given moment t. The plot $\mathscr{E}_i\ (t)$ is shown in Fig. 25 where $t_n = \sqrt{2\pi n/\beta}$.

3.293. $I_{\text{ind}} = \alpha/r$, where $\alpha = {}^1/_2\mu_0 lvI/\pi R$.

3.294. $\mathscr{E}_i = \frac{\mu_0}{4\pi} \frac{2Ia^2v}{x(x+a)}$.

3.295. $\mathscr{E}_i = {}^1/_2\ (\omega a^3B^3 + 2mg \sin \omega t)/aB$.

3.296. $v = \frac{mgR \sin \alpha}{B^2l^2}$.

3.297. $w = \frac{g \sin \alpha}{1 + l^2B^2C/m}$.

3.298. $\langle P \rangle = {}^1/_2\ (\pi\omega a^2B)^2/R$.

3.299. $B = {}^1/_2 qR/NS = 0.5$ T.

3.300. $q = \frac{\mu_0 aI}{2\pi R} \ln \frac{b+a}{b-a}$, i.e. is independent of L.

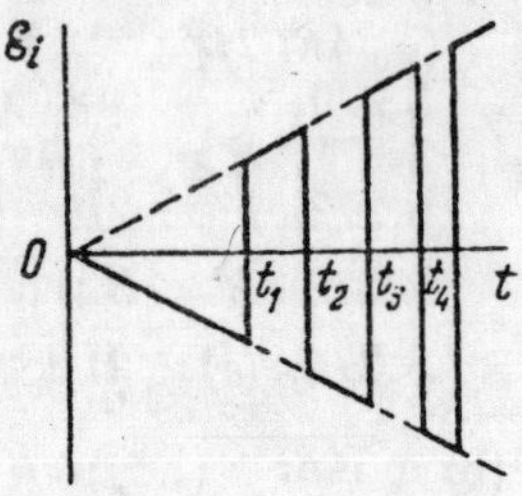

Fig. 25.

3.301. (a) $I = \frac{\mu_0 I_0 v}{2\pi R} \ln \frac{b}{a}$; (b) $F = \frac{v}{R}\left(\frac{\mu_0 I_0}{2\pi} \ln \frac{b}{a}\right)^2$.

3.302. (a) $s = v_0 mR/l^2B^2$, (b) $Q = {}^1/_2 mv_0^2$.

3.303. $v = \frac{F}{\alpha m}\ (1 - e^{-\alpha t})$, where $\alpha = B^2l^2/mR$.

3.304. (a) In the round conductor the current flows clockwise, there is no current in the connector; (b) in the outside conductor, clockwise; (c) in both round conductors, clockwise; no current in the connector, (d) in the left-hand side of the figure eight, clockwise.

3.305. $I = {}^1/_4 \omega B_0\ (a - b)/\rho = 0.5$ A.

3.306. $\mathscr{E}_{im} = {}^1/_3 \pi a^2 N \omega B_0$.

3.307. $\mathscr{E}_i = {}^3/_2 wl\ \dot{B} t^2 = 12$ mV.

3.308. $E = \begin{cases} {}^1/_2 \mu_0 n \dot{I} r & \text{for } r < a, \\ {}^1/_2 \mu_0 n \dot{I} a^2/r & \text{for } r > a. \end{cases}$

3.309. $I = {}^1/_4 \mu_0 nSd\dot{I}/\rho = 2$ mA, where ρ is the resistivity of copper.

3.310. $E = {}^1/_2 ab\ (\eta - 1)/(\eta + 1)$.

3.311. $\omega = -\frac{q}{2m} \mathbf{B}\ (t)$.

3.312. $F_{1\,max} = \frac{\mu_0 a^2 \mathscr{V}^2}{4rRlb^2}$.

3.313. $Q = {}^1/_3 a^2\tau^3/R$.

3.314. $I = {}^1/_4\ (b^2 - a^2)\ \beta h/\rho$.

3.315. $l = \sqrt{4\pi l_0 L/\mu_0} = 0.10$ km.

3.316. $L = \frac{\mu_0}{4\pi} \frac{mR}{l\rho\rho_0}$, where ρ and ρ_0 are the resistivity and the density of copper.

3.317. $t = -\frac{L}{R} \ln (1 - \eta) = 1.5$ s.

3.318. $\tau = \frac{\mu_0}{4\pi}\frac{m}{l\rho\rho_0} = 0.7$ ms, where ρ is the resistivity, ρ_0 is the density of copper.

3.319. $L_1 = \frac{\mu\mu_0}{2\pi}\ln\eta = 0.26$ μH/m.

3.320. $L = \frac{\mu_0}{2\pi}\mu N^2 a \ln\left(1+\frac{a}{b}\right)$.

3.321. $L_1 = \mu_0 h/b = 25$ nH/m.

3.322. $L_1 \approx \frac{\mu_0}{\pi}\ln\eta$.

3.323. (a) $I = \pi a^2 B/L$; (b) $A = {}^1/_2\pi^2 a^4 B^2/L$.

3.324. $I = I_0(1+\eta) = 2$ A.

3.325. $I = \frac{\pi a B}{\mu_0\left(\ln\frac{8a}{b} - 2\right)} = 50$ A.

3.326. $I = \frac{\mathscr{E}}{R}[1 + (\eta - 1)e^{-t\eta R/L}]$.

3.327. $I = \frac{\mathscr{E}}{R}(1 - e^{-tR/2L})$.

3.328. $I_1 = \frac{\mathscr{E}L_2}{R(L_1+L_2)}$, $\quad I_2 = \frac{\mathscr{E}L_1}{R(L_1+L_2)}$.

3.329. $L_{12} = \frac{\mu_0 b}{2\pi}\ln\left(1+\frac{a}{l}\right)$.

3.330. $L_{12} = \frac{\mu_0\mu h N}{2\pi}\ln\frac{b}{a}$.

3.331. (a) $L_{12} \approx {}^1/_2\mu_0\pi a^2/b$; (b) $\Phi_{21} = {}^1/_2\mu_0\pi a^2 I/b$.

3.332. $p_m = 2aRq/\mu_0 N$.

3.333. $L_{12} \approx {}^1/_2\mu_0\pi a^4/l^3$.

3.334. $I_2 = \frac{\alpha L_{12}}{R}(1 - e^{-tR/L_2})$.

3.335. $Q = \frac{L\mathscr{E}^2}{2R^2(1+R_0/R)} = 3$ μJ.

3.336. $W = {}^1/_2 N\Phi I = 0.5$ J.

3.337. $W = BH\pi^2 a^2 b = 2.0$ J, where $H = {}^1/_2\, NI/\pi b$.

3.338. (a) $W_{gap}/W_m \approx \mu b/\pi d = 3.0$; (b) $L \approx \frac{\mu_0 S N^2}{b + \pi d/\mu} = 0.15$ H.

3.339. $W_1 = \mu_0\lambda^2\omega^2 a^2/8\pi$.

3.340. $E = B/\sqrt{\varepsilon_0\mu_0} = 3\cdot 10^8$ V/m.

3.341. $w_m/w_e = \varepsilon_0\mu_0\omega^2 a^4/l^2 = 1.1\cdot 10^{-15}$

3.343. (a) $L_{total} = 2L$; (b) $L_{total} = L/2$.

3.344. $L_{12} = \sqrt{L_1 L_2}$.

3.346. $W_{12} = \frac{\mu_0\pi a^2}{2b} I_1 I_2\cos\theta$.

3.347. (a) $\mathbf{j}_d = -\mathbf{j}$; (b) $I_d = q/\varepsilon_0\varepsilon\rho$.

3.348. The displacement current should be taken into account in addition to the conduction current.

3.349. $E_m = I_m/\varepsilon_0\omega S = 7$ V/cm.

3.350. $H = H_m\cos(\omega t + \alpha)$, where $H_m = \frac{rV_m}{2d}\sqrt{\sigma^2 + (\varepsilon_0\varepsilon\omega)^2}$ and α is determined from the formula $\tan\alpha = \varepsilon_0\varepsilon\omega/\sigma$.

3.351. $j_d = \begin{cases} \frac{1}{2}\ddot{B}r & \text{for } r < R, \\ \frac{1}{2}\ddot{B}R^2/r & \text{for } r > R. \end{cases}$

Here $\ddot{B} = \mu_0 n I_m \omega^2 \sin \omega t$.

3.352. (a) $\mathbf{j}_d = \frac{2q\mathbf{v}}{4\pi r^3}$; (b) $\mathbf{j}_d = -\frac{q\mathbf{v}}{4\pi r^3}$.

3.353. $x_m = 0$, $j_{d\,max} = \frac{qv}{4\pi a^3}$.

3.354. $\mathbf{H} = \frac{q[\mathbf{vr}]}{4\pi r^3}$.

3.355. (a) If $\mathbf{B}(t)$, then $\nabla \times \mathbf{E} = -\partial \mathbf{B}/\partial t \neq 0$. The spatial derivatives of the field $\mathbf{E}$, however, may not be equal to zero ($\nabla \times \mathbf{E} \neq 0$) only in the presence of an electric field.

(b) If $\mathbf{B}(t)$, then $\nabla \times \mathbf{E} = -\partial \mathbf{B}/\partial t \neq 0$. But in the uniform field $\nabla \times \mathbf{E} = 0$.

(c) It is assumed that $\mathbf{E} = \mathbf{a} f(t)$, where $\mathbf{a}$ is a vector which is independent of the coordinates, $f(t)$ is an arbitrary function of time. Then $-\partial \mathbf{B}/\partial t = \nabla \times \mathbf{E} = 0$, that is the field $\mathbf{B}$ does not vary with time. Generally speaking, this contradicts the equation $\nabla \times \mathbf{H} = \partial \mathbf{D}/\partial t$ for in this case its left-hand side does not depend on time whereas its right-hand side does. The only exception is the case when $f(t)$ is a linear function. In this case the uniform field $\mathbf{E}$ can be time-dependent.

3.356. Let us find the divergence of the two sides of the equation $\nabla \times \mathbf{H} = \mathbf{j} + \partial \mathbf{D}/\partial t$. Since the divergence of a rotor is always equal to zero, we get $0 = \nabla \cdot \mathbf{j} + \frac{\partial}{\partial t}(\nabla \cdot \mathbf{D})$. It remains to take into account that $\nabla \cdot \mathbf{D} = \rho$.

3.357. Let us consider the divergence of the two sides of the first equation. Since the divergence of a rotor is always equal to zero, $\nabla \cdot (\partial \mathbf{B}/\partial t) = 0$ or $\frac{\partial}{\partial t}(\nabla \cdot \mathbf{B}) = 0$. Hence, $\nabla \cdot \mathbf{B} = \text{const}$ which does not contradict the second equation.

3.358. $\nabla \times \mathbf{E} = -[\boldsymbol{\omega}\mathbf{B}]$.

3.359. $\mathbf{E}' = [\mathbf{vB}]$.

3.360. $\sigma = \varepsilon_0 vB = 0.40$ pC/m^2.

3.361. $\rho = -2\varepsilon\omega B = -0.08$ nC/m^3, $\sigma = \varepsilon_0 a\omega B = 2$ pC/m^2.

3.362. $\mathbf{B} = \frac{\mu_0}{4\pi}\frac{q[\mathbf{vr}]}{r^3}$.

3.364. $\mathbf{E}' = b\mathbf{r}/r^2$, where r is the distance from the z' axis.

3.365. $\mathbf{B}' = \frac{a[\mathbf{rv}]}{c^2 r^2}$, where r is the distance from the z' axis.

3.367. (a) $E' = E\sqrt{\frac{1-\beta^2\cos^2\alpha}{1-\beta^2}} = 9$ kV/m; $\tan\alpha' = \frac{\tan\alpha}{\sqrt{1-\beta^2}}$, whence $\alpha \approx 51°$; (b) $B' = \frac{\beta E \sin\alpha}{c\sqrt{1-\beta^2}} = 14$ µT.

3.368. (a) $E' = \dfrac{\beta B \sin\alpha}{c\sqrt{1-\beta^2}} = 1.4$ nV/m;

(b) $B' = B\sqrt{\dfrac{1-\beta^2\cos^2\alpha}{1-\beta^2}} = 0.9$ T, $\alpha' \approx 51°$.

3.370. $B' = B\sqrt{1-(E/cB)^2} \approx 0.15$ mT.

3.371. Suppose the charge q moves in the positive direction of the x axis of the reference frame K. Let us pass into the frame K' at whose origin of coordinates this charge is at rest (the x and x' axes of the two frames coincide and the y and y' axes are parallel). In the frame K' the field of the charge has the simplest form: $\mathbf{E}' = \dfrac{1}{4\pi\varepsilon_0}\dfrac{q}{r'^3}\mathbf{r}'$, with the following components in the plane x, y

$$E'_x = \frac{1}{4\pi\varepsilon_0}\frac{q}{r'^3}x', \quad E'_y = \frac{1}{4\pi\varepsilon_0}\frac{q}{r'^3}y'.$$

Now let us make the reverse transition to the initial frame K. At the moment when the charge q passes through the origin of coordinates of the frame K, the x and y projections of the vector $\mathbf{r}$ are related to the x' and y' projections of the vector $\mathbf{r}'$ as

$$x = r\cos\theta = x'\sqrt{1-(v/c)^2}, \quad y = r\sin\theta = y'.$$

Besides, in accordance with the formulas that are reciprocal to Eqs. (3.6i),

$$E_x = E'_x, \quad E_y = E'_y/\sqrt{1-(v/c)^2}.$$

Solving simultaneously all these equations, we obtain

$$\mathbf{E} = E_x\mathbf{i} + E_y\mathbf{j} = \frac{1}{4\pi\varepsilon_0}\frac{q\mathbf{r}}{r^3}\frac{1-\beta^2}{(1-\beta^2\sin^2\theta)^{3/2}}.$$

Note that in this case ($\mathbf{v}$ = const) the vector $\mathbf{E}$ is collinear with the vector $\mathbf{r}$.

3.372. $v = \sqrt[3]{{}^9/_2\, ale/m} = 16$ km/s.

3.373. $\tan\alpha = \dfrac{al^2}{4}\sqrt{\dfrac{m}{2eV^3}}$.

3.374. (a) $x = 2E_0/a$; (b) $w = qE_0/m$.

3.375. $t = \dfrac{\sqrt{T(T+2m_0C^2)}}{ceE} = 3.0$ ns.

3.376. $w = \dfrac{eE}{m_0(1+T/m_0c^2)^3}$.

3.377. (a) $\tan\theta = \dfrac{eEt}{m_0v_0}\sqrt{1-(v_0/c)^2}$, where e and m_0 are the charge and the mass of a proton; (b) $v_x = v_0/\sqrt{1+(1-v_0^2/c^2)(eEt/m_0c^2)^2}$.

3.378. $\alpha = \arcsin\left(dB\sqrt{\dfrac{q}{2mV}}\right) = 30°$.

3.379. (a) $v = reB/m = 100$ km/s, $T = 2\pi m/eB = 6.5$ μs; (b) $v = c/\sqrt{1+(m_0c/reB)^2} = 0.51$ c, $T = \dfrac{2\pi m_0}{eB\sqrt{1-(v/c^2)}} = 4.1$ ns.

3.380. (a) $p = qrB$; $T = m_0c^2\left(\sqrt{1+(qrB/m_0c)^2}-1\right)$; (c) $w = \dfrac{c^2}{r\,[1+(m_0c/qrB)^2]}$.

3.381. $T = \eta m_0c^2$, 5 keV and 9 MeV respectively.

3.382. $\Delta l = 2\pi\sqrt{2mV/eB^2}\cos\alpha = 2.0$ cm.

3.383. $q/m = \dfrac{8\pi^2 V}{l^2\,(B_2-B_1)^2}$.

3.384. $r = 2\rho\,|\sin(\varphi/2)|$, where $\rho = \dfrac{mv}{eB}\sin\alpha$, $\varphi = \dfrac{leB}{mv\cos\alpha}$.

3.385. $r_{max} = ae^{v_0/b}$, where $b = \dfrac{\mu_0}{2\pi}\dfrac{e}{m}I$.

3.386. $v = \dfrac{V}{rB\ln(b/a)}$, $q/m = \dfrac{V}{r^2B^2\ln(b/a)}$.

3.387. (a) $y_n = \dfrac{2\pi^2 mEn^2}{qB^2}$; (b) $\tan\alpha = \dfrac{v_0B}{2\pi En}$.

3.388. $z = l\tan\sqrt{\dfrac{qB^2}{2mE}y}$; for $z \ll 1$ this equation reduces to $y = (2mE/ql^2B^2)\,z^2$.

3.389. $F = mEI/qB = 20$ μN.

3.390. $\Delta l = \dfrac{2\pi mE}{eB^2}\tan\varphi = 6$ cm.

3.391. $q/m = \dfrac{a\,(a+2b)\,B^2}{2E\Delta x}$.

3.392. (a) $x = a\,(\omega t - \sin\omega t)$; $y = a\,(1-\cos\omega t)$, where $a = mE/qB^2$, $\omega = qB/m$. The trajectory is a cycloid (Fig. 26). The

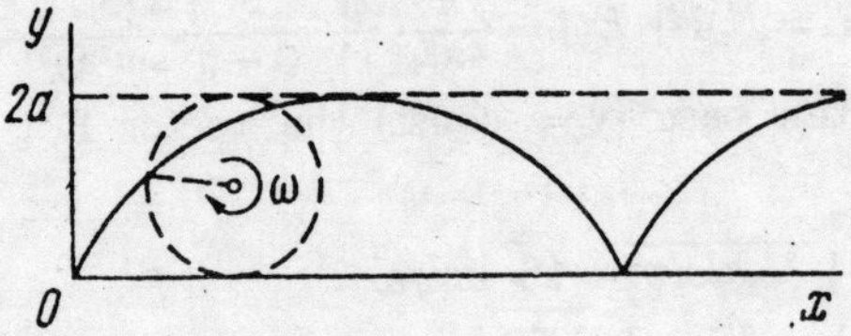

Fig. 26.

motion of the particle is the motion of a point located at the rim of a circle of radius a rolling without slipping along the x axis so that its centre travels with the velocity $v = E/B$; (b) $s = 8mE/qB^2$; (c) $\langle v_x\rangle = E/B$.

3.393. $V = 2\,\dfrac{e}{m}\left(\dfrac{\mu_0 I}{4\pi}\right)^2\ln\dfrac{a}{b}$.

3.394. $B \leqslant \dfrac{2b}{b^2-a^2}\sqrt{\dfrac{2m}{e}V}$.

3.395. $y = \dfrac{a}{2\omega}t\sin\omega t$, $x = \dfrac{a}{2\omega^2}(\sin\omega t - \omega t\cos\omega t)$, where $a = qE_m/m$. The trajectory has the form of unwinding spiral.

3.396. $V \gtrsim 2\pi^2\nu^2 mr\Delta r/e = 0.10$ MV.

3.397. (a) $T=\frac{(erB)^2}{2m}=12$ MeV; (b) $\nu_{min}=\frac{1}{\pi r}\sqrt{\frac{T}{2m}}=20$ MHz.

3.398. (a) $t=\frac{\pi^2\nu mr^2}{eV}=17$ μs; (b) $s\approx\frac{4\pi^3\nu^2mr^3}{3eV}=0.74$ km.

Instruction. Here $s\sim\sum_{n=1}^{N}v_n\sim\sum\sqrt{n}$, where v_n is the velocity of the particle after the nth passage across the accelerating gap. Since N is large, $\sum_1^N\sqrt{n}\approx\int_0^N\sqrt{n}\,dn$.

3.399. $n=2\pi\nu W/eBc^2=9$.

3.400. $\omega=\omega_0/\sqrt{1+at}$, where $\omega_0=qB/m$, $a=qB\Delta W/\pi m^2c^2$.

3.401. $v={}^1/_2rqB/m$, $\rho=r/2$.

3.402. $N=W/e\dot{\Phi}=5\cdot10^6$ revolutions, $s=2\pi rN=8\cdot10^3$ km.

3.403. On the one hand,

$$\frac{dp}{dt}=eE=\frac{e}{2\pi r}\frac{d\Phi}{dt},$$

where p is the momentum of the electron, r is the radius of the orbit, Φ is the magnetic flux acting inside the orbit.

On the other hand, dp/dt can be found after differentiating the relation $p=erB$ for $r=$ const. It follows from the comparison of the expressions obtained that $dB_0/dt={}^1/_2\,d\langle B\rangle/dt$. In particular, this condition will be satisfied if $B_0={}^1/_2\langle B\rangle$.

3.404. $r_0=\sqrt{2B_0/3a}$.

3.405. $dE/dr=\dot{B}(r_0)-{}^1/_2\langle\dot{B}\rangle=0$.

3.406. $\Delta W=2\pi r^2eB/\Delta t=0.10$ keV.

3.407. (a) $W=\left(\sqrt{1+(reB/m_0c)^2}-1\right)m_0c^2$; (b) $s=W\Delta t/reB$.

4.1. (a) See Fig. 27; (b) $(v_x/a\omega)^2+(x/a)^2=1$ and $w_x=-\omega^2x$.

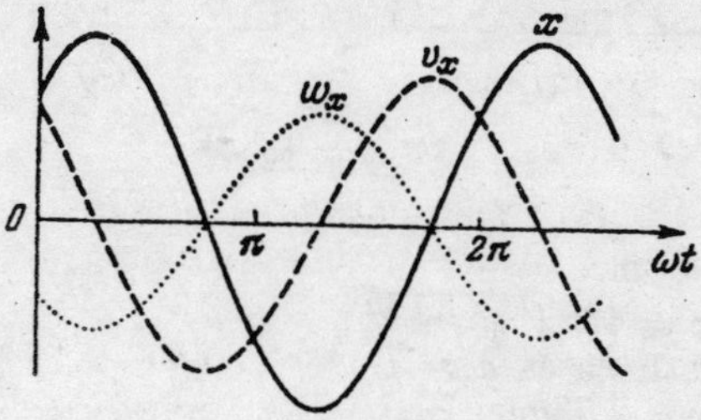

Fig. 27.

4.2. (a) The amplitude is equal to $a/2$, and the period is $T=\pi/\omega$, see Fig. 28*a*; (b) $v_x^2=4\omega^2x(a-x)$, see Fig. 28*b*.

4.3. $x=a\cos(\omega t+\alpha)=-29$ cm, $v_x=-81$ cm/s, where $a=\sqrt{x_0^2+(v_{x0}/\omega)^2}$, $\alpha=\arctan(-v_{x0}/\omega x_0)$.

4.4. $\omega=\sqrt{(v_1^2-v_2^2)/(x_2^2-x_1^2)}$, $a=\sqrt{(v_1^2x_2^2-v_2^2x_1^2)/(v_1^2-v_2^2)}$.

4.5. (a) $\langle v\rangle = 3a/T = 0.50$ m/s; (b) $\langle v\rangle = 6a/T = 1.0$ m/s.

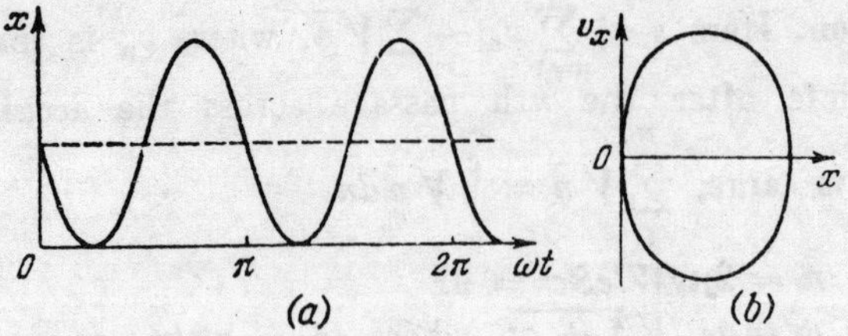

Fig. 28.

4.6. (a) $\langle v_x\rangle = \frac{2\sqrt{2}}{3\pi}a\omega$; (b) $|\langle \mathbf{v}\rangle| = \frac{2\sqrt{2}}{3\pi}a\omega$; (c) $\langle v\rangle = \frac{2(4-\sqrt{2})}{3\pi}a\omega$.

4.7. $s=\begin{cases} a\,[n+1-\cos(\omega t-n\pi/2)], & n \text{ is even,}\\ a\,[n+\sin(\omega t-n\pi/2)], & n \text{ is odd.}\end{cases}$

Here n is a whole number of the ratio $2\omega t/\pi$.

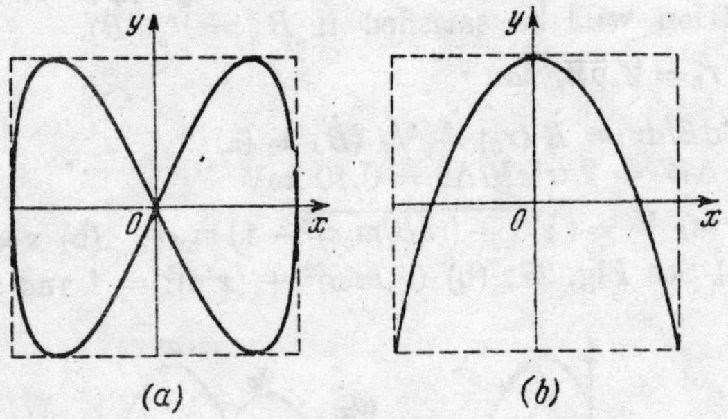

Fig. 29.

4.8. $s = 0.6$ m.

4.9. $dP/dx = 1/\pi\sqrt{a^2-x^2}$

4.10. In both cases $a = 7$.

4.11. $v_{max} = 2.73a\omega$.

4.12. 47.9 and 52.1 s^{-1}, 1.5 s.

4.13. 18 or 26 Hz.

4.14. (a) $x^2/a^2 + y^2/b^2 = 1$, clockwise; (b) $\mathbf{w} = -\omega^2\mathbf{r}$.

4.15. (a) $y^2 = 4x^2(1-x^2/a^2)$; (b) $y = a(1-2x^2/a^2)$. See Fig. 29.

4.16. $T = 2\pi\sqrt{m/a^2U_0}$.

4.17. $T = 4\pi a\sqrt{ma/b^2}$.

4.18. $T = \pi \sqrt{ml/F} = 0.2$ s.

4.19. $T = 2\pi \sqrt{\eta l / g(\eta - 1)} = 1.1$ s.

4.20. $T = 2\sqrt{l/g}\,[\pi/2 + \arcsin(\alpha/\beta)]$.

4.21. $t = \sqrt{\frac{2h}{w}}\,\frac{\sqrt{1+\eta} - \sqrt{1-\eta}}{1 - \sqrt{1-\eta}}$ where $\eta = w/g$.

4.22. $T = \sqrt{4\pi m/\rho g r^2} = 2.5$ s.

4.23. $T = 2\pi \sqrt{\eta(1-\eta)\, m/\varkappa} = 0.13$ s.

4.24. $T = 2\pi \sqrt{m/(\varkappa_1 + \varkappa_2)}$.

4.25. $T = 2\pi \sqrt{m/\varkappa}$, where $\varkappa = \varkappa_1 \varkappa_2/(\varkappa_1 + \varkappa_2)$.

4.26. $\omega = \sqrt{2T_0/ml}$.

4.27. $T = 2\pi \sqrt{m/S\rho g(1 + \cos\theta)} = 0.8$ s.

4.28. $T = \pi \sqrt{2l/kg} = 1.5$ s.

4.29. (a) $\ddot{x} + (g/R)\,x = 0$, where x is the displacement of the body relative to the centre of the Earth, R is its radius, g is the standard free-fall acceleration; (b) $\tau = \pi \sqrt{R/g} = 42$ min, (c) $v = \sqrt{gR} = 7.9$ km/s.

4.30. $T = 2\pi \sqrt{l/|\mathbf{g} - \mathbf{w}|} = 0.8$ s, where $|\mathbf{g} - \mathbf{w}| = \sqrt{g^2 + w^2 - 2gw\cos\beta}$.

4.31. $T = 2\pi/\sqrt{\varkappa/m - \omega^2} = 0.7$ s, $\omega \geqslant \sqrt{\varkappa/m} = 10$ rad/s.

4.32. $k = 4\pi^2 a/gT^2 = 0.4$.

4.33. (a) $\theta = 3.0° \cos 3.5t$; (b) $\theta = 4.5° \sin 3.5t$; (c) $\theta = 5.4° \cos(3.5t + 1.0)$. Here t is expressed in seconds.

4.34. $F = (m_1 + m_2)\,g \pm m_1 a\omega^2 = 60$ and 40 N.

4.35. (a) $F = mg\left(1 + \frac{a\omega^2}{g}\cos\omega t\right)$, see Fig. 30; (b) $a_{min} = g/\omega^2 = 8$ cm; (c) $a = \left(\omega\sqrt{2h/g} - 1\right) g/\omega^2 = 20$ cm.

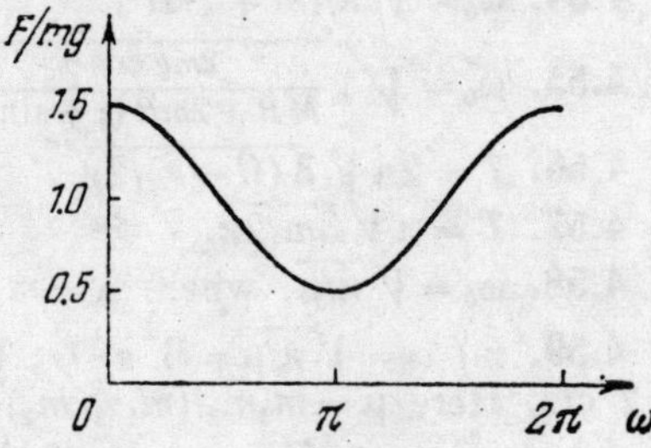

Fig. 30.

4.36. (a) $y = (1 - \cos\omega t)\, mg/\varkappa$, where $\omega = \sqrt{\varkappa/m}$; (b) $T_{max} = 2mg$, $T_{min} = 0$.

4.37. $(x/r_0)^2 + \alpha (y/v_0)^2 = 1$.

4.38. (a) $y = (1 - \cos\omega t)\, w/\omega^2$; (b) $y = (\omega t - \sin\omega t)\, \alpha/\omega^3$. Here $\omega = \sqrt{\varkappa/m}$.

4.39. $\Delta h_{max} = mg/k = 10$ cm, $E = m^2 g^2/2k = 4.8$ mJ.

4.40. $a = (mg/\varkappa)\sqrt{1 + 2h\varkappa/mg}$, $E = mgh + m^2 g^2/2\varkappa$.

4.41. $a = (mg/\varkappa)\sqrt{1 + 2h\varkappa/(m + M)g}$.

4.42. Let us write the motion equation in projections on the x and y axes:

$$\ddot{x} = \omega \dot{y}, \quad \ddot{y} = -\omega \dot{x}, \quad \text{where } \omega = a/m.$$

Integrating these equations, with the initial conditions taken into account, we get $x = (v_0/\omega)(1 - \cos\omega t)$, $y = (v_0/\omega)\sin\omega t$. Hence $(x - v_0/\omega)^2 + y^2 = (v_0/\omega)^2$. This is the equation of a circle of radius v_0/ω with the centre at the point $x_0 = v_0/\omega$, $y_0 = 0$.

4.43. Will increase $\sqrt{1 + {}^2/_5 (R/l)^2}$ times. It is taken into account here that the water (when in liquid phase) moves translationwise, and the system behaves as a *mathematical* pendulum.

4.44. $\omega = \sqrt{\frac{3g}{2l}\left(1 + \frac{2\varkappa l}{mg}\right)}$.

4.45. (a) $T = 2\pi\sqrt{l/3g} = 1.1$ s; (b) $E = {}^1/_2 mgl\alpha^2 = 0.05$ J.

4.46. $\varphi_m = \varphi_0\sqrt{1 + mR^2\dot{\varphi}_0^2/2k\varphi_0^2}$, $E = {}^1/_2 k\varphi_m^2$.

4.47. $\langle T\rangle = {}^1/_8 mgl\theta_0^2 + {}^1/_{12} ml^2\dot{\theta}_0^2$.

4.48. $T = 4\pi/\omega$.

4.49. $I = ml^2(\omega_2^2 - g/l)/(\omega_1^2 - \omega_2^2) = 0.8\ \mathrm{g\cdot m^2}$.

4.50. $\omega = \sqrt{(I_1\omega_1^2 + I_2\omega_2^2)/(I_1 + I_2)}$.

4.51. $x = l/2\sqrt{3}$, $T_{min} = 2\pi\sqrt{l/g\sqrt{3}}$.

4.52. $T = \pi\sqrt{2h/g}$, $l_{red} = h/2$.

4.53. $\omega_0 = \sqrt{3a\omega^2/2l}$.

4.54. $\omega_0 = \sqrt{\varkappa/(m + I/R^2)}$.

4.55. $\omega_0 = \sqrt{\frac{2mg\cos\alpha}{MR + 2mR(1 + \sin\alpha)}}$.

4.56. $T = 2\pi\sqrt{3(R - r)/2g}$.

4.57. $T = \pi\sqrt{3m/2\varkappa}$.

4.58. $\omega_0 = \sqrt{\varkappa/\mu}$, where $\mu = m_1m_2/(m_1 + m_2)$.

4.59. (a) $\omega = \sqrt{\varkappa/\mu} = 6\ \mathrm{s^{-1}}$; (b) $E = {}^1/_2\mu v_1^2 = 5$ mJ, $a = v_1/\omega = 2$ cm. Here $\mu = m_1m_2/(m_1 + m_2)$.

4.60. $T = 2\pi\sqrt{I'/k}$, where $I' = I_1I_2/(I_1 + I_2)$.

4.61. $\omega_2/\omega_1 = \sqrt{1 + 2m_O/m_C} \approx 1.9$, where m_O and m_C are the masses of oxygen and carbon atoms.

4.62. $\omega = S\sqrt{2\gamma p_0/mV_0}$, where γ is the adiabatic exponent.

4.63. $q = 4h\sqrt{\pi\varepsilon_0 mg(\eta^2 - 1)} = 2.0\ \mu\mathrm{C}$.

4.64. The induction of the field increased $\eta^2 = 25$ times.

4.65. $x = (v_0/\omega)\sin\omega t$, where $\omega = lB/\sqrt{mL}$.

4.66. $x = (1 - \cos\omega t)g/\omega^2$, where $\omega = lB/\sqrt{mL}$.

4.67. (a) a_0 and $a_0\omega$; (b) $t_n = \frac{1}{\omega}\left(\arctan\frac{\omega}{\beta} + n\pi\right)$, where $n = 0, 1, 2, \ldots$

4.68. (a) $\dot{\varphi}(0) = -\beta\varphi_0$, $\ddot{\varphi}(0) = (\beta^2 - \omega^2)\varphi_0$; (b) $t_n = \frac{1}{\omega}\left(\arctan\frac{\omega^2 - \beta^2}{2\beta\omega} + n\pi\right)$, where $n = 0, 1, 2, \ldots$

4.69. (a) $a_0 = \frac{|\dot{x}_0|}{\omega}$, $\alpha = \begin{cases} -\pi/2, & \text{when } \dot{x}_0 > 0, \\ +\pi/2, & \text{when } \dot{x}_0 < 0; \end{cases}$ (b) $a_0 = |x_0| \sqrt{1 + (\beta/\omega)^2}$, $\alpha = \arctan(-\beta/\omega)$, with $-\pi/2 < \alpha < 0$, if $x_0 > 0$ and $\pi/2 < \alpha < \pi$, if $x_0 < 0$.

4.70. $\beta = \omega \sqrt{\eta^2 - 1} = 5\ \text{s}^{-1}$.

4.71. (a) $v(t) = a_0 \sqrt{\omega^2 + \beta^2}\, e^{-\beta t}$; (b) $v(t) = |\dot{x}_0| \sqrt{1 + (\beta/\omega)^2}\, e^{-\beta t}$.

4.72. The answer depends on what is meant by the given question. The first oscillation attenuates faster in time. But if one takes the natural time scale, the period T, for each oscillation, the second oscillation attenuates faster during that period.

4.73. $\lambda = n\lambda_0 / \sqrt{1 + (1 - n^2)(\lambda_0/2\pi)^2} = 3.3$, $n' = \sqrt{1 + (2\pi/\lambda_c)^2} = 4.3$ times.

4.74. $T = \sqrt{(4\pi^2 + \lambda^2)\, \Delta x/g} = 0.70$ s.

4.75. $Q = \pi n / \ln \eta = 5 \cdot 10^2$.

4.76. $s \approx l(1 + e^{-\lambda/2})/(1 - e^{-\lambda/2}) = 2$ m.

4.77. $Q = {}^1\!/_2 \sqrt{\frac{4g\tau^2}{l \ln^2 \eta} - 1} = 1.3 \cdot 10^2$.

4.78. $T = \sqrt{{}^3\!/_2 (4\pi^2 + \lambda^2) R/g} = 0.9$ s.

4.79. $\omega = \sqrt{\frac{2\alpha}{mR^2} - \left(\frac{\pi\eta R^2}{m}\right)^2}$.

4.80. $\eta = 2\lambda h I / \pi R^4 T$.

4.81. $\tau = 2RI/a^4B^2$.

4.82. (a) $T = 2\pi \sqrt{m/\varkappa} = 0.28$ s; (b) $n = (x_0 - \Delta)/4\Delta = 3.5$ oscillations, here $\Delta = kmg/\varkappa$.

4.83. $x = \frac{F_0/m}{\omega^2 - \omega_0^2} (\cos \omega_0 t - \cos \omega t)$.

4.84. The motion equations and their solutions:

$$t \leqslant \tau,\ \ddot{x} + \omega_0^2 x = F/m, \qquad x = (1 - \cos \omega_0 t)\, F/k,$$

$$t \geqslant \tau,\ \ddot{x} + \omega_0^2 x = 0, \qquad x = a \cos[\omega_0 (t - \tau) + \alpha],$$

where $\omega_0^2 = k/m$, a and α are arbitrary constants. From the continuity of x and $\dot{x}$ at the moment $t = \tau$ we find the sought amplitude:

$$a = (2F/k)|\sin(\omega_0 t/2)|.$$

4.85. $\omega_{res} = \sqrt{\frac{1 - (\lambda/2\pi)^2}{1 + (\lambda/2\pi)^2} \frac{g}{\Delta l}}$, $a_{res} = \frac{\lambda F_0 \Delta l}{4\pi m g}\left(1 + \frac{4\pi^2}{\lambda^2}\right)$.

4.86. $\omega_{res} = \sqrt{(\omega_1^2 + \omega_2^2)/2} = 5.1 \cdot 10^2\ \text{s}^{-1}$.

4.87. (a) $\omega_0 = \sqrt{\omega_1 \omega_2}$; (b) $\beta = |\omega_2 - \omega_1|/2\sqrt{3}$, $\omega = \sqrt{\omega_1\omega_2 - (\omega_2 - \omega_1)^2/12}$.

4.88. $\eta = (1 + \lambda^2/4\pi^2)\,\pi/\lambda = 2.1$.

4.89. $A = \pi a F_0 \sin \varphi$.

4.90. (a) $Q = \frac{1}{2}\sqrt{\frac{4\omega^2\omega_0^2}{(\omega^2-\omega_0^2)^2\tan^2\varphi} - 1} = 2.2$; (b) $A = \pi m a^2 (\omega_0^2 - \omega^2)\tan\varphi = 6$ mJ. Here $\omega_0 = \sqrt{\varkappa/m}$.

4.91. (a) $\langle P\rangle = \frac{F_0^2\beta\omega^2/m}{(\omega_0^2-\omega^2)^2+4\beta^2\omega^2}$; (b) $\omega = \omega_0$, $\langle P\rangle_{max} = F_0^2/4\beta m$.

4.92. $\frac{\langle P\rangle_{max} - \langle P\rangle}{\langle P\rangle_{max}} = \frac{100}{\eta^2-1}$ %.

4.43. (a) $A = -\pi\varphi_m N_m \sin\alpha$; (b) $Q = \frac{\sqrt{(\cos\alpha + 2\omega^2 I\varphi_m/N_m)^2 - 1}}{2\sin\alpha}$.

4.94. $\omega = \sqrt{ne^2/\varepsilon_0 m} = 1.65\cdot 10^{16}$ s^{-1}.

4.95. $V^2 + I^2 L/C = V_m^2$.

4.96. (a) $I = I_m \sin\omega_0 t$, where $I_m = V_m\sqrt{C/L}$, $\omega_0 = 1/\sqrt{LC}$; (b) $\mathscr{E}_S = V_m/\sqrt{2}$.

4.97. $A = (\eta^2 - 1)\,W$.

4.98. (a) $T = 2\pi\sqrt{L(C_1+C_2)} = 0.7$ ms; (b) $I_m = V\sqrt{(C_1+C_2)/L} = 8$ A.

4.99. $V = \frac{1}{2}(1 \pm \cos\omega t)\,V_0$, where the plus sign refers to the left-hand capacitor, and the minus sign to the right-hand one; $\omega = \sqrt{2/LC}$.

4.100. $I = \frac{\Phi}{L}\cos(t/\sqrt{LC})$.

4.101. (a) $t_n = \frac{\pi n}{\omega}$; (b) $t_n = \frac{1}{\omega}\left[\arctan\left(-\frac{\beta}{\omega}\right) + \pi n\right]$. Here $n = 0, 1, 2, \ldots$

4.102. $V_0/V_m = \sqrt{1 - \frac{R^2C}{4L}}$.

4.103. $V_C = I_m\sqrt{L/C}\,e^{-\beta t}\sin(\omega t + \alpha)$ with $\tan\alpha = \omega/\beta$; $V_C(0) = I_m\sqrt{\frac{L}{C(1+\beta^2/\omega^2)}}$.

4.104. $W_L/W_C = L/CR^2 = 5$.

4.105. $L = L_1 + L_2$, $R = R_1 + R_2$.

4.106. $t = \frac{Q}{\pi\nu}\ln\eta = 0.5$ s.

4.107. $n = \frac{1}{2\pi}\sqrt{\frac{4L}{CR^2} - 1} = 16$.

4.108. $\frac{\omega_0 - \omega}{\omega_0} = 1 - \frac{1}{\sqrt{1 + 1/(2Q)^2}} \approx \frac{1}{8Q^2} = 0.5\%$.

4.109. (a) $W_0 = \frac{1}{2}\mathscr{E}^2(L + CR^2)/(r+R)^2 = 2.0$ mJ; (b) $W = W_0 e^{-tR/L} = 0.10$ mJ.

4.110. $t \approx \frac{Q}{2\pi\nu_0}\ln\eta = 1.0$ ms.

4.111. (a) $\omega = \sqrt{\frac{1}{LC} - \frac{1}{4R^2C^2}}$; (b) $Q = \frac{1}{2}\sqrt{\frac{4R^2C}{L} - 1}$. When solving the problem, it should be taken into account that $dq/dt = I - I'$, where q is the charge of the capacitor, I is the current in the coil winding, I' is the leakage current ($I' = V/R$).

4.112. $Q=\frac{V^2 m}{2\langle P\rangle}\sqrt{\frac{C}{L}}=1.0\cdot10^2$.

4.113. $\langle P\rangle = R\,\langle I^2\rangle = {}^1/_2 R I_m^2 = 20$ mW.

4.114. $\langle P\rangle = {}^1/_2 RCV_m^2/L = 5$ mW.

4.115. $\omega=\sqrt{\frac{1}{LC}-\frac{1}{4R^2C^2}}$; $R<\frac{1}{2}\sqrt{\frac{L}{C}}$.

4.116. $\frac{1}{L_1}+\frac{1}{L_2}=\frac{1}{L}$ and $\frac{1}{R_1}+\frac{1}{R_2}=\frac{1}{R}$.

4.117. $I=\frac{V_0}{L}te^{-t/\sqrt{LC}}$; $I=I_{max}=\frac{V_0}{e}\sqrt{\frac{C}{L}}$ at the moment $t_m=\sqrt{LC}$.

4.118. $I=\frac{V_m}{\sqrt{R^2+\omega^2L^2}}[\cos(\omega t-\varphi)-\cos\varphi\cdot e^{-tR/L}]$, $\tan\varphi=\omega L/R$.

4.119. $I=\frac{V_m}{\sqrt{R^2+1/(\omega C)^2}}[\cos(\omega t-\varphi)-\cos\varphi\cdot e^{-t/RC}]$, $\tan\varphi=-\frac{1}{\omega RC}$.

4.120. The current lags behind the voltage by phase angle φ, defined by the equation $\tan\varphi=\frac{\mu_0\pi^2\nu a}{4n\rho}$.

4.121. The current is ahead of the voltage by the phase angle $\varphi=60°$, defined by the equation $\tan\varphi=\sqrt{(V_m/RI_m)^2-1}$.

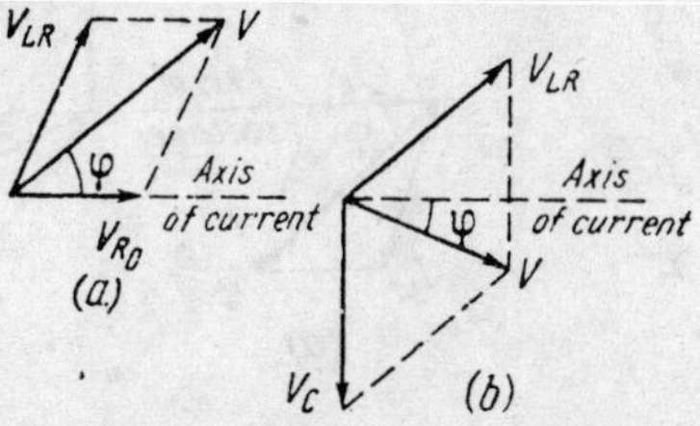

Fig. 31.

4.122. (a) $V'=V_0+V_m\cos(\omega t-\alpha)$, where $V_m=V_0/\sqrt{1+(\omega RC)^2}$, $\alpha=\arctan(\omega RC)$; (b) $RC=\sqrt{\eta^2-1}/\omega=22$ ms.

4.123. See Fig. 31.

4.124. (a) $I_m=V_m/\sqrt{R^2+(\omega L-1/\omega C)^2}=4.5$ A; (b) $\tan\varphi=\frac{\omega L-1/\omega C}{R}$, $\varphi=-60°$ (the current is ahead of the voltage); (c) $V_C=I_m/\omega C=0.65$ kV, $V_L=I_m\sqrt{R^2+\omega^2L^2}=0.50$ kV.

4.125. (a) $\omega=\sqrt{\omega_0^2-2\beta^2}$; (b) $\omega=\omega_0^2/\sqrt{\omega_0^2-2\beta^2}$, where $\omega_0^2=1/LC$, $\beta=R/2L$.

4.126. For $C=\frac{1}{\omega^2L}=28$ μF; $V_L=V_m\sqrt{1+(\omega L/R)^2}=0.54$ kV; $V_C=V_m\omega L/R=0.51$ kV.

4.127. $I=I_m\cos(\omega t+\varphi)$, where $I_m=\frac{V_m}{R}\sqrt{1+(\omega RC)^2}$ and $\tan\varphi=\omega RC$.

4.128. $\omega_0=\sqrt{\frac{L_2}{C(L_1L_2-L_{12}^2)}}$.

4.129. $Q=\sqrt{n^2-1/4}$.

4.130. $Q=\sqrt{\frac{\eta^2-1}{(n-1)^2}-\frac{1}{4}}$.

4.131. (a) $\omega_0=\sqrt{\omega_1\omega_2}$; (b) $Q=\sqrt{\frac{\omega_1\omega_2(n^2-1)}{(\omega_2-\omega_1)^2}-\frac{1}{4}}$.

4.133. $I_0/I = \sqrt{1 + (Q^2 + 1/4)(\eta^2 - 1)^2/\eta^2}$, 2.2 and 19 respectively.
4.134. $t = {}^1/_2 \pi t_0$.
4.135. (a) $I = \frac{2}{\sqrt{3}} I_0 \approx 1.15 I_0$; (b) $I = \frac{\pi}{\sqrt{8}} I_0 \approx 1.11 I_0$.
4.136. $\nu = \frac{R}{2\pi L}\sqrt{\eta - 1} = 2$ kHz.
4.137. The current lags behind the voltage by the phase angle $\varphi = \arccos\sqrt{1 - (X_L/Z)^2} \approx 37°$, $P = \frac{V^2}{Z^2}\sqrt{Z^2 - X_L^2} = 0.16$ kW.
4.138. For $R = \omega L - r = 0.20$ kΩ; $P_{max} = \frac{V^2}{2\omega L} = 0.11$ kW.
4.139. Increased by $\sqrt{n} - 1 \approx 30\%$.
4.140. For $Q \gg 1$ the ratio is $\Delta\omega/\omega_0 \approx {}^1/_2\sqrt{n - 1}/Q = 0.5\%$.

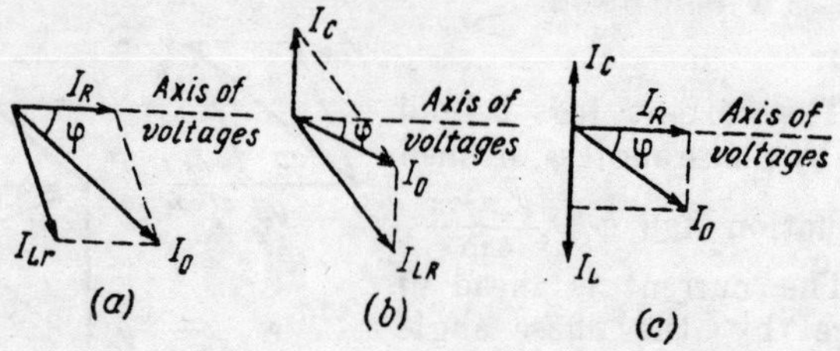

Fig. 32.

4.141. $P_2 = {}^1/_2 (V^2 - V_1^2 - V_2^2)/R = 30$ W.
4.142. $P_1 = {}^1/_2 (I^2 - I_1^2 - I_2^2) R = 2.5$ W.
4.143. $Z = R/\sqrt{1 + (\omega CR)^2} = 40$ Ω.
4.144. See Fig. 32.
4.145. (a) $\omega_{res} = \sqrt{\frac{1}{LC} - \frac{R^2}{L^2}} = 3 \cdot 10^4$ rad/s; (b) $I = VRC/L = 3$ mA, $I_L = V\sqrt{C/L} = 1.0$ A, $I_C = V\sqrt{\frac{C}{L} - \left(\frac{RC}{L}\right)^2} = 1.0$ A.
4.146. $\tan\varphi = \frac{\omega C(R^2 + \omega^2 L^2) - \omega L}{R}$.
4.147. $Z = \sqrt{\frac{R^2 + \omega^2 L^2}{(\omega CR)^2 + (1 - \omega^2 CL)^2}}$.
4.149. $\langle F_x \rangle = \frac{\omega^2 L_2 L_{12} I_0^2}{2(R^2 + \omega^2 L_2^2)} \frac{\partial L_{12}}{\partial x}$.
4.150. $t = \frac{2l}{\alpha(\sqrt{T_1} + \sqrt{T_2})}$.
4.151. $\Delta\varphi = \frac{\omega}{v} \mid (x_1 - x_2)\cos\alpha + (y_1 - y_2)\cos\beta + (z_1 - z_2)\cos\gamma \mid$.
4.152. $\mathbf{k} = \omega\left(\frac{\mathbf{e}_x}{v_1} + \frac{\mathbf{e}_y}{v_2} + \frac{\mathbf{e}_z}{v_3}\right)$.
4.153. $\xi = a\cos[(1 - V/v)\omega t - kx']$, where $v = \omega/k$.
4.155. (a) $a/\lambda = 5.1 \cdot 10^{-5}$; (b) $v_m = 11$ cm/s, $3.2 \cdot 10^{-4}$; (c) $(\partial\xi/\partial x)_m = 3.2 \cdot 10^{-4}$, $(\partial\xi/\partial t)_m = v(\partial\xi/\partial x)_m$, where $v = 0.34$ km/s is the velocity of the wave.

4.156. See Fig. 33.

4.157. $\Delta\varphi = -\frac{2\pi}{\gamma\lambda}\ln(1-\eta) \approx \frac{2\pi\eta}{\gamma\lambda} = 0.3$ rad.

4.158. $\mathbf{r} = (a_1\mathbf{r}_1 + a_2\mathbf{r}_2)/(a_1 + a_2)$.

4.159. (a) $\gamma = \frac{\ln(\eta r_0/r)}{r - r_0} = 0.08\ \text{m}^{-1}$; (b) $v_m = \frac{2\pi\nu a_0}{\eta} = 15$ cm/s.

4.160. (a) See Fig. 34*a*. The particles of the medium at the points lying on the solid straight lines ($y = x \pm n\lambda$, $n = 0, 1, 2, \ldots$)

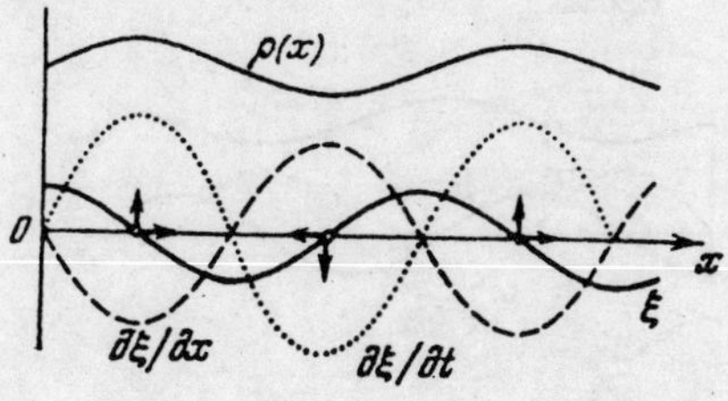

Fig. 33.

oscillate with maximum amplitude, those on the dotted lines do not oscillate at all.

(b) See Fig. 34*b*. The particles of the medium at the points lying on the straight lines $y = x \pm n\lambda$, $y = x \pm (n \pm 1/2)\lambda$ and $y = x \pm (n \pm 1/4)\lambda$ oscillate respectively along those lines, at

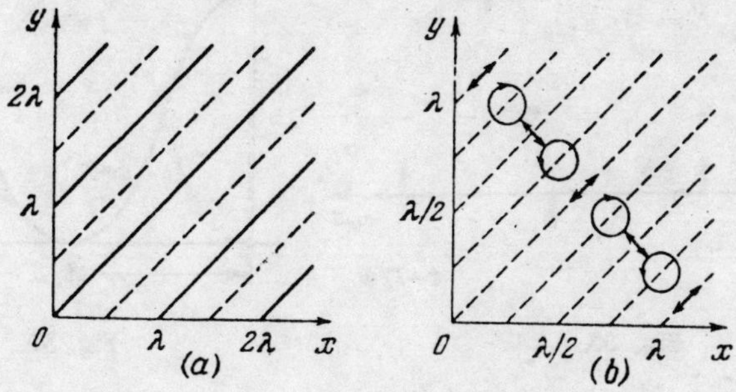

Fig. 34.

right angles to them, or move along the circles (here $n = 0, 1, 2, \ldots$). At all other points the particles move along the ellipses.

4.161. $\langle w \rangle = {}^2/_3 w_0$.

4.162. $\langle \Phi \rangle = 2\pi l^2 I_0 \left(1 - \frac{1}{\sqrt{1+(R/l)^2}}\right) = 20\ \mu\text{W}$.

4.163. $\langle \Phi \rangle = P/\sqrt{1+(2R/h)^2} = 0.07$ W.

4.164. Fee Fig. 35, for (a) and (b); see Fig. 36 for (c).

4.165. (a) $w_p = {}^1/_2\rho a^2\omega^2 \sin^2 kx \cdot \cos^2 \omega t$; (b) $w_k = {}^1/_2\rho a^2\omega^2 \times \cos^2 kx \cdot \sin^2 \omega t$. See Fig. 37.

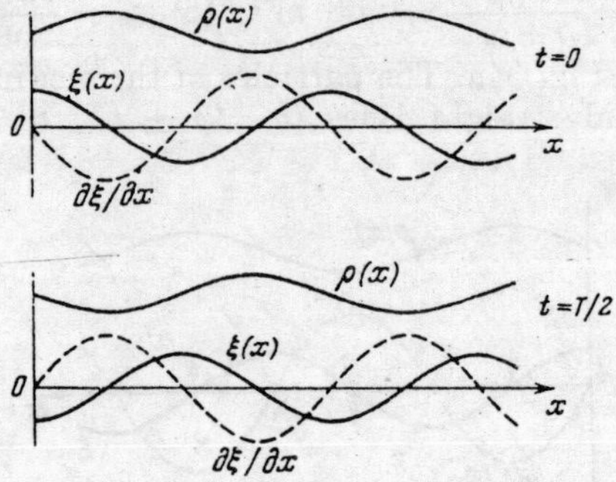

Fig. 35.

4.166. $a_{max} = 5$ mm; to the third overtone.

4.167. $\frac{\nu_2}{\nu_1} = \sqrt{\frac{\eta_2(1+\eta_1)}{\eta_1(1+\eta_2)}} = 1.4$.

4.168. Will increase $\eta = \frac{\sqrt{1-\Delta T/T}}{1+\Delta l/l} = 2$ times.

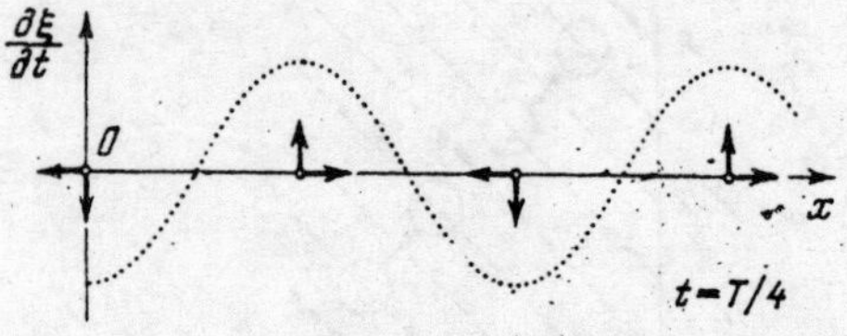

Fig. 36.

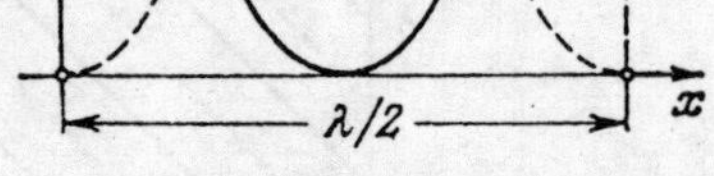

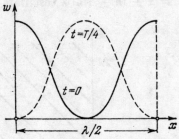

Fig. 37.

4.169. $v = 2l\nu = 0.34$ km/s.

4.170. (a) $\nu_n = \frac{v}{4l}(2n+1)$, six oscillations; (b) $\nu_n = \frac{v}{2l}(n+1)$, also six oscillations. Here $n = 0, 1, 2, \ldots$

4.171. $\nu_n = \frac{2n+1}{2l}\sqrt{\frac{E}{\rho}} = 3.8(2n+1)$ kHz; four oscillations with frequencies 26.6, 34.2, 41.8, and 49.4 kHz.

4.172. (a) $T_{max} = {}^1/_4 m\omega^2 a^2_{max}$; (b) $\langle T \rangle = {}^1/_8 m\omega^2 a^2_{max}$.

4.173. $W = {}^1/_4 \pi S\rho\omega^2 a^2/k$.

4.174. $\nu = 2\nu_0 vu/(v^2 - u^2) \approx 2\nu_0 u/v = 1.0$ Hz.

4.175. $u = \frac{v\nu_0}{\nu}\left(\sqrt{1+(\nu/\nu_0)^2}-1\right) \approx \frac{v\nu}{2\nu_0} = 0.5$ m/s.

4.176. $\omega = \frac{\nu_0 v}{a\Delta\nu}\left(\sqrt{1+(\Delta\nu/\nu_0)^2}-1\right) = 34\ \text{s}^{-1}$.

4.177. $\nu = \nu_0/\sqrt{1+2wt/v} = 1.35$ kHz.

4.178. (a) $\nu = \nu_0/(1-\eta^2) = 5$ kHz; (b) $r = l\sqrt{1+\eta^2} = 0.32$ km.

4.179. Decreases by $2u/(v+u) = 2.0\%$.

4.180. $\nu = 2\nu_0 u/(v+u) = 0.60$ Hz.

4.181. $\gamma = \frac{\ln(\eta r_1^2/r_2^2)}{2(r_2-r_1)} = 6\cdot 10^{-3}\ \text{m}^{-1}$.

4.182. (a) $L' = L - 20\gamma x \log e = 50$ dB; (b) $x = 0.30$ km.

4.183. (a) $L = L_0 + 20\log(r_0/r) = 36$ dB; (b) $r > 0.63$ km.

4.184. $\beta = \ln(r_B/r_A)/[\tau + (r_B - r_A)/v] = 0.12\ \text{s}^{-1}$.

4.185. (a) Let us consider the motion of a plane element of the medium of thickness dx and unit area of cross-section. In accordance with Newton's second law $\rho\, dx\ddot{\xi} = -dp$, where dp is the pressure increment over the length dx. Recalling the wave equation $\ddot{\xi} = v^2(\partial^2\xi/\partial x^2)$, we can write the foregoing equation as

$$\rho v^2 \frac{\partial^2\xi}{\partial x^2}dx = -dp.$$

Integrating this equation, we get

$$\Delta p = -\rho v^2\frac{\partial\xi}{\partial x} + \text{const}.$$

In the absence of a deformation (a wave) the surplus pressure is $\Delta p = 0$. Hence, const = 0.

4.186. $\langle\Phi\rangle = \pi R^2(\Delta p)_m^2/2\rho v\lambda = 11$ mW.

4.187. (a) $(\Delta p)_m = \sqrt{\rho v P/2\pi r^2} = 5$ Pa, $(\Delta p)_m/p = 5\cdot 10^{-5}$; (b) $a = (\Delta p)_m/2\pi\nu\rho v = 3\,\mu\text{m}$, $a/\lambda = 5\cdot 10^{-6}$.

4.188. $P = 4\pi r^2 e^{2\gamma r} I_0\cdot 10^L = 1.4$ W, where L is expressed in bels.

4.189. $\Delta\lambda = (1/\sqrt{\varepsilon}-1)c/\nu = -50$ m.

4.190. $t = 2(\sqrt{\varepsilon_1}-\sqrt{\varepsilon_2})\, l/c\ln(\varepsilon_1/\varepsilon_2)$.

4.191. $j/j_{dis} = \sigma/2\pi\nu\varepsilon\varepsilon_0 = 2$.

4.192. $\mathbf{H} = \frac{1}{k}\sqrt{\varepsilon_0/\mu_0}\,[\mathbf{k}\mathbf{E}_m]\cos(ckt)$, where c is the velocity of the wave in vacuum.

4.193. (a) $\mathbf{H} = \mathbf{e}_z E_m\sqrt{\varepsilon_0/\mu_0}\cos kx = -0.30\mathbf{e}_z$; (b) $\mathbf{H} = \mathbf{e}_z E_m\sqrt{\varepsilon_0/\mu_0}\cos(ckt_0 - kx) = 0.18\mathbf{e}_z$. Here $\mathbf{e}_z$ is the unit vector of the z axis, H is expressed in A/m.

4.194. $\mathcal{E}_m = 2\pi\nu l^2 E_m/c = 13$ mV.

4.196. $\langle\mathbf{S}\rangle = \frac{1}{2}\mathbf{k}\varepsilon_0 c^2 E_m^2/\omega$.

4.197. (a) $j_{dis} = \pi\sqrt{2}\varepsilon_0\nu E_m = 0.20$ mA/m²; (b) $\langle S\rangle = \frac{1}{2}\varepsilon_0 c E_m^2 = 3.3\ \mu\text{W/m}^2$.

4.198. Since $t \gg T$, where T is the period of oscillations, $W = \frac{1}{2}\sqrt{\varepsilon\varepsilon_0/\mu_0}E^2 m\pi R^2 t = 5$ kJ.
4.199. $\mathbf{B} = \mathbf{B}_m \sin kx \cdot \sin \omega t$, where $\mathbf{B}_m \perp \mathbf{E}_m$, with $B_m = E_m/c$.
4.200. $S_x = \frac{1}{4}\varepsilon_0 c E_m^2 \sin 2kx \cdot \sin 2\omega t$, $\langle S_x \rangle = 0$.
4.201. $W_m/W_e = \frac{1}{8}\varepsilon_0\mu_0\omega^2 R^2 = 5.0 \cdot 10^{-15}$.
4.202. $W_e/W_m = \frac{1}{8}\varepsilon_0\mu_0\omega^2 R^2 = 5.0 \cdot 10^{-15}$.
4.204. $\Phi_S = I^2 R$.
4.205. $S = I^2 \sqrt{m/2eU}/4\pi^2\varepsilon_0 r^2$.
4.207. To the left.
4.208. $\Phi = VI$.
4.209. $\langle \Phi \rangle = \frac{1}{2}V_0 I_0 \cos \varphi$.
4.211. The electric dipole moment of the system is $\mathbf{p} = \sum e\mathbf{r}_i = (e/m) M\mathbf{r}_C$, where M is the mass of the system, $\mathbf{r}_C$ is the radius vector of its centre of inertia. Since the radiation power $P \propto \ddot{\mathbf{p}}^2 \propto \ddot{\mathbf{r}}_C^2$, and in our case $\ddot{\mathbf{r}}_C = 0$, $P = 0$ too.
4.212. $\langle P \rangle = \frac{1}{4\pi\varepsilon_0}\frac{e^2 a^2 \omega^4}{3c^3} = 5 \cdot 10^{-15}$ W.
4.213. $P = \frac{1}{(4\pi\varepsilon_0)^3}\frac{2}{3c^3}\left(\frac{qe^2}{mR^2}\right)^2$.
4.214. $\Delta W \approx \frac{1}{(4\pi\varepsilon_0)^3}\frac{\pi e^4 q^2}{3c^3 m^2 v b^3}$.
4.215. $\Delta W/T = \frac{1}{3}e^3 B/\varepsilon_0 c^3 m^2 = 2 \cdot 10^{-18}$.
4.216. $T = T_0 e^{-\alpha t}$, where $\alpha = \frac{1}{3}e^4 B^2/\pi\varepsilon_0 c^3 m^3$. After $t_0 = \frac{1}{\alpha} =$

$$= \begin{cases} 2.5 \text{ s} & \text{for the electron,} \\ 1.6 \cdot 10^{10} \text{ s} = 0.5 \cdot 10^3 \text{ years} & \text{for the proton.} \end{cases}$$

4.217. $S_1/S_2 = \tan^2(\omega l/c) = 3$.
4.218. (a) Suppose that t is the moment of time when the particle is at a definite point x, y of the circle, and t' is the moment when the information about that reaches the point P. Denoting the observed values of the y coordinate at the point P by y' (see Fig. 4.40), we shall write

$$t' = t + \frac{l - x(t)}{c}, \quad y'(t') = y(t).$$

The sought acceleration is found by means of the double differentiation of y' with respect to t':

$$\frac{dy'}{dt'} = \frac{dy}{dt'} = \frac{dy}{dt}\frac{dt}{dt'}, \qquad \frac{d^2y}{dt'^2} = \frac{dt}{dt'}\frac{d}{dt}\left(\frac{dy'}{dt'}\right) = \frac{v^2}{R}\frac{v/c - y/R}{(1 - vy/cR)^3},$$

where the following relations are taken into account: $x = R \sin \omega t$, $y = R \cos \omega t$, and $\omega = v/R$.

(b) Energy flow density of electromagnetic radiation S is proportional to the square of the y projection of the observed acceleration of the particle. Consequently, $S_1/S_2 = (1 + v/c)^4/(1 - v/c)^4$.
4.219. $\langle P \rangle = \frac{8}{3}\pi r^2 S_0$.
4.220. $\langle w \rangle = \frac{3}{8}P_0/\pi r^2 c$.
4.221. $P = \frac{1}{6}p^2\omega^4/\pi\varepsilon_0 c^3$.

4.222. $\langle P\rangle/\langle S\rangle = (e^2/m)^2\mu_0^2/6\pi$.

4.223. $\langle P\rangle/\langle S\rangle = \frac{\mu_0^2}{6\pi}\frac{(e^2/m)^2\,\omega^4}{(\omega_0^2-\omega^2)^2}$.

4.224. $R = 3P/16\pi c\gamma\rho M_C \approx 0.6$ µm.

5.1. (a) 3 and 9 mW; (b) $\Phi = {}^1/_2\,(V_1 + V_2)\,\Phi_e/A = 1.6$ lm, where $A = 1.6$ mW/lm, V_1 and V_2 are the values of relative spectral response of an eye for the given wavelengths.

5.2. $E_m^2 = \sqrt{\mu_0/\varepsilon_0}\,A\Phi/2\pi r^2 V_\lambda$, hence $E_m = 1.1$ V/m, $H_m = 3.0$ mA/m. Here $A = 1.6$ mW/lm, V_λ is the relative spectral response of an eye for the given wavelength.

5.3. (a) $\langle E\rangle = {}^1/_2 E_0$; (b) $\langle E\rangle = \frac{1-\sqrt{1-(R/l)^2}}{1-R/l}\,\frac{I}{R^2} = 50$ lx.

5.4. $M = {}^2/_3\pi L_0$.

5.5. (a) $\Phi = \pi L\Delta S\sin^2\theta$; (b) $M = \pi L$.

5.6. $h \approx R$, $E = LS/4R^2 = 40$ lx.

5.7. $I = I_0/\cos^3\theta$, $\Phi = \pi I_0 R^2/h^2 = 3\cdot 10^2$ lm.

5.8. $E_{max} = (9/16\pi\sqrt{3})\,\rho ES/R^2 = 0.21$ lx, at the distance $R/\sqrt{3}$ from the ceiling.

5.9. $E = \pi L$.

5.10. $E = \pi L$.

5.11. $M = E_0\,(1 + h^2/R^2) = 7\cdot 10^2$ lm/m^2.

5.12. $E_0 = \pi LR^2/h^2 = 25$ lx.

5.13. $\mathbf{e}' = \mathbf{e} - 2(\mathbf{en})\,\mathbf{n}$.

5.14. Suppose $\mathbf{n}_1$, $\mathbf{n}_2$, $\mathbf{n}_3$ are the unit vectors of the normals to the planes of the given mirrors, and $\mathbf{e}_0$, $\mathbf{e}_1$, $\mathbf{e}_2$, $\mathbf{e}_3$ are the unit vectors of the incident ray and the rays reflected from the first, second, and the third mirror. Then (see the answer to the foregoing problem): $\mathbf{e}_1 = \mathbf{e}_0 - 2(\mathbf{e}_0\mathbf{n}_1)\,\mathbf{n}_1$, $\mathbf{e}_2 = \mathbf{e}_1 - 2(\mathbf{e}_1\mathbf{n}_2)\,\mathbf{n}_2$, $\mathbf{e}_3 = \mathbf{e}_2 - 2(\mathbf{e}_2\mathbf{n}_3)\,\mathbf{n}_3$. Summing termwise the left-hand and right-hand sides of these expressions, it can be readily shown that $\mathbf{e}_3 = -\mathbf{e}_0$.

5.15. $\theta_1 = \arctan n = 53°$.

5.16. $n_1/n_2 = 1/\sqrt{\eta^2-1} = 1.25$.

5.17. $x = [1 - \sqrt{(1-\sin^2\theta)/(n^2-\sin^2\theta)}]\,d\sin\theta = 3.1$ cm.

5.18. $h' = (hn^2\cos^3\theta)/(n^2 - \sin^2\theta)^{3/2}$.

5.21. $\Theta = 83°$.

5.22. From 37 to 58°.

5.23. $\alpha = 8.7°$.

5.24. $\Delta\alpha = \frac{2\sin(\Theta/2)}{\sqrt{1-n^2\sin^2(\Theta/2)}}\,\Delta n = 0.44°$.

5.27. (a) $f = l\beta/(1-\beta^2) = 10$ cm; (b) $f = l\beta_1\beta_2/(\beta_2-\beta_1) = 2.5$ cm.

5.28. $I' = \rho I_0 f^2\,(f-s)^2 = 2.0\cdot 10^3$ cd.

5.29. Suppose S is a point source of light and S' its image (Fig. 38). According to Fermat's principle the optical paths of all rays originating at S and converging at S' are equal. Let us draw circles with the centres at S and S' and radii SO and $S'M$. Consequently, the optical paths (DM) and (OB) must be equal:

$$n \cdot DM = n' \cdot OB. \qquad (*)$$

However, in the case of paraxial rays $DM \approx AO + OC$, where $AO \approx h^2/(-2s)$ and $OC \approx h'^2/2R$. Besides, $OB = OC - BC \approx$ $\approx h'^2/2R - h'^2/2s'$. Substituting these expressions into (*) and taking into account that $h' \approx h$, we obtain $n'/s' - n/s = (n'-n)/R$.

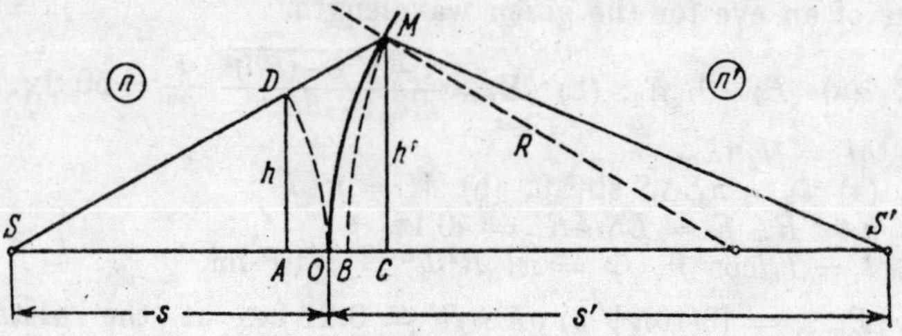

Fig. 38.

5.30. $x = \frac{nf}{n+1}\left(1 - \sqrt{1 - \frac{(n+1)\,r^2}{(n-1)\,f^2}}\right)$, $r_{max} = f\sqrt{(n-1)/(n+1)}$.

5.31. 6.3 cm.

5.32. (a) $\beta = 1 - d\,(n-1)/nR = -0.20$; (b) $E = \pi n^2 D^2 L/4d^2 =$ $= 42$ lx.

5.33. (a) $\Phi = \Phi_0\,(n - n_0)/(n-1) = 2.0$ D, $f' = -f = n_0/\Phi =$ $= 85$ cm; (b) $\Phi = {}^1/_2\Phi_0\,(2n - n_0 - 1)/(n-1) = 6.7$ D, $f =$ $= 1/\Phi \approx 15$ cm. $f' = n_0/\Phi \approx 20$ cm. Here n and n_0 are the refractive indices of glass and water.

5.35. $\Delta x \approx \Delta l f^2/(l - f)^2 = 0.5$ mm.

5.36. (a) $f = [l^2 - (\Delta l)^2]/4l = 20$ cm;
(b) $f = l\sqrt{\eta}/(1 + \sqrt{\eta})^2 = 20$ cm.

5.37. $h = \sqrt{h'h''} = 3.0$ mm.

5.38. $E = (1 - \alpha)\,\pi L D^2/4f^2 = 15$ lx.

5.39. (a) Is independent of D; (b) is proportional to D^2.

5.40. $f = n_0 R/2(n_1 - n_2) = 35$ cm, where n_0 is refractive index of water.

5.41. $f = R/2(2n - 1) = 10$ cm.

5.42. (a) To the right of the last lens at the distance 3.3 cm from it; (b) $l = 17$ cm.

5.43. (a) 50 and 5 cm; (b) by a distance of 0.5 cm.

5.44. $\Gamma = D/d$.

5.45. $\psi = \psi'/\sqrt{\eta} = 0.6'$.

5.46. $\Gamma' = (\Gamma + 1)\,\frac{n - n_0}{n_0\,(n-1)} - 1 = 3.1$, where n_0 is the refractive index of water.

5.47. $\Gamma \leqslant D/d_0 = 20$.

5.48. $\Gamma = 60$.

5.49. (a) $\Gamma = 2\alpha l_0/d_0 = 15$, where l_0 is the distance of the best vision (25 cm); (b) $\Gamma \leqslant 2\alpha l_0/d_0$.

5.50. The principal planes coincide with the centre of the lens. The focal lengths in air and water: $f = -1/\Phi = -11$ cm, $f' = n_0/\Phi = +15$ cm. Here $\Phi = (2n - n_0 - 1)/R$, where n and n_0 are the refractive indices of glass and water. The nodal points coincide and are located in water at the distance $x = f' + f = 3.7$ cm from the lens.

5.51. See Fig. 39.

5.54. (a) The optical power of the system is $\Phi = \Phi_1 + \Phi_2 - d\Phi_1\Phi_2 = +4$ D, the focal length is 25 cm. Both principal planes

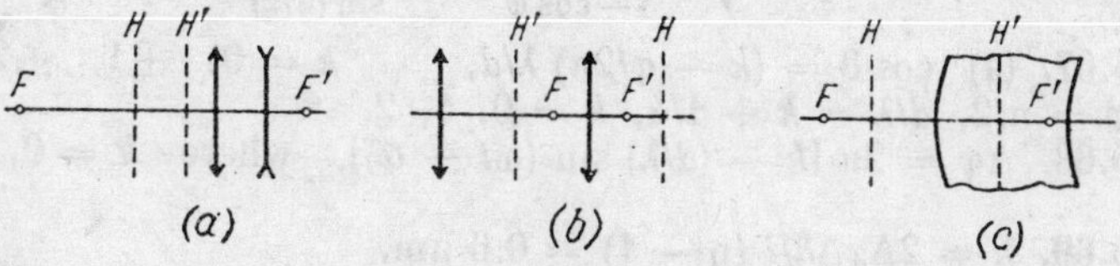

Fig. 39.

are located in front of the converging lens: the front one at a distance of 10 cm from the converging lens, and the rear one at a distance of 10 cm from the diverging lens ($x = d\Phi_2/\Phi$ and $x' = -d\Phi_1/\Phi$); (b) $d = 5$ cm; about 4/3.

5.55. The optical power of the given lens is $\Phi = \Phi_1 + \Phi_2 - (d/n)\Phi_1\Phi_2$, $x = d\Phi_2/n\Phi = 5.0$ cm, $x' = -d\Phi_1/n\Phi = 2.5$ cm, i.e. both principal planes are located outside the lens from the side of its convex surface.

5.56. $f = \dfrac{f_1 f_2}{f_1 + f_2 - d}$. The lens should be positioned in the front principal plane of the system, i.e. at a distance of $x = f_1 d/(f_1 + f_2 - d)$ from the first lens.

5.57. $\Phi = 2\Phi' - 2\Phi'^2 l/n_0 = 3.0$ D, where $\Phi' = (2n - n_0 - 1)/R$, n and n_0 are the refractive indices of glass and water.

5.58. (a) $d = n\Delta R/(n-1) = 4.5$ cm; (b) $d = 3.0$ cm.

5.59. (a) $\Phi = d(n-1)^2/nR^2 > 0$, the principal planes are located on the side of the convex surface at a distance of d from each other, with the front principal plane being removed from the convex surface of the lens by a distance of $R/(n-1)$; (b) $\Phi = (1/R_2 - 1/R_1) \times (n-1)/n < 0$; both principal planes pass through the common curvature centre of the surfaces of the lens.

5.60. $d = {}^1/_2 n (R_1 + R_2)/(n-1) = 9.0$ cm, $\Gamma = R_1/R_2 = 5.0$.

5.61. $\Phi = 2(n^2 - 1)/n^2 R = 37$ D.

5.63. $\rho = 3 \cdot 10^7$ m; $|\nabla n| = 1.6 \cdot 10^{-7}$ m^{-1}.

5.65. 1.9a.

5.66. Let us represent the kth oscillation in the complex form

$$\xi_k = a e^{i[\omega t + (k-1)\varphi]} = a_k^* e^{i\omega t},$$

where $a_k^* = a e^{i(k-1)\varphi}$ is the complex amplitude. Then the complex amplitude of the resulting oscillation is

$$A^* = \sum_{k=1}^{N} a e^{i(k-1)\varphi} = a\,[1 + e^{i\varphi} + e^{i2\varphi} + \ldots + e^{i(N-1)\varphi}] =$$
$$= a\,(e^{i\varphi N} - 1)/(e^{i\varphi} - 1).$$

Multiplying A^* by the complex conjugate value and extracting the square root, we obtain the real amplitude

$$A = a\sqrt{\frac{1 - \cos N\varphi}{1 - \cos\varphi}} = a\,\frac{\sin(N\varphi/2)}{\sin(\varphi/2)}.$$

5.67. (a) $\cos\theta = (k - \varphi/2\pi)\,\lambda/d$, $k = 0, \pm 1, \pm 2, \ldots$; (b) $\varphi = \pi/2$, $d/\lambda = k + 1/4$, $k = 0, 1, 2, \ldots$

5.68. $\Delta\varphi = 2\pi\,[k - (d/\lambda)\sin(\omega t + \alpha)]$, where $k = 0, \pm 1, \pm 2, \ldots$

5.69. $\lambda = 2\Delta x \Delta h/l\,(\eta - 1) = 0.6$ μm.

5.71. (a) $\Delta x = \lambda\,(b + r)/2\alpha r = 1.1$ mm, 9 maxima; (b) the shift is $\delta x = (b/r)\,\delta l = 13$ mm; (c) the fringe pattern is still sharp when $\delta x \leqslant \Delta x/2$, hence $\delta_{max} = (1 + r/b)\lambda/4\alpha = 43$ μm.

5.72. $\lambda = 2\alpha\Delta x = 0.64$ μm.

5.73. (a) $\Delta x = \lambda f/a = 0.15$ mm, 13 maxima; (b) the fringes are still sufficiently sharp when $\delta x \leqslant \Delta x/2$, where δx is the shift of the fringes from the extreme elements of the slit, hence, $\delta_{max} = \lambda f^2/2ab = 37$ μm.

5.74. $\lambda = 2a\,\Theta(n - 1)\,\Delta x/(a + b) = 0.6$ μm.

5.75. $\Delta x \approx \lambda/2\Theta\,(n - n') = 0.20$ mm.

5.76. The fringes are displaced toward the covered slit over the distance $\Delta x = hl\,(n - 1)/d = 2.0$ mm.

5.77. $n' = n + N\lambda/l = 1.000377$.

5.78. (a) Let **E**, **E**′, and **E**″ be the electric field vectors in the incident, reflected and transmitted waves. Select the x-, y-axes at the interface so that they coincide in direction with **E** and **H** in the incident wave.

The continuity of the tangential components across the interface yields

$$\mathbf{E} + \mathbf{E}' = \mathbf{E}''.$$

The minus sign before **H** appears because **H**′ ↑↓ **H**.

Rewrite the second equation taking into account that $\mathbf{H} \propto nE$. Solving the obtained and the first equation find:

$$\mathbf{E}'' = 2\mathbf{E}n_1/(n_1 + n_2).$$

Hence, we see that $\mathbf{E}''$ and $\mathbf{E}$ are collinear, that is. cophasal.

$$\text{(b) } \mathbf{E}' = \mathbf{E}(n_1 - n_2)/(n_1 + n_2),$$

that is at $n_2 > n_1$ and $\mathbf{E}' \uparrow\downarrow \mathbf{E}$ the phase abruptly changes by π at the interface. If $n_2 < n_1$ the phase jump does not occur.

5.79. $d = {}^1/_4\lambda\,(1+2k)\,/\sqrt{n^2 - \sin^2\theta_1} = 0.14\,(1+2k)$ µm, where $k = 0, 1, 2, \ldots$

5.80. $d_{min} = 0.65$ µm.

5.81. $d = {}^1/_4\lambda\,(1+2k)\,/\sqrt{n}$, where $k = 0, 1, 2, \ldots$

5.82. $d = \lambda\dfrac{\sqrt{n^2 - \sin^2\theta}}{\sin 2\theta \cdot \delta\theta} = 15$ µm.

5.83. $\lambda \approx \dfrac{d\,(r_i^2 - r_k^2)}{4nl^2\,(i-k)}$.

5.84. $\Delta x = \dfrac{\lambda \cos\theta_1}{2\alpha\sqrt{n^2 - \sin^2\theta_1}}$.

5.85. (a) $\Theta = {}^1/_2\lambda/n\Delta x = 3'$; (b) $\Delta\lambda/\lambda \approx \Delta x/l = 0.014$.

5.86. $\Delta r \approx {}^1/_4\lambda R/r$.

5.87. $r' = \sqrt{r^2 - 2R\Delta h} = 1.5$ mm.

5.88. $r = \sqrt{r_0^2 + (k - 1/2)\,\lambda R} = 3.8$ mm, where $k = 6$.

5.89. $\lambda = {}^1/_4\,(d_2^2 - d_1^2)/R\,(k_2 - k_1) = 0.50$ µm, where k_1 and k_2 are the numbers of the dark rings.

5.90. $\Phi = 2(n-1)(2k-1)\lambda/d^2 = 2.4$ D, where k is the number of the bright ring.

5.91. (a) $r = \sqrt{2k\lambda\,(n-1)/\Phi} = 3.5$ mm, where $k = 10$; (b) $r' = r/\sqrt{n_0} = 3.0$ mm, where n_0 is the refractive index of water.

5.92. $r = \sqrt{{}^1/_2\,(1+2k)\,\lambda R/n_2} = 1.3$ mm, where $k = 5$.

5.93. $k_{min} = {}^1/_2\lambda_1/(\lambda_2 - \lambda_1) = 140$.

5.94. The transition from one sharp pattern to another occurs if the following condition is met:

$$(k+1)\,\lambda_1 = k\lambda_2,$$

where k is a certain integer. The corresponding displacement Δh of the mirror is determined from the equation $2\Delta h = k\lambda_2$. From these two equations we get

$$\Delta h = \frac{\lambda_1\lambda_2}{2\,(\lambda_2 - \lambda_1)} \approx \frac{\lambda^2}{2\Delta\lambda} = 0.3 \text{ mm}.$$

5.95. (a) The condition for maxima: $2d\cos\theta = k\lambda$; hence, the order of interference k diminishes as the angle θ, i.e. the radius of the rings, increases (see Fig. 5.18). (b) Differenting both sides of the foregoing equation and taking into account that on transition from one maximum to another the value of k changes by unity, we obtain $\delta\theta = {}^1/_2\lambda/d\sin\theta$; this shows that the angular width of the fringes decreases with an increase of the angle θ, i.e. with a decrease in the order of interference.

5.96. (a) $k_{max} = 2d/\lambda = 1.0 \cdot 10^5$, (b) $\Delta\lambda = \lambda/k = \lambda^2/2d = 5$ pm.

5.97. $I_0 = \frac{2}{b\mathcal{N}\lambda} \int_0^\infty I(r)\, r\, dr$.

5.98. $b = ar^2/(k\lambda a - r^2) = 2.0$ m.

5.99. $\lambda = (r_2^2 - r_1^2)(a + b)/2ab = 0.60$ µm.

5.100. (a) $I \approx 4I_0$, $I \approx 2I_0$; (b) $I \approx I_0$.

5.101. (a) $I \approx 0$; (b) $I \approx I_0/2$.

5.102. (a) $I_1 \approx {}^9/_{16}\, I_0$, $I_2 = {}^1/_4\, I_0$, $I_3 = {}^1/_{16} I_0$, $I_4 = I_2$, $I \approx (1 - \varphi/2\pi)^2 I_0$; (b) $I_5 \approx {}^{25}/_{16}\, I_0$, $I_6 \approx {}^9/_4\, I_0$, $I_7 \approx {}^{49}/_{16}\, I_0$, $I_8 = I_6$, $I \approx (1 + \varphi/2\pi)^2\, I_0$. Here φ is the angle covered by the screen.

5.103. (a) $h = \lambda\,(k + 3/8)/(n - 1) = 1.2\,(k + 3/8)$ µm; (b) $h = 1.2\,(k + 7/8)$ µm, (c) $h = 1.2k$ or $1.2\,(k + 3/4)$ µm. Here $k = 0, 1, 2, \ldots$

5.104. $h = \lambda\,(k + 3/4)/(n - 1)$, where $k = 0, 1, 2, \ldots$, (b) $I_{max} \approx 8I_0$.

5.105. $h_{min} \approx \lambda\,(k + 5/8)/(n - 1) = 2.5$ µm, where $k = 2$.

5.106. $r = \sqrt{k\lambda f b/(b - f)} = 0.90\sqrt{k}$ mm, where $k = 1, 3, 5, \ldots$

5.107. $b' = b/\eta^2 = 1.0$ m.

5.108. (a) $y' = yb/a = 9$ mm; (b) $h_{min} \approx ab\lambda/D\,(a + b) = 0.10$ mm.

5.109. $f = ab/(a + b) = 0.6$ m. This value corresponds to the principal focal point, apart from which there are other points as well.

5.110. (a) $h = 0.60\,(2k + 1)$ µm; (b) $h = 0.30\,(2k + 1)$ µm. Here $k = 0, 1, 2, \ldots$

5.111. (a) $I_{max}/I_{min} \approx 1.7$, (b) $\lambda = 2\,(\Delta x)^2/b(v_2 - v_1)^2 = 0.7$ µm, where v_1 and v_2 are the corresponding values of the parameter along Cornu's spiral.

5.112. $I_{centr.}/I_{edge.} \approx 2.6$.

5.113. $\lambda = (\Delta h)^2/2b\,(v_2 - v_1)^2 = 0.55$ µm, where v_1 and v_2 are the corresponding values of the parameter along Cornu's spiral.

5.114. $h \approx \lambda\,(k + 3/4)/(n - 1)$, where $k = 0, 1, 2, \ldots$

5.115. $I_2/I_1 \approx 1.9$.

5.116. $I \approx 2.8I_0$.

5.117. $I_1 : I_2 : I_3 \approx 1 : 4 : 7$.

5.118. $I \approx I_0$.

5.119. $I_\theta \backsim (\sin^2\alpha)/\alpha^2$, where $\alpha = (\pi b/\lambda)\sin\theta$; $b\sin\theta = k\lambda$, $k = 1, 2, 3, \ldots$

5.120. The condition for a maximum leads to the transcendental equation $\tan\alpha = \alpha$, where $\alpha = (\pi b/\lambda)\sin\theta$. The solution of this equation (by means of plotting or selection) provides the following root values: $\alpha_1 = 1.43\pi$, $\alpha_2 = 2.46\pi$, $\alpha_3 = 3.47\pi$. Hence $b\sin\theta_1 = 1.43\lambda$, $b\sin\theta_2 = 2.46\lambda$, $b\sin\theta_3 = 3.47\lambda$.

5.121. $b\,(\sin\theta - \sin\theta_0) = k\lambda$; for $k = +1$ and $k = -1$ the angles θ are equal to 33° and 27° respectively.

5.122. (a) $\Delta\theta = \arcsin(n \sin\theta) - \theta = 7.9°$; (b) from the condition $b(\sin\theta_1 - n\sin\theta) = \pm\lambda$ we obtain $\Delta\theta = \theta_{+1} - \theta_{-1} = 7.3°$.

5.123. $\lambda \approx (\alpha^2 - \alpha_0^2)\, d/2k = 0.6$ μm.

5.125. 55°.

5.126. $d = 2.8$ μm.

5.127. $\lambda = (d \sin\Delta\theta)/\sqrt{5 - 4\cos\Delta\theta} = 0.54$ μm.

5.128. (a) 45°; (b)-64°.

5.129. $x = 2R/(n-1)\sqrt{(d/\lambda)^2 - 1} = 8$ cm.

5.130. From the condition $d[n\sin\theta - \sin(\theta + \theta_k)] = k\lambda$ we obtain $\theta_0 = -18.5°$, $\theta_{+1} = 0°$; $k_{max} = +6$, $\theta_{+6} = +78.5°$. See Fig. 40.

5.131. $h_k = \lambda(k - 1/2)/(n - 1)$, where $k = 1, 2, \ldots$; $a \sin\theta_1 = \lambda/2$.

5.132. $v = \lambda v f/\Delta x = 1.5$ km/s.

5.133. Each star produces its own diffraction pattern in the objective's focal plane, with their zeroth maxima being separated

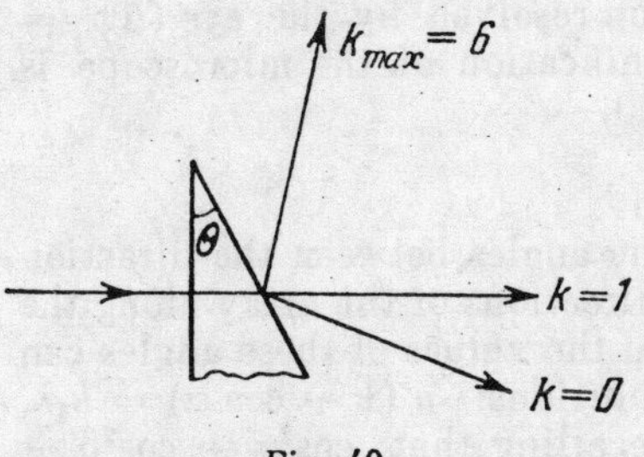

Fig. 40.

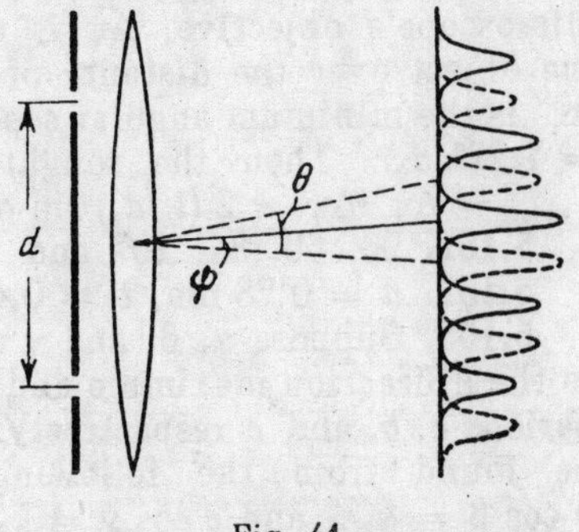

Fig. 41.

by an angle ψ (Fig. 41). As the distance d decreases the angle θ between the neighbouring maxima in each diffraction pattern increases, and when θ becomes equal to 2ψ, the first deterioration of visibility occurs: the maxima of one system of fringes coincide with the minima of the other system. Thus, from the condition $\theta = 2\psi$ and the formula $\sin\theta = \lambda/d$ we obtain $\psi = \lambda/2d \approx 0.06''$.

5.134. (a) $D = k/d\sqrt{1 - (k\lambda/d)^2} = 6.5$ ang. min/nm, where $k = 2$; (b) $D = k/d\sqrt{1 - (k\lambda/d - \sin\theta_0)^2} = 13$ ang. min/nm, where $k = 4$.

5.135. $d\theta/d\lambda = (\tan\theta)/\lambda$.

5.136. $\Delta\theta = 2\lambda/Nd\sqrt{1 - (k\lambda/d)^2} = 11''$.

5.139. $\theta = 46°$.

5.140. (a) In the fourth order; (b) $\delta\lambda_{min} \approx \lambda^2/l = 7$ pm.

5.141. (a) $d = 0.05$ mm; (b) $l = 6$ cm.

5.142. (a) 6 and 12 μm; (b) not in the first order, yes in the second order.

5.143. According to Rayleigh's criterion the maximum of the line of wavelength λ must coincide with the first minimum of the line of wavelength $\lambda + \delta\lambda$. Let us write both conditions for the least deviation angle in terms of the optical path differences for the extreme rays (see Fig. 5.28):

$$bn - (DC + CE) = 0, \quad b(n + \delta n) - (DC + CE) = \lambda + \delta\lambda.$$

Hence, $b\delta n \approx \lambda$. What follows is obvious.

5.144. (a) $\lambda/\delta\lambda = 2bB/\lambda^3$; $1.2\cdot10^4$ and $0.35\cdot10^4$ (b) 1.0 cm.

5.145. About 20 cm.

5.146. $R = 7\cdot10^4$, $\Delta y_{min} \approx 4$ cm.

5.147. About 50 m.

5.148. Suppose $\Delta\psi$ and $\Delta\psi'$ are the minimum angular separations resolved by the telescope's objective and the eye respectively ($\Delta\psi = 1.22\lambda/D$, $\Delta\psi' = 1.22\lambda/d_0$). Then the sought magnification of the telescope is $\Gamma_{min} = \Delta\psi'/\Delta\psi = D/d_0 = 13$.

5.149. $d_{min} = 0.61\lambda/\sin\alpha = 1.4$ µm.

5.150. Suppose d_{min} is the minimum separation resolved by the microscope's objective, $\Delta\psi$ is the angle subtended by the eye at the object over the distance of the best visibility l_0 (25 cm), and $\Delta\psi'$ is the minimum angular separation resolved by the eye ($\Delta\psi' = 1.22\lambda/d_0$). Then the sought magnification of the microscope is $\Gamma_{min} = \Delta\psi'/\Delta\psi = 2(l_0/d_0)\sin\alpha = 30$.

5.151. 26, 60, 84, 107 and 134°.

5.152. $a = 0.28$ nm, $b = 0.41$ nm.

5.153. Suppose α, β, and γ are the angles between the direction to the diffraction maximum and the directions of the array along the periods a, b, and c respectively. Then the values of these angles can be found from the following conditions: $a(1 - \cos\alpha) = k_1\lambda$, $b\cos\beta = k_2\lambda$, and $c\cos\gamma = k_3\lambda$. Recalling that $\cos^2\alpha + \cos^2\beta + \cos^2\gamma = 1$, we obtain

$$\lambda = \frac{2k_1/a}{(k_1/a)^2 + (k_2/b)^2 + (k_3/c)^2}.$$

5.154. $\lambda = \frac{2}{k}\sqrt[3]{\frac{m}{2\rho}}\sin\alpha = 244$ pm, where $k = 2$, m is the mass of a NaCl molecule.

5.155. $d = \frac{\lambda}{2\sin(\alpha/2)}\sqrt{k_1^2 + k_2^2 - 2k_1k_2\cos(\alpha/2)} = 0.28$ pm, where k_1 and k_2 are the orders of reflection.

5.156. $r = l\tan 2\alpha = 3.5$ cm, where α is the glancing angle found from the condition $2d\sin\alpha = k\lambda$.

5.157. $I_0/4$.

5.158. (a) I_0; (b) $2I_0$.

5.159. $E = \pi\Phi_0/\omega = 0.6$ mJ.

5.160. $\eta = \frac{1}{2}(\cos\varphi)^{2(N-1)} = 0.12$.

5.161. $I_0/I = \frac{2}{\tau^3\cos^4\varphi} \approx 60$.

5.162. $I_{pol}/I_{nat} = P/(1 - P) = 0.3$.

5.163. $P = (\eta - 1)/(1 - \eta \cos 2\varphi) = 0.8$.

5.164. (a) Let us represent the natural light as a sum of two mutually perpendicular components with intensities I_0. Suppose that each polarizer transmits in its plane the fraction α_1 of the light with oscillation plane parallel to the polarizer's plane, and the fraction α_2 with oscillation plane perpendicular to the polarizer's plane. The intensity of light transmitted through the system of two polarizers is then equal to

$$I_{\parallel} = \alpha_1^2 I_0 + \alpha_2^2 I_0,$$

when their planes are parallel, and to

$$I_{\perp} = \alpha_1\alpha_2 I_0 + \alpha_2\alpha_1 I_0,$$

when their planes are perpendicular; according to the condition, $I_{\parallel}/I_{\perp} = \eta$.

On the other hand, the degree of polarization produced separately by each polarizer is

$$P_0 = (\alpha_1 - \alpha_2)/(\alpha_1 + \alpha_2).$$

Eliminating α_1 and α_2 from these equations, we get

$$P_0 = \sqrt{(\eta - 1)/(\eta + 1)} = 0.905.$$

(b) $P = \sqrt{1 - 1/\eta^2} = 0.995$.

5.165. The relative intensity variations of both beams in the cases A and B are

$$(\Delta I/I)_A = 4 \cot(\varphi/2)\cdot\delta\varphi, \quad (\Delta I/I)_B = 4 \tan(\varphi/2)\cdot\delta\varphi.$$

Hence

$$\eta = (\Delta I/I)_A/(\Delta I/I)_B = \cot^2(\varphi/2), \quad \varphi = 11.5°.$$

5.166. 90°.

5.167. (a) $\rho = \frac{1}{2}(n^2 - 1)^2/(n^2 + 1)^2 = 0.074$;
(b) $P = \rho/(1-\rho) = \dfrac{(1+n^2)^2 - 4n^2}{(1+n^2)^2 + 4n^2} = 0.080$. Here n is the refractive index of glass.

5.168. $I = I_0(1 - \rho)/n = 0.721 I_0$, where n is the refractive index of water.

5.169. $\rho = [(n^2 - 1)/(n^2 + 1)] \sin^2\varphi = 0.038$, where n is the refractive index of water.

5.170. $P_1 = P_3 = 1$, $P_2 = \dfrac{\rho}{1-\rho} = 0.087$, $P_4 = \dfrac{2\rho(1-\rho)}{1 - 2\rho(1-\rho)} = 0.17$.

5.171. (a) In this case the coefficient of reflection from each surface of the plate is equal to $\rho = (n^2 - 1)^2/(n^2 + 1)^2$, and therefore $I_4 = I_0(1 - \rho)^2 = 16 I_0 n^4/(1 + n^2)^2 = 0.725 I_0$;
(b) $P = \dfrac{1-(1-\rho')^2}{1+(1-\rho')^2} = \dfrac{(1+n^2)^4 - 16n^4}{(1+n^2)^4 + 16n^4} \approx 0.16$, where ρ' is the coefficient of reflection for the component of light whose electric vector oscillates at right angles to the incidence plane.

5.172. (a) $P = (1 - \alpha^{4N})/(1 + \alpha^{4N})$, where $\alpha = 2n/(1 + n^2)$, n is the refractive index of glass; (b) 0.16, 0.31, 0.67, and 0.92 respectively.

5.173. (a) $\rho = (n - 1)^2/(n + 1)^2 = 0.040$; (b) $\Delta\Phi/\Phi = 1 - (1 - \rho)^{2N} = 0.34$, where N is the number of lenses.

5.175. (a) 0.83; (b) 0.044.

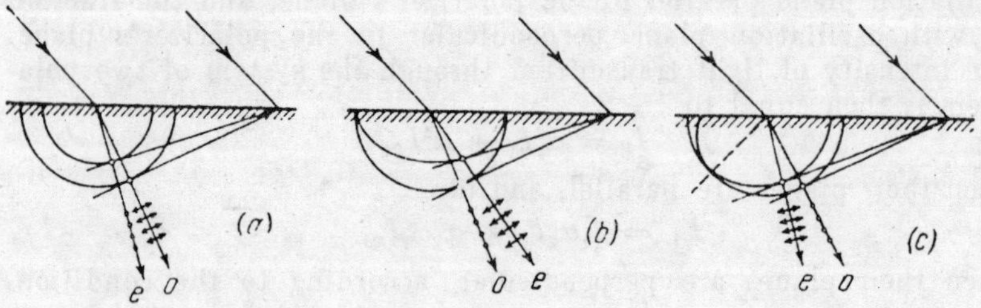

Fig. 42.

5.176. See Fig. 42, where o and e are the ordinary and extraordinary rays.

5.177. $\delta \approx 11°$.

5.178. For the right-handed system of coordinates:

(1) circular anticlockwise polarization, when observed toward the incoming wave;

(2) elliptical clockwise polarization, when observed toward the incoming wave; the major axis of the ellipse coincides with the straight line $y = x$;

(3) plane polarization, along the straight line $y = -x$.

5.179. (a) 0.490 mm; (b) 0.475 mm.

5.180. $\lambda = 4d\Delta n/(2k + 1)$; 0.58, 0.55 and 0.51 μm respectively at $k = 15$, 16 and 17.

5.181. Four.

5.182. 0.69 and 0.43 μm.

5.183. $d = (k - 1/2)\,\lambda_1/\Delta n = 0.25$ mm, where $k = 4$.

5.184. $\Delta n = \lambda/\Theta\Delta x' = 0.009$.

5.185. Let us denote the intensity of transmitted light by $I_\perp$ in the case of the crossed Polaroids, and by $I_\parallel$ in the case of the parallel Polaroids. Then

$$I_\perp = {}^1/_2 I_0 \sin^2 2\varphi \cdot \sin^2 (\delta/2),$$
$$I_\parallel = {}^1/_2 I_0 \,[1 - \sin^2 2\varphi \cdot \sin^2 (\delta/2)].$$

The conditions for the maximum and the minimum:

Polaroids	I_{max}	I_{min}
$\perp$	$\Delta = (k + 1/2)\,\lambda$, $\varphi = \pi/4$	$\Delta = k\lambda$, for any φ
$\parallel$	$\Delta = k\lambda$, for any φ	$\Delta = (k + 1/2)\,\lambda$, $\varphi = \pi/4$

Here Δ is the optical path difference for the ordinary and extraordinary rays, $k = 0, 1, 2, \ldots$

5.187. (a) The light with right-hand circular polarization (from the observer's viewpoint) becomes plane polarized on passing through a quarter-wave plate. In this case the direction of oscillations of the electric vector of the electromagnetic wave forms an angle of $+45°$ with the axis OO' of the crystal (Fig. 43*a*); in the case of left-hand polarization this angle will be equal to $-45°$ (Fig. 43*b*).

(b) If for any position of the plate the rotation of the Polaroid (located behind the plate) does not bring about any variation in the intensity of the transmitted light, the initial light is natural;

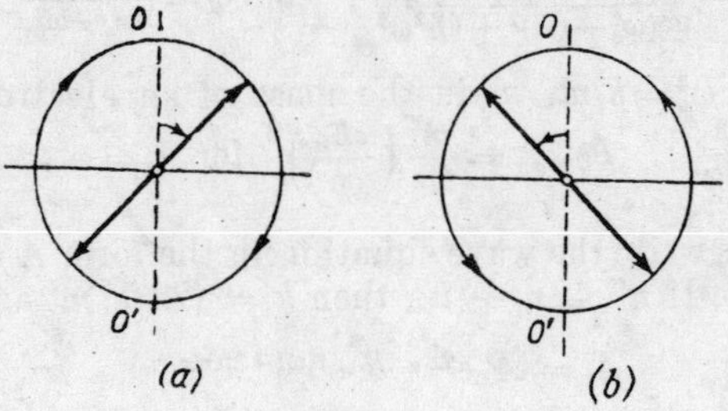

Fig. 43.

if the intensity of the transmitted light varies and drops to zero, the initial light is circularly polarized; if it varies but does not drop to zero, then the initial light is composed of natural and circularly polarized light.

5.188. (a) $\Delta x = {}^1/_2\lambda\,(n_e - n_o)\,\Theta$, (b) $d\,(n_o' - n_e') = -2\,(n_e - n_o)\,\Theta\delta x < 0$.

5.189. $\Delta n = \alpha\lambda/\pi = 0.71\cdot 10^{-4}$, where α is the rotational constant.

5.190. $\alpha = \pi/\Delta x \tan\Theta = 21$ ang. deg./mm, $I(x) \sim \cos^2(\pi x/\Delta x)$, where x is the distance from the maximum.

5.191. $d_{min} = (1/\alpha) \arcsin\sqrt{2\eta} = 3.0$ mm.

5.192. 8.7 mm.

5.193. $[\alpha] = 72$ ang. deg./(dm·g/cm³).

5.194. (a) $E_{min} = 1/\sqrt{4Bl} = 10.6$ kV/cm; (b) $2.2\cdot 10^8$ interruptions per second.

5.195. $\Delta n = 2cHV/\omega$, where c is the velocity of light in vacuum.

5.196. $V = {}^1/_2\,(\varphi_1 - \varphi_2)/lH = 0.015$ ang. min/A.

5.197. If one looks toward the transmitted beam and counts the positive direction clockwise, then $\varphi = (\alpha - VNH)\,l$, where N is the number of times the beam passes through the substance (in Fig. 5.35 the number is $N = 5$).

5.198. $H_{min} = \pi/4Vl = 4.0$ kA/m, where V is the Verdet constant. The direction along which the light is transmitted changes to the opposite.

5.199. $t = mc\omega_0/\lambda I = 12$ hours. Although the effect is very small, it was observed both for visible light and for SHF radiation.

5.200. (a) $a = eE_0/m\omega^2 = 5\cdot 10^{-16}$ cm, where $E_0 = \sqrt{2I/\varepsilon_0 c}$, $v = a\omega = 1.7$ cm/s; (b) $F_m/F_e = 2.9\cdot 10^{-11}$.

5.201. (a) $\varepsilon = 1 - n_0 e^2/\varepsilon_0 m\omega^2$, $v = c\sqrt{1 + (n_0 e^2/4\pi^2\varepsilon_0 mc^2)\lambda^2}$.

5.202. $n_0 = (4\pi^2\nu^2 m\varepsilon_0/e^2)(1 - n^2) = 2.4\cdot 10^7$ cm^{-3}.

5.203. $n - 1 = -n_0 e^2\lambda^2/8\pi^2\varepsilon_0 mc^2 = -5.4\cdot 10^{-7}$, where n_0 is the concentration of electrons in carbon.

5.204. (a) $x = a\cos(\omega t + \varphi)$, where a and φ are defined by the formulas

$$a = \frac{eE_0/m}{\sqrt{(\omega_0^2 - \omega^2)^2 + 4\beta^2\omega^2}}, \quad \tan\varphi = \frac{2\beta\omega}{\omega^2 - \omega_0^2}.$$

Here $\beta = \gamma/2m$, $\omega_0^2 = k/m$, m is the mass of an electron. (b) $\langle P\rangle = \frac{m\beta(eE_0/m)^2\omega^2}{(\omega_0^2 - \omega^2)^2 + 4\beta^2\omega^2}$, $\langle P\rangle_{max} = \frac{m}{4\beta}\left(\frac{eE_0}{m}\right)^2$ for $\omega = \omega_0$.

5.205. Let us write the wave equation in the form $A = A_0 e^{i(\omega t - kx)}$, where $k = 2\pi/\lambda$. If $n' = n + i\varkappa$, then $k = (2\pi/\lambda_0)n'$ and

$$A = A_0 e^{2\pi\varkappa x/\lambda_0} e^{i(\omega t - 2\pi n x/\lambda_0)},$$

or in the real form

$$A = A_0 e^{\varkappa' x}\cos(\omega t - k'x),$$

i.e. the light propagates as a plane wave whose amplitude depends on x. When $\varkappa < 0$, the amplitude diminishes (the attenuation of the wave due to absorption). When $n' = i\varkappa$, then

$$A = A_0 e^{\varkappa' x}\cos\omega t.$$

This is a standing wave whose amplitude decreases exponentially (if $\varkappa < 0$). In this case the light experiences total internal reflection in the medium (without absorption).

5.206. $n_0 = 4\pi^2\varepsilon_0 mc^2/e^2\lambda_0^2 = 2.0\cdot 10^9$ cm^{-3}.

5.208. (a) $u = {}^3/_2\, v$; (b) $u = 2v$; (c) $u = {}^1/_3\, v$.

5.209. $\varepsilon = 1 + A/\omega^2$, where A is a constant.

5.210. $v = c/n = 1.83\cdot 10^8$ m/s, $u = [1 + (\lambda/n)(dn/d\lambda)]\,c/n = 1.70\cdot 10^8$ m/s.

5.211. It is sufficient to discuss three harmonic components of the train of waves (most easily with the help of a plot).

5.212. $I = {}^1/_2 I_0 e^{-\varkappa l}\sin^2\varphi$, where $\varphi = VlH$.

5.213. (a) $I = I_0(1-\rho)^2(1 + \rho^2 + \rho^4 + \ldots) = I_0(1-\rho)^2/(1-\rho^2)$; (b) $I = I_0(1-\rho)^2\sigma(1 + \sigma^2\rho^2 + \sigma^4\rho^4 + \ldots) = I_0\sigma(1-\rho)^2/(1-\sigma^2\rho^2)$, where $\sigma = \exp(-\varkappa d)$.

5.214. $\varkappa = \frac{\ln(\tau_1/\tau_2)}{d_2 - d_1} = 0.35$ cm^{-1}.

5.215. $\varkappa = \frac{1}{lN}\ln\frac{(1-\rho)^{2N}}{\tau} = 0.034$ cm^{-1}.

5.216. $\tau = (1-\rho)^2\exp[-{}^1/_2(\varkappa_1 + \varkappa_2)\,l]$.

5.217. $I = I_0(1-\rho)^2 \frac{e^{-\varkappa_1 l} - e^{-\varkappa_2 l}}{(\varkappa_2 - \varkappa_1) l}$.

5.218. $\Delta\lambda = 2\lambda_0 \sqrt{(\ln \eta)/\alpha d}$.

5.219. $I = \frac{\Phi}{4\pi b^2}(1-\rho)^2 e^{-\varkappa(b-a)}$.

5.220. Will decrease $\exp(\mu d) = 0.6 \cdot 10^2$ times.

5.221. $d = 0.3$ mm.

5.222. $d = (\ln 2)/\mu = 8$ mm.

5.223. $N = (\ln \eta)/\ln 2 = 5.6$.

5.224. $c = 2lz(n_2 - n_1) = 3.0 \cdot 10^8$ m/s.

5.225. First of all note that when $v \ll c$, the time rate is practically identical in the reference frames fixed to the source and to the receiver. Suppose that the source emits short pulses with the intervals T_0. Then in the reference frame fixed to the receiver the distance between two successive pulses is equal to $\lambda = cT_0 - v_r T_0$, when measured along the observation line. Here v_r is the projection of the source velocity on the observation line ($v_r = v \cos\theta$). The frequency of received pulses $\nu = c/\lambda = \nu_0/(1 - v_r/c)$, where $\nu_0 = 1/T_0$. Hence $(\nu - \nu_0)/\nu_0 = (v/c)\cos\theta$.

5.226. $\Delta\lambda = -\lambda\sqrt{2T/mc^2} \cos\theta = -26$ nm.

5.227. $T = 4\pi R\lambda\, c\delta\lambda = 25$ days, where R is the radius of the Sun.

5.228. $d = (\Delta\lambda/\lambda)_m c\tau/\pi = 3 \cdot 10^7$ km, $m = (\Delta\lambda/\lambda)_m^3 c^3\tau/2\pi\gamma = 2.9 \cdot 10^{29}$ kg, where γ is the gravitational constant.

5.229. $\omega = \omega_0(1+\beta)/(1-\beta)$, where $\beta = V/c$; $\omega \approx \omega_0(1 + 2V/c)$.

5.230. $v = {}^1/_2\lambda\Delta\nu \approx 900$ km per hour.

5.231. Substituting the expressions for t' and x' (from the Lorentz transformation) into the equation $\omega t - kx = \omega' t' - k' x'$, we obtain

$$\omega = \omega'(1+\beta)/\sqrt{1-\beta^2}, \quad k = k'(1+\beta)/\sqrt{1-\beta^2},$$

where $\beta = V/c$. Here it is taken into account that $\omega' = ck'$.

5.232. From the formula $\omega' = \omega\sqrt{(1-\beta)/(1+\beta)}$ we get $\beta = v/c = 0.26$.

5.233. $v = c\frac{(\lambda/\lambda')^2 - 1}{(\lambda/\lambda')^2 + 1} = 7.1 \cdot 10^4$ km/s.

5.234. $\omega = \omega_0\sqrt{3/7}$.

5.235. $\Delta\lambda = \lambda T/m_0 c^2 = 0.70$ nm, where m_0 is the mass of the atom.

5.236. (a) $\omega = \omega_0/\sqrt{1-\beta^2} = 5.0 \cdot 10^{10}$ s^{-1}; (b) $\omega = \omega_0\sqrt{1-\beta^2} = 1.8 \cdot 10^{10}$ s^{-1}. Here $\beta = v/c$.

5.237. The charge of an electron and the positive charge induced in the metal form a dipole. In the reference frame fixed to the electron the electric dipole moment varies with a period $T' = d'/v$, where $d' = d\sqrt{1-(v/c)^2}$. The corresponding "natural" frequency is $\nu' = v/d'$. Due to the Doppler effect the observed frequency is

$$\nu = \nu' \frac{\sqrt{1-(v/c)^2}}{1-(v/c)\cos\theta} = \frac{v/d}{1-(v/c)\cos\theta}.$$

The corresponding wavelength is $\lambda = c/\nu = d\,(c/v - \cos\theta)$. When $\theta = 45°$ and $v \approx c$ the wavelength is $\lambda \approx 0.6$ μm.

5.238. (a) Let v_x be the projection of the velocity vector of the radiating atom on the observation direction. The number of atoms with projections falling within the interval v_x, $v_x + dv_x$ is

$$n\,(v_x)\,dv_x \sim \exp\,(-mv_x^2/2kT)\cdot dv_x.$$

The frequency of light emitted by the atoms moving with velocity v_x is $\omega = \omega_0\,(1 + v_x/c)$. From the expression the frequency distribution of atoms can be found: $n\,(\omega)\,d\omega = n\,(v_x)\,dv_x$. And finally it should be taken into account that the spectral radiation intensity $I_\omega \sim n\,(\omega)$. (b) $\Delta\omega/\omega_0 = 2\sqrt{(2\ln 2)\,kT/mc^2}$.

5.239. $u = \frac{c/n + V}{1 + V/cn}$. If $V \ll c$, then $u \approx \frac{c}{n} + V\left(1 - \frac{1}{n^2}\right)$.

5.240. $v = {}^1/_2 c\delta\theta = 30$ km/s.

5.242. $\theta' = 8°$.

5.243. The field induced by a charged particle moving with velocity V excites the atoms of the medium turning them into sources of light waves. Let us consider two arbitrary points A and B along the path of the particle. The light waves emitted from these points when the particle passes them reach the point P (Fig. 44) simultaneously and amplify each other provided the time taken by the light wave to propagate from the point A to the point C is equal to that taken by the particle to fly over the distance AB. Hence, we obtain $\cos\theta = v/V$, where $v = c/n$ is the phase velocity of light. It is evident that the radiation is possible only if $V > v$, i.e. when the velocity of the particle exceeds the phase velocity of light in the medium.

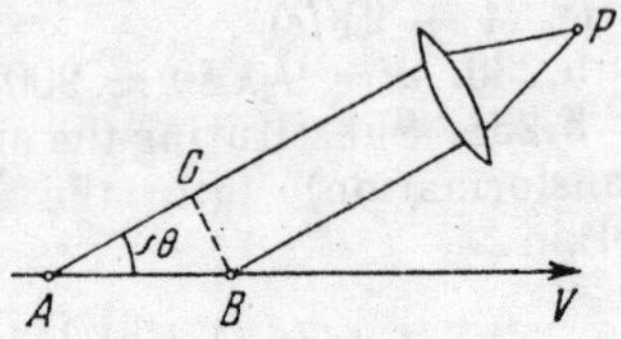

Fig. 44.

5.244. $T_{min} = (n/\sqrt{n^2-1} - 1)\,mc^2$; 0.14 MeV and 0.26 GeV respectively. For muons.

5.245. $T = \left(\frac{n\cos\theta}{\sqrt{n^2\cos^2\theta - 1}} - 1\right) mc^2 = 0.23$ MeV.

5.247. $T_2 = bT_1/(b + T_1\Delta\lambda) = 1.75$ kK.

5.248. $\lambda_m = 3.4$ μm.

5.249. $5\cdot 10^9$ kg/s, about 10^{11} years.

5.250. $T = \sqrt[3]{3cR\rho/\sigma M} = 2\cdot 10^7$ K, where R is the universal gas constant, M is the molar mass of hydrogen.

5.251. $t = (\eta^3 - 1)\, c\rho d/18\sigma T_0^3 = 3$ hours where c is the specific heat capacity of copper, ρ is its density.

5 252. $T_2 = T_1 \sqrt{d/2l} = 0.4$ kK.

5.253. (a) $C_V = (\partial U/\partial T)_V = 16\, \sigma T^3 V/c = 3$ nJ/K, where $U = 4\sigma T^4 V/c$; (b) $S = 16\sigma T^3 V/3c =$ [illegible] J/K.

5.254. (a) $\omega_{pr} = 3T/a = 7.85\cdot 10^{14}\ s^{-1}$; (b) $\lambda_{pr} = 2\pi ca/5T = 1.44$ μm.

5.255. (a) $u_\omega = (kT/\pi^2 c^3)\, \omega^2$; (b) $u_\omega = (\hbar/\pi^2 c^3)\, \omega^3 e^{-\hbar\omega/kT}$.

5.256. $u_\nu = \dfrac{16\pi^2\hbar}{c^3} \dfrac{\nu^3}{e^{2\pi\hbar\nu/kT} - 1}$, $u_\lambda = \dfrac{16\pi^2 c\hbar\lambda^{-5}}{e^{2\pi\hbar c/kT\lambda} - 1}$.

5.257. $\Delta P = 4\pi^2 c^2 \hbar T^5 \Delta\lambda / b^5 (e^{2\pi\hbar c/kb} - 1) = 0.31\ W/cm^2$, where b is the constant in Wien's displacement law.

5.258. (a) 1.1 μm; (b) 0.37; (c) $P_2/P_1 = (T_2/T_1)^4 (1 - y_2)/(1 - y_1) = 4.9$.

5.259. $n_\omega\, d\omega = \dfrac{1}{\pi^2 c^3} \dfrac{\omega^2\, d\omega}{e^{\hbar\omega/kT} - 1}$, $n_\lambda\, d\lambda = \dfrac{8\pi\lambda^{-4}\, d\lambda}{e^{2\pi\hbar c/kT\lambda} - 1}$.

5.260. (a) $\langle j \rangle = P\lambda/8\pi^2 c\hbar r^2 = 6\cdot 10^{13}\ cm^{-2}s^{-1}$; (b) $r = \sqrt{P\lambda/2\hbar n}/2\pi c = 9$ m.

5.261. $dp/dt = \Phi_e/c$.

5.262. $\langle p \rangle = 4\,(1 + \rho)\, E/\pi d^2 c\tau \approx 50$ atm.

5.263. $p = (E/c)\sqrt{1 + \rho^2 + 2\rho\cos 2\theta} = 35$ nN·s.

5.264. $p = (I/c)(1 + \rho)\cos^2\theta = 0.6\ nN/cm^2$.

5.265. $F = \pi R^2 I/c = 0.18$ μN.

5.266. $F = P/2c\,(1 + \eta^2)$.

5.267. (a) $\Delta p = \dfrac{2\hbar\omega}{c} \dfrac{\sqrt{1 - \beta^2}}{1 - \beta}$; (b) $\Delta p = \dfrac{2\hbar\omega}{c} \dfrac{1}{1 - \beta}$. Here $\beta = V/c$. It is evident that in the reference frame fixed to the mirror the latter obtains the smaller momentum.

5.268. $\sin(\theta/2) \approx E/mc\sqrt{gl}$, $\theta = 0.5°$.

5.269. $\Delta\omega/\omega_0 = -(1 - e^{-\gamma M/Rc^2}) < 0$, i.e. the frequency of the photon decreases.

5.270. $V = 2\pi\hbar c\,(1 - 1/\eta)/e\Delta\lambda = 16$ kV.

5.271. $V = \pi\hbar c/ed \sin\alpha = 31$ kV.

5.272. $\lambda_{min} = 2\pi\hbar/mc\,(\gamma - 1) = 2.8$ pm, where $\gamma = 1/\sqrt{1 - (v/c)^2}$.

5.273. 332 nm, $6.6\cdot 10^5$ m/s.

5.274. $A = 2\pi c\hbar \dfrac{(\eta^2 - \lambda_2/\lambda_1)}{\lambda_2(\eta^2 - 1)} = 1.9$ eV.

5.275. $\varphi_{max} = 4.4$ V.

5.276. $T_{max} = \hbar(\omega_0 + \omega) - A_f = 0.38$ eV.

5.277. $w = 2\pi c\hbar J/e\lambda = 0.020$.

5.278. $v_{max} = 6.4\cdot 10^5$ m/s.

5.279. 0.5 V; the polarity of the contact potential difference is opposite to that of external voltage.

5.280. $\hbar/mc$, the Compton wavelength for the given particle.

5.281. Let us write the energy and momentum conservation laws in the reference frame fixed to the electron for the moment preceding the collision with the photon: $\hbar\omega + m_0c^2 = mc^2$, $\hbar\omega/c = mv$, where $m = m_0\sqrt{1-(v/c)^2}$. From this it follows that $v = 0$ or $v = c$. The results have no physical meaning.

5.282. (a) Light is scattered by the free electrons; (b) the increase of the number of electrons that turn free (the free electrons have the binding energy much lower than the energy transferred to them by the photons); (c) the presence of a non-displaced component is due to scattering by the strongly bound electrons and the nuclei.

5.283. $\lambda = 4\pi\lambdabar_C\,[\sin(\theta_2/2) - \eta\sin(\theta_1/2)]/(\eta - 1) = 1.2$ pm.

5.284. $T = \hbar\omega\eta/(1+\eta) = 0.20$ MeV.

5.285. (a) $\omega' = 2\pi c/(\lambda + 2\pi\hbar/mc) = 2.2\cdot10^{20}$ rad/s;
(b) $T = \dfrac{2\pi c\hbar/\lambda}{1+\lambda mc/2\pi\hbar} = 60$ keV.

5.286. $\hbar\omega' = \dfrac{\hbar\omega}{1+2(\hbar\omega/mc^2)\sin(\theta/2)} = 0.144$ MeV.

5.287. $\sin(\theta/2) = \sqrt{mc(p-p')/2pp'}$. Hence $\theta = 120°$.

5.288. $\hbar\omega = \left[1+\sqrt{1+2mc^2/T\sin^2(\theta/2)}\right]T/2 = 0.68$ MeV.

5.289. $\lambda = (2\pi\hbar/mc)\left(\sqrt{1+2mc^2/T_{max}} - 1\right) = 3.7$ pm.

5.290. $\tan\varphi = \dfrac{\sqrt{4\pi\hbar/mc\Delta\lambda - 1}}{1+\hbar\omega/mc^2}$, $\varphi = 31°$.

5.291. $\rho = \dfrac{2\eta(1+\eta)mc}{(1+2\eta)eB} = 3.4$ cm.

5.292. $\Delta\lambda = (4\hbar/mc)\sin^2(\theta/2) = 1.2$ pm.

6.1. $r = 3e^2/2E = 0.16$ nm, $\lambda = (2\pi c/e)\sqrt{mr^3} = 0.24$ μm.

6.2. $b = 0.73$ pm.

6.3. (a) $r_{min} = 0.59$ pm; (b) $r_{min} = (2Ze^2/T)(1 + m_\alpha/m_{Li}) = 0.034$ pm.

6.4. (a) $\rho_{min} = (Ze^2/T)\cot^2(\theta/2) = 0.23$ pm; (b) $r_{min} = [1 + \operatorname{cosec}(\theta/2)]\,Ze^2/T = 0.56$ pm.

6.5. $p \approx 2\sqrt{2mT/[1+(2bT/Ze^2)^2]}$.

6.6. $T_e = m_pe^4/m_eb^2T = 4$ eV.

6.7. $b = \dfrac{Rn\sin(\theta/2)}{\sqrt{1+n^2-2n\cos(\theta/2)}}$, where $n = \sqrt{1+U_0/T}$.

6.8. (a) $\cos(\theta/2) = b/(R+r)$; (b) $dP = {}^1/_2\sin\theta\,d\theta$; (c) $P = 1/2$.

6.9. $3.3\cdot10^{-5}$.

6.10. $d = (4Jr^2T^2/nIZ^2e^4)\sin^4(\theta/2) = 1.5$ μm, where n is the concentration of nuclei.

6.11. $Z_{Pt} = Z_{Ag}\sqrt{\eta A_{Pt}/A_{Ag}} = 78$.

6.12. (a) $1.6\cdot10^6$; (b) $N = \pi nd\,(Ze^2/T)^2\cot^2(\theta_0/2)\,I_0\tau = 2.0\cdot10^7$, where n is the concentration of nuclei.

6.13. $P = \pi nd\,(Ze^2/mv^2)^2 = 0.006$, where n is the concentration of nuclei.

6.14. $\Delta N/N = 1 - \pi nZ^2e^4/T^2\tan^2(\theta_0/2) = 0.6$.

6.15. $\Delta N/N = \frac{\pi e^4}{4T^2}\left(0.7\,\frac{Z_1^2}{M_1} + 0.3\,\frac{Z_2^2}{M_2}\right)\rho d N_A \cot^2\frac{\theta}{2} = 1.4\cdot 10^{-3}$, where Z_1 and Z_2 are the atomic numbers of copper and zinc, M_1 and M_2 are their molar masses, N_A is Avogadro's number.

6.16. $\Delta\sigma = \pi\,(Ze^2/T)^2 \cot^2(\theta_0/2) = 0.73$ kb.

6.17. (a) 0.9 MeV; (b) $d\sigma/d\Omega = \Delta\sigma/4\pi \sin^4(\theta/2) = 0.64$ kb/sp.

6.18. $t = (3mc^3/2e^2\omega^2)\ln\eta = 15$ ns.

6.19. $t \approx m^2c^3r^3/4e^4 \approx 13$ ps.

6.21. $r_n = \sqrt{n\hbar/m\omega}$, $E_n = n\hbar\omega$, where $n = 1, 2, \ldots$, $\omega = \sqrt{k/m}$.

6.22.

	r_1, pm	v, 10^6 m/s	T, eV	E_b, eV	φ_i, V,	φ_1, V	λ, nm
H	52.9	2.18	13.6	13.6	13.6	10.2	121.5
He^+	26.5	4.36	54.5	54.5	54.5	40.8	30.4

6.23. $\omega = me^4Z^2/\hbar^3n^3 = 2.07\cdot 10^{16}\ s^{-1}$.

6.24. $\mu_n = ne\hbar/2mc$, $\mu_n/M_n = e/2mc$, $\mu_1 = \mu_B$.

6.25. $B = m^2e^7/c\hbar^5 = 125$ kG.

6.27. The Brackett series, $\lambda_{6\to 4} = 2.63$ μm.

6.28. (a) 657, 487 and 434 nm; (b) $\lambda/\delta\lambda \approx 1.5\cdot 10^3$.

6.29. For $n \gg 1$ $\sin\theta \approx n^3\pi c/lR$, whence $\theta \approx 60°$

6.30. He^+.

6.31. $N = {}^1/_2 n\,(n-1)$.

6.32. 97.3, 102.6 and 121.6 nm.

6.33. $n = 5$.

6.34. $R = \frac{176\pi c}{15Z^2\Delta\lambda} = 2.07\cdot 10^{16}\ s^{-1}$.

6.35. $Z = \sqrt{(176/15)\,\pi c/R\Delta\lambda} = 3$, Li^{++}.

6.36. $\lambda = (2\pi c/\Delta\omega)(Z\sqrt{R/\Delta\omega} - 1)/(2Z\sqrt{R/\Delta\omega} - 1) = 0.47$ μm.

6.37. $E_b = 54.4$ eV (He^+).

6.38. $E = E_0 + 4\hbar R = 79$ eV.

6.39. $v = \sqrt{2(\hbar\omega - 4\hbar R)/m} = 2.3\cdot 10^6$ m/s, where $\omega = 2\pi c/\lambda$.

6.40. $T_{min} = {}^3/_2\hbar R = 20.5$ eV.

6.41. $v = 3\hbar R/4mc = 3.25$ m/s, where m is the mass of the atom.

6.42. $(\varepsilon - \varepsilon')/\varepsilon \approx 3\hbar R/8mc^2 = 0.55\cdot 10^{-6}\%$, where m is the mass of the atom.

6.43. $v = 2\sqrt{\hbar R/m} = 3.1\cdot 10^6$ m/s, where m is the mass of the electron.

6.44. $v = 3R\Delta\lambda/8\pi\cos\theta = 0.7\cdot 10^6$ m/s.

6.45. (a) $E_n = n^2\pi^2\hbar^2/2ml^2$; (b) $E_n = n^2\hbar^2/2mr^2$; (c) $E_n = n\hbar\sqrt{\alpha/m}$; (d) $E_n = -m\alpha^2/2\hbar^2n^2$.

6.46. $E_b = \mu e^4/2\hbar^2$, $R = \mu e^4/2\hbar^3$, where μ is the reduced mass of the system. If the motion of the nucleus is not taken into account, these values (in the case of a hydrogen atom) are greater by $m/M \approx \approx 0.055\%$, where m and M are the masses of an electron and a proton.

6.47. $E_D - E_H = 3.7$ meV, $\lambda_H - \lambda_D = 33$ pm.

6.48. (a) 0.285 pm, 2.53 keV, 0.65 nm; (b) 106 pm, 6.8 eV, 0.243 μm.

6.49. 123, 2.86 and 0.186 pm.

6.50. 0.45 keV.

6.51. For both particles $\lambda = 2\pi\hbar\,(1 + m_n/m_d)/\sqrt{2m_nT} = 8.6$ pm.

6.52. $\tilde{\lambda} = 2\lambda_1\lambda_2/\sqrt{\lambda_1^2 + \lambda_2^2}$.

6.53. $\lambda = 2\pi\hbar/\sqrt{2mkT} = 128$ pm.

6.54. First, let us find the distribution of molecules over de Broglie wavelengths. From the relation $f(v)\,dv = -\varphi(\lambda)\,d\lambda$ where $f(v)$ is Maxwell's distribution of velocities, we obtain

$$\varphi(\lambda) = A\lambda^{-4}e^{-a/\lambda^2}, \quad a = 2\pi^2\hbar^2/nkT.$$

The condition $d\varphi/d\lambda = 0$ provides $\lambda_{pr} = \pi\hbar/\sqrt{mkT} = 0.09$ nm.

6.55. $\lambda = 2\pi\hbar/\sqrt{2mT\,(1 + T/2mc^2)}$, $T \leqslant 4mc^2\Delta\lambda/\lambda = 20.4$ keV (for an electron) and 37.5 MeV (for a proton).

6.56. $T = (\sqrt{2} - 1)\,mc^2 = 0.21$ MeV.

6.57. $\lambda = \lambda_{sh}/\sqrt{1 + mc\lambda_{sh}/\pi\hbar} = 3.3$ pm.

6.58. $v = 4\pi\hbar l/mb\Delta x = 2.0\cdot 10^6$ m/s.

6.59. $\Delta x = 2\pi\hbar l/d\sqrt{2meV} = 4.9$ μm.

6.60. $V_0 = \pi^2\hbar^2/2me\,(\sqrt{\eta} - 1)^2\,d^2\sin^2\theta = 0.15$ keV.

6.61. $d = \pi\hbar k/\sqrt{2mT}\cos(\theta/2) = 0.21$ nm, where $k = 4$.

6.62. $d = \pi\hbar k/\sqrt{2mT}\sin\theta = 0.23 \pm 0.04$ nm, where $k = 3$ and the angle θ is determined by the formula $\tan 2\theta = D/2l$.

6.63. (a) $n = \sqrt{1 + V_i/V} = 1.05$; (b) $V/V_i \geqslant 1/\eta\,(2 + \eta) = 50$.

6.64. $E_n = n^2\pi^2\hbar^2/2ml^2$, where $n = 1, 2, \ldots$.

6.66. $1\cdot 10^4$, $1\cdot 10$ and $1\cdot 10^{-20}$ cm/s.

6.67. $\Delta v \approx \hbar/ml = 1\cdot 10^6$ m/s; $v_1 = 2.2\cdot 10^6$ m/s.

6.69. $\Delta t \approx \eta ml^2/\hbar \approx 10^{-16}$ s.

6.70. $T_{min} \approx \hbar^2/2ml^2 = 1$ eV. Here we assumed that $p \approx \Delta p$ and $\Delta x = l$.

6.71. $\Delta v/v \sim \hbar/l\sqrt{2mT} = 1\cdot 10^{-4}$.

6.72. $F \approx \hbar^2/ml^3$.

6.73. Taking into account that $p \sim \Delta p \sim \hbar/\Delta x \sim \hbar/x$, we get $E = T + U \approx \hbar^2/2mx^2 + kx^2/2$. From the condition $dE/dx = 0$ we find x_0 and then $E_{min} \approx \hbar\sqrt{k/m} = \hbar\omega$, where ω is the oscillator's angular frequency. The rigorous calculations furnish the value $\hbar\omega/2$.

6.74. Taking into account that $p \sim \Delta p \sim \hbar/\Delta r$ and $\Delta r \sim r$, we get $E = p^2/2m - e^2/r \approx \hbar^2/2mr^2 - e^2/r$. From the condition

$dE/dr = 0$ we find $r_{eff} \approx \hbar^2/me^2 = 53$ pm, $E_{min} \approx -me^4/2\hbar^2 = -13.6$ eV.

6.75. The width of the image is $\Delta \approx \delta + \Delta' \approx \delta + \hbar l/p\delta$, where Δ' is an additional widening associated with the uncertainty of the momentum Δp_y (when the hydrogen atoms pass through the slit), p is the momentum of the incident hydrogen atoms. The function $\Delta(\delta)$ has the minimum when $\delta \approx \sqrt{\hbar l/mv} = 0.01$ mm.

6.76. The solution of the Schrödinger equation should be sought in the form $\Psi = \psi(x) \cdot f(t)$. The substitution of this function into the initial equation with subsequent separation of the variables x and t results in two equations. Their solutions are $\psi(x) \sim e^{ikx}$, where $k = \sqrt{2mE}/\hbar$, E is the energy of the particle, and $f(t) \sim e^{-i\omega t}$, where $\omega = E/\hbar$. Finally, $\Psi = ae^{i(kx-\omega t)}$, where a is a certain constant.

6.77. $P = 1/3 + \sqrt{3}/2\pi = 0.61$.

6.78. $$\psi = \begin{cases} A\cos(\pi n x/l), & \text{if } n = 1, 3, 5, \ldots, \\ A\sin(\pi n x/l), & \text{if } n = 2, 4, 6, \ldots \end{cases}$$

Here $A = \sqrt{2/l}$.

6.80. $dN/dE = (l/\pi\hbar)\sqrt{m/2E}$; if $E = 1$ eV, then $dN/dE = 0.8 \cdot 10^7$ levels per eV.

6.81. (a) In this case the Schrödinger equation takes the form

$$\frac{\partial^2\psi}{\partial x^2} + \frac{\partial^2\psi}{\partial y^2} + k^2\psi = 0, \quad k^2 = 2mE/\hbar^2.$$

Let us take the origin of coordinates at one of the corners of the well. On the sides of the well the function $\psi(x, y)$ must turn into zero (according to the condition), and therefore it is convenient to seek this function inside the well in the form $\psi(x, y) = a \sin k_1 x \times \sin k_2 y$, since on the two sides ($x = 0$ and $y = 0$) $\psi = 0$ automatically. The possible values of k_1 and k_2 are found from the condition of ψ turning into zero on the opposite sides of the well:

$$\psi(l_1, y) = 0, \quad k_1 = \pm(\pi/l_1)\, n_1, \quad n_1 = 1, 2, 3, \ldots,$$
$$\psi(x, l_2) = 0, \quad k_2 = \pm(\pi/l_2)\, n_2, \quad n_2 = 1, 2, 3, \ldots$$

The substitution of the wave function into the Schrödinger equation leads to the relation $k_1^2 + k_2^2 = k^2$, whence

$$E_{n_1 n_2} = (n_1^2/l_1^2 + n_2^2/l_2^2)\, \pi^2\hbar^2/2m.$$

(b) 9.87, 24.7, 39.5, and 49.4 units of $\hbar^2/ml^2$.

6.82. $P = 1/3 - \sqrt{3}/4\pi = 19.5\%$.

6.83. (a) $E = (n_1^2 + n_2^2 + n_3^2)\, \pi^2\hbar^2/2ma^2$, where n_1, n_2, n_3 are integers not equal to zero: (b) $\Delta E = \pi^2\hbar^2/ma^2$; (c) for the 6-th level $n_1^2 + n_2^2 + n_3^2 = 14$ and $E = 7\pi^2\hbar^2/ma^2$; the number of states is equal o six (it is equal to the number of permutations of a triad 1, 2, 3.)

6.84. Let us integrate the Schrödinger equation over a small interval of the coordinate x within which there is a discontinuity in $U(x)$, for example at the point $x = 0$:

$$\frac{\partial\psi}{\partial x}(+\delta) - \frac{\partial\psi}{\partial x}(-\delta) = \int_{-\delta}^{+\delta} \frac{2m}{\hbar^2}(E-U)\,\psi\, dx.$$

Since the discontinuity U is finite the integral tends to zero as $\delta \to 0$. What follows is obvious.

6.85. (a) Let us write the Schrödinger equation for two regions

$$0 < x < l, \quad \psi_1'' + k^2\psi_1 = 0, \quad k^2 = 2mE/\hbar^2,$$
$$x > l, \quad \psi_2'' - \varkappa^2\psi_2 = 0, \quad \varkappa^2 = 2m(U_0 - E)/\hbar^2.$$

Their common solutions

$$\psi_1(x) = a \sin(kx + \alpha), \quad \psi_2(x) = be^{-\varkappa x} + ce^{\varkappa x}$$

must satisfy the standard and boundary conditions. From the condition $\psi_1(0) = 0$ and the requirement for the finiteness of the wave

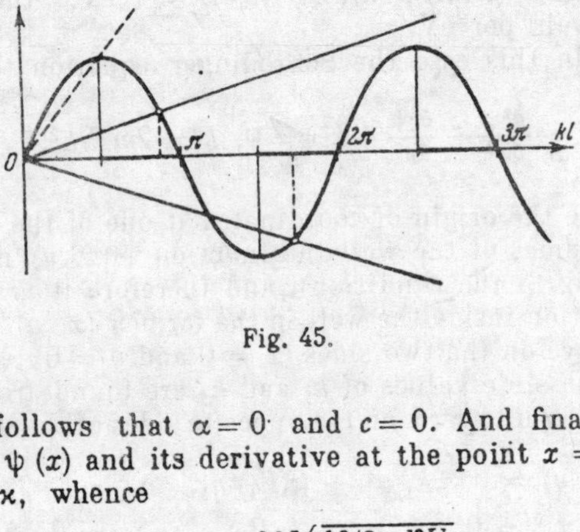

Fig. 45.

function it follows that $\alpha = 0$ and $c = 0$. And finally, from the continuity of $\psi(x)$ and its derivative at the point $x = l$ we obtain $\tan kl = -k/\varkappa$, whence

$$\sin kl = \pm kl\sqrt{\hbar^2/2ml^2U_0}.$$

Plotting the left-hand and right-hand sides of the last equation (Fig. 45), we can find the points at which the straight line crosses the sine curve. The roots of the equation corresponding to the eigenvalues of energy E are found from those intersection points $(kl)_i$ for which $\tan(kl)_i < 0$, i.e. the roots of that equation are located in the even quadrants (these segments of the abscissa axis are shown heavy in the figure). It is seen from the plot that the roots of the equation, i.e. the bound states of the particle, do not always exist. The dotted line indicates the ultimate position of the straight line.

(b) $(l^2U_0)_{1\,min} = \pi^2\hbar^2/8m$, $(l^2U_0)_{n\,min} = (2n-1)^2\pi^2\hbar^2/8m$.

6.86. Suppose that P_a and P_i are the probabilities of the particle being outside and inside the well. Then

$$\frac{P_a}{P_i}=\frac{\int_l^\infty b^2 e^{-2\varkappa x}\,dx}{\int_0^l a^2 \sin^2 kx\,dx}=\frac{2}{2+3\pi},$$

where the ratio b/a can be found from the condition $\psi_1(l)=\psi_2(l)$. Now it remains to take into account that $P_a+P_i=1$; then $P_a=2/(4+3\pi)=14.9\%$.

The penetration of the particle inte the region where its energy $E<U$ is a purely quantum phenomenon. It occurs owing to the wave properties of the particle ruling out the simultaneous precise magnitudes of the coordinate and the momentum, and consequently the precise division of the total energy of the particle into the potential and the kinetic energy. The latter could be done only within the limits set by the uncertainty principle.

6.87. Utilizing the substitution indicated, we get

$$\chi''+k^2\chi=0, \quad \text{where } k^2=2mE/\hbar^2.$$

We shall seek the solution of this equation in the form $\chi=a\sin(kr+\alpha)$. From the finiteness of the wave function ψ at the point $r=0$ it follows that $\alpha=0$. Thus, $\psi=(a/r)\sin kr$. From the boundary condition $\psi(r_0)=0$ we obtain $kr_0=n\pi$, where $n=1, 2, \ldots$ Hence, $E_n=n^2\pi^2\hbar^2/2mr_0^2$.

6.88. (a) $\psi(r)=\frac{1}{\sqrt{2\pi r_0}}\frac{\sin(n\pi r/r_0)}{r}$, $n=1, 2, \ldots$; (b) $r_{pr}=r_0/2$; 50%.

6.89. (a) The solutions of the Schrödinger equation for the function $\chi(r)$:

$$r<r_0,\quad \chi_1=A\sin(kr+\alpha),\quad \text{where } k=\sqrt{2mE}/\hbar,$$

$$r>r_0,\quad \chi_2=Be^{\varkappa r}+Ce^{-\varkappa r},\quad \text{where } \varkappa=\sqrt{2m(U_0-E)}/\hbar.$$

Since the function $\psi(r)$ is finite throughout the space, $\alpha=0$ and $B=0$. Thus,

$$\psi_1=A\frac{\sin kr}{r},\quad \psi_2=C\frac{e^{-\varkappa r}}{r}.$$

From the continuity of the function ψ and its derivative at the point $r=r_0$ we get $\tan kr_0=-k/\varkappa$, or

$$\sin kr_0=\pm\sqrt{\hbar^2/2mr_0^2U_0}\,kr_0.$$

As it was demonstrated in the solution of Problem 6.85, this equation determines the discontinuous spectrum of energy eigenvalues. (b) $r_0^2U_0=\pi^2\hbar^2/8m$.

6.90. $\alpha = m\omega/2\hbar$, $E = \hbar\omega/2$, where $\omega = \sqrt{k/m}$.

6.91. $E = -me^4/8\hbar^2$, i.e. the level with principal quantum number $n = 2$.

6.92. (a) The probability of the electron being at the interval r, $r + dr$ from the nucleus is $dP = \psi^2(r)\, 4\pi r^2 dr$. From the condition for the maximum of the function dP/dr we get $r_{pr} = r_1$; (b) $\langle F \rangle = 2e^2/r_1^2$; (c) $\langle U \rangle = -e^2/r_1$.

6.93. $\varphi_0 = \int (\rho/r)\, 4\pi r^2\, dr = -e/r_1$, where $\rho = -e\psi^2$ is the space charge density, ψ is the normalized wave function.

6.94. (a) Let us write the solutions of the Schrödinger equation to the left and to the right of the barrier in the following form:

$$x < 0, \quad \psi_1(x) = a_1 e^{ik_1x} + b_1 e^{-ik_1x}, \quad \text{where } k_1 = \sqrt{2mE}/\hbar,$$

$$x > 0, \quad \psi_2(x) = a_2 e^{ik_2x} + b_2 e^{-ik_2x}, \quad \text{where } k_2 = \sqrt{2m(E - U_0)}/\hbar.$$

Let us assume that the incident wave has an amplitude a_1 and the reflected wave an amplitude b_2. Since in the region $x > 0$ there is only a travelling wave, $b_2 = 0$. The reflection coefficient R is the ratio of the reflected stream of particles to the incident stream, or, in other words, the ratio of the squares of amplitudes of corresponding waves. Due to the continuity of ψ and its derivative at the point $x = 0$ we have $a_1 + b_1 = a_2$ and $a_1 - b_1 = (k_2/k_1)\, a_2$, whence

$$R = (b_1/a_1)^2 = (k_1 - k_2)^2/(k_1 + k_2)^2.$$

(b) In the case of $E < U_0$ the solution of the Schrödinger equation to the right of the barrier takes the form

$$\psi_2(x) = a_2 e^{\varkappa x} + b_2 e^{-\varkappa x}, \quad \text{where } \varkappa = \sqrt{2m(U_0 - E)}/\hbar.$$

From the finiteness of $\psi(x)$ it follows that $a_2 = 0$. The probability of finding the particle under the barrier has the density $P_2(x) = \psi_2^2(x) \sim e^{-2\varkappa x}$. Hence, $x_{eff} = 1/2\varkappa$.

6.95. (a) $D \approx \exp\left[-\frac{2l}{\hbar}\sqrt{2m(U_0 - E)}\right]$;

(b) $D \approx \exp\left[-\frac{8l\sqrt{2m}}{3\hbar U_0}(U_0 - E)^{3/2}\right]$.

6.96. $D \approx \exp\left[-\frac{\pi l}{\hbar}\sqrt{\frac{2m}{U_0}}(U_0 - E)\right]$.

6.97. -0.41 for an S term and -0.04 for a P term.

6.98. $\alpha = \sqrt{\hbar R/(E_0 - e\varphi_1)} - 3 = -0.88$.

6.99. $E_b = \hbar R/(\sqrt{R\lambda_1\lambda_2/2\pi c\Delta\lambda} - 1)^2 = 5.3$ eV.

6.100. 0.82 μm ($3S \rightarrow 2P$) and 0.68 μm ($2P \rightarrow 2S$).

6.101. $\Delta E = 2\pi\hbar c\Delta\lambda/\lambda^2 = 2.0$ meV.

6.102. $\Delta\omega = 1.05 \cdot 10^{14}$ rad/s.

6.103. $3S_{1/2}$, $3P_{1/2}$, $3P_{3/2}$, $3D_{3/2}$, $3D_{5/2}$.

6.104. (a) 1, 2, 3, 4, 5; (b) 0, 1, 2, 3, 4, 5, 6; (c) 1/2, 3/2, 5/2, 7/2, 9/2.

6.105. For the state ^4P: $\hbar\sqrt{3/2}$, $\hbar\sqrt{15/2}$, and $\hbar\sqrt{32/2}$; for the state ^5D: 0, $\hbar\sqrt{2}$; $\hbar\sqrt{6}$, $\hbar\sqrt{12}$, $\hbar\sqrt{20}$.

6.106. (a) $^2F_{7/2}$, $M_{max}=\hbar\sqrt{63/2}$, (b) $^3F_4$, $M_{max}=2\hbar\sqrt{5}$.

6.107. In the F state $M_s=\hbar\sqrt{6}$; for the D state it can be only found that $M_s \geqslant \hbar\sqrt{6}$.

6.108. 3, 4, 5.

6.109. (a) 1, 3, 5, 7, 9; (b) 2, 4, 6; (c) 5, 7, 9.

6.110. 31°.

6.111. $^3D_2$.

6.112. $^1P_1$, $^1D_2$, $^1F_3$, $^3P_{0,1,2}$, $^3D_{1,2,3}$, $^3F_{2,3,4}$.

6.113. The same as in the foregoing problem.

6.114. The second and the third term.

6.115. $g = 4 + 6 = 10$.

6.116. 4, 7 and 10.

6.117. $^3F_3$.

6.118. As.

6.119. (a) $^4S_{3/2}$; (b) $^3P_2$.

6.120. (a) $^4F_{3/2}$, $\hbar\sqrt{15/2}$; (b) $^4F_{9/2}$, $\hbar 3\sqrt{11/2}$.

6.121. (a) Two d electrons; (b) five p electrons; (c) five d electrons.

6.122. (a) $^3P_0$, (b) $^4F_{9/2}$.

6.123. $^4F_{3/2}$.

6.124. $\mu = \mu_B\sqrt{35}$ $(^6S_{5/2})$.

6.125. $\eta = n^2 e^{-\hbar\omega/kT} = 3\cdot 10^{-17}$, where $\omega = R\,(1 - 1/n^2)$.

6.126. $N/N_0 = (g/g_0)\, e^{-\hbar\omega/kT} = 1.14\cdot 10^{-4}$, where g and g_0 are the statistical weights (degeneracy ratios) of the levels $3P$ and $3S$ respectively ($g = 6$, $g_0 = 2$).

6.127. $\tau = l/v \ln \eta = 1.3$ μs.

6.128. $N = \lambda\tau P/2\pi c\hbar = 7\cdot 10^9$.

6.129. $\tau = (n\hbar\omega/P)\,(g/g_0)\, e^{-\hbar\omega/kT} = 65$ ns, where g and g_0 are the degeneracy ratios of the resonant and the basic level.

6.130. (a) $P_{ind}/P_{sp} = 1/(e^{\hbar\omega/kT} - 1) \approx 10^{-34}$, where $\omega = {}^3/_4 R$; (b) $T = 1.7\cdot 10^5$ K.

6.131. Suppose that I is the intensity of the passing ray. The decrease in this value on passing through the layer of the substance of thickness dx is equal to

$$-dI = \varkappa I\, dx = (N_1 B_{12} - N_2 B_{21})\,(I/c)\,\hbar\omega\, dx,$$

where N_1 and N_2 are the concentrations of atoms on the lower and upper levels, B_{12} and B_{21} are the Einstein coefficients. Hence

$$\varkappa = (\hbar\omega/c)\, N_1 B_{12}\,(1 - g_1 N_2/g_2 N_1).$$

Next, the Boltzmann distribution should be taken into consideration, as well as the fact that $\hbar\omega \gg kT$ (in this case N_1 is approximately equal to N_0, the total concentration of the atoms).

6.132. $\Delta\lambda_{Dop}/\Delta\lambda_{nat} \approx 4\pi\tau v_{pr}/\lambda \approx 10^3$, where $v_{pr} = \sqrt{2RT/M}$.

6.133. $\lambda = 154$ pm.

6.134. (a) 843 pm for Al, 180 pm for Co; (b) ≈ 5 keV.

6.135. Three.

6.136. $V = 15$ kV.

6.137. Yes.

6.138. $Z = 1 + 2\sqrt{(n-1)eV_1/3\hbar R(n - V_1/V_2)} = 29$.

6.139. $Z = 1 + \sqrt{4\Delta\omega/3R} = 22$, titanium.

6.140. $E_b = {}^3/_4\hbar R(Z-1)^2 + 2\pi c\hbar/\lambda_L = 5.5$ keV.

6.141. $E_L = \hbar\omega(2\pi c/\omega\Delta\lambda - 1) \approx 0.5$ keV, where $\omega = {}^3/_4 R(Z-1)^2$.

6.142. $T = {}^3/_4\hbar R(Z-1)^2 - 2\pi c\hbar/\lambda_K = 1.45$ keV, $v = 2.26\cdot 10^7$ m/s.

6.143. (a) $g = 2$, with the exception of the singlet state, where $g = 0/0$; (b) $g = 1$.

6.144. (a) $-2/3$; (b) 0; (c) 1; (d) 5/2; (e) 0/0.

6.145. (a) $\sqrt{12}\mu_B$; (b) $2\sqrt{3/5}\mu_B$; (c) $(8/\sqrt{3})\mu_B$.

6.146. $M_s = 2\sqrt{3}\hbar$.

6.147. $\mu = (8/\sqrt{3})\mu_B$.

6.148. $\mu = 3\sqrt{7/5}\mu_B$.

6.149. $\mu - (5\sqrt{5}/2)\mu_B$.

6.150. $M = \hbar\sqrt{3}/2$.

6.151. ${}^5F_1$.

6.152. $\omega = \mu_B gB/\hbar = 1.2\cdot 10^{10}$ rad/s, where g is the Landé factor.

6.153. $F_{max} = \mu_{B\,max}\cdot|\partial B/\partial z| = (3/\sqrt{8})\pi IgJ\mu_B/cr^2 = 4\cdot 10^{-27}$ N.

6.154. $F = 2I\mu_B/cr^2 = 3\cdot 10^{-26}$ N.

6.155. $\partial B/\partial z = 2T\delta/gJ\mu_B l_1(l_1 + 2l_2) = 15$ kG/cm.

6.156. (a) It does not split; (b) splits into 6 sublevels; (c) does not split ($g = 0$).

6.157. (a) 58 μeV; (b) $\Delta E = 2gJ\mu_B B = 145$ μeV.

6.158. (a) Normal; (b) anomalous; (c) normal; (d) normal (both terms have identical Landé factors).

6.159. $L = \Delta E/2\mu_B B = 3$; ${}^1F_3$.

6.160. $\Delta\lambda = \lambda^2 eB/2\pi mc^2 = 35$ pm.

6.161. $B_{min} = 4.0$ kG.

6.162. $B = \hbar\Delta\omega/g\mu_B = 3$ kG.

6.163. (a) 2 . 1 (the ratio of the corresponding Landé factors); (b) $B = 2\pi c\hbar\Delta\lambda/g\mu_B\eta\lambda^2 = 5.5$ kG.

6.164. $\Delta\omega = (\pm 1.3, \pm 4.0, \pm 6.6)\cdot 10^{10}$ s^{-1}, six components.

6.165. (a) Six (*1*) and four (*2*); (b) nine (*1*) and six (*2*).

6.166. $\Delta\omega = (m_1 g_1 - m_2 g_2)_{max} eB/mc = 1.0\cdot 10^{11}$ s^{-1}.

6.167. $\omega = 4\sqrt{2}\hbar/md^2 = 1.57\cdot 10^{11}$ s^{-1}, where m is the mass of the molecule.

6.168. 2 and 3.

6.169. $M = \sqrt{md^2 E/2} = 3.5h$, where m is the mass of the molecule.

6.1 0. $I = h/\Delta\omega = 193.10^{-40}$ g . cm^2, $d = 112$ pm.

6.1 1. 13 levels.

6.1 2. $N \approx \sqrt{2I\omega/h} = 33$ lines.

6.1 3. $dN/dE \approx \sqrt{I/2h^{-2}E}$, where I is the moment of inertia of the molecule. In the case of $J = 10$ $dN/dE = 1.0.10^4$ levels per eV.

6.1 4. $E_{vib}/E_{rot} = \omega\mu d^2/h$, where μ is the reduced mass of the molecule; (a) 36; (b) $1.7 \cdot 10^2$; (c) $2.9 \cdot 10^3$.

6.1 5. $N_{vib}/N_{rot} = 1/3^{0-h(\omega-2B)/kT} = 3.1 \cdot 10^{-4}$, where $B = h/2I$, I is the moment of inertia of the molecule.

6.1 6. According to the definition

$$(E) = \frac{\Sigma E_v \exp(-E_v/kT)}{\Sigma \exp(-E_v/kT)} = \frac{\Sigma E_v \exp(-\alpha E_v)}{\Sigma \exp(-\alpha E_v)}$$

were $E_v = h_\omega (v + 1/2)$ $\alpha = 1/kT$. The summation is carried out over v taking the values from 0 to ∞ as follows:

$$(E) = -\frac{\partial}{\partial\alpha} \ln \Sigma \exp(-\alpha E_v) = -\frac{\partial}{\partial a} = \frac{\exp(-\alpha h\omega/2)}{1-\exp(-\alpha h\omega)}$$

$$= \frac{h\omega}{2} + \frac{h\omega}{\exp(h\omega/kT)-1};$$

$$C_{vvib} = N\frac{\partial (E)}{\partial T} = \frac{R(h\omega/kT)^2 \theta^{h\omega/kT}}{(e^{h\omega/kT}-1)^2} = 0.56\,R,$$

where R is the universal gas constant.

6.1 . $d = \sqrt{2h/\mu\Delta\omega} = 0.13$ nm, where μ is the reduced mass of the molecule.

6.1 8. $\lambda = \lambda_0/(1 \mp \omega\lambda_0/2\pi c) = 423$ and 387 nm.

6.1 9. $\omega = \pi c(\lambda_r - \lambda_v)/\lambda_r\lambda_v = 1.37 \cdot 10^{14}$ rad/s, $x = 4.96$ N/cm,

6.180. $I_v/I_r = \exp(-h\omega/kT) = 0.067$. Will increase 3.9 times.

6.181. (a) See Fig. 46*a* in which the arrows indicate the motion directions of the nuclei in the molecule at the same moment. The oscillation frequencies are ω_1, ω_2, ω_3, with ω_3 being the frequency of two independent oscillations in mutually perpendicular planes. Thus, there are four different oscillations. (b) See Fig. 46b; there are seven different oscillations: three longitudinal ones (ω_1, ω_2, ω_3) and four transversal ones (ω_4, ω_5), two oscillations for each frequency.

6.182. $dN_\omega = (l/\pi v)\, d\omega$.

6.183. $dN_\omega = (S/2\pi v^2)\,\omega\, d\omega$.

6.184. $dN_\omega = (V/\pi^2 v^3)\,\omega^2\, d\omega$.

6.185. (a) $\Theta = (h/k)\,\pi v n_0$; (b) $\Theta = (h/k)\, v\sqrt{4\pi n_0}$; (c) $\Theta = (h/k)$ $v\sqrt[3]{6\pi^2 n_0}$.

6.186. $\Theta = (\hbar/k)\sqrt[3]{18\pi^2 n_0/(v_{\parallel}^{-3} + 2v_{\perp}^{-3})} = 470$ K, where n_0 is the concentration of the atoms.

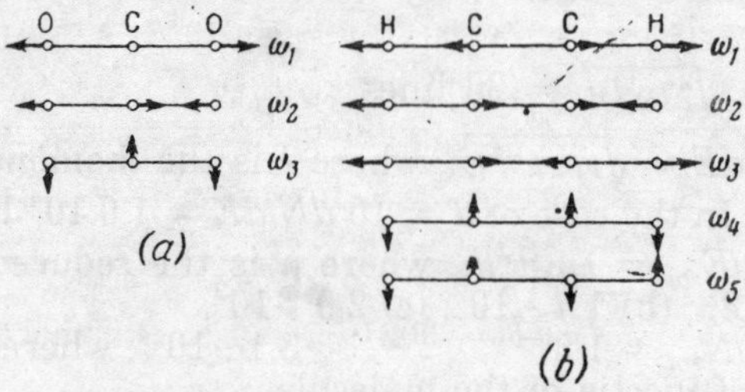

Fig. 46.

6.187. $v \approx k\Theta/\hbar\sqrt[3]{6\pi^2 n_0} = 3.4$ km/s, where n_0 is the concentration of the atoms. The tabulated values are: $v_{\parallel} = 6.3$ km/s, $v_{\perp} = 3.1$ km/s.

6.188. The oscillation energy of a mole of a "crystal" is

$$U = R\Theta\left[\frac{1}{4} + \left(\frac{T}{\Theta}\right)^2 \int_0^{\Theta/T} \frac{x\,dx}{e^x - 1}\right],$$

where $x = \hbar\omega/kT$. Hence the molar heat capacity is

$$C = R\left(\frac{2T}{\Theta}\int_0^{\Theta/T}\frac{x\,dx}{e^x - 1} - \frac{\Theta/T}{e^{\Theta/T} - 1}\right).$$

When $T \gg \Theta$, the heat capacity $C \approx R$.

6.189. (a) $dN/d\omega = 2l/\pi a\sqrt{\omega_{max}^2 - \omega^2}$; (b) $N = l/a$, i.e. is equal to the number of the atoms in the chain.

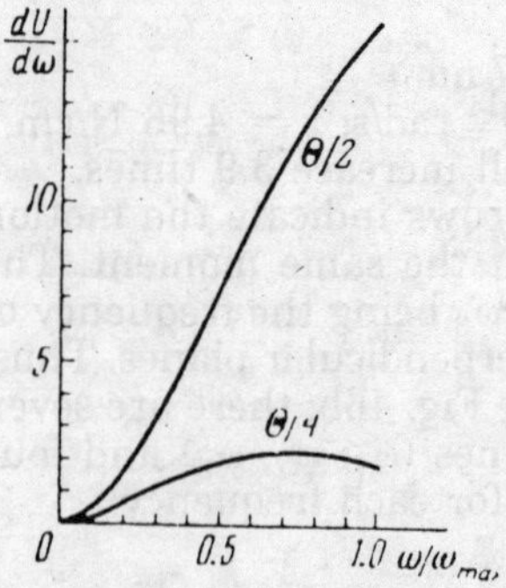

Fig. 47.

6.190. $U_0 = 9R\Theta/8\mu = 48.6$ J/g, where μ is the molar mass of copper.

6.191. (a) $\Theta \approx 220$ K; (b) $C \approx 10$ J/(mol·K); (c) $\omega_{max} = 4.1 \times 10^{13}$ rad/s.

6.193. Yes, because the heat capacity is proportional to T^3 at these temperatures.

6.194. $\langle E\rangle = {}^3/_8\, k\Theta$.

6.195. See Fig. 47.

6.196. $\hbar\omega_{max} = 28$ meV, $\hbar k_{max} \sim 10^{-19}$ g·cm/s.

6.197. (a) $T_{max} = (3\pi^2 n)^{2/3}\hbar^2/2m$; (b) $\langle T\rangle = {}^3/_5 T_{max}$.

6.198. $\eta = 1 - 2^{-3/2} \approx 65\%$.

6.199. 0.93.

6.200. $\approx 3\cdot 10^4$ K.

6.201. $\Delta E = 2\pi^2\hbar^2/mV\ (3\pi^2 n)^{1/3} = 2\cdot 10^{-22}$ eV.
6.202. (a) $dn_v = (m^3/\pi^2\hbar^3)\, v^2\, dv$; (b) $\langle v\rangle/v_{max} = 3/4$.
6.203. $dn_\lambda = 8\pi\lambda^{-4}\, d\lambda$.
6.204. $p = {}^2/_3 n\ \langle T\rangle = (\pi\sqrt[3]{9\pi}\hbar^2/5m)\ n^{5/3} \approx 5\cdot 10^4$ atm.
6.205. $A = kT\ (\eta T/\Delta T - 2) = 4.5$ eV.
6.206. $n = \sqrt{1 + U_0/T} = 1.02$, where $U_0 = T_{max} + A$, $T_{max} = (3\pi^2 n)^{2/3}\ \hbar^2/2m$. A is the work function.
6.207. $E_{min} = \dfrac{2kT_1T_2}{T_2 - T_1} \ln\eta = 0.33$ eV.
6.208. $\alpha = \dfrac{1}{\rho}\dfrac{\partial\rho}{\partial T} = -\dfrac{\pi c\hbar}{kT^2\lambda_r} = -0.05\ \text{K}^{-1}$, where $\rho \sim e^{\Delta E_0/2kT}$, ΔE_0 is the forbidden band width.
6.209. $\Delta E = -2k\dfrac{\Delta \ln\sigma}{\Delta(T^{-1})} = 1.2$ and 0.06 eV.
6.210. $\tau = t/\ln\dfrac{(\rho-\rho_1)\,\rho_2}{(\rho-\rho_2)\,\rho_1} = 0.01$ s.
6.211. $n = hBV/el\rho V_H = 5\cdot 10^{15}\ \text{cm}^{-3}$, $u_0 = lV_H/hBV = 0.05\ \text{m}^2/(\text{V}\cdot\text{s})$.
6.212. $|u_0^- - u_0^+| = 1/\eta B = 0.20\ \text{m}^2/(\text{V}\cdot\text{s})$.
6.213. $n^+/n^- = \eta^2 = 4.0$.
6.214. (a) $P = 1 - \exp(-\lambda t)$; (b) $\tau = 1/\lambda$.
6.215. About 1/4.
6.216. $1.2\cdot 10^{15}$.
6.217. $\tau \approx 16$ s.
6.218. $T = 5.3$ days.
6.219. $4.6\cdot 10^2$ part./min.
6.220. $\lambda = -(1/t)\ln(1-\eta) \approx \eta/t = 1.1\cdot 10^{-5}\ \text{s}^{-1}$, $\tau = 1/\lambda = 1.0$ years.
6.221. $T = 4.5\cdot 10^9$ years, $A = 1.2\cdot 10^4$ dis./s.
6.222. $4.1\cdot 10^3$ years.
6.223. About $2.0\cdot 10^9$ years.
6.224. $3.2\cdot 10^{17}$ and $0.8\cdot 10^5$ dis/(s·g) respectively.
6.225. $V = (A/A')\exp(-t\ln 2/T) = 6$ l.
6.226. 0.19%.
6.227. $T_1 = 1.6$ hours, $T_2 = 9.8$ hours; $N_2/N_1 = (T_2/T_1) \times \exp(\ln A_2 - \ln A_1) = 10$.
6.228. $t = -(T/\ln 2)\ln(1 - A/q) = 9.5$ days.
6.229. (a) $N_2(t) = N_{10}\dfrac{\lambda_1}{\lambda_2 - \lambda_1}(e^{-\lambda_1 t} - e^{-\lambda_2 t})$;
(b) $t_m = \dfrac{\ln(\lambda_1/\lambda_2)}{\lambda_1 - \lambda_2}$.
6.230. (a) $N_2(t) = \lambda N_{10} t \exp(-\lambda t)$; (b) $t_m = 1/\lambda$.
6.231. $N_3(t) = N_{10}\left(1 + \dfrac{\lambda_1 e^{-\lambda_2 t} - \lambda_2 e^{-\lambda_1 t}}{\lambda_2 - \lambda_1}\right)$.
6.232. $\dot N_\beta = N_0\lambda_1 \exp(-\lambda_1 t) = 0.72\cdot 10^{11}$ part./s, $\dot N_\alpha = N_0(e^{-\lambda_1 t} - e^{-\lambda_2 t})\,\lambda_1\lambda_2/(\lambda_2 - \lambda_1) = 1.46\cdot 10^{11}$ part./s. Here N_0 is the initial number of Bi^{210} nuclei.
6.233. (a) Pb^{206}; (b) eight alpha decays and six beta decays.

6.234. $v = \sqrt{2m_\alpha T_\alpha/m} = 3.4\cdot10^5$ m/s; 0.020.
6.235. 1.6 MJ.
6.236. 0.82 MeV.
6.237. (a) 6.1 cm; (b) $2.1\cdot10^5$ and $0.77\cdot10^5$ respectively.
6.238. $Q = \begin{cases} (M_p - M_d)c^2 \text{ for } \beta^- \text{ decay and } K\text{-capture}, \\ (M_p - M_d - 2m)\,c^2 \text{ for } \beta^+ \text{ decay}. \end{cases}$
6.239. 0.56 MeV and 47.5 eV.
6.240. 5 MJ.
6.241. 0.32 and 0.65 MeV.
6.242. $T \approx {}^1/_2 Q\,(Q + 2mc^2)/M_N c^2 = 0.11$ keV, where $Q = (M_N - M_C - 2m)\,c^2$, m is the mass of an electron.
6.243. 40 km/s.
6.244. 0.45 c, where c is the velocity of light.
6.245. $\Delta\varepsilon/\varepsilon = E/2mc^2 = 3.6\cdot10^{-7}$, where m is the mass of the nucleus.
6.246. $v \approx \varepsilon/mc = 0.22$ km/s, where m is the mass of the nucleus.
6.247. $v = gh/c = 65$ μm/s.
6.248. $h_{min} = \hbar c^2/g\varepsilon\tau = 4.6$ m.
6.249. $T = T_\alpha/[1 + (M - m)^2/4mM\cos^2\Theta] = 6.0$ MeV, where m and M are the masses of an alpha particle and a lithium nucleus.
6.250. (a) $\eta = 4mM/(m + M)^2 = 0.89$; (b) $\eta = 2m/(m + M) = 2/3$. Here m and M are the masses of a neutron and a deuteron.
6.251. $\theta_{max} = \arcsin(m_1/m_2) = 30°$, where m_1 and m_2 are the masses of a proton and a deuteron.
6.252. $2\cdot10^{11}$ kg/cm³; $1\cdot10^{38}$ nucl./cm³.
6.253. (a) d; (b) F^{17}; (c) α; (d) Cl^{37}.
6.255. Be^8, $E_b = 56.5$ MeV.
6.256. (a) 8.0 MeV; (b) 11.5 and 8.7 MeV; (c) 14.5 MeV.
6.257. $E_n - E_p = 0.22$ MeV.
6.258. $E = 20\varepsilon_{Ne} - 2\cdot4\varepsilon_\alpha - 12\varepsilon_C = 11.9$ MeV, where ε is the binding energy per nucleon in the corresponding nucleus.
6.259. (a) 8.0225 a.m.u.; (b) 10.0135 a.m.u.
6.260. $Q = (E_3 + E_4) - (E_1 + E_2)$.
6.261. (a) $8.2\cdot10^{10}$ kJ, $2.7\cdot10^6$ kg; (b) 1.5 kg.
6.262. $5.74\cdot10^7$ kJ, $2\cdot10^4$ kg.
6.263. 2.79 MeV; 0.85 MeV.
6.264. $Q = 8\varepsilon_\alpha - 7\varepsilon_{Li} = 17.3$ MeV.
6.265. $Q = (1 + \eta_p)\,T_p - (1 - \eta_\alpha)\,T_\alpha - 2\sqrt{\eta_p\eta_\alpha T_p T_\alpha} \times \cos\theta = -1.2$ MeV, where $\eta_p = m_p/m_O$, $\eta_\alpha = m_\alpha/m_O$.
6.266. (a) −1.65 MeV; (b) 6.82 MeV; (c) −2.79 MeV; (d) 3.11 MeV.
6.267. $v_\alpha = 0.92\cdot10^7$ m/s, $v_{Li} = 0.53\cdot10^7$ m/s.
6.268. 1.9 MeV.
6.269. $T_n = \dfrac{Q + (1 - m_\alpha/m_C)\,T}{1 + m_n/m_C} = 8.5$ MeV.
6.270. 9.1 MeV, 170.5°.

6.272. $T \geqslant E_b(m_p + m_d)/m_d = 3.3$ MeV.

6.273. Between 1.89 and 2.06 MeV.

6.274. $Q = -{}^{11}/_{12}\, T_{th} = -3.7$ MeV.

6.275. 1.88 and 5.75 MeV respectively.

6.276. 4.4 MeV; $5.3 \cdot 10^6$ m/s.

6.277. $T_\alpha = \frac{1}{m_3+m_4}\left[(m_4-m_1)T - \frac{m_2 m_4}{m_1+m_2} T_{th}\right] = 2.2$ MeV, where m_1, m_2, m_3, m_4 are the masses of neutron, a C^{12} nucleus, an alpha particle, and a Be^9 nucleus.

6.278. By $E_b/2mc^2 \simeq 0.06\%$, where m is the mass of a deuteron.

6.279. $E = Q + {}^2/_3 T = 6.5$ MeV.

6.280. $E_i = E_b + \frac{m_C}{m_d + m_C} T_i = 16.7$, 16.9, 17.5 and 17.7 MeV, where E_b is the binding energy of a deuteron in the transitional nucleus.

6.281. $\sigma = (M/N\rho\, d) \ln \eta = 2.5$ kb, where M is the molar mass of cadmium, N is the Avogadro number, ρ is the density of cadmium.

6.282. $I_0/I = \exp[(2\sigma_1 + \sigma_2) nd] = 20$, where n is the concentration of heavy water molecules.

6.283. $w = \{1 - \exp[-(\sigma_s + \sigma_a) nd]\}\, \sigma_s/(\sigma_s + \sigma_a) = 0.35$, where n is the concentration of Fe nuclei.

6.284. (a) $T = (w/k) \ln 2$; (b) $w = ATe/It \ln 2 = 2 \cdot 10^{-3}$.

6.285. (a) $t = \eta/\sigma J = 3 \cdot 10^6$ years; (b) $N_{max} = J\sigma N_0 T/\ln 2 = 1.0 \cdot 10^{13}$, where N_0 is the number of Au^{197} nuclei in the foil.

6.286. $N = (1 - e^{-\lambda t})\, Jn\sigma/\lambda$.

6.287. $J = Ae^{\lambda t}/\sigma N_0 (1 - e^{-\lambda t}) = 6 \cdot 10^9$ part./(cm$^2 \cdot$s), where λ is the decay constant, N_0 is the number of Au nuclei in the foil.

6.288. $N = N_0 k^{i-1} = 1.3 \cdot 10^5$, where i is the number of generations.

6.289. $N = \nu P/E = 0.8 \cdot 10^{19}$ s^{-1}.

6.290. (a) $N/N_0 = 4 \cdot 10^2$; (b) $T = \tau/(k-1) = 10$ s.

6.291. 0.05, 0.4, and 9 GeV respectively.

6.292. $\langle l \rangle = c\tau_0 \sqrt{\eta(\eta+2)} = 15$ m.

6.293. $\tau_0 = lmc/\sqrt{T(T + 2mc^2)} = 26$ ns, where m is the rest mass of a pion.

6.294. $J/J_0 = \exp[-lmc/\tau_0 \sqrt{T(T+2mc^2)}] = 0.22$, where m is the rest mass of a negative pion.

6.295*. $T_\mu = (m_\pi - m_\mu)^2/2m_\pi = 4.1$ MeV, $E_\nu = 29.8$ MeV.

6.296*. $T = [(m_\Sigma - m_n)^2 - m_\pi^2]/2m_\Sigma = 19.5$ MeV.

6.297*. $T_{max} = (m_\mu - m_e)^2/2m_\mu = 52.5$ MeV.

6.298*. $m = m_p + T + \sqrt{m_\pi^2 + T(T + 2m_p)} = 1115$ MeV, a Λ particle.

6.299*. $E_\nu = {}^1/_2 (m_\pi^2 - m_\mu^2)/(m_\pi + T) = 22$ MeV.

---

* In the answers to Problems 6.295 - 6.299 marked by an asterisk the quantity mc^2 is abbreviated as m.

6.300*. $m = \sqrt{m_\Sigma^2 + m_\pi^2 - 2(m_\Sigma + T_\Sigma)(m_\pi + T_\pi)} = 0.94$ GeV, neutron.

6.301*. $T_\pi = m_\pi [\operatorname{cosec}(\Theta/2) - 1]$, $E_\gamma = m_\pi/2 \sin(\Theta/2)$. For $\Theta = 60°$ the energy $T_\pi = E_\gamma = m_\pi$.

6.303*. $\cos(\Theta/2) = 1/\sqrt{1 + 2m/T}$, whence $\Theta = 99°$.

6.304*. (a) $\varepsilon_{th} = 4m_e = 2.04$ MeV; (b) $\varepsilon_{th} = 2m_\pi(1 + m_\pi/m_p) = 320$ MeV.

6.305*. (a) $T_{th} = 6m_p = 5.6$ GeV; (b) $T_{th} = m_\pi(4m_p + m_\pi)/2m_p = 0.28$ GeV.

6.306. (a) 0.90 GeV; (b) 0.77 GeV.

6.307. $S = -2$, $Y = -1$, Ξ^0 particle.

6.308. Processes 1, 2, and 3 are forbidden.

6.309. Processes 2, 4, and 5 are forbidden.

6.310. Process 1 is forbidden in terms of energy; in other processes the following laws of conservation are broken: of baryon charge (2), of electric charge (3), of strangeness (4), of lepton charge (5), and of electron and muon charge (6).

---

* In the answers to Problems 6.300-6.305 marked by an asterisk the quantity mc^2 is abbreviated as m.

APPENDICES

1. Basic Trigonometrical formulas

$\sin^2\alpha + \cos^2\alpha = 1$ $\sec^2\alpha - \tan^2\alpha = 1$ $\mathrm{cosec}^2\alpha - \cot^2\alpha = 1$ $\sin\alpha \cdot \mathrm{cosec}\,\alpha = 1$ $\cos\alpha \cdot \sec\alpha = 1$ $\tan\alpha \cdot \cot\alpha = 1$	$\sin(\alpha \pm \beta) = \sin\alpha\cos\beta \pm \cos\alpha\sin\beta$ $\cos(\alpha \pm \beta) = \cos\alpha\cos\beta \mp \sin\alpha\sin\beta$ $\tan(\alpha \pm \beta) = \dfrac{\tan\alpha \pm \tan\beta}{1 \mp \tan\alpha \cdot \tan\beta}$ $\cot(\alpha \pm \beta) = \dfrac{\cot\alpha\cot\beta \mp 1}{\cot\beta \pm \cot\alpha}$
$\sin\alpha = \dfrac{1}{\sqrt{1+\cot^2\alpha}}$ $\cos\alpha = \dfrac{1}{\sqrt{1+\tan^2\alpha}}$ $\sin 2\alpha = 2\sin\alpha\cos\alpha$ $\cos 2\alpha = \cos^2\alpha - \sin^2\alpha$ $\tan 2\alpha = \dfrac{2\tan\alpha}{1-\tan^2\alpha}$ $\cot 2\alpha = \dfrac{\cot^2\alpha - 1}{2\cot\alpha}$	$\sin\alpha + \sin\beta = 2\sin\dfrac{\alpha+\beta}{2}\cos\dfrac{\alpha-\beta}{2}$ $\sin\alpha - \sin\beta = 2\cos\dfrac{\alpha+\beta}{2}\sin\dfrac{\alpha-\beta}{2}$ $\cos\alpha + \cos\beta = 2\cos\dfrac{\alpha+\beta}{2}\cos\dfrac{\alpha-\beta}{2}$ $\cos\alpha - \cos\beta = -2\sin\dfrac{\alpha+\beta}{2}\sin\dfrac{\alpha-\beta}{2}$ $\tan\alpha \pm \tan\beta = \dfrac{\sin(\alpha\pm\beta)}{\cos\alpha\cos\beta}$ $\cot\alpha \pm \cot\beta = \pm\dfrac{\sin(\alpha\pm\beta)}{\sin\alpha\sin\beta}$
$\sin\dfrac{\alpha}{2} = \sqrt{\dfrac{1-\cos\alpha}{2}}$ $\cos\dfrac{\alpha}{2} = \sqrt{\dfrac{1+\cos\alpha}{2}}$	$2\sin\alpha\sin\beta = \cos(\alpha-\beta) - \cos(\alpha+\beta)$ $2\cos\alpha\cos\beta = \cos(\alpha-\beta) + \cos(\alpha+\beta)$ $2\sin\alpha\cos\beta = \sin(\alpha-\beta) + \sin(\alpha+\beta)$
$\sinh\alpha = \dfrac{e^{u} - e^{-u}}{2}$ $\cosh\alpha = \dfrac{e^{u} + e^{-u}}{2}$	$\tanh\alpha = \dfrac{e^{u} - e^{-u}}{e^{u} + e^{-u}}$ $\coth\alpha = \dfrac{e^{u} + e^{-u}}{e^{u} - e^{-u}}$

2. Sine Function Value

φ°	0′	20′	40′	φ°	0′	20′	40′
0	0.0000	0.0058	0.0116	45	0.7071	0.7112	0.7153
1	0.0175	0.0233	0.0291	46	0.7193	0.7234	0.7274
2	0.0349	0.0407	0.0465	47	0.7314	0.7353	0.7393
3	0.0523	0.0581	0.0640	48	0.7431	0.7470	0.7504
4	0.0698	0.0756	0.0814	49	0.7547	0.7585	0.7622
5	0.0872	0.0929	0.0987	50	0.7660	0.7698	0.7735
6	0.1045	0.1103	0.1161	51	0.7771	0.7808	0.7844
7	0.1219	0.1276	0.1334	52	0.7880	0.7916	0.7951
8	0.1392	0.1449	0.1507	53	0.7986	0.8021	0.8056
9	0.1564	0.1622	0.1679	54	0.8090	0.8124	0.8158
10	0.1736	0.1794	0.1851	55	0.8192	0.8225	0.8258
11	0.1908	0.1965	0.2022	56	0.8290	0.8323	0.8355
12	0.2079	0.2136	0.2196	57	0.8387	0.8418	0.8450
13	0.2250	0.2306	0.2363	58	0.8480	0.8511	0.8542
14	0.2419	0.2476	0.2532	59	0.8572	0.8601	0.8631
15	0.2588	0.2644	0.2700	60	0.8660	0.8689	0.8718
16	0.2756	0.2812	0.2868	61	0.8746	0.8774	0.8802
17	0.2924	0.2979	0.3035	62	0.8829	0.8857	0.8884
18	0.3090	0.3145	0.3201	63	0.8910	0.8936	0.8962
19	0.3256	0.3311	0.3365	64	0.8988	0.9013	0.9038
20	0.3420	0.3475	0.3529	65	0.9063	0.9088	0.9112
21	0.3584	0.3638	0.3692	66	0.9135	0.9159	0.9182
22	0.3746	0.3800	0.3854	67	0.9205	0.9228	0.9250
23	0.3907	0.3961	0.4014	68	0.9272	0.9293	0.9315
24	0.4067	0.4120	0.4173	69	0.9336	0.9356	0.9377
25	0.4226	0.4279	0.4331	70	0.9397	0.9417	0.9436
26	0.4384	0.4436	0.4488	71	0.9455	0.9474	0.9492
27	0.4540	0.4592	0.4643	72	0.9511	0.9528	0.9546
28	0.4695	0.4746	0.4797	73	0.9563	0.9580	0.9596
29	0.4848	0.4899	0.4950	74	0.9613	0.9628	0.9644
30	0.5000	0.5050	0.5100	75	0.9859	0.9674	0.9689
31	0.5150	0.5200	0.5250	76	0.9703	0.9717	0.9730
32	0.5299	0.5348	0.5398	77	0.9744	0.9757	0.9769
33	0.5446	0.5495	0.5544	78	0.9781	0.9793	0.9805
34	0.5592	0.5640	0.5688	79	0.9816	0.9827	0.9838
35	0.5736	0.5783	0.5831	80	0.9848	0.9858	0.9868
36	0.5878	0.5925	0.5972	81	0.9877	0.9886	0.9894
37	0.6018	0.6065	0.6111	82	0.9903	0.9911	0.9918
38	0.6157	0.6202	0.6248	83	0.9925	0.9932	0.9939
39	0.6293	0.6338	0.6383	84	0.9945	0.9951	0.9957
40	0.6428	0.6472	0.6517	85	0.9962	0.9967	0.9971
41	0.6561	0.6604	0.6648	86	0.9976	0.9980	0.9983
42	0.6691	0.6734	0.6777	87	0.9986	0.9989	0.9992
43	0.6820	0.6862	0.6905	88	0.9994	0.9996	0.9997
44	0.6947	0.6988	0.7030	89	0.9998	0.9999	1.0000

3. Tangent Function Values

φ°	0′	20′	40′	φ°	0′	20′	40′
0	0.0000	0.0058	0.0116	45	1.0000	1.012	1.024
1	0.0175	0.0233	0.0291	46	1.036	1.048	1.060
2	0.0349	0.0407	0.0466	47	1.072	1.085	1.098
3	0.0524	0.0582	0.0641	48	1.111	1.124	1.137
4	0.0699	0.0758	0.0816	49	1.150	1.164	1.178
5	0.0875	0.0934	0.0992	50	1.192	1.206	1.220
6	0.1051	0.1110	0.1169	51	1.235	1.250	1.265
7	0.1228	0.1287	0.1346	52	1.280	1.295	1.311
8	0.1405	0.1465	0.1524	53	1.327	1.343	1.360
9	0.1584	0.1644	0.1703	54	1.376	1.393	1.411
10	0.1763	0.1823	0.1883	55	1.428	1.446	1.464
11	0.1944	0.2004	0.2065	56	1.483	1.501	1.520
12	0.2126	0.2186	0.2247	57	1.540	1.560	1.580
13	0.2309	0.2370	0.2432	58	1.600	1.621	1.643
14	0.2493	0.2555	0.2617	59	1.664	1.686	1.709
15	0.2679	0.2742	0.2805	60	1.732	1.756	1.780
16	0.2867	0.2931	0.2994	61	1.804	1.829	1.855
17	0.3057	0.3121	0.3185	62	1.881	1.907	1.935
18	0.3249	0.3314	0.3378	63	1.963	1.991	2.020
19	0.3443	0.3508	0.3574	64	2.050	2.081	2.112
20	0.3640	0.3706	0.3772	65	2.145	2.177	2.211
21	0.3839	0.3906	0.3973	66	2.246	2.282	2.318
22	0.4040	0.4108	0.4176	67	2.356	2.394	2.434
23	0.4245	0.4314	0.4383	68	2.475	2.517	2.560
24	0.4452	0.4522	0.4592	69	2.605	2.651	2.699
25	0.4663	0.4734	0.4806	70	2.747	2.798	2.850
26	0.4877	0.4950	0.5022	71	2.904	2.960	3.018
27	0.5095	0.5169	0.5243	72	3.078	3.140	3.204
28	0.5317	0.5392	0.5467	73	3.271	3.340	3.412
29	0.5543	0.5619	0.5696	74	3.487	3.566	3.647
30	0.5774	0.5851	0.5930	75	3.732	3.821	3.914
31	0.6009	0.6088	0.6168	76	4.011	4.113	4.219
32	0.6249	0.6330	0.6412	77	4.331	4.449	4.574
33	0.6494	0.6577	0.6661	78	4.705	4.843	4.989
34	0.6745	0.6830	0.6916	79	5.145	5.309	5.485
35	0.7002	0.7089	0.7177	80	5.671	5.871	6.084
36	0.7265	0.7355	0.7445	81	6.314	6.561	6.827
37	0.7536	0.7627	0.7720	82	7.115	7.429	7.770
38	0.7813	0.7907	0.8002	83	8.144	8.556	9.010
39	0.8098	0.8195	0.8292	84	9.514	10.08	10.71
40	0.8391	0.8491	0.8591	85	11.43	12.25	13.20
41	0.8693	0.8796	0.8899	86	14.30	15.60	17.17
42	0.9004	0.9110	0.9217	87	19.08	21.47	24.54
43	0.9325	0.9435	0.9545	88	28.64	34.37	42.96
44	0.9657	0.9770	0.9884	89	57.29	85.94	171.9

4. Comon Logarithms

N	0	1	2	3	4	5	6	7	8	9
10	0000	0043	0086	0128	0170	0212	0253	0294	0334	0374
11	0414	0453	0492	0531	0569	0607	0645	0682	0719	0755
12	0792	0828	0864	0899	0934	0969	1004	1038	1072	1106
13	1139	1173	1206	1239	1271	1303	1335	1367	1399	1430
14	1461	1492	1523	1553	1584	1614	1644	1673	1703	1732
15	1761	1790	1818	1847	1875	1903	1931	1959	1987	2014
16	2041	2068	2095	2122	2148	2175	2201	2227	2253	2279
17	2304	2330	2355	2380	2405	2430	2455	2488	2504	2529
18	2553	2577	2601	2625	2648	2672	2695	2718	2742	2765
19	2788	2810	2833	2856	2878	2900	2923	2945	2967	2989
20	3010	3032	3054	3075	3096	3118	3139	3160	3181	3201
21	3222	3243	3263	3284	3304	3324	3345	3365	3385	3404
22	3424	3444	3464	3483	3502	3522	3541	3560	3579	3598
23	3617	3636	3655	3674	3692	3711	3729	3747	3766	3784
24	3802	3820	3838	3856	3874	3892	3909	3927	3945	3962
25	3979	3997	4014	4031	4048	4065	4082	4099	4116	4133
26	4150	4166	4183	4200	4216	4232	4249	4265	4381	4298
27	4314	4330	4346	4362	4378	4393	4409	4425	4440	4456
28	4472	4487	4502	4518	4533	4548	4564	4579	4594	4609
29	4624	4639	4654	4669	4683	4698	4713	4728	4742	4757
30	4771	4786	4800	4814	4829	4843	4857	4871	4886	4900
31	4914	4928	4942	4955	4969	4983	4997	5011	5024	5038
32	5051	5065	5079	5092	5105	5119	5132	5145	5159	5172
33	5185	5198	5211	5224	5237	5250	5283	5276	5289	5302
34	5315	5328	5340	5353	5366	5378	5391	5403	5416	5428
35	5441	5453	5465	5478	5490	5502	5514	5527	5539	5551
36	5563	5575	5587	5599	5611	5623	5635	5647	5658	5670
37	5682	5694	5705	5717	5729	5740	5752	5763	5775	5786
38	5798	5809	5821	5832	5843	5855	5866	5877	5888	5899
39	5911	5922	5933	5944	5955	5966	5977	5988	5999	6010
40	6021	6031	6042	6053	6064	6075	6085	6096	6107	6117
41	6128	6138	6149	6160	6170	6180	6191	6201	6212	6222
42	6232	6243	6253	6263	6274	6284	6294	6304	6314	6325
43	6335	6345	6355	6365	6375	6385	6395	6405	6415	6425
44	6435	6444	6454	6464	6474	6484	6493	6503	6513	6522
45	6532	6542	6551	6561	6571	6580	6590	6599	6609	6618
46	6628	6637	6646	6656	6665	6675	6684	6693	6702	6712
47	6721	6730	6739	6749	6758	6767	6776	6785	6794	6803
48	6812	6821	6830	6839	6848	6857	6866	6875	6885	6893
49	6902	6911	6920	6928	6937	6946	6955	6964	6972	6981
50	6990	6998	7007	7016	7024	7033	7042	7050	7059	7067
51	7076	7084	7093	7101	7110	7118	7126	7135	7143	7152
52	7160	7168	7177	7185	7193	7202	7210	7218	7226	7235
53	7243	7251	7259	7267	7275	7284	7292	7300	7308	7316
54	7324	7332	7340	7348	7356	7364	7372	7380	7388	7396

(Continued)

N	0	1	2	3	4	5	6	7	8	9
55	7404	7412	7419	7427	7435	7443	7451	7450	7466	7475
56	7482	7490	7497	7405	7513	7520	7528	7536	7543	7551
57	7559	7566	7574	7582	7589	7597	7604	7612	7619	7627
58	7634	7642	7649	7657	7664	7672	7679	7686	7694	7701
59	7709	7716	7723	7731	7738	7745	7752	7760	7767	7774
60	7782	7789	7796	7803	7810	7818	7825	7832	7839	7846
61	7853	7860	7868	7875	7882	7889	7896	7903	7910	7917
62	7924	7931	7938	7945	7952	7959	7966	7973	7980	7987
63	7993	8000	8007	8014	8021	8028	8035	8041	8048	8055
64	8062	8069	8075	8082	8089	8096	8102	8109	8116	8122
65	8129	8136	8142	8149	8156	8162	8169	8176	8182	8189
66	8195	8202	8209	8215	8222	8228	8235	8241	8248	8254
67	8261	8267	8274	8280	8287	8293	8299	8306	8312	8319
68	8325	8331	8338	8344	8351	8357	8363	8370	8376	8382
69	8388	8395	8401	8407	8414	8420	8426	8432	8439	8445
70	8451	8457	8463	8470	8476	8482	8488	8494	8500	8506
71	8513	8519	8525	8531	8537	8543	8549	8555	8561	8567
72	8573	8579	8585	8591	8597	8603	8609	8615	8621	8627
73	8633	8639	3645	8651	8657	8663	8669	8675	8681	8686
74	8692	8698	8704	8710	8716	8722	8727	8733	8739	8745
75	8751	8756	8762	8768	8774	8779	8785	8791	8797	8802
76	8808	8814	8820	8825	8831	8837	8842	8848	8854	8859
77	8865	8871	8876	8882	8887	8893	8899	8904	8910	8915
78	8921	8927	8632	8938	8943	8949	8954	8960	8965	8971
79	8976	8982	8987	8993	8998	9004	9009	9015	9020	9025
80	9031	9036	9042	9047	9053	9058	9063	9069	9074	9079
81	9085	9090	9096	9101	9106	9112	9117	9122	9128	9133
82	9138	9143	9149	9154	9159	9165	9170	9175	9180	9186
83	9191	9196	9201	9206	9212	9217	9222	9227	9232	9238
84	9243	9248	9253	9258	9263	9269	9274	9279	9284	9289
85	9294	9299	9304	9309	9315	9320	9325	9330	9335	9340
86	9345	9350	9355	9360	9365	9370	9375	9380	9385	9390
87	9395	9400	9405	9410	9415	9420	9425	9430	9435	9440
88	9445	9450	9455	9460	9465	9469	9474	9479	9484	9489
89	9494	9499	9504	9509	9513	9518	9523	9528	9533	9538
90	9542	9547	9552	9557	9562	9566	9571	9576	9581	9586
91	9590	9595	9600	9605	9609	9614	9619	9624	9628	9633
92	9638	9643	9647	9652	9657	9661	9666	9671	9675	9680
93	9685	9689	9694	9699	9703	9708	9713	9717	8722	9727
94	9731	9736	9741	9745	9750	9754	9759	9763	9768	9773
95	9777	9782	9786	9791	9795	9800	9805	9809	9814	9818
96	9823	9827	9832	9836	9841	9845	9850	9854	9859	9863
97	9868	9872	9877	9881	9886	9890	9894	9899	9903	9908
98	9912	9917	9921	9926	9930	9934	9939	9943	9948	9952
99	9956	9961	9965	9969	9974	9978	9983	9987	9991	9996

5. Exponential Functions

x	e^x	e^{-x}	x	e^x	e^{-x}
0.00	1.0000	1.0000	2.00	7.3891	0.1353
0.05	1.0513	0.9512	2.05	7.7679	0.1287
0.10	1.1052	0.9048	2.10	8.1662	0.1225
0.15	1.1618	0.8607	2.15	8.5849	0.1165
0.20	1.2214	0.8187	2.20	9.0250	0.1108
0.25	1.2840	0.7788	2.25	9.4877	0.1054
0.30	1.3499	0.7408	2.30	9.9742	0.1003
0.35	1.4191	0.7047	2.35	10.486	0.09537
0.40	1.4918	0.6703	2.40	11.023	0.09072
0.45	1.5683	0.6376	2.45	11.588	0.08629
0.50	1.6487	0.6065	2.50	12.182	0.08208
0.55	1.7333	0.5770	2.55	12.807	0.07808
0.60	1.8221	0.5488	2.60	13.464	0.07427
0.65	1.9155	0.5221	2.65	14.154	0.07065
0.70	2.0138	0.4966	2.70	14.880	0.06721
0.75	2.1170	0.4724	2.75	15.643	0.06393
0.80	2.2255	0.4493	2.80	16.445	0.06081
0.85	2.3396	0.4274	2.85	17.288	0.05784
0.90	2.4596	0.4066	2.90	18.174	0.05502
0.95	2.5857	0.3867	2.95	19.106	0.05234
1.00	2.7183	0.3679	3.00	20.086	0.04979
1.05	2.8577	0.3499	3.05	21.115	0.04736
1.10	3.0042	0.3329	3.10	22.198	0.04505
1.15	3.1582	0.3166	3.15	23.336	0.04285
1.20	3.3201	0.3012	3.20	24.533	0.04076
1.25	3.4903	0.2865	3.25	25.790	0.03877
1.30	3.6693	0.2725	3.30	27.113	0.03688
1.35	3.8574	0.2592	3.35	28.503	0.03508
1.40	4.0552	0.2466	3.40	29.964	0.03337
1.45	4.2631	0.2346	3.45	31.500	0.03175
1.50	4.4817	0.2231	3.50	33.115	0.03020
1.55	4.7115	0.2123	3.55	34.813	0.02872
1.60	4.9530	0.2019	3.60	36.598	0.02732
1.65	5.2070	0.1921	3.65	38.475	0.02599
1.70	5.4739	0.1827	3.70	40.447	0.02472
1.75	5.7546	0.1738	3.75	42.521	0.02352
1.80	6.0496	0.1653	3.80	44.701	0.02237
1.85	6.3598	0.1572	3.85	46.993	0.02128
1.90	6.6859	0.1496	3.90	49.402	0.02024
1.95	7.0287	0.1423	3.95	51.935	0.01925

(Continued)

x	e^x	e^{-x}	x	e^x	e^{-x}
4.00	54.598	0.01832	6.0	403.43	0.00248
4.05	57.397	0.01742	6.1	445.86	0.00224
4.10	60.340	0.01657	6.2	492.75	0.00203
4.15	63.434	0.01576	6.3	544.57	0.00184
4.20	66.686	0.01500	6.4	601.85	0.00166
4.25	70.105	0.01426	6.5	665.14	0.001503
4.30	73.700	0.01357	6.6	735.10	0.001360
4.35	77.478	0.01991	6.7	812.41	0.001231
4.40	81.451	0.01228	6.8	897.85	0.001114
4.45	85.627	0.01168	6.9	992.27	0.001008
4.50	90.017	0.01111	7.0	1096.6	0.000912
4.55	94.632	0.01057	7.1	1212.2	0.000825
4.60	99.484	0.01005	7.2	1339.4	0.000747
4.65	104.58	0.00956	7.3	1480.5	0.000676
4.70	109.95	0.00910	7.4	1636.0	0.000611
4.75	115.58	0.00865	7.5	1808.0	0.000553
4.80	121.51	0.00823	7.6	1998.2	0.000500
4.85	127.74	0.00783	7.7	2208.3	0.000453
4.90	134.29	0.00745	7.8	2440.6	0.000410
4.95	141.17	0.00708	7.9	2697.3	0.000371
5.00	148.41	0.00674	8.0	2981.0	0.000335
5.05	156.02	0.00641	8.1	3294.5	0.000304
5.10	164.02	0.00610	8.2	3641.0	0.000275
5.15	172.43	0.00580	8.3	4023.9	0.000249
5.20	181.27	0.00552	8.4	4447.1	0.000225
5.25	190.57	0.00525	8.5	4914.8	0.000203
5.30	200.34	0.00499	8.6	5431.7	0.000184
5.35	210.61	0.00475	8.7	6002.9	0.000167
5.40	221.41	0.00452	8.8	6634.2	0.000151
5.45	232.76	0.00430	8.9	7332.0	0.000136
5.50	244.69	0.00409	9.0	8103.1	0.000123
5.55	257.24	0.00389	9.1	8955.3	0.000112
5.60	270.43	0.00370	9.2	9897.1	0.000101
5.65	284.29	0.00352	9.3	10938	0.000091
5.70	298.87	0.00335	9.4	12088	0.000083
5.75	314.19	0.00318	9.5	13360	0.000075
5.80	330.30	0.00303	9.6	14765	0.000068
5.85	347.23	0.00288	9.7	16318	0.000061
5.90	365.04	0.00274	9.8	18034	0.000055
5.95	383.75	0.00261	9.9	19930	0.000050
			10.0	22026	0.000045

6. Greek Alphabet

Α, α—alpha	Ι, ι—Iota	Ρ, ρ—rho
Β, β—beta	Κ, κ—kappa	Σ, σ—sigma
Γ, γ—gamma	Λ, λ—lambda	Τ, τ—tau
Δ, δ—delta	Μ, μ—mu	Υ, υ—upsilon
Ε, ε—epsilon	Ν, ν—nu	Φ, φ—phi
Ζ, ζ—zeta	Ξ, ξ—xi	Χ, χ—Chi
Η, η—eta	Ο, ο—omicron	Ψ, ψ—psi
Θ, θ—theta	Π, π—pi	Ω, ω—omega

7. Numerical Constants and Approximation

Numerical constants	Approximate formulas (for $\alpha << 1$)
$\pi = 3.1416$	$(1 \pm \alpha)^n \approx 1 \pm n\alpha$
$\pi^2 = 9.8696$	$e^\alpha \approx 1 + \alpha$
$\sqrt{\pi} = 1.7725$	$\ln(1 + \alpha) \approx \alpha$
$e = 2.7183$	$\sin \alpha \approx \alpha$
$\log e = 0.4343$	$\cos \alpha \approx 1 - \alpha^3/2$
$\ln 10 = 2.3026$	$\tan \alpha \approx \alpha$

8. Some Data on Vectors

$$\mathbf{a}(\mathbf{b} + \mathbf{c}) = \mathbf{ab} + \mathbf{ac} \qquad [\mathbf{a}, \mathbf{b} + \mathbf{c}] = [\mathbf{ab}] + [\mathbf{ac}]$$

$$\mathbf{ab} = a_x b_x + a_y b_y + a_z b_z \qquad [\mathbf{a}[\mathbf{be}]] = \mathbf{b}(\mathbf{ac}) - \mathbf{c}(\mathbf{ab})$$

$$[\mathbf{ab}] \begin{bmatrix} \mathbf{i} & \mathbf{j} & \mathbf{k} \\ a_x & a_y & a_x \\ b_x & b_y & b_z \end{bmatrix} = (a_y b_z - a_z b_y)\,\mathbf{i} + (a_z b_x - a_x b_z)\,j + (a_x b_y - a_y b_x)\,\mathbf{k}$$

$$\frac{d}{dt}(a + b) = \frac{d\mathbf{a}}{dt} + \frac{d\mathbf{b}}{dt} \qquad \frac{d}{dt}(\alpha b) = \frac{d\mathbf{a}}{dt}\mathbf{b} + \mathbf{a}\frac{d\mathbf{b}}{dt}$$

$$\frac{d}{dt}(\alpha\, \mathbf{a}) = \frac{d\alpha}{dt}\mathbf{a} + \alpha\frac{d\mathbf{a}}{dt} \qquad \frac{d}{dt}[\mathbf{ab}] = \left[\frac{d\mathbf{a}}{dt}\mathbf{b}\right] + \left[\mathbf{a}\frac{d\mathbf{b}}{dt}\right]$$

9. Derivatives and Integrals

Function	Derivative	Function	Derivative	Function	Derivative
x^n	xn^{n-1}	$\sin x$	$\cos x$	$\arcsin x$	$\frac{1}{\sqrt{1-x^2}}$
$\frac{1}{x}$	$-\frac{1}{x^2}$	$\cos x$	$-\sin x$	$\arccos x$	$-\frac{1}{\sqrt{1-x^2}}$
$\frac{1}{x^n}$	$-\frac{n}{x^{n+1}}$	$\tan x$	$\frac{1}{\cos^2 x}$	$\arctan x$	$\frac{1}{1+x^2}$
$\sqrt{x}$	$\frac{1}{2\sqrt{x}}$	$\cot x$	$-\frac{1}{\sin^2 x}$	$\text{arccot}\, x$	$-\frac{1}{1+x^2}$
e^x	e^x	$\sqrt{u}$	$\frac{u'}{2\sqrt{u}}$	$\sinh x$	$\cosh x$
e^{nx}	ne^{nx}			$\cosh x$	$\sinh x$
a_x	$a^x \ln a$	$\ln u$	$\frac{u'}{u}$	$\tanh x$	$\frac{1}{\cosh^2 x}$
$\ln x$	$\frac{1}{x}$	$\frac{u}{v}$	$\frac{vu'-v'u}{v^2}$	$\coth x$	$-\frac{1}{\sinh^2 x}$

$$\int x^n\,dx = \frac{x^{n+1}}{n+1} \quad (n \neq -1)$$

$$\int \frac{dx}{x} = \ln x$$

$$\int \sin x\,dx = -\cos x$$

$$\int \cos x\,dx = \sin x$$

$$\int \tan x\,dx = -\ln \cos x$$

$$\int \cot x\,dx = \ln \sin x$$

$$\int \frac{dx}{\cos^2 x} = \tan x$$

$$\int \frac{dx}{\sin^2 x} = -\cot x$$

$$\int e^x\,dx = e^x$$

$$\int \frac{dx}{1+x^2} = \arctan x$$

$$\int \frac{dx}{\sqrt{1+x^2}} = \arcsin x$$

$$\int \frac{dx}{\sqrt{x^2-1}} \ln\left(x+\sqrt{x^2-1}\right)$$

Integration by parts: $\int u\,dv = uv - \int v\,du$

Some Definite Integrals

$\int_0^\infty x^n e^{-x}\,dx = \begin{cases} 1, & n=0 \\ ½\sqrt{\pi} & n=1/2 \\ 1, & n=1 \\ 2, & n=2 \end{cases}$	$\int_0^\infty x^n e^{-x2}\,dx = \begin{cases} ½\sqrt{\pi}, & n=0 \\ 1/2, & n=1 \\ ¼\sqrt{\pi}, & n=2 \\ 1/2, & n=3 \end{cases}$
$\int_0^\infty \frac{x^n\,dx}{e^x-1} = \begin{cases} 2.31, & n=1/2 \\ \pi^2/6, & n=1 \\ 2.405, & n=2 \\ \pi^4/15, & n=3 \\ 24.9, & n=4 \end{cases}$	$\int_0^\alpha \frac{x^2\,dx}{e^x-1} = \begin{cases} 0.225, & \alpha=1 \\ 1.18, & \alpha=2 \\ 2.56, & \alpha=3 \\ 4.91, & \alpha=5 \\ 6.43, & \alpha=10 \end{cases}$

10. Astronomical Data

Body	Mean radius, m	Mass, kg	Mean density, 10^3 kg/m3	Period of rotation about axis, days
Sun	6.95-10[illegible]	$1.97.10^{30}$	1.41	25.4
Earth	6.37-10[illegible]	$5.96.10^{24}$	5.52	1.00
Moon	1.74-10[illegible]	$7.30.10^{22}$	3.30	27.3

Planets of solar system	Mean distance from the sun, 10^6 km	Siderial period, years
Mercury	57.87	0.241
Venus	108.14	0.615
Earth	149.50	1.000
Mars	227.79	1.881
Jupiter	777.8	11.862
Saturn	1426.1	29.458
Uranus	2867.7	84.013
Neptune	4494	164.79

11. Density of Substances

Solids	ρ, g/cm^3	Liquids	ρ, g/cm^3
Diamond	3.5	Benzene	0.88
Aluminium	2.7	Water	1.00
Tungsten	19.1	Glycerin	1.26
Graphite	1.6	Castor oil	0.90
Iron (steel)	7.8	Kerosene	0.80
Gold	19.3	Mercury	13.6
Cadmium	8.65	Alcohol	0.79
Cobalt	8.9	Heavy water	1.1
Ice	0.916	Ether	0.72
Copper	8.9	**Gases (under standard Conditions)**	**ρ, kg/m^3**
Molibdenum	10.2		
Sodium	0.97	Nitrogen	1.25
Nickel	8.9	Ammonia	0.77
Tin	7.4	Hydrogen	0.09
Platinum	21.5	Air	1.293
Cork	0.20	Oxygen	1.43
Lead	11.3	Methane	0.72
Silver	10.5	Carbon dioxide	1.98
Titanium	4.5	Chlorine	3.21
Uranium	19.0		
Porcelain	2.3		
Zinc	7.0		

12. Thermal Expansion Coefficients
(at room temperatures)

Solids	Linear expansion coefficient; α 10^{-6} K^{-1}	Liquids	Bulk expansion coefficient; β 10^{-4} K^{-1}
Aluminium	22.9	Water	2.1
Brass	18.9	Glycerin	5.0
Copper	16.7	Kerosene	10.0
Steel (iron)	11	Mercury	1.8
Common glass	8.5	Ethyl alcohol	11.0

Note, $\alpha = \frac{1}{l}\frac{\partial l}{\partial T}$, $\beta = \frac{1}{V}\frac{\partial V}{\partial T}$

13. Elastic Constant, Tensile Strength

Material	Young's Modulus E, GPa	Shear Modulus G. GPa	Poisson's ratio μ	Tensile strength σ_m, GPa	Compressibility, β, GPa^{-1}
Aluminium	70	26	0.34	0.10	0.014
Copper	130	40	0.34	0.30	0.007
Lead	16	5.6	0.44	0.015	0.022
Steel (iron)	200	81	0.29	0.60	0.006
Glass	60	30	0.25	0.05	0.025
Water	—	—	—	—	0.49

Note. Compressibility $\beta = -\frac{1}{V}\frac{\partial V}{\partial p}$

14. Saturated Vapour Pressure

°C	Pressure, kPa	°C	Pressure, kPa	°C	Pressure, kPa
0	0.61	25	3.15	60	19.9
5	0.87	30	4.23	70	31.0
10	1.22	35	5.60	80	47.3
15	1.70	40	7.35	90	70.0
20	2.33	50	12.3	100	101.3

15. Gas Constants (under standard conditions)

Gas	Relative Molecular mass	$\gamma = \frac{C_p}{C_V}$	Heat conductivity x, $\frac{mW}{m.K}$	Viscosity η, μPa s	Molecular diameter d, nm	Van der Waals constants a, $\frac{atm.\ l^2}{mol^3}$	b, $\frac{l}{mol}$
He	4	1.67	141.5	18.9	0.20	—	—
Ar	40	1.67	16.2	22.1	0.35	1.30	0.032
H_2	2	1.41	168.4	8.4	0.27	0.24	0.027
N_2	28	1.40	24.3	16.7	0.37	1.35	0.039
O_2	32	1.40	24.4	19.2	0.35	1.35	0.032
CO_2	44	1.30	23.2	14.0	0.40	3.62	0.043
H_2O	18	1.32	15.8	9.0	0.30	5.47	0.030
Air	29	1.40	24.1	17.2	0.35	—	—

Note. This table quotes the mean values of molecular diameters. When performing more accurate calculations, it should be remembered that the values of d obtained from the coefficients of viscosity, heat conductivity, and diffusion, as well as the Van der Waals constant b, differ perceptibly from one another.

16. Some Parameters of Liquids and Solids

Substance	Specific heat capacity * c, $\frac{J}{g.K}$	Specific heat of vaporization ** q, J/g	Specific heat of melting q, J/g	Surface tension * α, mN/m
Water	4.18	2250	—	73
Glycerin	2.42	—	—	66
Mercury	0.14	284	—	490
Alcohol	2.42	853	—	22
Aluminium	0.90	—	321	—
Iron	0.46	—	270	—
Ice	2.09	—	333	—
Copper	0.39	—	175	—
Silver	0.23	—	88	—
Lead	0.13	—	25	—

* Under standard conditions.

** Under standard atmospheric pressure.

17. Perimitivities (relative values)

Dielectric	ε	Dielectric	ε
Water	81	Mica	7.5
Air	1.00058	Alcohol	26
Kerosene	2.0	Glass	6.0
Paraffin	2.0	Porcelain	6.0
Plexiglas	3.5	Ebonits	2.7
Polyethylene	2.3		

18. Resistivities of Conductors

Conductor	Resistivity (at 20°C) ρ, $n\Omega$.m	Temperature coefficient α, kK^{-1}
Aluminium	25	4.5
Tungsten	50	4.8
Iron	90	6.5
Gold	20	4.0
Copper	16	4.3
Lead	190	4.2
Silver	15	4.1

19. Magnetic Susceptibilities of Para- and Diamagnetics

Paramagnetic substance	μ-1, 10^{-6}	Diamagnetic substance	μ-1, 10^{-6}
Nitrogen	0.013	Hydrogen	—0.063
Air	0.38	Benzene	—7.5
Oxygen	1.9	Water	—9.0
Ebonite	14	Copper	—10.3
Aluminium	23	Glass	—12.6
Tungsten	176	Rock-salt	—12.6
Platinum	360	Quartz	—15.1
Liquid oxygen	3400	Bismuth	—176

20. Refractive Indices

Substance	n	Substance	n
Air	1.00029	Glass	1.50
Water	1.33	Diamond	2.42

Note. Since the refractive indices are known to depend on the nature of the substance and the wavelength of light, the values of n listed here should be regarded as conditional.

Wavelength λ, nm	Colour	Iceland spar		Quartz	
		n_e	n_o	n_e	n_o
687	red	1.484	1.653	1.550	1.541
656	orange	1.485	1.655	1.551	1.542
589	yellow	1.486	1.658	1.553	1.544
527	green	1.489	1.664	1.556	1.547
486	blue	1.491	1.668	1.559	1.550
431	indigo	1.495	1.676	1.564	1.554
400	violet	1.498	1.683	1.568	1.558

21. Rotation of the Plane of Polarization

Natural rotation in quartz (the thickness of the plate is 1 mm)

λ, nm	φ, deg	λ, nm	φ, deg	λ, nm	φ, deg
199.0	295.65	344.1	70.59	589.5	21.72
217.4	226.91	372.6	58.89	656.3	17.32
219.4	220.7	404.7	48.93	670.8	16.54
257.1	143.3	435.9	41.54	1040	6.69
274.7	121.1	491.6	31.98	1450	3.41
328.6	78.58	508.6	29.72	1770	2.28

Magnetic Rotation (λ = 589 nm). The Verdet Constant V:

Liquid	V, ang. min/A	Liquid	V, ang. min/A
Benzene	2.59	Carbon disulphide	0.053
Water	0.016	Ethyl alcohol	1.072

22. Work Function of Various Metals

Metal	A. eV	Metal	A. eV	Metal	A. eV
Aluminium	3.74	Gold	4.58	Potassium	2.15
Barium	2.29	Iron	4.36	Silver	4.28
Biasmuth	4.62	Lithium	2.39	Sodium	2.27
Cesium	1.89	Molybdenum	4.27	Titanium	3.92
Cobalt	4.25	Nickel	4.84	Tungsten	4.50
Copper	4.47	Platinum	5.29	Zinc	3.74

23. Band Absorption Edge

Z	Element	λ_K, pm	Z	Element	λ_K, pm
23	V	226.8	47	Ag	48.60
26	Fe	174.1	50	Sn	42.39
27	Co	160.4	74	W	17.85
28	Ni	148.6	78	Pt	15.85
29	Cu	138.0	79	Au	15.35
30	Zn	128.4	82	Pb	14.05
42	Mo	61.9	92	U	10.75

24. Mass Absorption Coefficients
(X-ray radiation, narrow beam)

λ, pm	Mass absorption coefficient μ/ρ, cm^2/g				
	Air	Water	Aluminium	Copper	Lead
10		0.16	0.16	0.36	3.8
20		0.18	0.28	1.5	4.9
30		0.29	0.47	4.3	14
40		0.44	1.1	9.8	31
50	0.48	0.66	2.0	19	54
60	0.75	1.0	3.4	32	90
70	1.3	1.5	5.1	48	139
80	1.6	2.1	7.4	70	
90	2.1	2.8	11	98	
100	2.6	3.8	15	131	
150	8.7	12	46	49	
200	21	28	102	108	
250	39	51	194	198	

25. Ionization Potentials of Atoms

Z	Atom	Ionization potential φ, V	Z	Atom	Ionization potential φ, V
1	H	13.59	7	N	14.54
2	He	24.58	8	O	13.62
3	Li	5.39	9	F	17.42
4	Be	9.32	10	Ne	21.56
5	B	8.30	11	Na	5.14
6	C	11.27	80	Hg	10.44

26. Mass of Light Atoms

Z	Isotope	Excess of mass of atom A_r - A, a.m.u.	Z	Isotope	Excess of mass of atom A_r - A, a.m.u.
0	n	0.00867	6	C^{11}	0.01143
1	H^1	0.00783		C^{12}	0
	H^2	0.01410		C^{13}	0.00335
	H^3	0.01605	7	N^{13}	0.00574
2	He^3	0.01603		N^{14}	0.00307
	He^4	0.00260		N^{15}	0.00011
3	Li^6	0.01513	8	O^{15}	0.00307
	Li^7	0.01601		O^{16}	—0.00509
4	Be^7	0.01693		O^{17}	—0.00087
	Be^8	0.00531	9	F^{19}	—0.00160
	Be^9	0.01219	10	Ne^{20}	—0.00756
	Be^{10}	0.01354	11	Na^{23}	—0.01023
5	B^{10}	0.01294		Na^{24}	—0.00903
	B^{11}	0.00930	12	Mg^{24}	—0.01496

Note. Here A_r is the relative atomic mass (in a.m.u.), A is the mass number.

27. Half-Life Values of Radionuclides

Z	Isotope	Kind of decay	Half-life
27	Cobalt Co^{60}	β	5.2 years
38	Strontium Sr^{90}	β	28 years
84	Polonium Po^{210}	α	138 days
86	Radon Rn^{222}	α	3.8 years
88	Radium Re^{226}	α	1620 years
92	Uranium U^{238}	α	$4.5.10^9$ years

28. Units of Physical Quantities

Names and symbols of certain quantities

A, ampere	H, henry	Oe, oersted
a.m.u., atomic mass unit	h, hour	Ω, ohm
	Hz, hertz	P, poise
B, bel	J, joule	Pa, pascal
b, barn	K, kelvin	rad, rdian
C, coulomb	l, litre	S, siemens
cd, candela	Im, lumen	s, second
D, diopter	lx, lux	sr, steradian
dyn, dyne	m, metre	St, stokes
eV, electron-volt	min, minute	T, tesla
F, farad	mol, mole	V, volt
G, gauss	Mx, maxwell	W, watt
g, gram	N, newton	Wb, weber

Decimal Prefixes

Factor	Name of prefix	Symbol	Factor	Name of prefix	Symbol
10^{12}	tera-	T	10^{-2}	centi-	c
10^{9}	giga-	G	10^{-3}	milli-	m
10^{6}	mega-	M	10^{-6}	micro-	μ
10^{3}	kilo-	k	10^{-9}	nano-	n
10^{2}	hecto-	h	10^{-12}	pico-	p
10	deca-	da	10^{-15}	femto-	f
10^{-1}	deci-	d	10^{-18}	atto-	a

SI and CGS Units

Physical quantity	Name of Unit		Conversion factor 1 SI unit/1 CGS unit
	SI	CGS	
Length	m	cm	100
Time	s	s	1
Velocity	m/s	cm/s	100
Acceleeration	m/s^3	cm/s^2	100
Oscillation frequency	Hz	Hz	1
Angular velocity	rad/s	rad/s	1
Angular frequency	s^{-1}	s^{-1}	1
Mass	kg	g	10^3
Density	kg/m^3	g/cm^3	10^{-3}
Force	N	dyn	10^5

(*Continued*)

Physical quantity	Name of Unit		Conversion factor 1 SI unit/1 CGS unit
	SI	CGS	
pressure, stress	Pa	dyn/cm^2	10
Momentum	kg.m/s	g.cm/s	10^6
Moment of force	N-m	dyn.cm	10^7
Energy, work	J	erg	10^7
Power	W	erg/s	10^7
Energy flux density	W/m^2	$erg/(s.cm^2)$	10^3
Angular momentum	$kg\text{-}m^2/s$	$g.cm^2/s$	10^7
Moment of inertia	$kg.m^2$	$g.cm^2$	10^7
Dynamic viscosity	Pa.s	P	10
Temperature	K	K	1
Heat capacity, entropy	J/K	erg/K	10^7
Electric charge	C	CGSE unit	3.109
Potential	V	CGSE unit	1/300
Electric field strength	V/m	CGSE unit	$1/(3.10^4)$
Electric induction	$C.m^2$	CGSE unit	$12\pi \, . \, 10^4$
Electric dipole moment	C/m	CGSE unit	$3..10^{11}$
Electric polarization	C/m^2	CGSE unit	3.10^5
Capacity	F	cm	9.10^{11}
Current	A	CGSE unit	3.10^9
Current density	A/m^2	CGSE unit	3.10^6
Resistance	Ω	CGSE unit	$1/(9.10^{11})$
Resistivity	Ω.m	CGSE unit	$1/(9.10^9)$
Conductance	S	CGSE unit	9.10^{11}
Magnetic induction	T	G	10^4
Magnetic flux	Wb	Mx	10^8
Magnetic field strength	A/m	Oe	$4p \, . \, 10^{-3}$
Magnetic moment	$A.m^2$	CGSE unit	10^3
Magnetization	A/m	CGSE unit	10^{-3}
Inductance	H	cm	10^9
Luminous intensity	cd	cd	1
Luminous flux	lm	lm	1
Illumination	lx		
Luminosity	lm/m^2		
Brightness	cd/m^2		

Note. The CGS electric and magnetic units are given here in the Gaussian system.

Some Extrasystem Units

1 year	= $3.11 \, . \, 10^7$ s	1 A	= 10^{-8} cm
1 atm	= 101.3 kPa; 760 mm Hg	1 b	= 10^{-24} cm^2
1 bar	= 100 kPa (precisely)	1 eV	= $1.6.10^{-19}$ j; $1.6.10^{-12}$ erg
1 mm Hg	= 133.3 Pa	1 a.m.u.	= $1.66.10^{-24}$ g; 9.31.4 MeV
1 l.atm	= 101.3 J	1 Ci (curie)	= $3.70.10^{10}$ dis./S
1 cal	= 4.18 J		

29. The Basic Formulas of Electrodynamics in the SI and Gaussian Systems

Name	SI	Gaussian system
Strength of the field of a point charge	$E = \frac{1}{4\pi\varepsilon_0}\frac{q}{r^2}$	$E = \frac{q}{r^2}$
Strength of the field of a plane capacitor	$E = \frac{\sigma}{\varepsilon_0\varepsilon}$	$E = \frac{4\pi\sigma}{\varepsilon}$
Potential of the field of a point charge	$\varphi = \frac{1}{4\pi\varepsilon_0}\frac{q}{r}$	$E = \frac{q}{r}$
Relation between **E** and φ	$\mathbf{E} = -\nabla\varphi,\ \varphi_1 - \varphi_2 = \int_1^2 E_l\, d_l$	
Electric dipole **p** in field E	$\mathbf{N} = [\mathbf{pE}],\ W = -\mathbf{pE}$	
Relation between **P** and **E**	$\mathbf{P} = x\varepsilon_0\mathbf{E}$	$\mathbf{P} = x\mathbf{E}$
Relation between σ′, **P**, and **E**	$\sigma' = P_n = x\varepsilon_0 E_n$	$\sigma' = P_n = xE_n$
Definition of the Vector **D**	$\mathbf{D} = \varepsilon_0\mathbf{E} + \mathbf{P}$	$\mathbf{D} = \mathbf{E} + 4\pi\mathbf{P}$
Relation between ε and x	$\varepsilon = 1 + x$	$\varepsilon = 1 + 4\pi x$
Relation between **D** and **E**	$\mathbf{D} = \varepsilon_0\varepsilon\mathbf{E}$	$\mathbf{D} = \varepsilon\mathbf{E}$
Gauss theorem for the vector **D**	$\oint D_n\, dS = q$	$\oint D_n\, dS = 4\pi q$
Capacitance of a capacitor	$C = q/V$	
Capacitance of a plane capacitor	$C = \frac{\varepsilon_0\varepsilon S}{d}$	$C = \frac{\varepsilon S}{4\pi d}$
Energy of a system of charges	$W = 1/2\ \Sigma\ q_i\ \varphi_i$	
Energy of a capacitor	$W = CV^2/2$	
Energy density of electric field	$w = \frac{ED}{2}$	$w = \frac{ED}{8\pi}$
Ohm's law	$= \sigma\mathbf{E}$	
Joule's law	$w = \sigma E^2$	
Magnetic moment of a current carrying loop	$p_m = IS$	$p_m = \frac{1}{c}\ IS$
Magnetic dipole $\mathbf{p}_m$ in the field B	$\mathbf{N} - [p_m\mathbf{B}],\ W = -\mathbf{p}_m\ \mathbf{B}$	

(Continued)

Name	SI	Gaussian system
Biot and Savarts law	$dB = \frac{\mu_0}{4\pi}\frac{I[dl, r]}{r^3}$	$dB = \frac{1}{c}\frac{I[dl, r]}{r^3}$
Induction of the field produced		
(a) by direct current	$B = \frac{\mu_0}{4\pi}\frac{2I}{r}$	$B = \frac{1}{c}\frac{2I}{r}$
(b) In the centre of a loop	$B = \frac{\mu_0}{4\pi}\frac{2\pi I}{r}$	$B = \frac{1}{c}\frac{2\pi I}{r}$
(c) in a solenoid	$B = \mu_0 nI$	$B = \frac{4\pi}{c} nI$
Definition of the vector H	$H = B/\mu_0 - J$	$H = B - 4\pi J$
Circulation of the vector H in a constant field	$\oint H_l dl = I$	$\oint H_l dl = \frac{4\pi}{c} I$
Relation between J and H	$J = \chi H$	
Relation between μ and χ	$\mu = 1 + \chi$	$\mu = 1 + 4\pi\chi$
Relation between B and H	$B = \mu_0 \mu H$	$B = \mu H$
Lorentz force	$F = q\,[vB]$	$F = \frac{q}{c}[vB]$
Ampere's law	$dF = I[dl, B]$	$dF = \frac{I}{c}[dl, B]$
Force of interaction of paralel currents	$F = \frac{\mu_0}{4\pi}\frac{2I_1 I_2}{d}$	$F = \frac{1}{c^2}\frac{2I_1 I_2}{d}$
Emf of induction	$\xi_i = -\frac{d\Phi}{dt}$	$\xi_i = -\frac{1}{c}\frac{d\Phi}{dt}$
Inductance	$L = \Phi/I$	$L = c\Phi/I$
Inductane of a solenoid	$L = \mu_0 \mu n^2 V$	$L = 4\pi\mu n^2 V$
Ener of the magnetic fiel l produced by current	$W = \frac{LI^2}{2}$	$W = \frac{1}{c^2}\frac{LI^2}{2}$
Energy density of magnetic field	$w = \frac{BH}{2}$	$w = \frac{BH}{8\pi}$

(Continued)

Nature	SI	Gaussian system
Maxwell's equations in integral form	$\oint D_n\, dS = \int \rho dV$ $\oint E_l dl = -\int \dot{B}_n\, dS$ $\oint B_n\, dS = 0$ $\oint H_l dl = \int (j_n + \dot{D}_n) dS$	$\oint D_n dS = 4\pi \int \rho dV$ $\oint E_l dl = -\frac{1}{c}\int \dot{B}_n\, dS$ $\oint B_n\, dS = 0$ $\oint H_l dl = \frac{4\pi}{c}\int \left(j_n + \frac{\dot{D}_n}{4\pi}\right) dS$
Maxwell's equations in differential form	$\nabla \cdot D = p$ $\nabla \times \mathbf{E} = -\dot{B}$ $\nabla . \mathbf{B} = 0$ $\nabla \times \mathbf{H} = \mathbf{j} + \dot{D}$	$\nabla . D = 4\pi\rho$ $\nabla \times \mathbf{E} = -\frac{1}{c}\dot{B}$ $\nabla . \mathbf{B} = 0$ $\nabla \times H = \frac{4\pi}{c}\left(j + \frac{\dot{D}}{4\pi}\right)$
Velocity of an electromagnetic wave in a medium	$v = 1/\sqrt{\varepsilon_0\mu_0\varepsilon\mu}$	$v = c/\sqrt{\varepsilon\mu}$
Relation between E and H in an electromagnetic wave	$E\sqrt{\varepsilon_0\varepsilon} = H\sqrt{\mu_0\mu}$	$\mathbf{E}\sqrt{\varepsilon} = H\sqrt{\mu}$
Poynting vector	$\mathbf{S} = [\mathbf{EH}]$	$\mathbf{S} = \frac{c}{4\pi}[\mathbf{EH}]$

30. Fundamental Constants

Velocity of light in vacuum	$c = 2.998.10^8$ m/s
Gravitational constant	$\lambda = \begin{cases} 6.67 . 10^{-11}\ m^3/(kg.3^2) \\ 6.67 . 10^{-8}\ cm^3/(g.s^2) \end{cases}$
Free fall acceleration (standard value)	$g = 9.9.807\ m/s^2$
Avogardro constant	$N_A = 6.023 . 10^{23}\ mol^{-1}$
Molar volume of ideal gas at stp	$V_0 = 22.4$ l/mol
Loschmidt's number	$n_0 = \begin{cases} 2.69 . 10^{25}\ m^{-3} \\ 2.69 . 10^{19}\ cm^{-3} \end{cases}$
Universal gas constant	$R = \begin{cases} 8.314\ J/(K-mol) \\ 8.314 . 10^7\ erg/mol \\ 0.082\ l.atm/mol \end{cases}$
Boltzmann constant	$k = \begin{cases} 1.380 . 10^{-23}\ J/K \\ 1.380 . 10^{-14}\ erg/K \end{cases}$
Faraday constant	$F = \begin{cases} 0.865 . 10^5\ C/kg . equiv. \\ 2.90 . 10^{14}\ CGSE/g.equ\ iv. \end{cases}$
Elementary charge	$e = \begin{cases} 1.602 . 10^{-19}\ C \\ 4.803 . 10^{-10}\ CGSE \end{cases}$
Electron test mass	$m_e = \begin{cases} 0.911 . 10^{30}\ C \\ 0.911 . 10^{-27} g \\ 0.511\ MeV \end{cases}$
Specific charge of electron	$\frac{e}{m_e} = \begin{cases} 1.76 . 10^{11}\ C/kg \\ 5.27 . 10^{17}\ CGSE/g \end{cases}$
Proton rest mass	$m_p = \begin{cases} 1.672 . 10^{-27}\ kg \\ 1.672 . 10^{-24}\ g \end{cases}$
Specific charge of proton	$\frac{e}{m_p} = \begin{cases} 0.959 . 10^8\ C/kg \\ 2.87 . 10^{14}\ CGSE/g \end{cases}$
Stefan-Boltzmann constant	$\sigma = 5.67 \cdot 10^{-8}\ W/(m^2 . K^4)$
Constant in Wien's displacement law	$b = 0.29$ cm . K
Planck constant	$h = \begin{cases} 1.054 . 10^{-34}\ , J.s \\ 1.054 . 10^{-27}\ erg.s \\ 0.659 . 10^{-15}\ eV.s \end{cases}$
Rydberg constant	$R = \frac{me^4}{2h^3} = 2.07 \cdot 10^{16}\ s^{-1}$ $R' = R/2\pi c = 1.097 . 10^5\ cm^{-1}$
First Bohr radius	$r_1 = \hbar^2/me^2 = 0.529 . 10^{-3}$ cm
Binding energy of electron in a hydrogen atom	$E = me^4/2\hbar^2 = 13.56$ eV
Compton wavelength of an electron	$\lambda_C = \hbar/mc = 3.86 . 10^{-11}$ cm
Classical electron radius	$r_e = e^2/mc^2 = 2.82 . 10^{-18}$ cm
Bohr magneton	$\mu_B = \frac{eh}{2m_e c} = 0.927 . 10^{-30}$ erg/G
Nuclear magneton	$\mu_N = \frac{eh}{2m_p c} = 5.05 . 10^{-24}$ erg/G

(*Continued*)

Proton magnetic moment	$\mu_p = 2.7928\ \mu N$
Neutron magnetic moment	$\mu_n = -1.913\ \mu N$
Atomic mass unit	1 a.m.u. = $\begin{cases} 1.660 \,.\, 10^{-24}\ g \\ 931.4\ MeV \end{cases}$
Permittivity of vacuum	$\varepsilon_0 = 0.855 \,.\, 10^{-11}$ F/m $1/4\pi_0 = 9.10^9$ m/F
Permeability of vacuum	$\mu_0 = 1.257 \,.\, 10^6$ H/m $\mu_0/4\pi = 10^{-7}$ 11/m